22- 5

SELECTED PAPERS IN SOIL FORMATION AND CLASSIFICATION

S591
.D72
1968

SELECTED PAPERS IN SOIL FORMATION AND CLASSIFICATION

J. V. DREW, Editor

R. B. GROSSMAN   H. W. SMITH

J. L. RETZER   M. E. SPRINGER

R. W. SIMONSON

Associate Editors

R. C. DINAUER, Managing Editor

MATTHIAS STELLY, Coordinating Editor

Number 1 in the

SSSA SPECIAL PUBLICATION SERIES

Soil Science Society of America, Inc., Publisher

Madison, Wisconsin, USA

1967

INDIANA
UNIVERSITY
LIBRARY
JUL 1 3 1977
NORTHWEST
AUG - 9 1977

Copyright © 1967, by the Soil Science Society of America, Inc.
ALL RIGHTS RESERVED.
No part of this book may be reproduced in any form, by photostat, microfilm, or any other means, without written permission from the publisher.

Second Printing 1968
Third Printing 1970

The Soil Science Society of America, Inc.,
677 South Segoe Road, Madison, Wisconsin, USA 53711

Library of Congress Catalog Card Number: 67-22346

Printed in the United States of America

FOREWORD

Selected Papers in Soil Formation and Classification is, in a very real sense, an experiment in publication by the Soil Science Society of America. It is an attempt to assemble under one cover some of the best papers published and to make them available to students, both in college and on the job, who do not have access to the original publications. If this collection of papers meets a real need, the evidence will be in how well this first special publication of the Society is used. Success on this project may call for an updated version and be an encouragement to enter into other subdisciplines of soil science with similar ventures.

In view of the food scarcity in many countries now and the impending general World food shortage, this book is timely. Man depends on the land for food. The sea has never contributed much and probably will not become more important as a food source. Not in the foreseeable future will we shift over to algae grown in tanks or to micro-organisms grown on sewage to sustain ourselves. Instead, our future depends on the better use of the land now in cultivation and on the use of land not now used intensively for agriculture. We not only need land to grow food on but we need land to dwell on, travel on and play on. Best use of the soil for these purposes depends on its proper classification so that we can make valid comparisons of one place with another. We need to know about the processes that caused the soil to get the way it is so that we can better understand how what we do to it will eventually affect it. If these carefully selected papers help us better to understand and to use our soil resources, they will have served a noble purpose.

This publication had its official conception when the editorial committee was appointed in a letter by President Nyle C. Brady on August 12, 1964. Needless to say, many of the committee members and others had spent much time earlier on the project. Work on the selection of papers was continued by the committee under Society presidents R. W. Pearson and W. P. Martin. The current officers of the Society express their appreciation to the editorial committee, the past officers and board members of the Society, and to Executive Secretary Stelly and Editor R. C. Dinauer who made the publication possible. Finally, we express our thanks to the authors and their publishers who permitted reproduction of their papers.

Although most of the expenses of publication were paid from general funds of the Society, the residue of the Marbut fund was used to pay initial costs, including composition of this publication, as authorized by the Board of Directors.

March 1967

FRANK G. VIETS, JR.
President

PREFACE

The purpose of this volume is to bring together source material dealing with modern concepts in soil formation and classification. In recent years, considerable progress has been made in recognizing genetic soil groups, in understanding specific mechanisms involved in soil formation and in developing concepts in soil classification. Of course, it is possible to assemble in a single volume only a small sample of papers dealing with these advances. It is hoped, however, that papers presented on the following pages will provide some understanding of concepts and problems in pedology for students of soil science or related fields. This book is not intended to present an integrated analysis of recent research, but it is designed to provide text material or supplemental reading for a course in soil formation and classification.

Papers composing the volume have been grouped under several headings. The introductory paper provides some general ideas of important changes involved in soil formation and the possible relationships of these changes to environmental factors. The second section brings together papers describing a number of soils that occur in areas ranging from the forests, grasslands, and deserts of North America south to the tropics and north to the arctic tundra. A third section provides examples of the interpretation of relationships among certain soil characteristics and the factors involved in soil formation, and the fourth section illustrates some specific mechanisms and changes involved in soil genesis. The final section is concerned with recent approaches to the problem of soil classification.

Many excellent papers could not be included in this collection. It is hoped, however, that the volume will stimulate interest in the study of soil genesis, and that certain papers may provide points of departure for further advances in understanding soil formation and classification.

March 1967

J. V. DREW, University of Nebraska, Lincoln, Nebr., *Editor*

Associate Editors

R. B. GROSSMAN, Soil Survey Laboratory, Soil Conservation Service, USDA, Lincoln, Nebr.

J. L. RETZER, University of Wisconsin, Madison, Wis.

R. W. SIMONSON, Soil Conservation Service, U.S. Dept. of Agriculture, Hyattsville, Maryland.

H. W. SMITH, Washington State University, Pullman, Wash.

M. E. SPRINGER, University of Tennessee, Knoxville, Tenn.

CONTENTS

PART III
SOIL FORMING FACTORS — CONCEPTS AND INTERPRETATIONS

Part I

INTRODUCTION

SOIL FORMATION

E. Crompton

(School of Agriculture, University of Durham, Newcastle-upon-Tyne)

The natural supply of essential plant nutrients by a fertile soil is a complex process well demonstrated by the exacting requirements of hydroponics. How soil profiles of value in agriculture—as well as mediocre ones—arise from parent rocks is treated under the headings: weathering, translocation and the organic cycle, special reference being made to the formation of clay minerals with characteristic structures and properties.

Ecologists have described in detail the fascinating succession of vegetation from the first colonizing plants on a bare surface of rock, sand or clay to the ultimate establishment of complex and closely integrated climax communities. Few people seem to have realized that parallel developments are occurring beneath the surface. It is true, nevertheless, that the random masses of mineral particles in which colonizing plants begin to grow are gradually transformed by successions of changes just as fascinating, orderly and meaningful as those above ground. The resulting soil profiles reveal organized dynamic systems that reflect the interplay of environmental factors, and perhaps also some relic features of former conditions.

Dokuchaev established the science of pedology by his recognition that soils display consistent and distinctive morphological characteristics which are the result of the integrated effects of climate, parent rock, vegetation and associated organisms, relief of the land, and time; where these five soil-forming factors are the same the soils must be the same since they are in fact "a mere function of the soil-forming factors" (1). From the time of Dokuchaev a great deal of increasingly detailed study of soils in relation to environments has confirmed the validity of his philosophy, and inferences can even be made concerning environments of remote past ages from the morphology of the fossil soils of buried land surfaces. Some quantitative relationships between soil properties and single features of the environment have been established (2, 3). The work of Walker and his colleagues (6, 7, 8) suggests that such studies can be of direct significance to farming as well as to academic pedology.

Although an understanding of soil variety in terms of the soil-forming factors appears likely to remain the unifying philosophy of "pure" pedology, it is well to remember that correlations between soils and their environments, even when clearly shown to be causative relationships, do not in themselves explain any of the mechanisms whereby external factors such as climate and relief actually produce the morphology of a soil profile. The immediate causes of a particular succession of soil horizons lie rather in the physical, chemical and biological processes at work within that particular profile. These are the instruments which actually fashion the character of a soil and upon which its development and fertility depend. The factors set the conditions but internal processes produce the profile.

Reproduced with permission from *Outlook on Agriculture,* Vol. 3, 1962, p. 209-218.
Published by Imperial Chemical Industries Limited, London, England.

Just as each of the accepted soil-forming factors is, in fact, a complex group, so it is convenient to consider the other processes in four main groups. Rock material is decomposing with some constituents passing into solution in a process which we can call weathering. The products of weathering may be removed or redistributed in the soil profile by translocation. Plants and other organisms absorb some of the products of weathering and return them to the surface or to other parts of the profile, adding at the same time an organic residue composed largely of elements gathered from the atmosphere—mechanisms which we can consider under the organic cycle. Under the influence of gravity, wind and running water the surface of every soil is losing or receiving material. The development of a soil profile depends on the first three processes being allowed to operate in the absence of excessive erosion or deposition.

WEATHERING

Mechanisms such as freezing and thawing, heating and cooling, wetting and drying, and physical disintegration by plant roots are some of the means by which solid rock is reduced to masses of small particles. These changes are chiefly important because they increase the surface area of rock material exposed to chemical weathering, in which a number of reactions are involved, chief among them being hydrolysis, hydration, solution and oxidation-reduction.

The igneous rocks, from which other rocks are ultimately derived, consist almost entirely of silicate minerals in which the structural unit is the silica tetrahedron. This consists of four closely-packed oxygen atoms enclosing a silicon atom which is of such dimensions that it fits almost exactly into the space between the four oxygen ones. Each of the four bonds of the Si^{++++} is attached to one bond of each O^{--} leaving every O^{--} with a spare bond by which it may be attached to ions outside its tetrahedral group. Such tetrahedra may thus be linked together through other cations lying between them, or they may be more firmly linked directly by elimination of some oxygen atoms, to form chain, ribbon, sheet or framework structures as one, two, three or four of the tetrahedral oxygen atoms are shared between pairs of silicon atoms, or between one silicon atom and a metal cation. Thus there is an increasing proportion of silicon and a decreasing proportion of other cations, such as aluminium, iron, calcium, magnesium, and potassium, in proportion to the amount of direct linkage as we pass from the isolated tetrahedra of olivine through the chain structures of augite, the ribbon structures of hornblende, the sheet structures of the micas, to the framework of quartz. (Figures 1 and 2.)

The very important group of minerals, the felspars, are also framework structures but they illustrate another important variation, the substitution of Al^{+++} for Si^{++++} in the tetrahedron. This leaves an excess negative charge which requires another positive ion in the structure to maintain electrical neutrality. In orthoclase a quarter of the silicon atoms is replaced by aluminium and the charge is balanced by potassium ions, in plagioclase half the silicon atoms is replaced, and calcium ions restore the neutrality. Substitution of aluminium for silicon occurs in other types of mineral besides the felspars and the adjustment required always involves a weakening of the mineral structure.

In the presence of rain water, surface chemical reactions gradually bring the constituents of the minerals into solution. The most important reaction is hydrolysis by which various cations are replaced by hydrogen ions. Following this, sooner or later a portion of the mineral structure becomes unstable and the components pass into solution as ions, molecules, or small colloidal groups. The minerals most susceptible to hydrolysis are (a) those in which the stable silica tetrahedra are linked by cations that can be replaced—olivine is, therefore, very unstable and quartz extremely stable; and (b) those with a high degree of substitution of Al^{+++} for Si^{++++}. The calcium felspars are thus more easily weathered than the potash felspar, orthoclase.

Among igneous rocks, the acid granites and rhyolites, which contain a high proportion of quartz and orthoclase, are chemically the most resistant. Susceptibility to weathering becomes greater the more basic the rocks; in the gabbros and basalts quartz is absent, calcium felspars are generally important, while the chain-structured pyroxenes, the ribbon-structured amphiboles, and olivine of isolated tetrahedral structure may be abundant. So basic rocks are richer in both bases and iron, important soil constituents, and are likely to release them more readily into the soil solution. In general these rocks are also richer in apatite, almost the sole original source of phosphorus, so necessary an element in plant growth.

Soils developed from sedimentary deposits may include primary minerals eroded from igneous rocks, new minerals such as calcite, and poorly-crystalline cementing materials. Their plant nutrient content ranges from siliceous sandstones composed entirely of quartz and virtually barren, to some phosphatic, base-rich sediments of high potential fertility.

Parent soil materials, therefore, vary widely in potential but their quality is governed by decomposition rate, which depends on rock porosity and texture, on temperature, and on the extent to which the acidity of the soil solution is affected by vegetation. Soluble decomposition products may be supplemented by solutions seeping down from adjacent slopes. All these factors combine to influence the rate at which materials enter the soil solution at a given point in a particular soil profile; once in solution the constituents are mobile and subject to processes of translocation.

TRANSLOCATION

From an examination of river waters flowing from areas of known rock composition Polynov (5) and later Perelman (4) were able to estimate the relative mobilities of the elements. Polynov's figures are shown in the Table. The figure for SiO_2 is estimated from the combined silica in the rock on the assumption that quartz is almost inert.

It appears that the elements tend to form mobility phases with relatively small differences within each phase compared with the differences between one phase and the next. It should be possible, therefore, for drainage waters to remove the greater part of the chlorides and sulphates from a weathering material without depleting the chemical elements in the other phases to a great extent. Subsequently those in phase II would be selectively taken away, followed by combined silica, yielding a sesquioxide-rich residue containing the very inert minerals.

Polynov argued that climate does not alter the order in which the elements are leached but only the intensity of the process, the greater temperatures of the humid

(a) Isolated tetrahedra representing silicon atoms each surrounded by four oxygen atoms.
Example: olivine.

(b) Chain structure of tetrahedra. Example: augite.

(c) Ribbon (double chain) structure of tetrahedra.
Example: hornblende.

(d) Sheet structure of tetrahedra. Such sheets, in combination with aluminium octahedra, are characteristic of the clay minerals.
Example: muscovite.

Fig. 1—Structure of silicate minerals (pictorial).

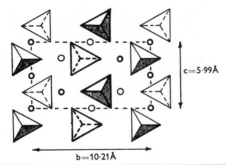

(a) Isolated tetrahedral groups linked together through bonds of intermediate metal ions (Mg^{++}, Fe^{++}). Heavy lines indicate units centred on top and bottom of cell, light ones those of half height. Example: olivine.

$c = 5.99\text{Å}$

$b = 10.21\text{Å}$

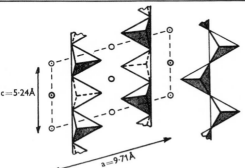

(b) Chain silicate, cross linked with Ca^{++} (dotted circles) and Mg^{++} (open circles). Heavy circles indicate positions above, light ones those below, the medial line of the chains. Example: diopside. (Right) Face view of single chain as in pyroxene group.

$c = 5.24\text{Å}$

$a = 9.71\text{Å}$

(c) Double chain silicate. Face view as in amphibole group.

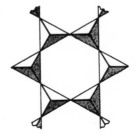

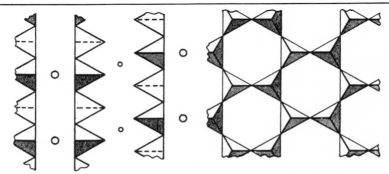

(d) Layer silicates—the micas and clay minerals—built up of indefinitely extended sheets of tetrahedra linked together in inwardly-facing pairs by small metal ions (Mg^{++}, Fe^{++}, Al^{+++}), the sandwiches so formed being joined back-to-back by large metal ions (K^+, Na^+, Ca^{++}) or by interlayer water or other polar molecules.

Fig. 2—Structure of silicate minerals (diagrammatic).

RELATIVE MOBILITIES OF MINERAL ELEMENTS

Chemical substance	Relative mobility	Mobility phase
Cl^- SO_4^{--}	100·00 57·00	I
Ca^{++} Na^+ Mg^{++} K^+	3·00 2·40 1·30 1·25	II
SiO_2	0·20	III
Fe_2O_3 Al_2O_3	0·04 0·02	IV

tropics accelerating the decomposition of primary minerals and thereby facilitating the more rapid removal of their constituents. He distinguished sharply between weathering and translocation, though these cannot be separated in nature. It is clear, however, that the rate of breakdown of minerals and the rate of removal of their constituents need not keep in step: under hot and moderately humid conditions, for example, weathering may be rapid but, if little excess water passes through the soil, translocation may be slight, and the constituents released from decomposing minerals may remain *in situ* to form new combinations; under low temperatures and strong leaching, on the other hand, the released materials may be largely removed in solution so dilute that formation of new compounds is unlikely.

Under the variety of climates in the world many combinations of weathering and translocation are possible: from those in hot, dry regions where intense weathering for short periods follows infrequent rains, insufficient to remove the weathered products, to those in cool, wet climates where every ion released is likely to be leached away unless, like iron and aluminium, it immediately forms a new, insoluble product.

These effects are influenced by relief: weathered products from higher sites may be leached into depressions, there to enrich the soil solution. Differential absorption of certain elements by vegetation may tend to concentrate them in the upper part of the soil.

We therefore arrive at the concept of *richness of weathering*, which is the product of the quantity and variety of elements in the parent material capable of being brought into the soil solution and those effects of temperature, site, vegetation, etc., which tend to bring them into solution. The richness of weathering is offset by *intensity of leaching*, an outcome of the rainfall/evapo-transpiration balance and soil permeability.

When richness of weathering and intensity of leaching are considered together (Figure 3), the principles that govern the occurrence of new products in soils may be viewed in a greatly simplified form. In positions of rich weathering, due for instance to intense hydrolysis, perhaps assisted by seepage of solutions into depressions, the soil solution is enriched in such elements as sodium, potassium, calcium, magnesium, chlorides, sulphates and bicarbonates, and if leaching is weak, as in desert areas, a variety of new combinations of soluble salts may form and accumulate in the upper parts of the soil profile. Under somewhat less rich weathering or

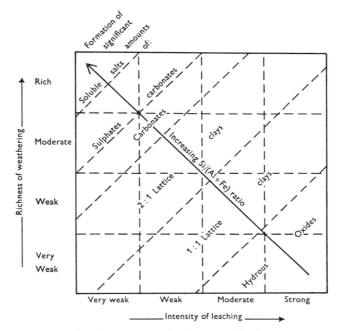

Fig. 3—Joint action of weathering and leaching.

slightly stronger leaching, the chlorides and sulphates may be removed, at least from the upper horizons of the profile, but the bases may combine with CO_2 produced by the organic cycle, and secondary carbonates may be formed even in the upper soil horizons.

At this stage there are also being formed the most important secondary products of soils—the clay minerals. These resemble the primary micas in consisting of sheets of silica tetrahedra (Figure 1 (d)) combined with sheets of alumina octahedra, often with some degree of substitution of aluminium for silicon, and iron and magnesium for aluminium, with various other cations included in the framework.

The clay minerals are commonly considered in two main divisions. In the kaolin group, the 1:1 clay minerals, one sheet of silica tetrahedra is bonded to one sheet of alumina octahedra through mutually shared oxygen atoms. These pairs of sheets are stacked above each other and held together rather firmly by hydrogen bonds.

In the other main clay group, that of the 2:1 clay minerals, there are stacks of three-fold layers comprising two sheets of silica tetrahedra with one sheet of alumina octahedra between, as in the primary micas. In illite successive three-fold layers are bonded by potassium and do not expand on wetting. In vermiculite there is much substitution in the lattice. Cations, such as Ca and Mg, which link the three-fold layers to each other, are surrounded by water molecules varying in quantity and permitting expansion and contraction of the lattice in some circumstances. In montmorillonite the bonding between successive three-fold layers is very weak and the lattice readily expands on wetting.

Some of the micas of the primary rock appear to be able to weather directly by exchange of cations to clay minerals of the 2:1 lattice type, of similar structure, but relatively stable in soil conditions. In soils still containing primary micas, therefore, there are likely to be some clay minerals, such as illite and vermiculite, from this source. But much of the clay formed in soils must arise by recrystallization from solution, the constituents being derived from hydrolysis of felspars and ferromagnesian minerals.

As shown in Figure 3, if the weathering/leaching ratio is such that some bases and ample silica remain, 2:1 lattice type minerals of the illite and montmorillonite groups are likely to be formed; but with a lower weathering/leaching ratio the bases tend to be leached out as fast as they are released, as also does some of the silica, so that 1:1 lattice type kaolin minerals are the more likely product. With intense leaching all the constituents released by silicate hydrolysis are removed in dilute solution as quickly as they are weathered, except iron and aluminium which readily form very insoluble hydrous oxides.

In circumstances to be explained later, in which a very acid humus layer is developed on the surface of the soil, the movement of iron and aluminium appears to be accelerated, probably in associations with organic complexes, in the process known as podzolization. Although the siliceous residue which remains is generally composed mainly of primary quartz grains, there is some evidence suggesting that secondary silica also accumulates.

One other deviation which is very widespread results from anaerobic conditions caused by waterlogging. By both bacterial and chemical action iron and manganese are reduced to ferrous and manganous forms and become soluble and more mobile. Where seasonal drying allows the re-oxidation of these materials, they are redeposited as yellow and rusty spots and streaks of ferric iron, or as black manganese concretions, characteristic of many of these gleyed soils (Figure 5 (c)).

The way in which podzolization and gleying modify the effects of the balance between richness of weathering and intensity of leaching is shown in simplified form in Figure 4.

On weathering, rock material yields particles of various sizes, from large boulders to colloidal clay. The clay fraction of the soil has many distinctive and valuable

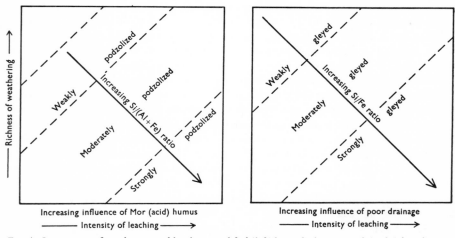

Fig. 4—Joint action of weathering and leaching modified (left) by podzolization and (right) by gleying.

properties arising from its very fine state of sub-division and platy character. It can absorb great quantities of water, partly as a film surrounding the particles, and partly within the lattice if the clay mineral has an expanding structure. The clay becomes plastic and sticky when damp, and smooth and slippery as the wet platelets slide over each other; on drying it shrinks and hardens, and may adhere firmly to adjacent objects. The properties of expansion and contraction, stickiness and hardness increase with fineness of sub-division and type of clay from kaolin through illite and vermiculite to montmorillonite.

In coarse sandy soils even the closest packing leaves cavities large enough for quick draining by gravity after rain. On freely-drained sites such soils are well aerated and respiration of the roots presents no problem; the only difficulties are those arising from low retention of water and nutrients.

On the other hand, if clays are closely packed the cavities between the particles are so small that the thin films of water held by surface tension fill them almost entirely: movement of air and water is suppressed. Such a "shaken down" condition makes plant growth impossible, and explains the serious effect of cultivating a clay soil in a wet state.

Fortunately the property of expansion and shrinkage enables a clay in a "shaken down" condition to shrink and crack on drying, producing fissures through which air and water can move. The first cracks to appear when a uniform mud is dried tend to form perpendicular to the surface. But soon the wall of the crack itself becomes a drying surface and cracks develop horizontally, and then further cracks perpendicular to them. Eventually the clay becomes a mass of isolated blocks of various sizes with fissures between, or fissures of various shapes and sizes surrounding residual blocks of soil material. Other forces, such as frost and the action of roots and earthworms, contribute to the fissuring, and in some circumstances may even dominate the formation of the complex mass of fissures and aggregates which we term soil structure.

A well-developed structure ensures the continuity of larger cavities, which drain quickly after rain and provide essential aeration channels for root respiration; it also affords many fine capillaries by which water is retained for plants even during dry weather. Physically the soil is in a good condition to sustain the growth of larger plants.

Clays can be of vital chemical importance to plant growth. Owing largely to isomorphous substitution in the lattice structure, they carry a negative charge that is satisfied by a swarm of cations absorbed on their surfaces. Some of the cations are able to enter the surrounding solution and an equilibrium is established. As cations are withdrawn from the solutions by plant roots they are replaced by others dissociating from the clay surfaces. Mineral weathering releases new supplies to replenish the reserve of exchangeable cations. The clay thus acts as a reservoir of available plant nutrients without which the steady growth of larger plants would not be possible.

With its variety of weathered products the soil is in a position, both physically and chemically, to support continuous plant growth, and to maintain the organic cycle without which it could scarcely be regarded as soil.

Before we look at the organic cycle, however, another important phenomenon of translocation remains to be considered. In some circumstances the fine clay particles of the soil may be washed down in suspension from the upper layers and deposited in fissures and channels lower in the profile. This process is most marked when the exchange complex contains large quantities (more than 20 percent) of absorbed sodium, or perhaps magnesium; the clay becomes highly dispersed and percolates downwards in suspension. The process seems, however, to be a more general one, for it tends to occur in other soils, particularly at neutral to slightly acid pH levels. In more alkaline conditions free bicarbonate ions, and in more acid conditions aluminium ions and dissociating basic ferric hydroxide, encourage flocculation and inhibit movement. Where clay shift occurs, however, the subsoil texture becomes heavier and may impede internal drainage, leading to a chain of other changes. That it may be of practical significance in certain agricultural soils of poor structure is a possibility that should not be overlooked.

THE ORGANIC CYCLE

Many rock materials can provide all the mineral nutrients that plants require from the soil except nitrogen, which is generally present in extremely limited quantities. Small amounts are received annually in the rain and may build up to considerable totals during the full period of soil development. It is significant, however, that the first colonists of a newly exposed geological surface are generally plants with some nitrogen-fixing mechanisms: lichens with associated blue-green algae are among the first to establish on solid rock, while legumes with associated nitrogen-fixing nodule bacteria are prominent on newly-exposed unconsolidated deposits. The remains of these plants decompose and release nitrogen for other kinds of vegetation, and also leave humus in the soil, forming a reserve nitrogen supply.

The kind of organic material produced in a particular situation, and its amount, depend on the natural environment as well as on the type of vegetation. Production ranges from virtually nothing in deserts to 10 or 20 tons of dry matter per annum in tropical forests, and largely depends on rainfall and temperature; but in any climatic region wide variations reflect the fertility of the soil.

An important distinction between grasslands and forests is the difference in distribution of organic matter returned to the soil. Grasses produce enormous masses of roots of relatively short life, and as these die and decay great quantities of organic matter are added directly to the soil throughout a considerable depth. Trees, on the other hand, tend to have an enduring root system from which the annual decomposition is slight. Organic matter from the foliage reaches the surface soil and tends to accumulate there.

Mineral nutrients that have been absorbed from the soil, perhaps from the lower horizons, are released from decomposing residues and returned to the surface. This mechanism selectively counteracts the leaching downwards of certain soluble soil constituents in percolating rain-water. Its efficiency depends very much on the nature of the vegetation: fertile grassland species tend to produce nutrient-rich residues; deciduous forest trees, especially ash, elm and hazel, produce a litter rich in bases and nitrogen; but coniferous forest and acid heath plants leave residues of low mineral content. The litter of an individual species may be affected by soil fertility, so that no simple precise order of quality, or efficiency of organic circulation of nutrients, can be established.

The decomposition of plant litter is brought about by grazing animals, earthworms, insects and bacteria and fungi in great variety.

(a) Podzol (humus-iron) on sand showing current bedding.

(b) Peaty-gleyed podzol. A soil common in upland Britain in which podzolization and gleying combine to give a peaty top and a very thin dense layer of iron accumulation or iron pan.

(c) Gleyed soil showing the effects of water-logging.

(d) Brown Earth. The result of free drainage and a good return of nutrients to the surface in an active organic cycle.

Fig. 5—Soil profiles.

Plant litter that falls on the surface of the soil may either accumulate *in situ* or decompose and be incorporated with the mineral soil. All the environmental factors influence the situation: high temperatures and base-rich litter favour extreme decomposition and mineralization; low temperatures and nutrient-deficient litter, such as acid heath and coniferous residues, encourage accumulation, as does extreme waterlogging; moderate temperature and moisture, with nutrient-rich grassland and the better deciduous forest, favour the incorporation of humus with the mineral particles. The wet surface accumulations are known as peat, the drier ones as mor humus, and the well-incorporated intimate mixtures, generally associated in Britain with high earthworm activity, as mull. Mull has a carbon/nitrogen ratio in the region of 10, compared with 20 or so in mor and peat, has a higher exchange capacity even than fine clay, provides a ready reserve of nitrogen, and is therefore the most desirable humus form.

The principles outlined above help us to understand soil profiles and may be illustrated by a brief reference to certain British soils. Under natural conditions the lowlands of Britain would be clothed with deciduous forests and the freely-drained soils would mainly belong to the broad group of Brown Earths (Fig. 5d). These are soils having a strong organic cycle in which deep-rooted trees and their undergrowth return a rich litter to the soil surface. The material is readily decomposed by earthworms and micro-organisms with the rapid circulation of phosphorus, nitrogen and other plant nutrients. The high biological activity of the soil helps to maintain the mull humus with its good structure and its excellence as a medium for plant growth, and the moderate loss of nutrients through leaching is balanced by the moderate rate of release of further supplies from rock decomposition. This dynamic system under natural forest is capable of conversion to stable agriculture without great change in the intensity of processes.

In upland Britain the much higher rainfall leaches the soil more strongly, and the lower temperatures reduce the rate of weathering of the rocks. The combination leads to acidity and an adapted vegetation, such as moorland heath, which circulates only small quantities of nutrients and yields an unpalatable litter giving rise to a mor humus or acid peat (Fig. 5b). The podzol so produced may be changed by liming and manuring, equivalent to speedier weathering, but the whole dynamic tendency is towards podzolization, as would quickly become apparent if farming were neglected.

Different kinds of rocks may modify the weathering pattern in lowlands or uplands. Here and there in the lowlands the poorer weathering process, for example that on a siliceous sandstone (Fig. 5a), often fails to compensate for even moderate leaching; acidity increases, conifers or heaths with their poor organic cycle form the natural vegetation and the resulting mor humus leads to podzolization. The richer weathering from soft limestone or chalk, on the other hand, may fully compensate for leaching, and maintain the rich, calcium-saturated, dark mull of a typical rendzina soil. If this occurs in the uplands, Brown Earths of lowland character may develop.

Other factors may also influence the soil pattern, as when the planting of conifers on a former deciduous forest site increases acidity, or where a steep slope lowers the leaching intensity by shedding some of the rain from the surface, and so maintains Brown Earths surrounded by podzols on the flatter ground.

ACKNOWLEDGMENT

The assistance of Mr. F. Hunter and Mr. D. Robson of King's College, Newcastle-upon-Tyne, in preparing the paper for publication, after the decease of Mr. E. Crompton, is gratefully acknowledged by Mr. A. Crompton, the author's brother.

REFERENCES

1. Afanasiev, J. N. 1927. The classification problem in Russian soil science. U.S.S.R. Acad. Sci. Russian Pedological Investigations, V.
2. Dickson, B. A. and Crocker, R. L. 1953. J. Soil Sci., 4, 123.
3. Jenny, H. 1941. Factors of soil formation. New York, McGraw-Hill.
4. Perelman, A. I. 1955. C. R. Acad. Sci. U.S.S.R., 103, 669.
5. Polynov, B. B. 1937. The cycle of weathering. (Tr. A. Muir). London, Thos. Murby.
6. Walker, T. W. and Adams, A. F. R. 1958. Soil Sci., 85, 307.
7. Walker, T. W. and Adams, A. F. R. 1959. Soil Sci., 87, 1.
8. Walker, T. W., Thapa, B. K. and Adams, A. F. R. 1959. Soil Sci., 87, 135.

Part II

CHARACTERICS OF SOME GENETIC SOIL GROUPS

MAJOR KINDS OF PROFILES AND THEIR RELATIONSHIPS IN NEW YORK[1]

Marlin G. Cline[2]

ABSTRACT

The Zonal soils of New York are members of the Gray-Brown Podzolic, Brown Podzolic, and Podzol great soil groups. Each dominates the best-drained sites of extensive areas, but each is associated locally with a complete catena controlled by ground-water relationships. In addition, Brown Forest soils occupy the best-drained sites on some highly calcareous materials, and Alluvial soils occur on recent alluvium. Each of these is also associated with a complete catena.

THE NORMAL PROFILES

Under this heading are included the Podzols, Brown Podzolic, Gray-Brown Podzolic, and Brown Forest soils. Lyford's descriptions of Podzol and Brown Podzolic profiles of New England (4) fit these soils in New York. The Brown Podzolic soils are much like weakly expressed Podzols (2) and are included with "weak Podzols" for convenience throughout the remainder of this paper. The Gray-Brown Podzolic soils differ from Baldwin's description (1) mainly in the presence of a yellowish-tinged A_{21} horizon in the most acid members. The Brown Forest soils have been described in another paper (2) and are remarkably similar to "minimal" Prairie soils discussed by Smith, Allaway, and Riecken (8).

Figure 1 indicates well-defined zonation of normal soils, but segregation is far from perfect and correlation with climatic zones is not consistent. This is not surprising when one considers that the State lies mainly in a tension zone between the principal regions of Gray-Brown Podzolic soils to the South and Podzols to the North. Under these circumstances local factors of the environment may determine which of two contrasting kinds of Zonal soils develops.

Figure 1 shows how closely Brown Forest and Gray-Brown Podzolic soils parallel outcrops of calcareous rocks or deposits of lime-bearing marine and lacustrine clays. Except in area G3, the distribution of Gray-Brown Podzolic and Brown Forest soils coincides precisely with deposits of calcareous glacial material derived from adjacent outcrops of calcareous rocks. Conversely, Podzols are confined to acid material, and those that overlie calcareous bedrock are developed in acid materials transported from adjacent outcrops of acid rocks. The distance of such transport and the general direction of ice movement may be inferred from figure 1.

---

[1]Contribution from the Department of Agronomy, Cornell University Agricultural Experiment Station, Ithaca, N. Y. First received for publication September 6, 1951; publication delay due to loss of original manuscript in the mail. Presented before Section V, Soil Science Society of America, State College, Pa., August 28, 1951.

[2]Professor of Soil Science.

Reproduced with permission from *Soil Science Society of America Proceedings*, Vol. 17, 1957, p. 123-127. Published by the Soil Science Society of America, Madison, Wisconsin, USA.

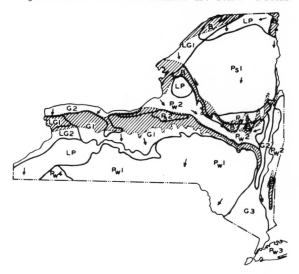

Fig. 1—Major Soil Associations of New York in relation to calcareous bedrock and direction of glaciation.

B. *Brown Forest with Gley soils* from calcareous drift on undulating to rolling plains and in valleys.
G. *Gray-Brown Podzolic with Gley soils*
    G1. From calcareous drift on undulating to rolling plains.
    G2. From calcareous lacustrine deposits on undulating plains.
    G3. From acid or calcareous drift on undulating plains.
Pw. *Podzols, weakly to moderately expressed, with Gley soils*
    Pw1. From medium-textured drift on hilly dissected plateaus.
    Pw2. From medium-textured drift on undulating to rolling plains.
    Pw3. From coarse-textured drift on level to hilly terrain.
    Pw4. From medium-textured residuum on hilly dissected plateaus.
Ps. *Podzols, strongly to moderately expressed, with Half Bog*
    Ps1. From coarse-textured drift on hilly terrain.
    Ps2. From lacustrine sands and silts on undulating plains.
LG. *Low-Humic Gley with Gray-Brown Podzolic soils*
    LG1. From lacustrine or marine deposits on nearly level plains.
    LG2. From drift on gently sloping plains.
LP. *Low-Humic Gley with Podzols,* from medium-textured drift on gently to strongly sloping plains.
    Shaded Areas—Calcareous bedrock (6)
    Arrows—General direction of ice movement (7)

It is characterstic of the drift that lime is at a maximum on some area near the southern edge of each calcareous outcrop and decreases both to the south and to the north in proportion to increasing dilution with acid material. This has made it possible to study the effects of decreasing lime within a limited area, and such studies have been reported for transects through area G1 in west-central New York (2, 3, 5). Figure 2 summarizes the classification, morphology[3], and interrelation-

---

[3]Subscripts "t" and "ir" in horizon designations refer to contrasting silicate-clay and iron concentrations respectively but not exceptional concentrations relative to those of zonal soils as commonly defined.

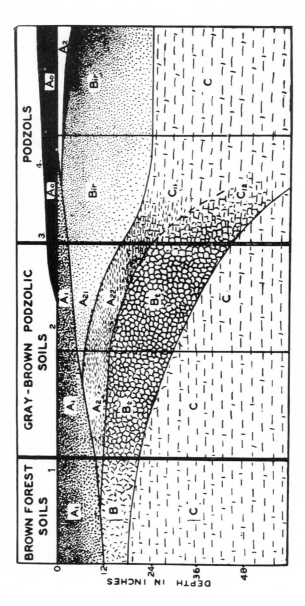

Fig. 2—Relationships among profiles of normal soils in New York.

Table 1—Selected physical and chemical properties of normal soils on glacial till in New York.*

Horizon	Depth, inches	pH	Clay, %	Organic matter, %	N, %	C:N ratio	Bulk density	Dominant type of clay mineral
Profile 1. Fenner silt loam—A Brown Forest soil†								
A11	0–5	7.0	17.9	7.9	0.32	14.2	1.0	
A12	5–9	7.3	17.4	1.9	0.14	10.9		
B2	9–15	7.5	19.4	1.4	0.08	11.0	1.4	
B3	15–19	7.8	16.4	1.0	0.07	9.1	1.6	
C1	19–24	7.8		1.1	0.07	9.9	1.6	
C2	24–30	8.3	12.4	0.4	0.03	10.0	1.8	
Profile 2. Ontario loam—A Gray-Brown Podzolic soil								
A1	0–5	6.1	13.3	6.7	0.24	16.2	1.1	Illite
A21	5–10	4.8	12.5	1.7	0.05	19.4	1.4	
A22	10–14	5.1	16.7	1.2	0.03	23.3	1.6	Illite
A3/B1	14–19	5.3	20.3	0.4	0.03	7.4	1.6	
Bt1	19–26	5.6	33.5	0.5	0.04	6.7	1.6	Illite
Bt2	26–34	6.1	43.6	0.5	0.04	6.7	1.7	
Bt3	34–40	7.7	37.8	0.6	0.04	7.3	1.7	
C1	40–76	8.0	27.5	0.3	0.04	8.5	1.8	Illite
C2	76–80	8.1	23.5	0.2	0.03	5.7		Illite
Profile 3. Sodus loam-Ontario loam intergrade—A weak Podzol within a Gray-Brown Podzolic solum								
A0	3–0	4.0		27.0	0.81	19.4		
A2/A1	0–½	4.5	9.8	4.5	0.15	17.3		
Bir1	½–12	4.8	14.0	2.8	0.18	9.2	1.0	Illite and X‡
Bir2	12–19	5.5	14.3	1.0	0.06	9.5	1.4	
Bir3	19–26	5.3	15.5	0.4	0.04	6.6	1.5	Illite
A2	26–32	5.8	18.7	0.5	0.03	8.8	1.4	
Bt1	32–39	6.1	24.2	0.3	0.04	4.6	1.7	Illite
Bt2	39–54	6.9	29.4	0.4	0.04	5.3	1.7	
C1	54–73	8.2	21.6	0.3	0.03	5.7	1.6	Illite
C2	73–80	8.2	19.5	0.02	0.03	4.4	1.7	Illite
Profile 4. Sodus fine sandy loam—A weak Podzol on low-lime till								
A0	3–0	4.0		25.8	0.86	17.5	0.5	
A2	0–1	4.5	9.2	3.5	0.12	16.8	1.1	X‡
Bir1	1–15	4.7	4.8	1.7	0.06	15.7	1.2	
Bir2	15–25	4.8	5.7	0.5	0.03	9.4	1.4	X‡
B3	25–31	5.1	11.7	0.1	0.02	3.2	1.6	
C11	31–45	4.9	8.0	0.3		8.5	1.7	Illite
C12	45–57						1.8	Illite
C13	57–65						1.8	Illite
C2	65–84	7.8	8.9	0.0	0.0			

*pH, organic matter, and bulk density of all samples and per cent clay of profile 1 by S. B. McCaleb, research assistant, Cornell University. Nitrogen and carbon-nitrogen ratios by F. F. Peterson, research assistant, Cornell University. Mechanical analyses of profiles 2–4 by V. J. Kilmer, U. S. Dept. Agr. X-ray determination of clay mineral species by J. G. Cady, U. S. Dept. Agr.

†Means of values for 3 profiles.

‡A "mica intermediate" with greater spacing than illite, interpreted as a weathering product of illite, which appears to be the principal type inherited from parent material.

ships of profiles along these transects. Table 1 presents previously unpublished data for profiles along a transect northeastward from area G1 into area Pw2 (figure 1) on ground moraine of the Cary substage (7) of Wisconsin glaciation. The profile numbers in table 1 correspond with numbered positions in figure 2.

Locally on strongly calcareous material in this area, carbonates have been lost only to shallow depths and organic matter has accumulated in large amounts. Although weathering has occurred below the principal zone of organic accumulation, no well-defined horizon of silicate-clay accumulation has developed. These are the neutral uniform-textured Brown Forest soils (profile 1 of figure 2). Most commonly, however, Gray-Brown Podzolic soils occur on such material in this part of the State; a clay maximum has developed in the B, and A_2 horizon is apparent below the A_1 although the soil may be only slightly acid throughout the solum. Where the A_2 is strongly acid, as in profile 2, the textural profile is strongly expressed and yellowish iron films appear on primary particles in the upper, most acid part of the A_2. This property of the A_{21} is interpreted as the first sign of incipient Podzol development. In this profile, illite-type clays dominate in all horizons.

Where the entire solum has become strongly acid, as in profile 3, figure 2, a weak Podzol profile occurs above a clay concentration characteristic of Gray-Brown Podzolic B horizons; the humus layer is a mor instead of a mull, and the horizon of clay concentration appears to be degrading from the top downward. In this profile there is evidence of alteration of illite in the upper most acid mineral horizon. Where the entire solum is very strongly acid and only the deep substratum is high in bases, as in profile 4, cursory examination suggests only a normal Podzol profile. Frei (3) has shown remnants of clay concentrations, resembling those in a Gray-Brown Podzolic B, deep in what would normally be considered C_1 horizon. In these profiles there is strong evidence of alteration of illite-type clays in all horizons above these remnants of clay concentration. On originally acid material there is no evidence of any clay concentration deep in the profile.

Variations from the relationships described above may be attributed to differences of climate, time, and mineralogy of parent materials. The contrasts among profiles are most strongly expressed in area G1 in western New York on drift of the Cary substage of Wisconsin glaciation (7). Here the mean growing season temperature ranges from 60 to 68 F, the length of the growing season is 150 to 180 days, and mean annual precipitation is 28 to 40 inches. Brown Forest soils occur only locally in this area. Eastward at higher elevations in area G1, the relationship holds, but the textural profile of Gray-Brown Podzolic soils is less strongly expressed. Here the growing season is about 15 days shorter and the drift is probably younger.

In northern New York, Brown Forest soils occupy a higher proportion of the well-drained sites and the Gray-Brown Podzolic profile is less strongly expressed on medium-textured calcareous drift than on comparable material in western New York. These soils are on the youngest glacial deposits of the State and are in areas with growing seasons 15 to 30 days shorter than those of western New York. Locally in this region the Brown Forest soils grade through an acid variant directly to Podzols with no intermediate Gray-Brown Podzolic profile. This situation appears to be confined to materials high in quartz and low in clays or clay-forming minerals. Gray-Brown Podzolic profiles occur on the fine-textured lacustrine and marine deposits throughout the region.

The southern part of Area G3 of figure 1, is the outstanding exception to the relationship described, for here Gray-Brown Podzolic soils occur on both acid and calcareous material. This is one of the warmest areas in the State with a growing season of 180 to 195 days—an area slightly warmer and 10 inches per year more humid than the warmest part of western New York. It appears to be the northern limit of the main body of Gray-Brown Podzolic soils of Eastern United States, where this kind of profile is not confined to calcareous material. The profiles here have no evidence of incipient Podzol development within a degrading Gray-Brown Podzolic solum although the drift is more deeply weathered and apparently older than the Cary drift of western New York. It should be noted, however, that strongly expressed Podzols occur on coarse-textured deposits on Long Island in areas with equally warm and equally humid climates.

The differences of degree of expression of the Podzol profile on areas of acid drift are associated with climatic differences. The area of strong Podzols has a growing season of only 85 to 145 days and mean annual temperatures 5 to 8 degrees lower than the main area of weakly expressed Podzols farther south. On material of similar texture, the degree of development of the Podzol profile is much greater in the colder area.

THE LOCAL ASSOCIATIONS

On a given farm or within a field, the most common differences among profiles are those associated with differences of topographic position and ground water. Each of the well-drained normal profiles has moderately well, imperfectly, poorly, and very poorly drained associates. The moderately well and imperfectly drained profiles have the same kinds of master horizons as the well-drained normal soil, but characteristics associated with gleying are superimposed on them. In the poorly and very poorly drained members, characteristics of gleying are dominant.[4]

Catenas With Gray-Brown Podzolic and Brown Forest Soils

Figure 3 is a diagram of a catena with a Gray-Brown Podzolic soil like profile 2 of figure 2. The separation between well and moderately well-drained soils is made where faint mottling appears in the upper part of the C or lower part of the B horizon as evidence of a temporary water table deep in the profile. This mottling is usually some shade of yellowish brown. It appears higher in the profile and increases in amount and contrast as the surfaces of the aggregates in the B become lighter brown with increasing periods of waterlogging. In the well and moderately well-drained profiles, the blocky aggregates of the B_2 have faces darker than interiors. The division between moderately well and imperfectly drained soils is made where aggregate surfaces become as light as the interiors and yellowish-brown mottling becomes prominent in both the A_2 and B horizons. The imperfectly drained

---

[4] "G" is used to designate strongly gleyed horizons which change color upon exposure to air. When used in conjunction with A, B, or C, as "BG", it indicates strong gleying transitional to G. The subscript "g" indicates weak or moderate gleying superimposed on characteristics associated with the master horizon designation to which it is applied.

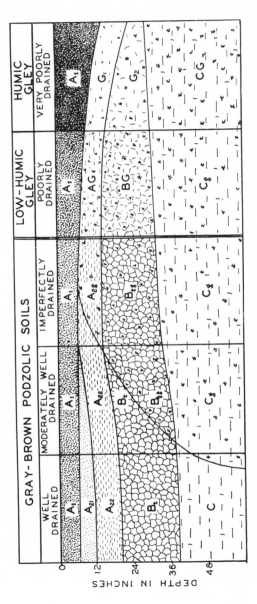

Fig. 3.–Catenary associations with Gray-Brown Podzolic soils in New York.

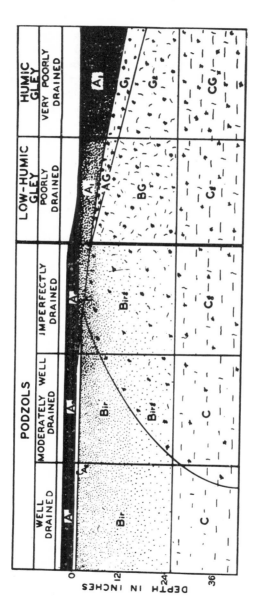

Fig. 4—Catenary associations with weakly expressed Podzols in New York.

soil retains the surface-soil color, textural and pH profiles, and general sequence of master horizons typical of its better-drained associates.

In the poorly and very poorly drained profiles, characteristics associated with gleying are dominant. The separation between imperfect and poor drainage corresponds with the differentiation of Gray-Brown Podzolic and Low-humic Gley soils. It is made where grayish colors indicative of prolonged gleying dominate the profile.

The A_1 horizon of the Low-humic Gley is typically very dark grayish brown moist and grayish brown when dry. The matrix of the AG is light gray or light brownish gray with high-contrast yellowish-brown mottling. The B horizon is weakly or moderately blocky but only slightly more clayey than horizons above. Each aggregate has a gray or brownish gray prominently mottled skin over a gray and brown mottled interior; the color sequence from the outside inward is like that from the AG to the BG of the whole soil in miniature. Roots are largely concentrated on aggregate faces. These soils are saturated to the surface for long periods, and increasing periods of waterlogging within the range of the group are reflected in increasing grayness of the entire profile.

The separation between poor and very poor drainage is made where the base colors approach neutral gray in the moist soil and subject to change toward brownish tints upon drying. This corresponds with the separation between Low-humic and Humic Gley soils, the latter having a thick very dark gray or black A_1 horizon over an intensively gleyed G horizon.

The same general relationships hold for catenas with Brown Forest soils, the major difference being the lack of a distinct clay maximum in the B horizons of the well, moderately well, and imperfectly drained members. On material of comparable texture within a moderate range of rock composition, the same series are used for the Low-humic and Humic Gley associates of both Gray-Brown Podzolic and Brown Forest soils.

Catenas With Podzols

Figure 4 is a diagram of a catena with a weakly expressed Podzol like that of profile 4 in figure 2 and table 1.

Criteria used to differentiate among catena members differ from those described for catenas with Gray-Brown Podzolic soils mainly in features associated with differences of the normal soils. The dominant yellowish-brown colors of the Podzol B horizon carry through the well, moderately well, and imperfectly drained members. Low-contrast mottling at depths ranging from as little as 10 to as much as 30 inches is the principle criterion for differentiating the moderately well from well-drained profiles. In the imperfectly drained member, low-contrast mottling extends to the A_0, but darker yellowish-brown color associated with infiltration of organic matter in the B horizon is commonly as good a criterion of imperfect drainage as is mottling alone. The mottling is indistinct against the yellowish-brown base until gray mottles become prominent as the drainage approaches poor.

In the poorly drained member, gray or grayish brown is the dominant color but yellowish-brown mottles are prominent. Most commonly the A_0 of better-drained members is replaced by 3 to 6 inches of A_1, but a thin A_0 may occur over the mixture of organic and mineral soil. The most strongly gleyed horizon occurs immediately under the A_1. The color and textural profile so nearly resembles that of poorly drained profiles associated with Gray-Brown Podzolic soils that both are tentatively being considered Low-humic Gley. The very poorly drained associate of weakly expressed Podzols is also commonly much like the soil of similar drainage in Gray-Brown Podzolic areas and is tentatively being included with Humic Gley.

Departures from this general relationship occur mainly in the region of strongly developed Podzols, and are most common on sandy material. Here a ground-water Podzol may replace the soil shown in imperfectly to poorly drained positions of figure 4. On very sandy material the most strongly expressed Podzol profiles are commonly on moderately well-drained sites where ground water is at depths ranging from 4 to 8 feet. In these areas also, the very poorly drained member of the catena may have a "peaty" humus layer, commonly with an A_1 below it, and would properly be classified as Half Bog.

Topographic and Ground-water Relationships

Drainage classes within any given catena are reflections of ground-water conditions, which depend largely on topographic position and soil or substratum permeability. The capacity of the watershed to supply water as seepage or surface flow in addition to that which falls as rain or snow and the ability of the soil to dispose of excess water internally or externally are the major contributing factors. Steepness of slope, as such, is commonly less significant than configuration and location within the larger landscape, though all are important.

On slowly permeable material, such as ground moraine, perched temporary water tables are dominant factors. On such material, the well-drained soil is typically on convex slopes where runoff disposes of an appreciable proportion of the water that falls on the soil and little water is contributed from adjacent watersheds. Such areas may be the convex crests of knolls on gently undulating to rolling plains or the upper parts of hills with greater local relief. Slope gradient does not have so great an effect on degree of expression of horizons as reported for Prairie soils of the middle west (8), and some series range from nearly level to steep.

The moderately well-drained profiles occur on similar-appearing convex slopes but commonly in positions where water is received from adjacent higher-lying land. The mottling of the B and upper C horizons is associated with temporary perched water tables just above slowly permeable material. Such areas may be the lower-lying knolls of undulating plains or moderately steep convex portions of hillsides with watersheds above them. Slope gradients as great as 25 percent are common. The imperfectly drained soils most commonly occur on uniform to slightly convex gentle slopes with a small contributing watershed and are uncommon in areas with high local relief.

The poorly drained soils on slowly permeable material may occupy nearly level areas with little contributing watershed or gently sloping to moderately steep, uniform or slightly concave lower portions of long slopes. In either case, a perched water table saturates the soil to the surface until late in the spring and may occur for shorter periods during the summer. Slope gradients range from nearly level to moderately steep. The very poorly drained soils may be either in concave depressions or in areas of nearly perennial seepage on slopes as great as 15 percent.

On rapidly permeable material, such as glacial outwash or deltaic sands, profiles with characteristics of restricted drainage are most commonly associated with regional ground-water tables connected with permanent zones of saturation. The essential feature is low gradient to some feature governing the base-level of the area. Basins or plains floored with slowly permeable clays, till, or bedrock are typical situations. The members of these catenas follow systematically from well to poorly drained along the gently upward-trending ground-water level from each incised drainage-way in level plains. Local differences in elevation of only one or two feet within such plains may account for differences of one drainage class. Although these are the most common situations, perched water tables above an unconforming slowly permeable stratum are factors locally.

LITERATURE CITED

1. Baldwin, M. First Internatl. Cong. Soil Sci. Proc. and Papers, Comm. V:276. 1927.

2. Cline, M. G. Soil Sci. 68:259. 1949.

3. Frei, E., and Cline, M. G. Soil Sci. 68:333. 1950.

4. Lyford, W. H., Jr. Soil Sci. Soc. Amer. Proc. 1946. 11:486. 1947.

5. McCaleb, S. B., and Cline, M. G. Soil Sci. 70-315. 1949.

6. Merrill, F. J. Geologic map of New York State. New York State Museum. 1901.

7. National Research Council. Glacial map of North America. Geol. Soc. Amer. 1945.

8. Smith, G. D., et al. Adv. in Agron. 2:157. Academic Press, New York. 1950.

GENESIS OF MIAMI SILT LOAM[1]

James Thorp, John G. Cady, and Erling E. Gamble[2]

ABSTRACT

Miami silt loam and other Gray-Brown Podzolic soils of the United States and Canada are developed from calcareous parent materials of glacial, glacial-fluvial or loessial origin; a large proportion of these materials were deposited during the Wisconsin stage of glaciation. Study of thin sections with polarized light shows clearly that much of the clay of the B_2 horizon has been carried in by water and deposited. Studies of the clay fraction of the soil and parent material indicate that much of the clay was either unaltered or has been transformed from clay originally present, but that some was formed by weathering of primary minerals. Characteristics of the A horizon may be ascribed to the joint effects of leaching, eluviation, and the influence of the broad-leaved deciduous forest and the associated macro- and micro-fauna. Recent leaching experiments, using "undisturbed" soil columns of Miami silt loam, suggest that B horizons are developed primarily through translocation of suspended fine clay and some humus, especially after the periods of soil drying in late summer and early autumn.

Miami silt loam is the best-known of the well-drained and well-developed soils of the north-central states. It is the prototype of the great soil group known as Gray-Brown Podzolic soils as named and described first by Mark Baldwin (2). Many samples have been analyzed physically and chemically and much has been written regarding its morphology and genesis. This paper reviews briefly the morphology of the Miami silt loam, presents new data from recent analyses and laboratory experiments, and offers hypotheses regarding its genesis. It is based on some results of a soil genesis project carried on jointly by members of the staffs of Earlham College, Richmond, Indiana, and the Soil Survey Laboratory, Beltsville, Maryland.

The Miami silt loam at Richmond, Indiana, is developed from medium-textured, highly calcareous glacial till with a silty overlay. The silt cap averages < 1 foot in thickness, but in places is up to 2 feet thick. The till contains calcitic and dolomitic limestone pebbles, sand and silt in amounts ranging from 25 to 55 percent as determined by analysis. The silt fraction of the till contains less than half as much lime as the fraction > 1 mm. in diameter. If the silt fraction of the loess source

[1]Contribution from the Soil Conservation Service, USDA, Beltsville, Md. Presented before Div. V, Soil Science Society of America, Nov. 18, 1957, at Atlanta, Ga. Received Dec. 22, 1958. Approved Jan. 16, 1959. The authors acknowledge the assistance of W. F. Holton in the laboratory work, especially in making the thin sections.
[2]Head, Dept. of Geology and Soil Science, Earlham College, Richmond, Ind., and Soil Scientist, Soil Survey Investigations, SCS, USDA, Washington, D. C.; Soil Scientist, Soil Survey Laboratory, SCS, USDA, Beltsville, Md.; and Soil Scientist, Soil Survey Investigations, SCS, USDA, Earlham College, Richmond, Ind., respectively.

Reproduced with permission from *Soil Science Society of America Proceedings,* Vol. 23, 1959, p. 65-70. Published by the Soil Science Society of America, Madison, Wisconsin, USA.

was similar to that of the till, the loess cap was probably less calcareous than the underlying till before weathering began.

The area studied is within the system of ground moraines and generally weak end-moraines shown by Leverett (7) as lying between the outermost Wisconsin drift, which he called the Shelbyville, and his Bloomington morainic system. This implies that the Miami silt loam in the Whitewater Valley lies on Leverett's Champaign drift. Certainly it is within the age limits of the Tazewell drift indicated by Wayne (10). South of the area where this study was conducted are the soils of the Russell catena, developed on earlier Tazewell drift with a thicker capping of loess.

Present rainfall averages 40 inches a year with about 8.3 inches in the winter, 11.2 inches each in the spring and summer months, and about 9.3 inches in the autumn. Winter temperatures average 28.5 F and summer temperatures average 71.5 F. Soils seldom freeze in virgin forest areas of Whitewater valley, and then only to a depth of 2 or 3 inches, but freezing goes much deeper in open fields during cold winters.

The native vegetation on Miami silt loam in Wayne County, Indiana, before settlement by white men, was a dense deciduous forest, dominated by oaks, sugar maple, hickories, beech, and black walnut, with other less-abundant species; but the composition of present wooded areas had been modified drastically by selective cutting. Studies by James B. Cope and Merrill Carrigan of Earlham College (report in preparation) show that oaks were much more important in the composition of the original forest than in present woodlots.

As noted by Baldwin (1), only a small fraction of the fallen leaves of one season remains on the surface by the time the next crop of leaves falls. Between one autumn and the next a succession of insects, myriapods, crustaceans, worms, protozoa, bacteria and fungi feed on the leaves, twigs, branches and fallen trees, on the organic material in the feces, or on the remains of predecessors. All take part in the transformation and partial exhaustion of the organic matter. Much of the dark humus of the A_1 horizon comprises feces of small animals, doubtless modified by molds and bacteria. Each user of the humus extracts part of the energy and leaves behind a product in which the energy is less available than in the preceding form. A dynamic near-equilibrium is reached between the addition of leaves to the surface and their decomposition to humus, water and gases.

Relatively few earthworms were found in Miami and associated soils of Lewis' Woods where these studies were conducted; apparently other animals are more active transformers there than are earthworms. The field studies of James Joyner (unpublished) and others have shown that worms are much more active in some other wooded areas of Miami silt loam, especially in grazed woodlands, than they appear to be in Lewis' Woods. Leaves are consumed more rapidly and "earthworm mull" is more noticeable where earthworms are abundant.

Some of the soluble organic matter leached from leaves and wood and formed by biological activity is carried into the soil by percolating water where it combines with the clay and moves along with it. The clay skins of the B horizon have a dark brown color imparted by organic matter. Ribbons of this dark-brown clay extend along joints a few feet into the C horizon of much of the Miami silt loam. We have noted that the "clay skins" on the soil blocks and lining rootholes in Miami B_2 horizons are lighter colored in soils long cultivated than in virgin woodlands. We believe that this is the result of more active decomposition in cultivated fields.

THE SOIL

The Miami silt loam profile discussed in this report was sampled and studied in "Lewis' Woods," 3/16 mile northeast of the southwest corner of Section 8, Twp. 15 N., Range 14 E., about 1 mile S. S. E. of Williamsburg, Wayne County, Indiana. This eighty acres of woods has never been grazed nor cleared but mature timber has been cut from time to time. Samples were collected from eight horizons and sub-horizons from one new profile and four samples of major horizons were collected from the site reported on by Brown and Thorp (4) in the same woods.

The following profile description sums up the morphological characteristics of the soil.

Horizon	Depth, Inches	Morphology
A_1	0-3	Very dark gray to dark grayish-brown (10YR 3/1 to 4/2, moist) silt loam; moderate fine crumb structure; friable when moist; soft when dry; boundary gradual and wavy; pH 6.3.
A_2	3-8	Very pale brown (10YR 7/3, dry) to brown (10YR 5/3, moist) silt loam; weak thin platy structure; friable when moist; slightly hard when dry and slightly sticky when wet; porous; lower boundary gradual; pH 5.8.
A_3-B_1	8-12	Light yellowish-brown to brown (10YR 6/4, 5/4, moist) silt loam to silty clay loam; weak to moderate fine subangular blocky structure with higher clay content and stronger structure in lower part; boundary irregular with intertonguing; pH 4.9.
B_{21}	12-19	Brown (10YR 5/3, 4/3, moist) silty clay loam; strong medium to coarse subangular blocky structure with thin streaks of pale brown heavy silt loam on upper block surfaces; firm when moist, hard when dry, sticky when wet; rock fragments present; lower boundary wavy; pH 5.5.
B_{22}	19-26	Dark brown (7.5YR 3/2 to 10YR 3/4) clay loam; coarse prismatic breaking to strong coarse to very coarse subangular blocky structure; firm when moist, hard when dry, sticky when wet; clay skins on surfaces of blocks are darker than interiors and they thicken toward lower part of horizon; lower boundary rather abrupt but irregular with tongues extending into horizon below; pH 6.1.
C_1	26-31	Light yellowish brown (2.5Y 6/4 to 10YR 6/4) loam glacial till. Some of the lime is leached out and dark brown clay films are present in joints and root and worm holes; pH 7.0.
C_2	31+	Strongly calcareous pale brown to grayish brown (10YR 6/3 to 10YR 5/3) loam till; about 40 percent limestone fragments. A few dark brown clay films in vertical cracks; pH 7.7.

Horizon thicknesses are variable. The thickness of the A_2 and A_3-B_1 transition is difficult to define closely. The depth to the C horizon may range from 25 inches to as much as 40 inches where tongues of B_{22} horizon penetrate into it. The samples were collected from a rather shallow representative of the series, and include some transitional horizons, so depths given in the thin section descriptions and

Table 1–Particle size distribution, pH, and organic carbon for Miami silt loam.

Depth	Horizon	Particle size distribution										pH 1:1	Organic Carbon
		Very coarse sand 2-1 mm.	Coarse sand 1-0.5 mm.	Medium sand 0.5-0.25 mm.	Fine sand 0.25-0.10 mm.	Very fine sand 0.10-0.05 mm.	Silt 0.05-0.002 mm.	Clay <0.002 mm.	0.2-0.02 mm.	0.02-0.002 mm.	> 2 mm.		
in.		%	%	%	%	%	%	%	%	%	%	%	%
0-3	A$_1$	1.8	4.0	6.2	12.1	7.1	52.2	16.6	29.2	36.8	4	6.6	3.58
3-7	A$_2$	1.4	3.9	6.2	12.0	7.6	52.6	16.3	31.7	35.2	3	5.0	0.82
7-13	A$_3$-B$_1$	1.4	3.9	5.9	11.9	7.6	47.4	21.9	27.8	33.9	5	4.8	0.58
13-18	B$_{21}$	1.5	3.6	5.3	10.8	7.0	32.3	39.5	24.0	21.3	3	5.1	0.40
18-23	B$_{22}$	1.9	4.2	6.1	11.9	7.5	26.6	41.8	22.8	18.0	6	5.4	0.34
23-31	B$_{22}$-B$_3$	2.4	5.0	7.2	15.7	10.2	26.5	33.0	30.1	15.4	7	6.8	0.44
37-41	B$_3$-C$_1$	1.5	4.7	7.6	18.5	12.0	24.3	31.4	32.3	14.7	5	6.0	0.33
36-40	C	4.4	6.0	6.0	13.6	11.9	41.1	17.0	39.1	22.0	12	7.7	0.20
						Recalculated on the Clay-Free Basis							
0-3		2.2	4.8	7.4	14.5	8.5	62.9		35.0	44.1			
3-7		1.7	4.7	7.4	14.3	9.1	62.8		37.9	42.1			
7-13		1.8	5.0	7.6	15.2	9.7	60.6		35.6	43.4			
13-18		2.5	5.9	8.8	17.8	11.6	53.4		39.6	35.4			
18-23		3.3	7.2	10.5	20.4	12.9	45.7		39.4	30.9			
23-31		3.6	7.5	10.7	23.4	15.2	39.6		45.1	23.0			
37-41		2.2	6.9	11.1	27.0	17.5	35.4		47.2	21.4			
36-40		5.3	7.2	7.2	16.4	14.3	49.5		47.1	26.5			

in table 1 may not agree exactly with the horizon depths indicated in the profile description.

LABORATORY PROCEDURES

Particle size distribution was determined by the pipette method as described by Kilmer and Alexander (6). The organic carbon method is described in (8). Separates saved after mechanical analysis were used for petrographic examination and clay mineral identification. Clays were examined by X-ray diffraction with a Geiger-counter diffractometer, as oriented aggregates on glass slides. A series of slides was analyzed which had been Mg^{++} and K^+ saturated, glycerol solvated, and heated stepwise to 500 C to identify the various minerals present. Thin sections were prepared after impregnation of blocks with a polystyrene resin. High montmorillonite content of some horizons made it necessary to dry-grind the specimens.

HORIZON DIFFERENTIATION

Table 1 shows the particle-size distribution of Miami silt loam and demonstrates the rather sharp contrast in silt percentage between the A-plus-B_1 and the B_2 horizons, and between the upper horizons and parent till. The contrasts are confirmed by examination of the particle-size composition calculated on the clay-free basis, and support the idea that material in the uppermost 12 to 14 inches was accumulated by wind action. The presence of a little very coarse sand and occasional small stones in this part of the profile is explained by mixing of upper and lower layers of soil when trees are uprooted and by the action of larger fauna. The low clay and high silt content of the till may not be real values for comparison with the other horizons because the analysis was run on whole material without removing the lime. Some clay is cemented into larger particles by lime.

The contrast in clay, silt, and sand content among the A, B, and C horizons in this Miami silt loam profile is shown clearly by figure 1.

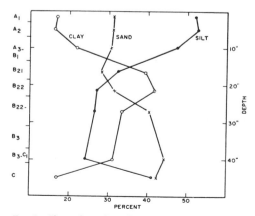

Fig. 1—Clay, silt, and sand content of Miami silt loam.

Note the concentration of silt in the A_1 to A_3 horizons and the heavy concentration of clay in the B_{22} horizon. A great deal of research and speculation has revolved around the genesis of this "textural B horizon" of Miami silt loam, and those of many soils in other forested regions, as well as in many soils of grasslands and deserts. An explanation of the "clay bulge" in Miami silt loam will probably be applicable to some of these other soils.

CLAY MINERALOGY AND WEATHERING

Montmorillonite, vermiculite, illite, and kaolinite are present in all horizons of this Miami silt loam profile. Relative amounts differ greatly among horizons. Illite is dominant in the till and the other minerals are in minor amounts. Illite is also fairly abundant in the lower B horizon but decreases upward in the profile to minor amounts in the A horizon. Montmorillonite is dominant in the horizons showing clay accumulation, being highest in the B_{21}, B_{22}, and B_3-C_1. Very little montmorillonite is present in the A_2 but the A_1 contains somewhat more of a very disordered, poorly crystallized variety. Vermiculite is present in all horizons, but is dominant in the A_1, A_2, and A_3-B_1 horizons, minor in the B, and slightly more abundant in the C horizon. Kaolin content is low throughout the profile, but is highest in the A_{21} indicating some accumulation as other minerals are removed. This distribution together with consideration of the properties of montmorillonite suggests that much of the clay which has moved and accumulated in the B horizon is montmorillonite; its particle-size is small; it is physically and chemically active, being capable of swelling and of forming complexes with organic compounds. The changes in illite and vermiculite concentration suggest that illite is weathering to vermiculite which in turn may be weathering to montmorillonite, although some illite could weather directly to montmorillonite. A part of the montmorillonite may be forming through weathering of ferromagnesian minerals. Analyses of soils and parent materials derived from loess by other workers (3) and by the Soil Survey Laboratory show that loess from sources presumably similar to that of the silt cap on this Miami profile contain relatively more montmorillonite than the unweathered till beneath. Hence, there are several possible sources of the clay present in the whole profile as well as the clay accumulated in the B horizon. The observed weathering sequence and the information obtained from clay mineralogy along with the lack of pronounced weathering

Table 2—Feldspar and hornblende percentages of 0.075 to 0.15 mm. sand,* Miami silt loam, Lewis' Woods.

	Horizons	\"New Pit\"							
		A_1	A_2	A_3-B_1	B_{21}	B_{22}	B_{22}-C_1	B_3-C_1	C_1
Feldspars		20	17	14	16	19	24	22	18
Hornblende		6	4	7	6	4	5	4	4

	Horizons	\"Old Pit\"		
		A_1-A_2	B_{21}	B	C
Feldspars		23	16	29	27
Hornblende		4	7	5	4

*Analysis by Hsin-yuan Tu.

of sand and coarse silt grains indicate that most of the clay can be accounted for by weathering and movement of clay minerals originally present in the till and loess.

As an indicator of weathering of primary minerals as a possible source of clay, a percentage analyses was obtained by counting several hundred grains of the dominant non-quartz minerals in the 0.075- to 0.15-mm. size range. The results in table 2 show a fairly large variation due to sampling errors and the natural variability of the till. However, the results suggest that a part of the feldspar of this size has weathered out of the lower A and upper B horizons. Examination of the heavy minerals of the coarse silt showed a lower hornblende content in the A_2 horizon but this is believed to be a feature of the loess composition. However, some of the hornblende was etched and corroded, indicating attack by acid solutions.

MICROMORPHOLOGY

Thin sections of oriented samples with undisturbed structure were examined with a petrographic microscope for evidences of weathering of mineral grains and movement and redeposition of clay. Following are descriptions of the micromorphology of the different horizons in sequence from the calcareous glacial till upward to the upper A_2 horizon. No thin sections could be made of the loose granular A_1 horizon.

1. *C horizon—Calcareous glacial till; sampled below a depth of 40 inches.*—This horizon is compact and has rather low porosity. Calcite and dolomite are present in all sizes from large pebbles down to micron-sized material spread through interstices. In the parts with highest lime content no segregation of minerals or particle sizes is evident and no pockets or skins or patches of clay appear in holes or as coatings around sand grains. However, in some areas which are lower in lime, there are spots, pockets, and streaks containing accumulations of clay which has been moved and redeposited. These are "skins" of oriented silicate clays along walls of cracks and crevices and lining pores. Most of these skins do not have lime in them, but some do. Many of them are lying against limy material; one was traced some distance along the surface of a limestone pebble.

   This does not settle the question about whether clay can move in the presence of lime, but it indicates that it can move in close proximity to it. The other possibility is that lime was removed locally, clay moved in, and later, lime was moved in and was reprecipitated. However, some of this "moved" clay is in close association with coarse limestone fragments.

2. *C_1—Calcareous but sampled near boundary to leached B_3-C_1 horizon at a depth of 36 to 40 inches.*—This sample is more variable than Number 1. Parts of the sections are very highly calcareous, densely packed, and contain lime even in the smallest grain sizes. Some fairly large portions of the horizon appear to be somewhat leached because the fine lime is removed and the coarser remains. In these latter areas there is a darkening or increase in opaqueness possibly due to an increase in concentration of clay. Also in these latter areas there are some crevice and pore fillings of "moved" clay mixed with lime or close to lime as described in 1 above.

   Some fairly large areas are leached almost free of lime and in these are copious thick skins of dark reddish-brown well-oriented laminated clay films. Here, as in the previously-described horizon, clay skins and lime particles are close together or even mixed. Well-developed clay skins are adjacent to lime fragments and particles. In one case, a large calcite rhomb had fractured into several pieces. The pieces were jagged with pinnacles and points having a very corroded appearance. These were surrounded by the brown clay films as if the clay itself were the attacking agent.

In places clay skins along crevices are interrupted where large surfaces of calcite are exposed in the wall, and then continue on the other side of the calcite. In some areas calcite has been removed without any accumulation of oriented clay; but there is usually a crevice with clay skin nearby indicating a place where solutions were moving.

3. B_3-C_1 transition; core depth 37 to 41 inches, taken from a deeper-leached tongue 3 feet away from Number 2.—The lime is gone, but apparently the matrix has not collapsed appreciably because the sections are full of holes which have the size and shape of sand grains. These pores are not the result of grains tearing out of the sections during preparation; they are not angular or ragged and there is no other evidence of damage. The main feature of the pores is the presence in almost all of them of a brownish skin of well-oriented laminated clay. This forms a skin of rather uniform thickness around the pore. Usually there is a relationship between size of pore and thickness of skin, small pores having thin skins, larger pores, thicker ones. In addition to these clay skins, oriented clay lines the cracks and channels. Linings are thin in small channels, and range up to thick masses in larger ones. Some of the quartz grains have thin films of oriented clay around them.

Away from the holes (there is not much area away from holes, they are so numerous) the clay is in small scaly aggregates packed among the other grains. Some areas show a reticulate pattern with simultaneous extinction between crossed nicols which may be the result of pressure. It is estimated that well over half of the clay present is in oriented skins in the pore linings, crack fills, and root holes.

Some of the feldspar and ferromagnesian minerals are etched and corroded at edges and converted to a clayey or micaceous substance. Grains so altered are relatively few and the effect is slight.

4. B_{22} —C transition; core depth 26 to 30 inches, above Number 2. Taken across a sharp contact between B_{22} and calcareous material. The thin sections came from the top of the calcareous part of the core.—In spite of being collected from a shallower depth, at least parts of this sample are less altered than Number 3. Some limestone fragments are still present, mostly remnants of larger grains of coarse sand size, and there are some fine sand-size calcite grains in the matrix. Most of these are being dissolved as shown by ragged edges, spaces between grains in compound particles, or a small corroded fragment remaining in a large pore. Some of these spaces contain no clay and no concentration of clay is in the vicinity, indicating that clay often starts to fill the pores only after the lime is gone. Little, if any, evidence of weathering of feldspars or hornblende can be seen.

Other parts of the sections are much like Number 3, but there is less evidence of clay having moved and lined pores. However, clay-flows of oriented reddish-brown clay are locally abundant in various types of crevices, pores and openings.

5. B_{22} horizon; core depth 19 to 23 inches.—This horizon is more heavily impregnated with brownish-red "moved" clay than the horizons below. It has the appearance of being "stuffed" with clay, which not only fills cracks and crevices and lines

pores as oriented skins, but also seems to have infiltrated the matrix away from visible openings. Open pores with clay linings are still fairly abundant, but the linings are thick and many pores are completely filled. Oriented skins around coarse grains are general. Clay has even infiltrated into porous ghosts of siliceous limestone pebbles. Skins can be easily traced completely around the surfaces of peds.

One bleached, collapsed spot, apparently a tongue of A_2 or a filled root channel or worm hole, is made up largely of silt, with little clay. Its boundary is very sharp.

Some feldspar grains are weathered around the edges.

6. *B_{21} horizon; core depth 14 to 18 inches.*—This horizon is considerably different from the horizons below in some ways and it is much more variable. The major part of the sections examined are like the B_{22} and have the densely impregnated appearance of being stuffed with reddish-brown moved clay. There are thick clay skins on aggregate surfaces, thick pore linings and skins around grains, and there is rather heavy impregnation throughout the matrix itself.

Other parts of the sections are siltier and contain less clay. Oriented skins are thinner, when present. Most of the clay present is in single separate chips and flakes of silt size. There are gradations in degree of these two conditions, but boundaries are often sharp between the two. For instance, one side of a crack has dense clay impregnation, while the other side is lighter colored and contains no oriented clay.

Some aggregates are densely impregnated inside but are bounded by cracks where clay skins would be expected. However, when the cracks are traced out the skins disappear, leaving empty channels. The grayish leached areas still have some thin pale clay skins in small pores and small crevices.

Some feldspar grains show weathering in place but these are the minority of total feldspar. One grain was seen which was weathering along cleavage and twinning planes in such a way that it would tend to reduce size of grains. If dispersed, it would break along the weathered planes to make several smaller grains. A part of the increase in silt in the surface could be due to such disintegration of feldspars, but we saw no evidence of any process that would make fine sand or silt grains out of coarse quartz grains.

7. *A_3-B_1 transition; core depth 8 to 12 inches.*—This horizon is considerably more leached and eluviated than Number 6. Most of the material on the slide has a bleached appearance with little organized clay in skins, pore fills, cracks or in any sort of pockets or patches. As mentioned in the discussion of the horizon below, what clay is present is in randomly-scattered small flakes and chips.

These are spots which have an appearance exactly like the B_2—these are packed with brownish, thickly laminated clay with oriented pore linings and clay skins. These are being attacked around the edges; channels, cracks and crevices are being stripped and there is a decrease in density of clay impregnation from the centers outward.

One of the most striking features is the general absence of clay skins in cracks and along aggregate boundaries. Places which in the B_2 would have skins are bare. There are some thin oriented skins in some smaller cracks. Some of these are discontinuous, can be traced a short distance, then disappear. Often there is a concentration of oriented clay *near* the wall of a crack but the surface of the wall itself is stripped and bleached. (In the B_2 where there are thick clay skins the oriented clay is abundant in the matrix parallel to the wall as well as in the crack itself.) This stripping may account for the silty powdery coatings seen on peds where the degradation process is going on.

These thin sections show very convincingly the breakdown of the upper B horizon with loss of clay. The residual areas with a high content of oriented clay are evidence that what is now the A_3-B_1 was once full of clay like the present B_2. The stripping of the aggregate surfaces and pore fills is very apparent and the effect is quite striking.

Some collapse of the stripped parts has occurred, shown by the close packing of the grains and the near-absence of visible pore space. It looks as if some silt had worked down into this horizon.

Feldspars weathering in place are common, but most of the feldspar grains are fresh and clean.

8. *A_2 horizon; core depth 3 to 7 inches.*—This horizon is siltier than the others. There is no segregation of components into any structure; their arrangement is uniform and randomly packed. Clay is uniformly distributed in form of little chips and flakes, and as unoriented packing between silt grains. Abundant black and dark brown flecks appear to be organic matter and charcoal. Round, opaque MnO_2-Fe_2O_3 concretions are common.

Many of the feldspar and hornblende grains are corroded and weathered but many are still fresh. This is the only horizon with much weathered hornblende.

One small area contained some oriented clay—a skin of oriented clay in a large pore with some patchy reddish-brown clay skins in crevices and around large grains nearby. We believe this is a small residue of B horizon material because of color and structure. It could easily have been brought here by burrowing animals or by an overturned tree or it could be the last vestige of B horizon at this depth. In the vicinity there were a few other pores with traces of clay concentrated near their walls, suggesting that this aggregate was once larger and is being destroyed by eluviation of clay. In most of the rest of the sections of this horizon there are no such clay-lined pores and crevices.

LEACHING EXPERIMENTS

Experiments, designed to find out how the clay content is increased in the B_2 horizon as compared to the other horizons in the profile, have been reported by Thorp et al. (9). Water and extracts of tree leaves were passed through tubes filled with crumbled clay loam from Miami B_2 horizon. Clay moved in suspension in the tubes and some, emerging at the base, lent the effluent a slightly "milky" color. Visible films of clay were deposited in lower parts of the soil columns.

In a later series of experiments distilled water and a water extract of sugar-maple leaves were passed through columns of structurally undisturbed samples, each pair taken in duplicate to overlap adjacent horizons. Details of these experiments will appear elsewhere. Earliest effluents from these undisturbed columns were visibly turbid, demonstrating that fine clay was moved through the columns in suspension. As the soil became wet, clay movement decreased, indicated by the reduced turbity of the effluents. The leaching was repeated after the soil had been dried out by growing a wheat plant in each column with the same result except that effluent from the column overlapping the B_2 and C_1 horizons was clear.

If the soil contains even a small percentage of clays that shrink and swell with moisture changes, the wetted surface of a dry ped will swell quickly and may exfoliate (peel off) from the ped. In the process, some of the fine clay goes into suspension and causes the water to become turbid. In natural soil columns, of course, the breakdown is less severe and complete than in isolated or loose peds because of the limited space for expansion. Qualitatively, it appeared that the greatest amount of clay movement was from the columns that overlap the A_3 and B_1 horizons. We believe the mechanical effect of peeling off is a partial explanation for the dispersion of clay in the columns. Maple-leaf extract mobilized more clay than did the distilled water. The formation of complexes between organic matter and clay, especially montmorillonite, is possibly another factor. Whatever the cause, it is clear that clay is brought into suspension and moves through the soil as individual clay particles.

CONCLUSIONS

From field and laboratory observations we conclude that clay accumulation in B horizons in Miami silt loam and in closely related soils is due primarily to movement in suspension from upper to generally lower horizons where much of the clay is deposited by drying or as a result of differences in chemical environment. Three years of weekly observations of water levels in soils in Lewis' Woods (to be reported later in detail) demonstrate that water passes completely through Miami silt loam and into the ground water only occasionally and especially in winter and spring. More frequently, except in winter and spring, the plants use up all of the "free" water before it goes out of reach of roots. Any suspended clay is left behind to be added to that which is already there. Only occasionally is the clay carried deeper, to be deposited in joints of the underlying glacial till.

Morphology of Miami silt loam shows that the original blocks of the upper part of the B horizon have lost most of the clay coats they may have had and now are dull in color and sprinkled with whitish silt. Lower in the B horizon, the lower parts of the blocks are covered with shiny clay and finally in the B_{22}, the brown "clay skins" cover all surfaces and line root holes and fill most other cavities. Examination of the clay skins with the petrographic microscope shows clearly that the clay crystals of these "skins" are oriented with the C-axis perpendicular to the surfaces which they cover. Clay minerals in water suspension can be laid down as an oriented film either by evaporation of the liquid or by a filtering action as turbid water is sucked into dry ped interiors from the cracks, pores, and channels as the dry soil is wetted.

In addition to the clay that has obviously been moved, as shown by optical orientation, the thin sections show "flakes" and "chips" of clay in the matrix that were either part of the original clay in the till or have been formed in place, probably by weathering of small grains of primary minerals, especially mica, and perhaps fine shale chips. In general, this clay-in-place is much less than half of the total in the B_{21} and B_{22} horizons, but is a large part of the total in the C and A horizons.

Eluviation ("stripping") of clay from the A, and illuviation in the B horizon account for most of the differences in clay content among horizons.

The thin sections show clearly also that some feldspars are in the early process of breaking down to clay, especially in the lower parts of the A and the upper parts of the B horizon; but they appear to have made only a small contribution to the total clay content in the B horizons.

The distribution of relative proportions of the clay minerals in the horizons of the profile suggests that illite is weathering to vermiculite and in turn to montmorillonite. In the A and upper B horizons the montmorillonite because of its small size and greater reactivity is rendered mobile and is removed to progressively lower depths.

Vermiculite and to some extent kaolinite accumulate in the clay fraction of the A_2 and A_3-B_1 transition. Some of the montmorillonite was originally present in the till, some has been formed by weathering of other clay minerals, and some is being fed into the system by weathering of primary minerals.

Evidence from the leaching columns substantiates evidence from soil morphology and micromorphology that clay is being removed gradually from the A_3 and B_1 horizons where acidity is strongest, and is carried down and largely deposited in the B_2 horizon, where reaction is less acid, probably with some loss of clay from the profile as a whole. Thus, the upper B horizon is gradually converted into an A_2 horizon as much of the clay is removed and coarser fractions remain behind.

LITERATURE CITED

1. Baldwin, Mark. The Miami profile. Am. Soil Survey Assoc. Bull. VIII, pp. 28-34. 1937.

2. ————. The Gray-Brown Podzolic soils of the eastern United States. Trans. Intern. Cong. of Soil Sci. 1st Cong. Washington. IV:276-282. 1928.

3. Beavers, A. H. Source and deposition of clay minerals in Peorian loess. Science 126:1285. 1957.

4. Brown, I. C., and Thorp, James. Morphology and composition of some soils of the Miami family and the Miami catena. USDA Tech. Bul. 834. 1942.

5. Gooding, A. M. Pleistocene terraces in the upper Whitewater drainage basin, southeastern Indiana. Earlham College Sci. Bull. 2, Richmond, Indiana. 1957.

6. Kilmer, V. J., and Alexander, L. T. Methods of making mechanical analyses of soils. Soil Sci. 68:15-24. 1949.

7. Leverett, Frank, and Taylor, F. B. The Pleistocene of Indiana and Michigan. Monographs of the U. S. Geological Survey 53:87-121. 1915.

8. Peech, M., Alexander, L. T., Dean, L. A., and Reed, J. F. Methods of soil analysis for soil fertility investigations. USDA Circ. 757. 1947.

9. Thorp, James, Strong, L. E., and Gamble, Erling E. Experiments in soil genesis—the role of leaching. Soil Sci. Soc. Am. Proc. 21:99-102. 1957.

10. Wayne, W. J. Wisconsin stratigraphy of central and eastern Indiana (abstract). Indiana Acad. Sci. Proc. 63, pp. 199-200. 1954.

FRAGIPAN SOILS OF ILLINOIS:
I. GENERAL CHARACTERIZATION AND FIELD RELATIONSHIPS OF HOSMER SILT LOAM[1]

R. B. Grossman, J. B. Fehrenbacher, and A. H. Beavers[2]

ABSTRACT

Bisequal soils with fragipans are common in southern Illinois. The purpose of this introductory paper is to set the general framework for understanding the nature and occurrence of these soils through the description of the morphology, chemical and physical properties, and field relationships of Hosmer silt loam, a soil with moderate fragipan expression.

The bisequal nature and expression of the fragipan increase with decreasing loess thickness and with latitude from north to south. Maximal expression is in the low, moderately well-drained, topographic positions. It is suggested that these soils in Illinois are part of an interstate sequence extending southward into Mississippi, within the loess-derived soils of the Mississippi River Valley.

The moderately well- and well-drained, loess-derived soils of southern Illinois developed under forest vegetation include modal Gray-Brown Podzolics and Gray-Brown Podzolics intergrading to Red-Yellow Podzolics. The Intergrade soils are commonly bisequal[3] and contain a fragipan or "fragizone" within the lower sequum. The purpose of this paper is to present morphological, physical, and chemical data for Hosmer silt loam, a soil containing a medial fragipan, and, with this as a point of reference, to describe the change in morphology as related to the depth of loess, latitude, and topographic position. Subsequent papers will deal with the mineralogy of the solum as it is related to parent material uniformity and with the micromorphology (10, 11).

---

[1]Contribution from the Department of Agronomy, Illinois Agr. Exp. Sta., Urbana. Published with the approval of the Director of the Illinois Agr. Exp. Sta. Presented before Div. V, Soil Science Society of America, Atlanta, Ga., Nov. 20, 1957. Received Apr. 11, 1958. Approved Aug. 14, 1958.

[2]Graduate Assistant, Assistant Professor, and Assistant Professor, respectively. Senior author now Soil Scientist, Soil Conservation Service, USDA, Beltsville, Md.

[3]"Sequum" refers to a "sequence of an eluvial horizon and its related illuvial horizon." The sola of the soils containing fragipans in Illinois are composed of two sequa or are "bisequal." (Terminology from mimeograph report of the National Cooperative Soil Survey Technical Work-planning Conference, 1955.) For purposes of discussion, the lower sequum shall be denoted by a prime; a complete horizon sequence would be A_p, A_2, B_1, B_2, A'_2, B'_2, B'_3, and C. In this notation, the B'_3 horizon exhibits the maximum pan-like morphology.

Reproduced with permission from *Soil Science Society of America Proceedings*, Vol. 23, 1959, p. 65-70. Published by the Soil Science Society of America, Madison, Wisconsin, USA.

The term "fragipan" is defined in the Soil Survey Manual (32) mainly on the basis of certain physical properties: high bulk density, relatively low clay percentage, massiveness, and a pronounced, reversible induration. The fragipans in Illinois meet these physical criteria. A "fragipan soil," however, as the concept is employed in Illinois, involves at least two additional morphological features: (1) the fragipan is found within the lower sequum of a bisequal solum; and (2) the occurrence in the lower sequum of a polygonal network of gray, silt loam that extends downward from the A'_2 horizon and delineates prismatic structural units (see figures 2 and 3).

In subsequent discussion, reference will be made to "incipient," "moderate," and "strongly" expressed fragipans and A'_2 horizons. An incipient A'_2 horizon contains weak, gray coatings on the surface of well-expressed subangular or blocky structural units. The zone is not sensibly coarser in texture than either the horizons directly above or below. At the other extreme, a strongly expressed A'_2 horizon has a definite gray color, is usually coarser in texture than the horizons above or below, and tends to be either massive or platy, although remnants of blocky peds are not uncommon. Criteria for increasing fragipan expression are a decrease in structural grade, an increase in the size of the structural units, and a change in shape from blocky or subangular blocky to prismatic, coupled with an increase in the resistance of the peds to rupture. Thus, a weak or incipient fragipan (B'_3 horizon) or fragizone might have moderate, medium, blocky structure and firm consistence, compared with the moderate, coarse, prismatic structure and extremely firm consistence of a strongly expressed fragipan. Associated with a progressive expression of the fragipan are increasingly distinct gray planes and more intense mottling of the lower sequum.

LITERATURE REVIEW

This review is limited to the pertinent literature on bisequal soils and soils with fragipans of the eastern United States and eastern Canada.

Bisequal sola, in which the upper sequum is a Brown Podzolic or a Podzol and the lower is a Gray-Brown Podzolic, have been described in eastern Canada by Stobbe (33), in Michigan by Veatch and Millar (41), Allen and Whiteside (1), and Gardner and Whiteside (6), and in New York by Cline (3), Frei and Cline (5), McCaleb and Cline (21), and McCaleb (20). These bisequal sola are considered as intergrades between the Gray-Brown Podzolic and Podzol or Brown Podzolic great soil groups.

Fragipans are common in soils developed from medium- to coarse-textured, acid parent materials. The pans described by Stobbe (34) in Quebec, by Foster et al. (4) in Michigan, and by Taylor (36) in Pennsylvania and New York could probably be considered fragipans. More recently, Carlisle[4], Knox (17), and Grossman and Cline (9) have studied the morphology, genesis, and basis for rigidity of the pan for several fragipan soils in New York State. Tamura (35) has suggested that the compact C horizons found in several Connecticut soils resemble fragipans.

---

[4]Carlisle, F. J., Characteristics of soils with fragipans in a Podzol region. Ph.D. thesis, Cornell University, Ithaca, New York, 1954.

Soils that are apparently bisequal and contain a fragipan in the lower sequum have been reported in the coastal plain of southern Maryland by Nikiforoff (23, 24), in West Virginia by Smith and Browning (30), in Indiana by Bushnell (2) and Ulrich et al. (38), in Tennessee by Winters (42), and in Missouri by Krusekopf (18).

Although recognition of fragipan horizons in Illinois has occurred only recently, the A'$_2$ horizon (or the then "gray layer") was noted in southern Illinois soils over 35 years ago. According to Norton (25), Marbut called attention to it during a field trip in the area during 1925. Norton interpreted this "gray silty band" in the middle of the B horizon of several southern Illinois soils as a podzolized zone of a buried soil profile. This interpretation has merit in cases where well-developed soils are present in several different, superimposed geological materials. However, the "gray band" described by Norton at a depth of 25 to 30 inches in profiles developed within Peorian loess, is currently considered the lower, eluvial horizon of a conforming bisequum. Evidence for this interpretation for Hosmer silt loam will be presented in a subsequent paper.

Norton et al. (27), in the soil report of Jackson county, Illinois, noted that the depth to mottling increases with the greater thickness of loess closer to the Mississippi River Valley loess source; this was attributed to the loess being of more recent origin nearer the source. Though the "gray layer" is not specifically mentioned, recent field study of the soils in the area indicates the mottle-free zone corresponds to the upper sequum of present terminology, and the mottled, gray-coated lower subsoil is the lower sequum, that contains a fragipan.

MATERIALS AND METHODS

Standard nomenclature was employed in describing Hosmer silt loam, as set forth in the Soil Survey Manual (32); colors refer to the moist condition.

Hosmer Silt Loam

Location: T9S-R2E Sec. 19, NW 160, NE 40, NW10 on N side of railroad cut in Williamson county, Illinois.

Slope: 4 to 5% to north.

Vegetation: Originally hardwood forest, but the sampling site has been cultivated and the cover is now bluegrass and weeds.

Horizon	Depth, inches	Description
A$_p$	0-8	Brown (10YR 4/3) friable silt loam with weak, fine crumb structure and abrupt smooth boundary.
A$_2$	8-15	Brown to yellowish brown (10YR 5/3 to 5/4) friable silt loam with weak, fine platy structure and an abrupt smooth boundary.
B$_2$	15-25	Strong brown (7.5YR 4/6) firm, fine silt loam. Moderate, medium subangular blocky structure. Clear smooth boundary.
A'$_2$	25-28	Brown (7.5YR 5/4) with dark brown (7.5YR 4/4) clay coatings and common, pale brown (10YR 6/3) distinct, fine mottles. Periphery of peds commonly light gray (10YR 7/2) fine sand and silt. Firm

silty clay loam with moderate, medium subangular blocky structure and clear smooth boundary.

B'$_2$ 28-36   Brown (7.5YR 5/4) with many, medium pale brown and yellowish brown (10YR 6/3 and 5/8) mottles. Dark brown (7.5YR 4/4) clay coatings and some fine Fe-Mn concretionary mottles present. Periphery of peds often light gray (10YR 7/2) fine sand and silt, particularly along vertical cleavage planes. Very firm silty clay loam with moderate, medium to coarse prismatic structure breaking to coarse blocky and subangular blocky peds. Gradual smooth boundary.

B'$_3$ 36-48   Dark brown and brown (7.5YR 4/4 and 5/4) with many medium pale brown (10YR 6/3) mottles. Some dark brown (7.5YR 4/4) clay coatings and Fe-Mn concretionary mottles; weakly expressed light gray (10YR 7/2) ped peripheries. Very firm, fine silt loam with moderate coarse blocky aggregates, having a weak prismatic tendency; aggregates show some vesicularity. Gradual smooth boundary.

C$_1$ 48-56   Brown (7.5YR 5/4) with few, distinct pale brown (10YR 6/3) mottles. Firm silt loam. Massive leached Peorian loess. Gradual smooth boundary.

D$_1$ 56-70   Reddish brown (5YR 4/4) with some streaks of light brownish gray (10YR 6/2). Firm silt loam. Massive leached Farmdale loess. Clear smooth boundary.

D$_2$ 70-85   Dark brown (7.5YR 4/4) firm silt loam containing some fine sand. Massive leached Illinoian till soil. An A horizon with some mixing of loess. Gradual smooth boundary.

D$_3$ 85-95+   Yellowish brown and dark yellowish brown (10YR 5/4 and 4/4) with mottlings of very pale brown and dark yellowish brown (10YR 7/4 and 3/4). Firm, coarse silty clay loam to clay loam. Massive leached Illinoian till soil B horizon.

Polygonal cracks filled with light gray (10YR 7/2) silt and clay occur in the B'$_2$ and extend downward, becoming thinner and less pronounced in the underlying Illinoian till soil. This profile is considered maximal Hosmer grading towards the Ava soils.

Mechanical analysis data supplied by the Bureau of Plant Industry were obtained by the method of Kilmer and Alexander (15); the remaining determinations were made by the method as outlined by Gieseking (8). Bulk density was determined by the paraffin clod method. Each value give in table 1 is the average of three clods. The moisture percentages closely approximate the moisture status of the profile at the time of sampling, which was early in the spring, when the solum was near field capacity. With slight modifications, hydraulic conductivity[5] was determined by the method as outlined by Uhland and O'Neal (37); values reported in table 1 are the average of the initial and final runs.

In the "drop-shatter" test (Marshall and Quirk, 19), roughly spherical, air-dry, undisturbed soil units, weighing between 200 and 400 g., were dropped 2 m. onto a concrete floor covered with heavy wrapping paper. Excessive scattering was prevented by a barrier, approximately 2 feet square. The soil material was dropped and sieved a succession of 3 times; this was found to give the best compromise

---

[5] As defined in "Report of Definitions Approved by the Committee on Terminology, Soil Science Society of America," 1956 (31).

Table 1—Physical properties of Hosmer silt loam.

Sample number	Horizon	Depth	Particle size distribution*					Moisture content	Bulk density		Hydraulic conductivity	Drop-shatter Log-geometric mean
			2-0.05 mm.	0.05-0.02 mm.	0.02-0.002 mm.	<0.002 mm.	<0.0002 mm.		Moist	Air-dry		
		in.	%	%	%	%	%	%	g/cc.	g/cc.	in./hr.	mm.
17963	A_p	0-8	4.5	38.1	42.6	14.8	—	19.1	1.40	1.45	3.58	—
17964	A_2	8-15	2.0	31.9	48.0	18.1	—	17.8	1.50	1.48	1.05	—
17965	B_2	15-25	1.6	27.5	43.5	26.6	14.2	19.1	1.47	1.66	0.29	12
17966	A_2'	25-28	2.4	26.9	42.9	27.6	16.9	23.9	1.53	1.58	0.40	10
17967	B_2'	28-36	1.6	27.6	40.0	30.3	21.2	23.4	1.55	1.69	0.01	19
17968	B_3'	36-48	1.0	28.6	43.9	26.5	—	21.2	1.58	1.68	0.01	23
17969	C_1	48-56	1.0	31.7	44.3	23.0	—	17.1	1.63	1.70	0.01	36
17970	D_1	56-70	14.1	34.5	32.4	18.4	11.3	15.5	1.62	1.68	0.03	—
17971	D_2	70-85	18.6	31.9	28.6	20.7	12.5	—	1.57	—	—	—
17972	D_3	85-95	40.1	20.1	20.7	19.2	11.1	15.6	1.64	—	—	—
Gray material from A_2'		25-28	2.1	29.6	43.2	24.4	16.2	—	—	—	—	—

*Particle-size distribution for samples 17963, 17964, 17968, and 17969 determined by members of the Soil Mangement and Irrigation Division, Bureau of Plant Industry, Soils and Agricultural Engineering, ARS, USDA; where entries are not given, determinations were not made.

Table 2—Chemical properties of Hosmer silt loam.*

Sample number	Horizon	Depth	pH	Organic carbon	Cation-exchange capacity	Base saturation	Exchangeable cations (me./100g.)				Ca/Mg ratio
							Ca	Mg	K	Na	
		in.		%	me./100g.	%					
17963	A_p	0-8	6.5	0.71	13.2	66	6.8	1.6	0.1	0.2	4.2
17964	A_2	8-15	5.0	0.31	—	—	—	—	—	—	—
17965	B_2	15-25	4.7	0.05	14.9	32	2.6	1.7	0.2	0.2	1.5
17966	A_2'	25-28	4.6	0.04	—	—	—	—	—	—	—
17967	B_2'	28-36	4.6	0.04	24.0	38	3.7	4.5	0.3	0.5	0.8
17968	B_3'	36-48	4.6	0.01	—	—	—	—	—	—	—
17969	C_1	48-56	4.7	0.01	20.3	59	5.8	5.3	0.3	0.6	1.1
17970	D_1	56-70	5.4								
17971	D_2	70-85	5.4								
17972	D_3	85-95	5.1								
Gray material from A_2'		25-28	4.5								

*Determinations by members of the Soil Management and Irrigation Division, Bureau of Plant Industry, Soils and Agricultural Engineering, ARS, USDA; where entries are not given, determinations were not made.

between a maximum of discrimination and a minimum of effort. The average, cumulative weight-percent oversize for six samples was plotted on log-normal paper as a function of sieve opening size (see Gardner, 7). The log-geometric mean as obtained from these plots is reported in table 1. Deviations from linearity make this analysis of the data somewhat questionable and further work is required on the best procedure to analyze and express data of this nature.

Chemical analyses (table 2) were performed by Bureau of Plant Industry personnel using the methods as outlined by Peech et al. (28), with Na and K determinations by the flame photometer. Exceptions are the pH values for samples 17970 through 17972, plus the "gray material from the A'_2" which were obtained by the authors, using a Beckman pH meter and a 1:1 soil-water suspension.

The "weathering numbers" given in figure 3 were calculated from the relationship, $R \times D_{wt}/E_p$, in which R is the rainfall in millimeters, D_{wt} is the relative hydrolysis constant for water at the temperature in question as obtained from Ramann (29), and E_p is the evaporative power of the environment, calculated from the equation,

$$E_p = \text{Vapor Pressure at T (°C.)} \times (100 - RH)/100$$

in which the vapor pressure is expressed in millimeters of mercury (13) and RH is the relative humidity for the temperature in question. The quotient, R/E_p, is identical with Meyer's NS Quotient, as discussed by Jenny (14)[6].

Weather data were obtained from the following twelve stations (16, 39, 40) located between latitude 32 degrees and latitude 44 degrees and within 200 miles east and west of the Mississippi River: LaCrosse, Wis.; Moline, Ill.; Peoria, Ill.; Springfield, Ill.; St. Louis, Mo.; Cairo, Ill.; Jonesboro, Ark.; Blytheville, Ark.; Union City, Tenn.; Memphis, Tenn.; Jackson, Miss.; Vicksburg, Miss. With one exception, rainfall and temperature records were for over 25 years; relative humidity records were for shorter periods with a minimum of 10 years. The mean daily relative humidity was approximated from the average of the 6:30 a.m. and 12:30 p.m. readings. Relative humidity at second-order stations, and that for St. Louis, a first-order station, was calculated from the average of the two bracketing first-order stations.

The equation for the regression between weathering number and latitude was
$$1332 - 19.1 \text{ (degrees latitude)}$$
with a correlation coefficient, r, of 0.92 for 11 degrees of freedom. From this regression, the weathering numbers given in figure 3 were obtained.

RESULTS AND DISCUSSION

Physical data.—There is a definite though not pronounced clay maximum in the B'_2 horizon. As the field description indicates, the A'_2 horizon contains elements both similar to the B'_2 horizon and gray, silty material, rather characteristic of an A_2 horizon. This would account for the difference in clay percentage between the bulked A'_2 horizon and the so-called "gray material from the A'_2." If the latter is

---

[6]The idea for the calculation of a weathering number was obtained from Hallsworth (12), whose symbolism has been largely followed. Hallsworth introduces the term D_{wt} as the reciprocal, and so his "Acidification Index" is different from the weathering number.

considered the true A'_2 horizon, there is a minimum in clay percentage between the B horizons of the two sequa. The B'_3 horizon is a fine silt loam (medium textured), the broad textural class of soils in which fragipans appear to have best expression (43).

The moist bulk density values show a regular increase with depth, whereas the air-dry values for the B horizons of the two sequa are roughly comparable. Values for the B'_3 horizon are within the range reported by Smith and Browning (30) and somewhat less than those given by Nikiforoff (24) and Carlisle.[7]

Hydraulic conductivity values for the B'_2 and B'_3 horizons of the lower sequum are below those for the upper sequum. The low hydraulic conductivity of the C_1 and D_1 horizons suggests, however, that relatively, weakly altered loess may have hydraulic conductivities of the same order as the fragipan. Values for the lower sequum are of the same order of magnitude as those reported by Smith and Browning (30) and by Winters and Simonson (43).

The results of the "drop-shatter" test given in table 1 indicate a progressive increase in resistance to fracture from the upper sequum through the lower sequum to the C_1 horizon. There is a fairly good correlation between the decrease in structural grade and class as observed in the field (see field description), and the increase in mean size of the shattered material, particularly if comparisons are restricted to within the lower sequum. The high value of the C_1 horizon suggests that, when dry, weakly altered loess is more resistant to fracture than the fragipan proper. When moist, however, as the field description indicates, the C_1 is less resistant to rupture than the fragipan (B'_3 horizon). Thus, the results would suggest that somewhat weathered loess, may express a greater degree of reversible induration than a fragipan. This, in turn, suggests that reversible induration may be a property inherent in the nature of loessial parent materials and is not specific to the fragipan developed therein.

Chemical properties.—With the exception of the A_p, which has been limed, the low pH, percent base saturation, and Ca/Mg ratio of the solum are indicative of a rather advanced degree of weathering. Both the percent base saturation and the Ca/Mg ratio of the B'_2 horizon are lower than at the comparable depth of maximum clay percentage in Winfield and related soils (Group IV) of the Mississippi Valley, as discussed in Illinois Bulletin 587 (22).

Field Relationships

Areal distribution of the major soil associations of southern Illinois is shown in figure 1. The terrace and bottomland area (Area A) is the presumed major loess source. Area B includes Gray-Brown Podzolic soils (Alford) without a fragipan, or at most with incipient fragipan and A'_2 expression where they grade into the soils of Area C. Area C soils (Hosmer) have moderate fragipan and A'_2 development, and Area E soils (Grantsburg) have the most strongly developed fragipans and bisequal character. Area D soils (Ava), because of the relatively shallow depths to the underlying Illinois till, are variable in fragipan expression. The northern boundary of the area with bisequal soils containing fragipans is the Shelbyville (Wisconsin) terminal moraine on the east and a diffuse zone of loess-derived soils on the west,

---

[7] Carlisle, F. J. *Op. Cit.*

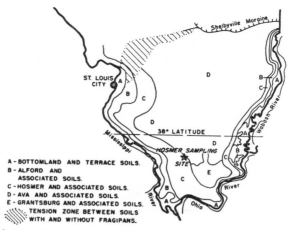

Fig. 1—Areal distribution of various soils associations in southern Illinois in relation to the major rivers and main loess sources (A areas).

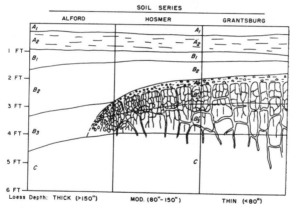

Fig. 2—Expression of bisequal sola and associated fragipans in relation to loess depth near 37.5 degree latitude.

as indicated by the cross-hatched region in figure 1. The banded nature of these soil associations along the principal loess sources is a reflection of the loess-thinning pattern away from the source.

Figure 2 is a transect from Area B, through C, to Area E, near 37.5 degrees latitude, that illustrates the increasing bisequal nature and expression of the fragipan with increasing distance from the loess source or decreasing loess thickness. This suggests that the expression of a bisequal solum and fragipan bears a relationship to the effective age of the soil, in a manner analogous to the concept developed previously for the Brunizem, Brunizem-Planosol Intergrade, and Planosol "maturity" sequence (25).

Considering soils sufficiently distant from the loess sources to exhibit a bisequal nature and a fragipan (Areas C, D, and E of figure 1), there is a progressive increase in the expression of these features from north to south (as illustrated in figure 3). This change in expression with latitude in the loess-derived soils of the Mississippi Valley, continues southward beyond the Illinois border, as both the thickness and expression of the A'_2 horizon and the development of the fragipan progressively increase. In conjunction, the nature of the B'_2 horizon changes, decreasing in clay and exhibiting weaker structural expression, until, at the latitude of northern Mississippi, the B'_2 horizon as described for Hosmer has largely disappeared and the A'_2 horizon rests directly on a well-developed fragipan horizon. It would thus appear that the fragipan soils of southern Illinois may be considered the northern segment of an interstate, climatic sequence.

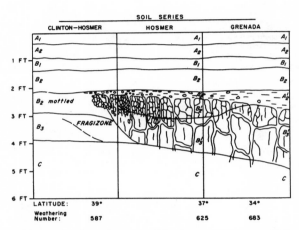

Fig. 3—Expression of bisequal sola and associated fragipans in Mississippi Valley loessial soils as function of latitude; dependence of weathering environment on latitude expressed as "weathering number."

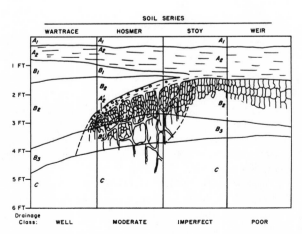

Fig. 4—Expression of bisequal sola and associated fragipans in relation to topographic or catenary position, within moderately thick loess belt near 37.5 degree latitude.

The "weathering numbers" given in figure 3 are an attempt to give quantitative expression to the relative weathering environment as determined by differences in climate within soils derived from similar parent material. This number is composed of two factors, R/E_p, which is presumed proportional to the amount of leaching, and D_{wt}, the relative hydrolysis constant of water. In more general chemical terms, the former (R/E_p) may be considered as proportional to the rate of end-product removal, and the latter (D_{wt}) is the temperature dependence of the reaction, analogous to the Van't Hoff Q_{10} expression.

Within the C, D, and E Areas of figure 1, bisequal and fragipan expression varies with natural soil drainage (see figure 4). Fragipans and the associated A'_2 horizon are most highly developed in moderately well-drained soils. In poorly drained sites, fragipan-claypan intergrades are usually found. From observation, it seems that soils grading from moderately well to imperfectly drained have the most highly expressed fragipans and bisequal nature.

LITERATURE CITED

1. Allen, B. L., and Whiteside, E. P. The characteristics of some soils on tills of Cary and Mankato age in Michigan. Soil Sci. Soc. Am. Proc. 18:203-206. 1948.

2. Bushnell, T. M. An outline of the classification of Indiana soils. Proc. Indiana Acad. Sci. 55: 151-158. 1940.

3. Cline, M. G. Profile studies of normal soils of New York: I. Soil profile sequences involving Brown Forest, Gray-Brown Podzolic, and Brown Podzolic soils. Soil Sci. 68:259-272. 1949.

4. Foster, Z. C., Veatch, J. O., and Schoenmann, L. R. Soil survey of Iron County, Michigan. USDA Ser. 1930, No. 46, 1937.

5. Frei, E., and Cline, Mg. G. Profile studies of normal soils of New York: II. Micromorphological studies of the Gray-Brown Podzolic-Brown Podzolic soil sequence. Soil Sci. 68:333-344. 1949.

6. Gardner, D. R., and Whiteside, E. P. Zonal soils in the transition region between the Podzol and Gray-Brown Podzolic regions in Michigan. Soil Sci. Soc. Am. Proc. 16:137-141. 1952.

7. Gardner, W. R. Representation of soil aggregate-size distribution by a logarithmic-normal distribution. Soil Sci. Soc. Am. Proc. 20:151-153. 1956.

8. Gieseking, J. E. The mechanical analysis of noncalcareous soils. Agron. Dept., Univ. of Illinois, AG 1406. 1949.

9. Grossman, R. B., and Cline, M. G. Fragipan horizons in New York: II. Relationships between rigidity and particle size distribution. Soil Sci. Soc. Am. Proc. 21:322-325. 1957.

10. ...., Stephen, I., Fehrenbacher, J. B., Beavers, A. H., and Parker, J. M. Fragipan soils of Illinois: II. Mineralogy in reference to parent material uniformity of Hosmer Silt Loam. Soil Sci. Soc. Am. Proc. 23:70-73. (this issue) 1959.

11. ...., ..., ..., and Beavers, A. H. Fragipan soils of Illinois: III. Micromorphological studies of Hosmer Silt Loam. Soil Sci. Soc. Am. Proc. 23:73-75. (this issue) 1959.

12. Hallsworth, E. G. An interpretation of the soil formations found on basalt in the Richmond-Tweed region of New South Wales. Australian J. Agr. Research 2:411-427. 1951.

13. Hodgman, C., ed., Handbook of Chemistry and Physics, 31st Edition, Chemical Rubber, Cleveland, Ohio p. 1852. 1949.

14. Jenny, H. Factors of Soil Formation. McGraw-Hill, New York, N. Y. p. 109. 1941.

15. Kilmer, V. J., and Alexander, L. T. Methods of making mechanical analyses of soils. Soil Sci. 68:15-24. 1949.

16. Kincer, J. B. Climate and weather data for the United States. In Climate and Man, USDA Yearbook of Agriculture, U.S. Government Printing Office, Washington, D. C., p. 695-1228. 1941.

17. Knox, E. G. Fragipan horizons in New York soils: III. The basis of rigidity. Soil Sci. Soc. Am. Proc. 21:326-330. 1957.

18. Krusekopf, H. H. The hardpan soils of the Ozark region. Soil Sci. Soc. Am. Proc. (1942) 7: 434-436. 1943.

19. Marshall, T. J., and Quirk, J. P. Stability of structural aggregates of dry soil. Australian J. Agr. Research 1:266-275. 1950.

20. McCaleb, S. B. Profile studies of normal soils of New York: IV. Mineralogical properties of the Gray-Brown Podzolic-Brown Podzolic soil sequence. Soil Sci. 77:319-333. 1954.

21. ...., and Cline, M. G. Profile studies of normal soils of New York: III. Physical and chemical properties of Brown Forest and Gray-Brown Podzolic soils. Soil Sci. 70:315-328. 1950.

22. Muckenhirn, R. J., et al. Field descriptions and analytical data of certain loess-derived Gray-Brown Podzolic soils in the upper Mississippi River Valley. Illinois Agr. Exp. Sta. Bul. 587. 1955.

23. Nikiforoff, C. C. Hardpan soils of the coastal plain of southern Maryland. U.S. Geol. Survey, Prof. Paper 267B:45-63.1955.

24. ...., Humbert, R. P., and Cady, J. G. The hardpan in certain soils of the coastal plain. Soil Sci. 65L135-153. 1948.

25. Norton, E. A. Succession of soil profiles along the Mississippi River in Illinois. Amer. Soil Survey Assoc. Bul. 11:158-160. 1930.

26. .... The genesis and morphology of the prairie soils. Amer. Soil Survey Assoc. Bul. 14:40-42. 1933.

27. ...., Smith, R. S., DeTurk, E. E., Bauer, F. C., and Smith, L. H. Jackson County soils. Illinois Agr. Exp. Sta. Soil Rept. No. 55, p. 16-19. 1933.

28. Peech, M., Alexander, L. T., Dean, L. A., and Reed, J. F. Methods of soil analysis for soil fertility investigations. USDA Circ. 757. 1947.

29. Ramann, E. Bodenkunde. Julius Springer, Berlin. p. 23. 1911.

30. Smith, R. M., and Browning, D. R. Occurrence, nature, and land-use significance of silt-pan subsoils in West Virginia. Soil Sci. 62:307-317. 1946.

31. Soil Science Society of America. Committee on Terminology. Report of definitions approved by the committee on terminology. Soil Sci. Soc. Am. Proc. 20:430-440. 1956.

32. Soil Survey Staff. Soil survey manual, USDA Handbook 18. 1951.

33. Stobbe, P. C. Adaptation of apple sites in Quebec to special soil types. Sci. Agr. 17:329-332. 1936.

34. .... The morphology and genesis of the Gray-Brown Podzolic and related soils of eastern Canada. Soil Sci. Soc. Am. Proc. 16:81-84. 1952.

35. Tamura, T. Physical, chemical and mineralogical properties of Brown Podzolic soils in southern New England: Paxton and Merrimac series. Soil Sci. 81:287-300. 1956.

36. Taylor, A. Profile studies of soils derived from glacial, sandstone and shale materials in Ohio, Pennsylvania, and New York. Am. Soil Survey Assoc. Bul. 12:104-110. 1931.

37. Uhland, R. E. and O'Neal, A. M. Soil permeability determinations for use in soil and water conservation. USDA SCS-TR-101. 1951.

38. Ulrich, H. P., Bushnell, T. M., Kunkel, D. R., Miller, J. T., and Fitzpatrick, E. G. Soil Survey of Pike County, Indiana. USDA Ser. 1930. No. 47. 1938.

39. U.S. Dept. Commerce, Weather Bureau. Climatography of United States, No. 11-B: Climatic summary of the United States—supplement for 1931-1952. Government Printing Office, Washington, D.C.

40. U.S. Dept. Commerce, Weather Bureau. Local climatological data, annual survey, 1955. Government Printing Office, Washington, D.C.

41. Veatch, J. O., and Millar, C. E. Some characteristics of mature soils in Michigan. Amer. Soil Survey Assoc. Bul. 15:42-44. 1934.

42. Winters, E. Silica hardpan development in the Red and Yellow Podzolic soil region. Soil Sci. Soc. Am. Proc. (1942) 7:437-440. (1943).

43. ...., and Simonson, R. W. The subsoil. In A. G. Norman ed., Advances in Agronomy. Academic Press, Inc. N. Y., N. Y. 3:1-92. 1951.

SOLS BRUNS ACIDES OF THE NORTHEASTERN UNITED STATES[1]

A. J. Baur and W. H. Lyford[2]

ABSTRACT

Sols Bruns Acides is the name now used in Belgium, France, and possibly other European countries for a class of soils at the great soil group level. Similar soils have developed under forest vegetation in the Northeastern United States, and it is proposed that the same name be applied here. In the past these soils have been included with Brown Podzolic, weak Podzol, weak Gray-Brown Podzolic or Red-Yellow Podzolic soil groups. Morphologically, Sols Bruns Acides have a thin A_1 horizon; a paler A_2 or A_2-like horizon (possibly a B_1 horizon) which is poorly differentiated from the B_2 horizon; a B_2 horizon with uniform color from top to bottom, weak subangular blocky structure, and silicate clay accumulation not evident or appearing only in traces. Sola of these soils are strongly to very strongly acid and have low base status. Distinction between Sols Bruns Acides and the Gray-Brown Podzolic and Red-Yellow Podzolic soils rests mainly on amounts of clay accumulation in the B horizon. Sols Bruns Acides differ from weak Podzols and Brown Podzolic soils mainly in color and structure of the B horizon. The latter have in the upper B horizon strong colors which fade with depth and weak, fine granular structure.

Certain soils of the Northeastern United States have properties intermediate between Brown Podzolic and Gray-Brown Podzolic soils. Prior to about 1953 they were classified with either one or the other of the above, or with weak Podzols; now they are known to be like the Sols Bruns Acides of Belgium. It is the pupose of this paper to describe the morphology and distribution of these soils in the Northeastern United States.

The term, Sols Bruns Acides, is used here for a class of soils at the great soil group level. Although horizon expression is weak these soils have a unique combination of characteristics that serves to differentiate them from weak Podzols, Brown Podzolic, Gray-Brown Podzolic and Red-Yellow Podzolic soils with which they were classed (2, 6) prior to about 1953. Morphologically they exhibit: (a) uniform colors in the B horizon rather than a more intense color in the upper part of the B horizon such as characterizes Podzols and Brown Podzolic soils; (b) weak subangular blocky structure throughout the B horizon rather than granular structure like that

---

[1]Contribution from the Soil Survey, Soil Conservation Service, U.S.D.A. Presented before Div. V. Soil Science Society of America, Cincinnati, Ohio, Nov. 15, 1956. Received Dec. 31, 1956. Approved April 4, 1957.

[2]Principal and Senior Soil Correlators, respectively, Soil Conservation Service, U.S.D.A., Ithaca, New York and Durham, New Hampshire.

Reproduced with permission from *Soil Science Society of America Proceedings*, Vol. 21, 1957, p. 533-536. Published by the Soil Science Society of America, Madison, Wisconsin, USA.

characteristic of the upper B horizon of most Podzols and Brown Podzolic soils; and (c) uniform texture throughout the solum contrasting in this respect with Gray-Brown Podzolic and Red-Yellow Podzolic soils which have silicate clay accumulation in the B horizon.

Particular attention was called to these soils by the Belgian soil scientists, R. Tavernier and A. Pecrot, during their visit to the Northeastern United States in 1953. Soils in the Hudson River Valley and in the vicinity of the New York-Pennsylvania State Line previously considered to be transitional or intergrade soils, were identified as identical with rather extensive soils in Belgium which had been named Sols Bruns Acides (8).

Because of this positive identification of our soils with those of Belgium, the name Sols Bruns Acides is used in this paper in preference to the translated name Acid Brown Earths used by Cline (3).

DISTRIBUTION IN THE NORTHEAST

A line projected from Boston, Massachusetts, westward through Central New York marks the approximate northern limit of the Sols Bruns Acides in the Northeast. Immediately south of this line, these soils are found along with Brown Podzolic and gleyed soils. From the Southern Hudson Valley and from Pennsylvania to West Virginia they are found with Gray-Brown Podzolic and Red-Yellow Podzolic soils and their Low Humic-Gley, Humic-Gley and Lithosol associates. The southward and westward limits have not been determined. Observations by others than the authors indiciate that the Sols Bruns Acides group may occur as far west as Minnesota.

Certain soil series or segments of them in the Northeast have been identified recently as belonging to the Sols Bruns Acides great soil group. Data are presented in this paper for the Dekalb, Mardin, Lordstown, and Wethersfield soils. In addition, the Chatfield and Rockaway series studied by Krebs[3], and the Wethersfield by Tamura and Swanson (9) probably represent Sols Bruns Acides. Cline (3) in a key to the soil series of New York lists between 15 and 20 series as Acid Brown Earths (Sols Bruns Acides).

GENERAL FEATURES OF THE REGION

Sols Bruns Acides developed under forest cover. The strongest morphological expression of these soils is found where oaks are a major component of the forest. Tree species occurring in the region of Sols Bruns Acides include white, red, black, and chestnut oaks, hickories, beech, white pine, hemlock, and formerly chestnut. The northern range of these soils extends into the region of northern hardwoods. Here the original tree stand was dominantly beech, sugar maple, yellow birch, hemlock, and white pine with some red oak as transitional species (1).

Average annual rainfall ranges from 35 to 45 inches in the region where Sols Bruns Acides are developed. Precipitation is distributed fairly uniformly through

---

[3]Krebs, R. D. Seven soil profiles in northern New Jersey; A study of the factors in their genesis as shown by certain of their morphological, physical, chemical, and mineralogical characteristics. Unpublished thesis, Rutgers University, New Brunswick, N.J. 1955.

the year. Soils are always moist enough to support good growth of trees and agricultural crops except during occasional midsummer periods of low rainfall. Length of the frost-free period ranges from 125 to 175 days. Temperatures drop low enough during the winter so that soils are frozen at the surface and usually to a depth of 3 to 12 inches or more, depending on prevailing temperature and protective cover. Sols Bruns Acides can be found on all exposures and slopes ranging from nearly level to steep. In unplowed forested areas there is a hummocky microrelief due to windthrow as described by Denny and Goodlett (4). Well and moderately well drained soils with good moisture-holding capacity are most common, but a few excessively drained as well as somewhat poorly drained soils have been recognized as possessing major features of Sols Bruns Acides.

These soils are developed on parent materials originating principally from non-calcareous or weakly calcareous sandstones, siltstones, slates, granite, schist, and quartzite. Part of the region has been glaciated and the soils occur both north and south of the limits of the continental ice sheets. In the areas of glacial drift these soils are found on early and late Wisconsin deposits. None have been identified with certainty on pre-Wisconsin drift. South of the drift in Pennsylvania, Maryland, and West Virginia they are found on materials which appear to have been in place a relatively short time. Disturbance, movement, and redeposition of these materials probably took place in Pleistocene or Recent Time as a result of colluvial, frost, or other forces (4).

CENTRAL CONCEPT OF SOLS BRUNS ACIDES IN THE NORTHEASTERN UNITED STATES

In general, unplowed Sols Bruns Acides as found in the Northeastern United States have a thin A_1 horizon; an A_2 which is poorly differentiated; a B_2 with uniform color, weak subangular blocky structure, and silicate clay accumulation not evident or appearing only in traces. Moderately coarse to medium textures are most common in the sola of these soils, but they also develop with coarse textures. Fragipan horizons occur in many Sols Bruns Acides. Where present, these horizons may have a distinct accumulation of clay and a much higher percent base saturation than horizons above.

Horizon	Description
A_{00} and A_0	Forest floor—consists of a thin layer of loose leaves, which in most places nearly disappears in the fall before new leaf drop; in some places underlain by a dark brown weakly fibrous mor consisting mostly of matted leaf remains ½ to 1 inch thick. Contains many mites, spiders, and ants. Near cultivated fields, earthworms have invaded the soil.
A_1	A 1- or 2-inch thick very dark grayish brown horizon, highly enriched with organic matter through biological activity; full of fine roots and mycelia. It has weak to moderately developed fine granular structure and is very friable.
A_2	The A_2 horizon ranges in thickness from 3 to 10 inches. It differs but slightly from the B_2 horizon below and especially when moist may be

overlooked or considered as a B_1 or B_{21}. When dry it is slightly paler than the horizon below, but the color difference is small; in the order of one or less Munsell color unit in value and chroma or a slight change in hue, for example 10YR to 7.5YR. Structure is weak fine platy or granular or both. The fine platy structure is especially distinctive in slightly moist or nearly dry fine sandy loam, loam and silt loam textures, but may not be evident in moist or wet soils. The peds are porous and crush easily.

In many plowed soils this horizon is entirely incorporated in the plow layer and no trace remains. Plow layers generally have chroma of 3 or 4.

The weakness in development of the A_2 cannot be emphasized too strongly; in fact, in many places A_3 or B_1 might be better horizon notation than A_2. Furthermore, there is some field evidence that the A_2 horizon may be transient. Detailed studies might show that the color of this horizon changes seasonally.

B_1 An intergrade horizon is found only where the A_2 is fairly distinct. If present, it represents a color and structure gradation.

B_2 The B_2 horizon ranges from 12 to 20 inches in thickness. Where the soils are developed on parent material with 10YR to 5Y hues, this horizon when moist is dark yellowish brown 10YR 4/4 or dark brown 7.5YR 4/4. A value of 5 when moist is found in some cases; chroma of 6 is rarely reached. This horizon has about the same clay content as the A_2; if clay content is greater the difference is not more than 1 or 2 percent. Silicate clay in the form of clay flow or coatings is seldom visible to the unaided eye. If present in this form it occurs as faint discontinuous or spotty deposits in pores and on the outsides of peds. In sandy loam, loams, and silt loams this horizon generally has weak medium subangular blocky structure but the structure may be moderately well developed in some places. In coarse textures the structure is very weak. Peds are porous and crush easily. Soil material in some cases becomes firm in the lower part. A firm to very firm, brittle fragipan has developed in the lower B horizon of some Sols Bruns Acides, usually with a higher content of clay than the horizons above.

C   Generally the parent material is somewhat coarser textured than the solum. It is acid, but in some localities carbonates are present at 5 to 8 feet. Shale, gravel, cobbles, and stones may be present, commonly ranging from 1 to 50 percent by volume.

Additional characteristics common to the Sols Bruns Acides are indicated by the data in table 1. The percent of clay below 2 microns in diameter in the B_2 horizons, excluding fragipan horizons marked with subscript m, is approximately the same as in the A_2 horizon. In no case does the clay in the B exceed that in the A_2 by more than 1.7 percent. The percentage of free iron oxides remains about the same in the A_2 and B_2 horizons. Organic carbon is high in the A_1 horizon, decreases sharply in the A_2, and decreases successively in each lower horizon. All of the A and B_2 horizons are strongly and very strongly acid and low in base status.

In contrast, the Gray-Brown Podzolic soil in table 1 exhibits distinct clay accumulation in the B horizon and the Brown Podzolic soil a greater free iron oxide content in the upper B horizon. Lajoie and DeLong (5) show a similar content and distribution of free iron oxide for Brown Podzolic soils. Other soils, however, which have been classed as Brown Podzolic fail to show a distinct maximum of iron oxides in the upper B horizon.[4]

RELATIONSHIPS TO OTHER SOILS

As clay accumulation in the B horizon increases and clay films on peds and in pores become more distinct and continuous, the soils tend toward the Gray-Brown Podzolic or Red-Yellow Podzolic group. Changes in base status and acidity may accompany changes in clay accumulation in the B_2 horizon. Distinctions between Sols Bruns Acides on the one hand and Gray-Brown Podzolic and Red-Yellow Podzolic soils on the other, rest mainly on differences in amounts of clay between the A and B horizon and on the nature of clay films in the B horizon. A noticeable increase in clay from the A_2 to the B horizon or the presence of faint and continuous or distinct and discontinuous clay film is considered sufficient basis for placing a given soil series into either the Gray-Brown Podzolic or Red-Yellow Podzolic group, depending upon other characteristics.

Some thick solum soils have Sol Brun Acide A and B horizons in the upper part underlain by a zone having the clay accumulation and structure of a Gray-Brown Podzolic or Red-Yellow Podzolic B_2 horizon (other than a fragipan). Thus, it appears that the upper Sol Brun Acide sequence of horizons occupies the position of a very thick A_2. Depth to and prominence of the lower B or zone of clay accumulation varies. Several alternatives exist for classifying soils with these horizon sequences. They may be considered as Sols Bruns Acides—Gray-Brown Podzolic or Sols Bruns Acides—Red-Yellow Podzolic intergrades because of the Sol Brun Acide characteristics in the upper solum and the B_2 horizon of one of the other groups at some depth. Another alternative, if the clay accumulation is weak and occurs at depths below 30 or 36 inches, is to disregard this feature and simply class the soil as Sol Brun Acide.

Shallow Sols Bruns Acides in contrast to Lithosols have discrete B_2 horizons. If the content of coarse fragments increases until it reaches such proportions that structure and other features of the B horizon can no longer be identified the soil is classed as a Lithosol.

In many places unplowed areas of Sols Bruns Acides have a micropodzol 2 to 4 inches thick, directly below the A_1 horizon. This is destroyed by plowing and may be disregarded in classifying the soils at the great soil group level.

In regions where Sols Bruns Acides merge with Brown Podzolic soils, color and structure differences which characterize the two classes largely disappear. As the soils tend to Brown Podzolic the faintly paler A_2 or A_2-like horizon of Sols Bruns Acides may appear only as a spotty or discontinuous horizon. In places where the A_2 horizon is not discernible colors are uniform from the A_1 to the C horizon or they may be slightly darker and stronger immediately under the A_1 due to staining by organic matter or a weak accumulation of iron and humus complexes. In

---

[4]Unpublished data. U.S.D.A., B.P.I.S.&A.E., Division of Soil Management and Irrigation Agriculture, Beltsville, Maryland. March 1952.

Table 1—Physical and chemical data for representative Sols Bruns Acides, Gray-Brown Podzolic, and Brown Podzolic soils.*

Soil type and location	Horizon	Depth	Silt 0.05-0.002 mm.	Clay < 0.002 mm.	Free iron oxides	Organic carbon	pH	Base saturation
		inches	%	%	%	%		%
			Sols Bruns Acides					
Dekalb stony loam† (field name Dekalb stony sandy loam) Monongalia Co., W. Va.	A_1	0-1½	29.7	30.4	2.3	10.5	3.9	6
	A_2	1½-7	51.6	18.8	2.5	2.09	4.4	4
	B_{21}	7-13	49.5	18.0	2.7	0.65	4.6	3
	B_{22}	13-22	42.3	18.9	3.0	0.24	4.7	10
	B_3	22-30	44.5	18.2	3.0	0.11	4.9	10
	C_1	30-40	31.2	11.7	2.2	0.07	4.9	20
Lordstown channery silt loam† Tioga Co., N.Y.	A_p	0-8	56.0	13.4	1.44	2.64	4.8	12
	A_2	8-12	57.2	12.2	1.20	0.49	5.1	14
	B_1 (or B_2)	12-22	58.6	13.6	1.44	0.33	5.2	15
	B_{21} (or B_3)	22-48	54.1	9.6	1.04	0.16	5.2	20
	B_{22} (or C_1)	48-72	54.4	8.8	1.20	0.03	5.2	38
	C	72-84	48.4	7.8	1.20	0.14	5.3	44
			Sols Bruns Acides with fragipan					
Mardin channery silt loam† Tioga Co., N.Y.	A_1	0-4	65.0	23.4	1.60	7.30	4.9	23
	A_2	4-6	66.9	21.9	1.92	1.19	4.8	12
	B_1	6-10	64.1	22.6	1.84	0.63	4.7	14
	B_{21}	10-16	63.1	20.5	1.60	0.46	4.7	17
	B_{22}gm‖	16-24	55.3	25.9	1.84	0.16	4.8	18
	B_{23}m	24-48	53.3	26.9	1.84	0.15	5.2	39
	B_{24}m	48-54	54.1	27.2	2.00	0.24	5.7	52
Weathersfield stony silt loam†,‡ Hartford Co., Conn.	A_0	1-0	—	—	—	—	5.8	—
	A_1	0-½	—	—	0.84	26.8	4.2	9
	A_2	½-1	48.2	12.4	1.63	7.0	4.2	4
	B_1	1-6	53.3	14.3	1.88	2.33	4.6	3
	B_{21}	6-18	41.8	11.1	1.92	0.39	4.8	1
	B_{22}	18-24	42.1	10.1	1.80	0.23	4.6	5
	C_1 (or B_{23} m)‖	24-36	42.0	15.8	2.12	0.04	5.2	67

(continued on next page)

Table 1—continued

	Horizon	Depth					
Gray-Brown Podzolic soil							
Ontario loam§	A_1	0-5	—	13.3	6.7¶	6.1	—
Cayuga Co., N.Y.	A_{21}	5-10	—	12.5	1.7	4.8	—
	A_{22}	10-14	—	16.7	1.2	5.1	—
	A_3/B_1	14-19	—	20.3	0.4	5.3	—
	B_{t1}	19-26	—	33.5	0.5	5.6	—
	B_{t2}	26-34	—	43.6	0.5	6.1	—
	B_{t3}	34-40	—	37.8	0.6	7.7	—
	C_1	40-76	—	27.5	0.3	8.0	—
	C_2	76-80	—	23.5	0.2	8.1	—
Brown Podzolic soil							
Paxton loam†,‡	A_1	0-4	2.00	30.6	4.28	4.0	3
Hillsboro Co., N.H.	B_2	4-16	3.00	28.7	1.25	4.7	4
	B_3	16-24	1.72	27.1	0.27	4.6	6
	C	24-36	1.12	23.2	0.19	5.0	6

*For descriptions and data on representative Red-Yellow Podzolic soils see U.S.D.A. Soil Survey Laboratory Memo No. 2, Washington, D.C. 1954.

†Determinations made by U.S.D.A., S.C.S., Soil Survey Laboratory, Beltsville, Md. 1952.

‡Data from U.S.D.A. Soil Survey Laboratory Memo No. 1, Beltsville, Md. 1952.

§Data from M.G. Cline. Major Kinds of Profiles and Their Relationships in New York, Soil Sci. Soc. Amer. Proc. 17:123-127, Table 1, Profile 2. 1953.

‖Fragipan horizons indicated by subscript m.

¶Figures for Ontario loam are percent organic matter determined by wet oxidation.

this region of mergence subangular blocky structure is weakly expressed and it is replaced to a large extent by granular structure. Soils with these characteristics might be classed as Sols Bruns Acides—Brown Podzolic intergrades or the range of the Sols Bruns Acides might be extended to include them as such. In contrast, Brown Podzolic soils as defined by Lyford (6) have distinct, strong colors in the upper B horizon and these colors fade with depth. This horizon has weak fine granular structure.

It seems that the eventual limits between the Sols Bruns Acides and the Brown Podzolic groups might be made on characteristics known to be a measure of sesquioxide and humus accumulation or genesis and for which we now do not have adequate methods of measurement. Unpublished[5] free iron oxide data on some thin Podzol and Brown Podzolic B_{ir} horizons and data by Matthews et al. (7) indicate that the strong color of these upper B horizons may be due principally to organic matter rather than iron—at least as measured on the soil fraction less than 2 mm. in diameter.

Further work is necessary to characterize Sols Bruns Acides in terms of genetic processes. Information is needed, especially on (1) silicate clay formation and movement, and (2) generation and mobility or lack of mobility of sesquioxide and humus complexes. Such information should help explain the peds in the B horizon, usually found where there is clay accumulation, and the color profile usually associated with the presence or accumulation of sesquioxide and humus.

---

[5] U.S.D.A., Soil Conservation Service, Soil Survey Laboratory, Beltsville, Maryland.

LITERATURE CITED

1. Braun, E. Lucy. Deciduous forests of Eastern North America. Blakiston Co. 1950.
2. Cline, M. G. Major kinds of profiles and their relationships in New York. Soil Sci. Soc. Amer. Proc. 17:123-127. 1953.
3. .... Soils and soil associations of New York. Cornell Ext. Bul. 930. 1955.
4. Denny, C. S. Surficial geology and geomorphology of Potter County, Pennsylvania. U.S. Dept. of Interior, Geological Survey Prof. Paper 288:59-66. 1956.
5. Lajoie, P. G. and DeLong, W. A. The acid-oxalate extracts of Podzols and Podzolic soils. Sci. Agr. 25:215-220. 1945.
6. Lyford, W. H. Characteristics of some Podzolic soils of the Northeastern United States. Soil Sci. Soc. Amer. Proc. 16:231-234. 1952.
7. Matthews, B. C., Reid, R. F., and Olding, A. B. Genesis and morphology of the Oneida and Haldimand series—Gray-Brown Podzolic soils in Ontario. Canadian Jour. of Agr. Sci. 35:500-510. 1955.
8. Pecrot, A., and Avril, P. Les Sols Ardennais. Etude Morphologique et genetique des sols bruns acides et des sols podzoliques du Plateau de Saint-Hubert. Bull. L'Institut Agron. Gembloux 22, 1-2:52-75. 1954.
9. Tamura, Tsuneo, and Swanson, C. L. W. Chemical and mineralogical properties of a Brown Podzolic soil. Soil Sci. Soc. Amer. Proc. 18:148-153. 1954.

THE GENESIS OF THE RED-YELLOW PODZOLIC SOILS[1]

Stanley B. McCaleb[2]

ABSTRACT

Mineralogical, chemical, physical, and morphological data are given for 18 profiles of Red-Yellow Podzolic soils. These soils represent 3 profiles each of 2 sequences, one derived from acid crystalline rocks and the other from sandstones. Six profiles of Reddish Brown Lateritic soils are included for comparison where appropriate.

Differences between sequences and within sequences are due either to inherited or to genetic properties, both of which are related to or limited by parent material. All properties studied follow the same kind of distribution with depth. Differences in magnitude reflect inherited differences, whereas the kind of distribution reflects similar genetic differences under uniform environments. Apparent discrepancies in the distribution with depth of clay content, exchange capacity, and associated properties occur as differences in parent materials. Differences in secondary products are also related to differences in parent materials and in turn are related to the observed differences.

Suggested mechanisms for the genesis of these soils and their characteristic mottling are presented. The Red-Yellow Podzolic soils are compared to the Gray-Brown Podzolic soils in terms of probable genesis.

The Red and Yellow Podzolic soils were combined as the Red-Yellow Podzolic Group in 1949. At that time, Thorp and Smith (10) cited the following definition of this group: "A group of well-developed, well-drained acid soils having thin organic (A_0) horizons over a light-colored bleached (A_2) horizon, over a red, yellowish-red, or yellow and more clayey (B) horizon. Parent materials are all more or less siliceous. Coarse reticulate streaks or mottles of red, yellow, brown, and light gray are characteristic of deep horizons of the Red-Yellow Podzolic soils where parent materials are thick."

The Reddish-Brown Lateritic soils, as presently defined (1, 10), do not fit the above description. However, there is increasing evidence (7) that they should be grouped with the Red-Yellow Podzolic soils. They are discussed here, where appropriate, to show their genetic relationships in North Carolina.

[1]Contribution from Department of Soils, North Carolina Agr. Exp. Sta., Raleigh, and USDA Soil Conservation Service. Part of the work reported here was supported by National Research Foundation Grant MSF-G1106. This aid is gratefully acknowledged. Paper presented before Div. V, Soil Science Society of America, Nov. 18, 1957, at Atlanta, Ga. Received Feb. 25, 1958. Approved Aug. 12, 1958.

[2]Clay Mineralogist, Sun Oil Company, Richardson, Texas.

Reproduced with permission from *Soil Science Society of America Proceedings,* Vol. 23, 1959, p. 164-168. Published by the Soil Science Society of America, Madison, Wisconsin, USA.

The early concepts of the genesis of Red and Yellow Podzolic soils were reviewed and evaluated by Simonson (8) in 1950. Simonson postulated, as a result, that the dominant process in the development of these soils was the formation of clay minerals at great depths in the altering parent material and their gradual disappearance in the sola as the rate of destruction exceeded the rate of formation. He concluded that the A horizons were too thin to have supplied the accumulation of clay in the B horizons.

EXPERIMENTAL METHODS

Summarized data presented here are the results of 6 years of extensive field and laboratory studies in North Carolina. Detailed profile descriptions, methods, and interpretations are presented elsewhere (5). Large numbers of deep samples (8 to 24 feet) were taken during this period to study clay accumulation and alteration of parent materials within these groups. These studies were considered necessary to clarify some of the conclusions that resulted from previous investigations.

Laboratory determinations included petrographic studies of undisturbed soil cores, sand separates, and alteration products of primary minerals. X-ray, differential thermal analysis (DTA), electron microscopy, and selected chemical procedures were used to study the silt and clay fractions. Mechanical analyses, cation-exchange capacities and cation distribution, pH, and free iron oxides were determined for whole soils.

Criteria and nomenclature in the Soil Survey Manual (9) were used for profile descriptions and horizon definition as modified by the following:

A horizons were adequately described and delineated if Manual criteria were rigidly applied. Clay skins usually appear near the A_3 transition in pores and as patches on ped surfaces. Pores are generally clean except for organic residues in the A_1 horizon.

B_1 horizons typically have increases in hue, value, or chroma over that in the A, but the relative increase is less than from B_1 to B_2 horizons. Structural units increase in size and stability but not so much as in the B_2 horizon. Structural changes are accompanied by increases in clay content and the number and and thickness of clay skins on ped surfaces. Clay skins are readily apparent, but are not continuous or as thick as they are in the B_2 horizon.

B_2 horizons are defined as having prominent, continuous, and usually thick clay skins. The maximum thickness occurs along vertical ped surfaces and in the large vertical pores and root channels. When the maximum percentage of clay did not occur in this horizon, clay skin criteria were used for definition. Subdivisions are made by Manual criteria except for the additional use of clay skin development.

B_3 horizons are usually mottled in these soils. Clay contents may be higher than in the B_2 horizon, but they never have the degree of clay skin development which defines the latter. Mottling is frequently associated with clay skin de-

velopment. Structural units are weakly expressed. Clay accumulations are mainly *in situ* alterations. Illuvial clay may fill pores and coat peds. Remnant geological structures, if present, are disrupted by weakly developed pedological structures.

C_1 *horizons* are composed of severely altered material which may retain original geological structures. Clay content never exceeds that of the B horizon. Illuvial clay occurs only as tongues which are controlled by large cracks and root channels. Clay is dominantly from *in situ* alterations and local segregations. Clay mineral concentrations are greater in silt and sand sizes than in the clay-sized fraction. Sedimentation differences are shown by textural changes, compositional differences, etc., and constitute criteria for D horizons. Metamorphic rocks frequently have bands of ferro-magnesian minerals which alter to products of high clay mineral contents.

The above criteria were formulated and used to give uniformity in profile descriptions and to try to clarify obvious discrepancies in published laboratory data and conclusions which do not support the field evidence.

The Red-Yellow Podzolic group is the dominant well-drained soil in North Carolina (2, 6). The characteristic appearance of a sequence of soils having red, reddish-yellow, and yellow B horizons on all siliceous material indicates a distribution pattern which is not accidental. The causes of these differences led to the initiation of this study in 1950. Preliminary field studies showed that certain morphological features and their associated chemical and physical properties were common to the three kinds of soil profiles regardless of the origin of the siliceous parent material.

Detailed studies were made of each of 18 profiles representing two such sequences —the Cecil, Appling and Durham series from acid crystalline rocks and the Wadesboro, Mayodan, and Granville series from Triassic sediments. Similar studies were made on six Reddish Brown Lateritic soils by Nyun and McCaleb (7). Large numbers of other soils were studied throughout the state to evaluate this group.

RESULTS

Figure 1 is a schematic presentation of the average original mineral content by great soil groups and subdivisions on B horizon color of the Podzolic group. Minor differences in color, consistence, amount and kind of clay, texture, and structure are associated with changes in mineral content.

The presence, development, and thickness of the A_2 horizons are correlated with the potential supply of available resistant minerals in the original material. The groups in figure 1 progressively have no A_2 horizon on the left to the thickest on the right for the yellow B horizon member. Quartz increases from almost none in the same manner. In general, the degree of alteration (amount of alteration per unit volume) is the most intense on the left and is progressively less toward the right. The original amount of weatherable mineral decreases as the quartz content increases. Essentially no ferromagnesian minerals are identifiable in the sola of any profile studied. Feldspars and micas in various stages of alteration are present throughout.

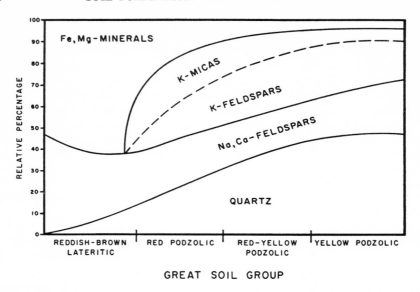

Fig. 1—Schematic average mineral composition of slightly altered parent material of acid crystalline and sedimentary origin.

Petrographic studies indicate that feldspars alter to kaolinite and/or halloysite but intermediate stages were not detected. Biotite and muscovite apparently alter through a vermiculite intermediate to kaolinite. These stages were observed in the fine sand fractions petrographically and were confirmed by X-ray and DTA on hand-picked specimens from that fraction. Pyroxenes and amphiboles were so completely altered that decomposition products were not detected. Iron segregation as amorphous materials occurs during the alteration of these minerals. DTA, X-ray and electron diffraction analysis of clay fractions showed little or no crystalline iron oxide materials. Step-wise heating of the clay fractions for 3 hours at 2, 3, 4, and 5 hundred degrees C. gave significant amounts of goethite and hematite. These data were interpreted as conversion of amorphous or poorly crystallized material to minerals detectable by the methods used. These materials appear to be similar to the cold-precipitated hydrated ferric oxides reported by Mackenzie (3).

Differences observed in the mottling characteristics of the three members of each sequence indicate that the base color is the original *in situ* alteration material. Secondary colors are confined to pores, interstitial spaces and root channels, and are due to materials physically or chemically transported from the horizon above in well-drained soils. Local segregation occurs in the parent material which indicates movement from adjacent areas. The contrasting colors from horizons above are more continuous and reticulate (dendritic) and follow the pore distribution pattern. These mottlings normally have the same Munsell color as the above horizon. Local movement gives a smeary, poorly oriented material which fills solution cavities and peripheral areas around the original site of the coloring material. Diffusion seems to be the important process during this segregation. Iron oxides are distributed throughout the profile as very finely divided coatings on all particles, but are more concentrated as mixtures with the clay-sized materials. Discrete layers of higher oxide concentration occur within the layered, oriented clays. Localized areas of earthy-appearing oxides occur as *in situ* alterations and segregations throughout the profile.

Redder hues are associated with the higher, original ferromagnesian contents; reddish yellow hues with mixtures, and the yellow with low contents. Mineralogically, higher ferromagnesian content minerals are associated with the more soluble plagioclase feldspars and low quartz content. In figure 1 the left profile has little or no yellow mottling, the next faint yellow mottling. The reddish-yellow profile may have either red or yellow mottling depending upon the composition of the original material. The yellow profile is strongly mottled with red. The more uniform distribution of iron-bearing minerals throughout the rock appears to give a red color upon alteration, whereas the random-occurring iron minerals in the right hand members yield yellow alteration products as a matrix color.

The average clay mineral content of two sizes each of silt and clay (< 50, 20, 2.0 and 0.2μ) were estimated using X-ray, DTA, and electron microscopy. Kaolinite was the dominant clay material with varying amounts of halloysite in both sequences. The Reddish Brown Lateritic and the Red Podzolic profiles of igneous origin had 70 to 90 percent kaolinite. The halloysite component of the kaolinite increased from 10 percent in the A to 40 percent in the C horizon. Vermiculite and gibbsite made up minor amounts in these two groups with no gibbsite below the C_{12} horizon. Kaolinite and vermiculite were present in all fractions including the fine sands.

The intermediate profiles ranged from 40 to 60 percent kaolinite and from 30 to 40 percent vermiculite. Halloysite was restricted to the B_2 horizon and below with the exception of the A_2 horizon and did not exceed 20 percent. No gibbsite occurred below the B_{31} horizon. The yellow profiles ranged from 40 to 80 percent kaolinite and 20 to 40 percent vermiculite throughout the profile. Gibbsite exceeded kaolinite in the C horizon.

Profiles from sedimentary rocks varied from the above as follows: Essentially no gibbsite occurred below the B_2 horizon except for the B_{31} horizon of the red member. Kaolinite was greater or equal to vermiculite in all profiles. Illite was present in the intermediate and yellow members throughout but none was present in the red member. Montmorillonite appeared in small amounts in the lower C and D horizons in all profiles as the shale component was encountered.

Table 1 summarizes the thickness data for the 18 profiles studied. The A horizon increases in thickness from the red to the yellow profile. The B_2 horizon thickness is relatively constant within each group. The ratios emphasize the increasing thickness of the A over the B in progressing from the red to the yellow member.

Table 1—Average[*] thickness of horizons for Red, Red-Yellow, and Yellow Podzolic soils.

Horizon	Group	Thickness, inches		
		Red	Red-Yellow	Yellow
A	Ign	10.3	13.3	19.7[†]
	Sed	13.0	13.7	18.3
B_2	Ign	24.3	22.3	25.0
	Sed	19.3	15.0	16.3
B_2/A	Ign	2.4	1.7	1.3
	Sed	1.5	1.1	0.9

[*]Average for three profiles. [†]Sum of all A horizons.

Table 2—Average* total clay, cation-exchange capacities, and free iron oxide content by groups and horizons.

Horizon	Group	Percent total clay < 2μ			Cation-exchange capacity me./100 g. soil			Percent free iron oxides‡		
		Red	Red-Yellow	Yellow	Red	Red-Yellow	Yellow	Red	Red-Yellow	Yellow
A_1	Ign	9.4	4.6	6.3	5.6	5.8	3.5	1.2	0.4	0.6
	Sed	7.6	5.3	6.4	5.7	4.2	6.3	0.7	0.3	0.3
A_2	Ign	10.2	6.3	6.4	3.2	2.3	1.7	1.4	0.6	0.6
	Sed	12.8	4.9	4.0	3.3	1.6	1.6	1.0	0.4	0.4
B_2	Ign	49.3	46.4	42.5	11.3	11.4	10.0	5.1	3.4	3.2
	Sed	52.7	40.4	33.5	18.5	15.1	13.4	4.4	3.7	2.7
C_1	Ign	22.7	27.0	23.0	5.1	6.6	4.4	3.0	1.2	4.0
	Sed	16.6	21.6	23.1	8.6	15.9†	25.3†	2.7	2.6	1.4
C_2	Ign	6.5	6.6	—				1.3	0.9	5.4
	Sed	5.1	16.3†	15.8†				1.3	—	1.7

*Average of three profiles.
†Increased mixing of shales with sandstone.
‡Kilmer modification of Deb method.

Table 2 gives the average clay content by horizons for the 18 profiles. All profiles have textural B_2 horizons. Clay percentages for the C_1 horizons are indicative of the amount of *in situ* clay formation over that in the C_2 horizon and relative to the B_2. These values may be high because of increases in mica and shales in metamorphic and sedimentary rocks. Average cation-exchange capacities are also given in table 2. Distributions are typically Podzolic; minimum values occur in the A_2 horizons and maximum values in the B_2 horizons.

Table 2 gives the free iron oxide percentages by horizons determined by the sodium bisulfite reduction method. The A horizon of the Red Podzolic soil has twice the content of the other two groups. B_2 horizons show large increases over the A and maxima compared with the C horizon, with the exception of the Durham profiles. These profiles show a steady increase with depth and may be associated with somewhat slower internal drainage.

Average pH values in table 3 show the rise in pH from minimum values in the A of the Red-Yellow Podzolic soils to a maxima in the B_2 horizon with a decrease below. Reddish Brown Lateritic profiles, in contrast, show a steady decrease with depth and are not so acid above the B_2 horizon. Table 4 gives average exchangeable Al values for selected horizons. The acid crystalline sequence has much lower

Table 3—Average pH by groups and horizons.

Horizon	Group	pH values[*]			
		RBL[†]	RP[†]	RYP[†]	YP[†]
A_1	Ign	5.6	4.3	4.5	4.4
	Sed		4.4	4.2	4.2
B_1	Ign	5.5	4.9	5.1	4.4
	Sed		4.7	4.7	5.0
B_2	Ign	5.4	5.3	5.1	4.9
	Sed		5.1	4.7	4.9
B_3	Ign	5.3	5.2	5.0	4.8
	Sed		5.0	4.5	4.8
C_{12}	Ign	5.1	5.0	4.9	4.6
	Sed		4.7	4.2	4.5

[*]pH determined on 1:5 ratio with Beckman glass electrode.
[†]RBL-Reddish Brown Lateritic; RP-RYP-YP are Red to Yellow Podzolic sequence.
Average of 5 profiles for first and 3 for each of others.

Table 4—Average exchangeable Al by groups and horizons.

Horizon	Group	me./100g. soil		
		Red	Red-Yellow	Yellow
A_1	Ign	0.76	0.96	0.86
	Sed	—	—	3.82
B_2	Ign	0.75	2.10	3.30
	Sed	5.21	10.98	11.24
C	Ign	3.29	3.76	3.15
	Sed	9.21	21.10	15.10

values than the younger sequence from sedimentary rocks. The red profile horizons have less exchangeable Al than the associated intermediate and yellow members in both sequences.

DISCUSSION

The concept of the Red-Yellow Podzolic Group has changed periodically with changes in theories of genesis and with advances in soil classification. Since the publication of Marbut's data (4), the statement has been frequently made that the C horizon of these soils contains more clay-sized material than the solum above. This is the premise of the hypothesis advanced by Simonson (8). It would seem more reasonable that, if such concentrations did exist, they would be associated with materials unlike those which apparently gave rise to the profile, or are developed from shales or fine-grained sediments.

Clay distributions with depth do not confirm the hypothesis advanced by Simonson (8). Evidence is presented to show the formation of clay in the C horizon, as well as in the solum, and that movement from the A to the B horizon is significant and is largely by physical means. Undoubtedly some chemical solution and breakdown occurs, although little physical evidence was obtained to indicate this as a major process now.

The mechanism of movement of secondary alteration products in the profile seems to be largely physical. Alterations of minerals *in situ* in the C and throughout the solum are responsible for a large percentage of the total clay mineral content. Pore size, shape, and distribution seem to be the controlling factors in the ultimate distribution of secondary transported material. The decrease in clay-sized particles in the A horizon has been accelerated by the greater rate of alteration and the increase in large pore space which facilitates easy exit from the alteration sites.

There is no direct evidence of clay mineral destruction being higher in the yellow than in the red members of the sequence to account for clay content differences, as was postulated by Simonson (8). Initially, clay movement follows channels until sufficient clay is accumulated to produce sieving action in the lower horizons. With time, the B_2 horizon becomes largely clay-sized materials and the amount of large pore space decreases to a minimum. The red members in both sequences represent this stage. In one of the six red profiles there was a higher base status and more large pores which resulted in a higher proportion of mottling in the B_3 horizon than in the other profiles. The fabric of the B_2 horizon thus becomes a mass of clay-sized materials formed *in situ* with multiple layers of secondary clay in channels, pores, and on ped surfaces.

It is postulated that movement of materials from higher horizons in the profile were initially responsible for the mottling in the lower solum and C horizon. The same process is still in operation where large root channels are formed due to root decomposition. These channels are filled with mixtures of materials but are largely composed of oriented clay skins. This layered material is different in appearance than the alteration products formed *in situ* and differs in color depending upon its source in the profile. These pore-filling materials are of different ages and give rise to mottled colors dependent upon the source, time of filling, and the conditions of aging.

The distribution of chemical properties with depth is characteristic of Podzolic soils. Colloid distribution shows the typical concentration of the organic fractions in the A horizon with rapid decrease with depth and the clay maximum in the B_2 horizon. Exchange capacities and distribution of cations are directly related to these colloid distributions. Bases are low throughout all profiles and all profiles are strongly to extremely acid. The pH ranges from 4.2 to 5.3 with some values as low as 3.5 in the surface horizon of 3 profiles.

With time and increased leaching the bases are almost completely removed and the colloids become H- and Al-saturated. In the A horizons, where most of the easily weatherable material has been lost, the more resistant minerals weather slowly. More Al is produced by weathering with time and is either leached to lower horizons or converted to gibbsite. Thus, the A horizon becomes dominantly H-saturated. As the clay content increases in the B horizon, the Al saturation increases over that in the A horizon and gibbsite is formed. In the B_3 and C horizons, where the proportion of weatherable minerals is still high, relatively high exchangeable Al contents are observed. Values observed were much higher for the sedimentary than the acid crystalline sequence. The high exchangeable Al associated with little or no gibbsite in the C horizon is indicative of the active alteration in progress. Few recognizable ferromagnesian minerals remain as source materials for Fe or Al. Thus, these materials must be segregated as oxides and clays at an early stage of alteration. The Al sources remaining are largely from micas and feldspars. These occur in the B horizon as well, but are more completely altered and leached. Fe and Al have maximum values in the B_2 horizons as free oxides in all-sized fractions, and as exchangeable ions in the case of Al. Minimum values for both occur in the A_2 horizon.

Differences in the magnitude of exchange properties between soil series and within series are due to differences in the amount and kind of clay present. All profiles were dominantly kaolinitic but the amount of soil vermiculite increased from the red to the yellow end of the sequence. The Wadesboro had more vermiculite than the Cecil series while the Mayodan and Granville series had illite in addition. The absence of gibbsite and the increased halloysite in the C horizon suggests either resilication of gibbsite to halloysite or halloysite as an intermediate to kaolinite. Increased gibbsite with kaolinite in the sola favors the second alternative. Exchange data are related to these differences and the effects of clay differences are intensified in the lower B and C horizon where parent material effects are more apparent. The stage of development based on clay contents and the clay mineral suites present would indicate that the sedimentary sequence was younger than the other sequence.

CONCLUSIONS

Red-Yellow Podzolic soils have developed under intense weathering conditions in humid, warm temperate, and tropical climates. Initially easily weatherable minerals are altered to secondary clays, oxides, and ions. As the bases are lost, segregation of insoluble oxides as amorphous materials occurs. Clays are apparently concurrently formed in place, the kind depending upon the source minerals, differential rates of solubility or weathering, and the ionic environment prevailing at the time. With time and changing environment, alterations proceed step-wise (7) to form kaolinite in the instance investigated. Other clay species are assumed to be remnants of incomplete reactions and inherited differences associated with differences in environment. Thus step-wise mineral suites are observed within soil series associated with their position in time. The closer the look the greater are the differences observed.

Morphological changes also occur step-wise in response to differences in physical, chemical, and biological environments in time. Matrix colors seem dependent upon kind of original minerals, distribution in the original rock, and the time and environment sequence in which formed. As large pores are filled and B_2 horizons are thickened, mechanical filling and orientation of clays occurs. *In situ* alteration produces the bulk of the clay minerals and oxides with a large percentage remaining in place in the B_2 horizon because of mechanical filling from earlier formed and transported A horizon alteration products. Fluctuating moisture contents seem to be responsible for both the transportation and oriented deposition. With time, the thickness and continuity of clay-skin development proceeds upward in the profile. As lower areas are sealed off from effective movement, local rearrangement occurs in the B_2 horizon between grains and in small pores. Thus, the upward boundary of the B horizon is limited by the potential source of weatherable material in the A horizon. Transitionally from the bottom of the B_2 horizon, the clay-skin occurrence and development reflects this premise.

The B_3 horizon has thick continuous skins which are largely on vertical ped walls and in large pores. Horizontal ped surfaces have thinner skins as a result of dependence on local production and movement of end products formed *in situ*, C horizons show little oriented clay because movement is confined to interstitial cavities and small pores. Old root channels have oriented clay skins formed from horizons above.

It is suggested that criteria for the separation of B horizons be modified to include the distribution and mode of occurrence in addition to the total amount of clay present. Reticulate mottling in itself should not be a criterion for horizon delineation. Laboratory data confirm the field separations made, based upon the suggested horizon nomenclature changes.

The genesis of Red-Yellow and Gray-Brown Podzolic soils seems to be alike in kind, but differs considerably in the degree and intensity of expression of similar horizon sequences formed under quite different environments. The Red-Yellow soils of the United States are older genetically than the Gray-Brown Podzolic soils. This maturity is expressed in terms of degree of primary mineral alteration, dominant clay minerals suites present, amount of clay and its distribution, profile development, and the extreme acid conditions resulting from base depletion.

LITERATURE CITED

1. Baldwin, M., Kellogg, C. E., Thorp, J., and Soil Survey Div. Staff, Bureau Chemistry and Soils. In Soils and Men, Yearbook of Agriculture. U.S. Government Printing Office, Washington, D.C. 1938.
2. Lee, W. D. Soils of North Carolina. North Carolina Agr. Exp. Sta. Tech. Bull. No. 115. 1956.
3. Mackenzie, R. C. Investigations on cold-precipitated hydrated ferric oxides and its origin in clays. AIME symposium: Problems of Clay and Laterite Genesis. pp. 65-75. 1952.
4. Marbut, C. F. Soils of the United States. Atlas of American Agriculture. Part III. 1935.
5. McCaleb, S. B. Properties and genesis of Red-Yellow Podzolic soils. North Carolina Agr. Exp. Sta. Tech. Bull. (Manuscript)

6. ...., and Lee, W. D. Soils of North Carolina: I: Factors of soil formation and the distribution of great soil groups. Soil Sci. 82:419-431. 1956.

7. Nyun, M.A., and McCaleb, S. B. The Reddish-Brown Lateritic soils of the North Carolina Piedmont Region: Davidson and Hiwassee series. Soil Sci. 80:27-41. 1955.

8. Simonson, R. W. 1949. Genesis and classification of Red-Yellow Podzolic soils. Soil Sci. Soc. Am. Proc. (1949) 14:316-319. 1950.

9. Soil Survey Staff. Soil Survey Manual. USDA Handbook 18, 1951.

10. Thorp, James, and Smith, Guy D. Higher categories of soil classification: Order, suborder, and great soil group. Soil Sci. 67:117-126. 1949.

THE RED AND YELLOW SOILS OF THE TROPICAL AND SUBTROPICAL UPLANDS

J. Bennema

Food and Agriculture Organization of the United Nations (Brazil) [1]
Received for publication May 8, 1962

The red and yellow soils of the tropical and subtropical uplands cover an important part of the world. Although their agricultural potential is utilized to only a very small extent, the economic importance of these soils is enormous. They represent a vast resource that is either untouched or is used only for an extensive type of agriculture. With the growing demand to feed the world's rapidly increasing population, these soils will prove to be an important factor in the development of most tropical countries.

Knowledge of these soils is increasing, but it is still only a fraction of what it should be for the most effective development of agriculture on them. Among the numerous questions which must be answered in order to utilize these red and yellow tropical soils to the full extent of their potentialities, are many directly related to their properties. The research which remains to be done represents one of great challenge to the soil scientist.

Only those red and yellow soils that are typical of the tropical and subtropical uplands will be included in this paper and special attention will be given to those of humid and subhumid regions. The latosols, lateritic podzolic soils, and red-yellow Mediterranean soils will be discussed in particular detail (see also Ref. No. 4).

The terms "red" and "yellow" refer to the color of the subsurface horizon, which has a hue that is either yellow with high chroma or red. The two colors indicate the presence of a fair amount of ferric iron, which, as the term implies, is indicative of good drainage conditions.

LATOSOLS

The most extensive red and yellow soils of the tropics and subtropics are those known among others as latosols, the greatest areas of which are found in South America and in Africa.

In the system of Aubert and Duchaufour (2) the latosols belong mainly to the "sols ferralitiques"; and in the 7th Approximation of the United States Department of Agriculture (11) to the "oxisols." In the legend of the Soil Map of Africa by D'Hoore[2] the sols ferralitiques consist mainly of latosols.

[1] Soil Survey Specialist, Rua Jardim Botanico 1008, Rio de Janeiro, Brazil.

[2] J. D'Hoore. The Soil Map of Africa South of the Sahara. Working paper, Intern. Congr. Soil Sci., 7th Congr., Madison, 1960. (Published in *Transactions* 4:11-19.)

Reproduced with permission from *Soil Science,* Vol. 95, 1963, p. 250-257. Copyright © 1963, The Williams and Wilkins Company, Baltimore, Maryland 21202, USA.

The concept of these soils and their characteristics have been the subject of general lectures during two congresses of the International Society of Soil Science. The first occasion was in Amsterdam in 1950, when Kellogg (9) presented a paper on the general concept of these soils and discussed their characteristics and management problems. They were discussed a second time (1954) in Leopoldville, when Aubert (1) reviewed existing knowledge of these soils. The vast areas of latosols in the tropics and the great possibilities they offer for agricultural production justify our discussing again their classification and properties.

Constitution of the Mineral Soil Mass

The fundamental characteristic of these soils is the nature and constitution of the mineral soil mass. This soil mass consists of sesquioxides; 1:1 lattice silicate clay minerals, quartz, and other minerals highly resistant to weathering. Primary silicate minerals less resistant to weathering are either absent or are present to only a small extent, as are 2:1 lattice clay minerals and those allophanes that have high base-exchange capacities. Free aluminum oxides are often present, but not always. The silt content of the samples in the solum is generally low. Some latosols, for example terra roxa, may, however, have a somewhat higher silt content. Concretions of iron, manganese, or aluminum oxides may be present in the soil mass. This constitution of the soil mass indicates a soil that is thoroughly weathered.

Characteristics and Properties

A great many of the characteristics and properties of the latosols can be ascribed to the constitution of the soil mass. Some of their properties and characteristics are:

1. Indistinct horizon differentiation with often diffuse or gradual transitions between the horizons.
2. Absence, or scarcity, of distinct silicate clay skins on peds or distinct silicate clay linings in the channels.
3. Low cation-exchange capacities of the clays due to absence, or near absence of 2:1 lattice clay minerals, and the absence, or near absence, of allophanes with high base-exchange capacities.
4. Red, yellow, or brown colors of the subsurface horizon or part of the subsurface horizon.
5. Absence, or near absence, of electro negative "natural clay" in those parts of the subsurface horizon that have a carbon clay ratio of less than 0.015 (natural clay is the clay obtained by shaking with distilled water, without dispersion agents).

In addition to these characteristics and properties, typical latosols have:

1. Absence of well-developed blocky or prismatic structure. The structural elements are often very fine granules that may be more or less coherent, forming together

a porous, friable, massive soil mass. A weak, or moderately blocky structure, or a seemingly massive structure without much visible porosity, may be found in latosols intergrading to other soils.

2. Deep solum.
3. Consistency in the moist state: very friable or friable.
4. High porosity and high permeability.
5. Low base saturation in the whole profile, or at least in the subsoil (cases of high base saturation throughout the profile are rare).
6. Relatively high anion-exchange capacity and high phosphorus-fixing power.
7. Relatively low amounts of exchangeable aluminum, due to the low effective base-exchange capacities of the clays.
8. High resistance to gully erosion, due to their porous structure and deep solum.

Many forms of soft or hard laterite (soft or hard plinthite) may be present in the lower part of the solum, or below the solum, but do not constitute an essential characteristic of a latosol.

The brown, yellow, and red colors, the absence of a well-developed blocky or prismatic structure and the absence of distinct clayskins, the porosity, the high friability, the indistinct horizon differentiation, and, frequently, the great depth of the solum, are the best and most easily recognizable morphological characteristics of typical latosols.

Agricultural Possibilities and Limitations

The aforementioned characteristics and properties of the latosols give an indication of their agricultural possibilities and limitations. They are, in general, soils with rather good physical conditions for plant growth. The great depth and high porosity of most of these soils are favorable to root development, although in some cases the topsoil may become too loose and open. The depth and porosity, together with the stable structure of most latosols, causes them to be less susceptible to erosion than many other soils with the same slope. Exceptions to this rule are the shallow latosols as well as the more sandy latosols. Typical latosols are easy to work with because they are mostly found in friable conditions.

The moisture equivalent of the latosols is generally medium to high, if the texture is not too sandy. Even with a high field capacity, latosols often become easily dry if they are found in a climate which has a dry period. The reasons may be sought in a great direct evaporation from the soil. Or it may be that the available water is not so high as the field capacity suggests; much water may still be present at the wilting point.

Fertility is normally medium to very low. Some latosols have such low natural fertility (especially in some savannah regions) that if no fertilizers are applied they are entirely unsuitable for agriculture.

The natural fertility of many latosols is restricted to the A horizon and related to the organic matter content; it can easily be lost by erosion or incorrect management practices. With better management practices, the latosols will retain their fertility longer, but if the practices do not include the use of fertilizers this state too will deteriorate after a time.

The primary nutrients, nitrogen and phosphorus, and to some extent potassium, are often deficient in latosols, as also are such secondary nutrients as calcium, magnesium, and sulfur, and such micronutrients as zinc and boron. Manganese can reach levels that are toxic. Correction of acidity may be necessary. Liming and the application of fertilizers involves many difficulties because of the often high fixing power of phosphorus, the low effective base-exchange capacity, and the easily upset balance between the different nutrients.

The Different Latosols

Although many different latosols have been identified and described, no generally acceptable classification of these soils has yet been developed. Some latosols, however, appear to be sufficiently distinct from others as to justify their separation at a high level of classification. These latosols are:

1. Yellow latosols with low amounts of sesquioxides; gibbsite is absent, or almost absent, and the iron oxide content is less than about 10 per cent of the clay fraction.
2. Latosols with a very low content of silicate clay minerals and with pH KCl of the sub-surface horizon greater than pH H_2O.
3. Terra roxa legitima, to which partially may also belong the "low humic latosols." This soil is derived from basalts and diabases and is characterized by low aluminum-iron oxide ratios and often relatively high amounts of manganese and titanium oxides.
4. Brown latosols of the somewhat higher altitudes.
5. Red-yellow latosols, humic red-yellow latosols, and dark red latosols, which will be described here together as a fifth group.

The textures in most of these groups may vary from clay to sand. The development of the A horizon is from weak to strong.

These units of the latosols can be found under different climatic conditions. We assume that these differences in climatic conditions also influence the profile morphology and the analytical characteristics. But morphological and analytical differences other than the moisture regime in the soil, which are constantly related to the climatic conditions under which the soils occur, are still not well known. It therefore does not appear to be convenient to use, for the description of the morphological and analytical features of these soils, a division based on differences of climate or of moisture regime. If we did so, we would have to repeat, for every class of moisture regime, almost the same morphological and analytical descriptions.

To evaluate their agricultural possibilities, however, a further division of these soils according to moisture regime or climatic conditions must be made.

Yellow Latosols with Low Amounts of Sesquioxides

Yellow latosols with low amounts of sesquioxides are mostly found on unconsolidated sediments. The texture varies from sandy loam to clay. Some difference in the clay content between the A horizon and the subsurface horizon is a common occurrence. The presence of red and white mottled clays in the lower part of the solum, or below the solum, can often be observed. The structure is somewhat less porous than the structure of many other latosols; weakly developed subangular blocks are often present, but clay skins, if present, are not well developed. They are also found in tropical climates both with and without dry climatic periods. The color of the B horizon in the regions with no marked dry period tends often to be somewhat paler [mostly brownish yellow, reddish yellow, or yellow (10 YR or 7.5 YR 6/6, 6/8 or 7/6)] than in the regions where there is a dry period; in the latter regions the color is normally strong brown or yellowish brown (7.5 YR 8/6 or 10 YR 5/6).

The A horizon is, for the most part, very weakly developed, but some latosols of this group occur with a more pronounced development of the A horizon.

In addition to the above-mentioned variations, transitions to regosols, ground-water latosols, red-yellow podzolic soils, and red-yellow latosols occur.

The relief, which is mostly undulating, is suitable for agriculture. The latosols of this group are mostly the poorest latosols of the region; normally base saturation is low and only in the transition areas to the arid regions may higher base saturation in surface layers and sub-surface layers be found.

The main limitation to agricultural use is the low natural fertility. In the regions with a dry season, water also can be a limiting factor. Response to fertilizers is often very favorable.

For the most part, these soils are still under the natural vegetation, especially under tropical forest. In other areas they are used for strip-cropping or grasslands; only in smaller areas is more intensive agriculture to be found. They have a great extension in the Amazon region and in the Congo basin.

Latosols with Very Low Amounts of Silicate Clay Minerals and pH KCl Greater Than pH H$_2$O

Some latosols show a near or total absence of silicate clay minerals (as is expressed in the silica aluminum oxide ratio, which is lower than 0.5). The morphology of the profile is often the same as that of other typical latosols, and it is difficult to separate them in the field. One useful individual characteristic in recognizing them is their very "earthy" feeling—the small aggregates feel somewhat "raw." Another more reliable characteristic, which can be useful in field work, is that in those samples in which the organic matter content is low, which is mainly the case in the subsurface horizon, the pH KCl 1:1 ratio is by definition higher than the pH H$_2$O 1:1

These latosols can have different colors, for example dusky red, dark red, red, or yellowish brown. They are often soils of savannah regions occurring on old land surfaces with level or gently undulating relief. They are found on different types of parent materials.

Latosols where the silicate clay minerals are partially or totally absent are not very suitable for agriculture. These are poor soils in which the latosolic properties are most pronounced, and thus difficulties of plant nutrition and complications involved in their fertilization are considerably increased.

These soils are rather rare. They are known to occur, among others, in South Africa and in Latin America. The well-known experimental station for coffee in

Ribeirao Preto is situated on these soils. They are the same as the "Acrox" of the 7th Approximation (11).

Terra Roxa

There are, in fact, a number of soils known as terra roxa (3). One of these is the terra roxa estruturada. The terra roxa estruturada has a blocky structure and clay skins, and in the present text is not considered as a latosol.

The terra roxa legitima has all the characteristics of a latosol. A small area of terra roxa legitima belongs to the latosols that have low amounts of silicate clay minerals and pH KCl greater than pH H_2O. The remainder, which is the more common terra roxa, will be described herein under the name terra roxa.

The soil mass of the terra roxa is different from that of the latosols, which will be described hereafter. This terra roxa has a high iron oxide content and a relatively high content of titanium and manganese oxides. The profiles are further characterized by their depth, very indistinct horizons, clayey texture, often dusky red color, little coherence between the fine granules, and absence (or slight difference) of texture between the A and B horizons. They are formed on basalts and diabase, or on drift from these rocks.

The natural vegetation is a tropical evergreen or semideciduous forest. Secondary vegetation may be savannah. A dry period of three to six months is normal.

These soils rank among the best latosols for agricultural production, because of their often smooth relief and relatively high fertility for a latosol. They are often intensively utilized for coffee and sugarcane planting.

Fertilization of these soils presents many problems, especially because of their high iron content, relatively high manganese content, and low effective base-exchange capacity.

The reddish brown latosols should perhaps be classified together with the terra roxa, as should the krasnozems and a part of the humic latosols described by Cline et al. (7), Tamura, Jackson, and Sherman (13) and Sherman and Alexander (10).

Brown Latosols

In the cooler and humid climates of the somewhat higher altitudes, latosols with a brown or brownish color of the subsurface horizon often occur to a large extent and form the highest zones of the latosols. These brown latosols are less deep than many other latosols, and the solum is normally less than 1 M. The A horizon is often (but not always) well developed. These soils are known to occur in the volcanic regions of southeast America and Central America on volcanic ash(4).

The soils described for Brazil under the name of "soils Campos Jordao" (Commissao de Solos, 1960), formed on siliceous parent rocks such as gneisses and phyllites, forming a zone above the red-yellow latosols, may be partly identified with these brown latosols. The color of the subsurface horizon of these soils is normally deep brown or yellowish brown (7.5 or 10 YR 5/6 or 5/8). They have a higher chroma than the brown latosols from the volcanic regions (8) which is brown (7.5 YR 5/4 or 4/4).

The natural vegetation of the brown latosols is tropical rain forest, often containing many species peculiar to the higher altitudes.

Although it is possible to define these soils in a general way and to cite their location in the vertical zonality of the tropical soils, it is not yet possible to distinguish them clearly from other latosols of the same color that occur under other climatic conditions.

Land use is greatly influenced by topography, which is hilly to mountainous, and by the wet and somewhat cooler climate. Large extensions of these soils are still under forest, functioning as protection for the watershed area. In other regions they are used for rice, bananas, tea, and mixed farming.

Red-Yellow Latosols and Dark Red Latosols

The differences between red-yellow latosols on the one hand and dark red latosols on the other, as expressed in their color and associated characteristics, are due to a difference in parent material. The red-yellow latosols are derived from acid parent rocks and sediments with small amounts of ferromagnesium minerals, such as many gneisses, granites, and phyllites, and from sediments derived from these rocks. On gneisses with higher quantities of ferromagnesium minerals, and also on some sedimentary rocks, dark red latosols are found. In addition to the difference in color, other differences between the red-yellow latosols and dark red latosols exist. The red-yellow latosols have mainly a lighter texture, and normally there is a greater difference in clay percentage between the A horizon and subsurface horizon than is the case with dark red latosols, and their fertility is, on an average, somewhat lower. These differences, however, represent tendency more than actual differentiation, and thus cannot be used as a criterion by which red-yellow and dark red latosols can be placed separately on a high level of the classification. In this paper, therefore these soils will be considered together as a group. As a group, red-yellow and dark red latosols are characterized by their mineral soil mass. They are soils with medium high amounts of iron oxides and varying amounts of gibbsite and 1:1 lattice clay minerals. They occur under a wide range of climatic conditions and under a great variety of natural vegetation.

The use and possibilities for agriculture of the latosols of this group differ widely according to the landform, climate, and natural fertility. The landform varies from hilly to gently undulating. The soils with a relief suitable for agriculture have, for the most part, the lowest fertility. Latosols with an undulating topography occur extensively in Latin America and probably also in Africa in regions with a well-defined dry period. They are at present used extensively, but their yields would be increased considerably if fertilizers were applied. Under the latosols with steeper slopes more fertile members can often be found, especially among the red members intergrading to podzolic soils.

Although large areas of the red-yellow and dark red latosols are in use for intensive agriculture, especially in regions where irrigation water is available, important areas are used for extensive grazing or more extensive agriculture, and some parts are still under natural vegetation. These soils are most extensive in the humid and subhumid tropics and are to be found in every part of the tropics.

LATERITIC PODZOLIC SOILS

With Lower Base Saturation in the B Horizon

Following the latosols, the most important red and yellow soils of the tropical and subtropical uplands are the lateritic podzolic soils. The term podzolic soil is used here in a broad sense. It is comprised of soils with a clayey subsurface horizon, heavier in texture than the A horizon (textural B horizon) with a well-developed blocky or prismatic structure and clay skins. It also may include soils with more sandy B horizons but with a marked difference in texture between the A and B horizons.

The best known lateritic podzolic soils of the tropics are the red-yellow podzolic soils (14). They are to be found mostly on siliceous, mainly acid, parent materials. The soils of the modal concept have a well-developed lightly textured A_2 horizon, and a clayey, blocky B horizon which often shows red or yellow colors in the upper part and a redder color in the lower part. The base saturation of the B horizon is low and that of the A horizon is normally medium. The clay minerals comprise iron oxides and silicate clay minerals which have mainly a 1:1 lattice, although some clay minerals with a 2:1 lattice may be present, as is the case with weatherable primary minerals. Aluminum oxides are normally not present in appreciable amounts. The base-exchange capacity of the clay minerals is higher, and often larger amounts of exchangeable aluminum are present than in most of the latosols with the same texture.

Natural clay is mostly present in the B horizon, which indicates a less stable aggregation than in the latosols. Permeability is less than in the latosols; drainage conditions are often moderate.

The topography of these soils is hilly to undulating. They occur under a wide variation of climatic conditions but normally a dry period is present. The natural vegetation in the tropical areas is mostly a semideciduous or deciduous forest or a savannah.

There are many other variations among the lateritic podzolic soils with lower base saturation. The soils described as rubrozems (6) may be seen as the members with an extremely developed A horizon. The reddish brown lateritic soils are the members developed from less siliceous parent material. Normally in this kind of soil an A_2 horizon is lacking.

Agricultural conditions of the latosolic podzolic soils of low base saturation are, in many aspects, similar to those of many red-yellow latosols. Differences in physical properties include the somewhat lower permeability and less stable aggregation which causes the soils to be more susceptible to erosion than most latosols. Some water stagnation in or on the B horizon may also, in extreme cases, prejudice root development.

The natural fertility can be rather low, but it is never as low as in the poorest latosols; it is, however, rarely higher than medium and may disappear easily. A high content of exchangeable aluminum, which is more rare in latosols, may prejudice plant production. Similar to latosols, they often have a strong phosphorus fixation, and a deficiency of available water frequently constitutes a moderate to rather strong limitation to agriculture.

Great areas of these soils are extensively used for pasture. Those parts which are not too steep are being used, to a large extent, for more intensive agriculture such as the growing of tobacco, corn, citrus, and fruits.

With Medium to High Base Saturation in the B Horizon

The red-yellow podzolic soils have been defined in this paper as soils with a low base saturation in the B horizon. Soils having almost the same morphology, and mainly 1:1 lattice silicate clay minerals, but with a medium to high base saturation in the B horizon, which often decreases but which may also increase with depth, have been separated here in order to stress the importance of these soils for tropical agriculture. As a rule these soils are found on less-acid parent materials, in a tropical or subtropical climate with a pronounced dry season. The natural vegetation is often a moist deciduous forest or a transition between moist deciduous forest and evergreen forest. The A_1 horizon is weakly to rather strongly developed. Weatherable minerals may be present, but the amounts are normally low or rather low. An A_2 horizon may be present, but it is often absent. A large part of the soils known as terra roxa estruturada belong to this group, as also do the podzolic soils on calcareous sandstone in Sao Paulo State, Brazil, a part of the soils described as red-yellow podzolic soils, and also a part of the red-yellow Mediterranean soils. The podzolic soils with medium to high base saturation in the B horizon may have properties in common with some sols ferrugineux tropicaux (2).

These soils, with a higher base saturation, show the same physical properties as the red-yellow podzolic soils and reddish brown lateritic soils with a low base saturation. The higher fertility gives them, however, a far greater value for the tropical and subtropical agriculture that exists. If the relief is favorable, they may be considered as the best tropical soils for agriculture. Most of Brazil's coffee plantations are to be found on these soils.

RED AND YELLOW MEDITERRANEAN SOILS

The soils already discussed are soils with silicate clay minerals with mainly a 1:1 lattice. In the tropics and subtropics there exist some red and yellow soils with greater amounts of 2:1 lattice clay minerals. The red-yellow Mediterranean soils represent one type, in which here we include the noncalcic brown soils. These soils are mainly found in transition zones of semihumid and semiarid climates and in semiarid climates under a deciduous forest or shrub vegetation.

These soils have a textural B, with medium to high base saturation, and, if they are not too sandy, they present a well-developed angular blocky structure. The color of this B horizon is often red, but under poorer drainage conditions or in more temperate climates it may be yellowish or brownish. Primary weatherable minerals are normally present to a larger extent. The A horizon is often massive, porous, and if dry, hard. The transition of this horizon to the heavier-textured B horizon is generally rather sharp.

The parent material ranges from acid to basic, and from siliceous to poor in silicium. The topography varies from undulating to hilly.

The main limitations of these soils for agriculture are a lack of water during a great part of the year and a great susceptibility to erosion.

They are used for a great variety of crops, but large areas, especially in the tropics, are only used for an extensive type of agriculture or are still under natural vegetation. Erosion control and water conservation practices play an important part in the management of these soils. Irrigation often gives very good results. Its success depends not only on the availability of water but also to a large extent on the permeability of the soils and subsoils, which varies from rapid to slow.

REDDISH PRAIRIE SOILS

In the somewhat more humid subtropical and tropical areas another type of soil, much like the red-yellow Mediterranean soils, can be found, which has a better-developed, often granular, A_1 horizon. These soils are only found on somewhat more basic rocks or rocks with a high content of ferromagnesium minerals. They are comparable to or alike, the reddish prairie soils. They often occur under a subhumid climate with a dry period. The principal limitations to agricultural production are generally the relief, and, if present, the dry period. Notwithstanding the latter limitations, these soils are often intensively used because of their high natural fertility. Management practices to combat erosion and to conserve water are very important for these soils.

CONCLUSION

The red and yellow soils of the tropical and subtropical uplands are, as we have seen, numerous, and their potentialities for agriculture are extremely diverse. It is also apparent that within each of these major groups conditions for plant growth may vary according to differences in natural fertility, texture, depth, slope, and climate.

Such a discrimination at a higher level of generalization as has been attempted in this paper offers only a general idea of the agricultural potentialities of each of these soils. In order to assist the farmers on how to best use their land, more precise soil information is necessary, and detailed soil surveys represent the best means of obtaining it. The shortage of well-trained soil surveyors, however, makes it almost impossible to meet present needs for detailed soil survey work. This situation can be partially remedied by following a middle course in the surveys of the tropical and subtropical areas in which medium to high levels of soil classification categories are used in the surveys, together with those phases which have important agricultural significance.

It has been found that reconnaissance mapping may supply the preliminary necessary knowledge for the classification of the soils at higher and medium levels to which the phases should be added. This is particularly applicable to the red and yellow soils of the tropical and subtropical uplands which often form extensive and rather homogeneous land units. Detailed maps of selected areas will show local patterns of soil distribution and the important phases to be considered for extension work. The increasing knowledge of the range of properties and characteristics of the different red and yellow soils will, in this way, supply valuable information for land use even if detailed soil surveys are lacking.

REFERENCES

1. Aubert, G. 1954 Les sols lateritiques. Trans. Intern. Congr. Soil Sci. 5th Congr. Leopoldville I: 103-118.
2. ...., and Duchaufour, P. 1956 Projet de classification des sols. Trans. Intern. Congr. Soil Sci. 6th Congr. Paris. E: 597-604.
3. Bramao, D. L. 1956 Terra Roxa and Rubrozem Soils of Brazil. FAO/56/1/374, mimeographed.
4. ...., and Dudal, R. 1958 Tropical soils. Proc. Pacific Sci. Congr. Pacific Sci. Assoc. 9th Congr. 20:46-50.
5. ...., and Lemos, P. 1960 Soil map of South America. Trans. Intern. Congr. Soil Sci. 7th Congr. Madison 4 (Comm. 5):1-8.
6. ...., and Simonson, R. W. 1956 Rubrozem—a proposed great soil group. Trans. Intern. Congr. Soil Sci. 6th Congr. Paris E: 25-29.
7. Cline, M. G., et al. 1955 Soil Survey of the Territory of Hawaii. U.S. Dep. Agr. Soil Survey Series 1939, No. 25.
8. Dudal, R., and Soepraptchardjo, M. 1960 Some considerations on the genetic relationship between latosols and andosols in Java (Indonesia). Trans. Intern. Congr. Soil Sci. 7th Congr. Madison 4 (Comm. 5): 229-234.
9. Kellogg, C. E. 1950 Tropical soils. Trans. Intern. Congr. Soil Sci. 4th Congr. Amsterdam 1950 1:266-276.
10. Sherman, G. D., and Alexander, L. T. 1959 Characteristics and genesis of low humic latosols. Soil Sci. Soc. Am. Proc. 23:168-170.
11. Soil Survey Staff 1960 Soil Classification, A Comprehensive System 7th Approximation. U.S. Dep. Agr. Soil Conservation Service.
12. Comissao de Solos do Brasil 1960 Levantamento de Reconhecimento dos Solos do Estado Sao Paulo. In press.
13. Tamura, T., Jackson, M. L., and Sherman, G. D. 1953 Mineral content of low humic, humic and hydrol humic latosols of Hawaii. Soil Sci. Soc. Am. Proc. 17:343-346.
14. Thorp, J., and Smith, G. D. 1949 Higher categories of soil classification: Order, suborder, and great soil groups. Soil Sci. 67:117-126.

CHERNOZEMS AND ASSOCIATED SOILS OF EASTERN NORTH DAKOTA: SOME PROPERTIES AND TOPOGRAPHIC RELATIONSHIPS[1]

McClelland,[2][3] C. A. Mogen,[2] W. M. Johnson,[2] F. W. Schroer[4] and J. S. Allen[2]

ABSTRACT

Chernozems may be associated with Humic-Gley soils, Calcium Carbonate Solonchaks and Regosols and, less commonly, with solonetzic soils. The morphology of these soils, particularly of the Chernozems and Calcium Carbonate Solonchaks, is discussed. Some chemical and physical data are presented.

An extensive area of northern Chernozem soils occurs in the states of North Dakota, South Dakota and Minnesota and in the provinces of Manitoba, Saskatchewan and Alberta, Canada. These soils have been described briefly in several soils textbooks and in more detail in various soil survey reports. The current interest in revising the system of soil classification in North America and abroad has pointed out the need for disseminating more detailed information about these and many associated soils. This paper was undertaken to meet this need for northern Chernozem soils as they occur in eastern North Dakota. Because northern Chernozems are intimately associated with Calcium Carbonate Solonchaks, they will also be discussed in some detail. Reference will be made to Chernozemic Regosols, Humic-Gley and solonetzic soils, all of which are common associates although not so extensive.

DESCRIPTION OF AREA

Chernozem soils are extensive in eastern North Dakota, an area that lies east of the Altamont Moraine (figure 1). The entire area has been glaciated and it is likely that the Mankato ice sheet covered the entire area as recently as 12,000 years ago (4). Except where isolated areas of preglacial sediments have been exposed through erosion, calcareous glacial deposits mantle the landscape. These consist of gently rolling plains of ground moraine, hilly terminal and recessional moraines, and nearly level areas of outwash and lacustrine sediments. The lacustrine deposits

[1] Joint contribution North Dakota Agr. Exp. Sta. and Soil Conservation Service, USDA. Presented before Div. V, Soil Science Society of America, Nov. 21, 1957, at Atlanta, Ga. Received May 23, 1958. Approved Sept. 2, 1958.

[2] Soil Scientists, Soil Conservation Service, USDA.

[3] Formerly Soil Scientist employed jointly by North Dakota Agr. Exp. Sta. and Soil Conservation Service, USDA.

[4] Assistant Soil Scientist, North Dakota Agr. Exp. Sta.

Reproduced with permission from *Soil Science Society of America Proceedings,* Vol. 23, 1959, p. 51-56. Published by the Soil Science Society of America, Madison, Wisconsin, USA.

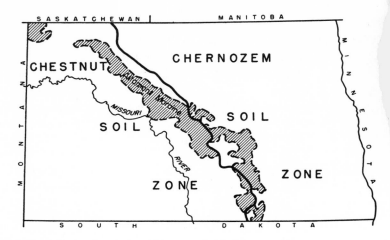

Fig. 1—Soil zones of North Dakota.

are extensive because much of eastern North Dakota drains towards the north. The glacier blocked this drainage causing large glacial lakes to be ponded along the southern margin of the ice.

The relief in eastern North Dakota is low except in a few places where the glacier overrode relatively high preglacial erosional remnants and in terminal or recessional moraines. The Red and Souris Rivers drain the eastern and northwestern portions of the area to the north and the James River provides drainage to the south. However, in most of eastern North Dakota an adequate drainage system has not developed since glaciation and much of the runoff collects in undrained depressions.

CLIMATE OF THE AREA

Eastern North Dakota has a cool-temperate, dry-subhumid climate characterized by cold dry winters, and warm relatively moist summers. Mean annual rainfall ranges from about 15 inches in the northwestern portion of the area to over 21 inches in the eastern portion. Rainfall gradually increases in March to a maximum in June and decreases to a minimum in December through February. Mean relative humidity at noon in January is about 73 to 83 percent; and in July, 47 to 52 percent. Mean annual temperatures are about 39 ± 3 F. with January averages of 4 ± 6 F. and July averages of 68 ± 2 F. The average frost free season is about 105 to 138 days, being longest in the southern portion. Mean annual evaporation from evaporation tanks ranges from 35 inches near the Chernozem-Chestnut boundary to about 28 inches in the northeastern portion. About 3 feet of snow is normal in the winter months. In many years most of the snow melts when the ground is frozen and as a consequence much of this moisture runs off. Average depth of frost penetration varies within the area from $3\frac{1}{2}$ to $4\frac{1}{2}$ feet. Climatic deviations are common. The soils are driest in late August and September because of high transpiration and evaporation rates combined with a decline in rainfall from the June maximum.

NATIVE VEGETATION

Native vegetation on the till plain consisted of tall and midgrasses, legumes and forbs on the better drained soils. Dominant grass species were needle and thread *(Stipa comata),* blue grama *(Bouteloua gracilis),* little bluestem *(Andropogon scoparius),* western wheatgrass *(Agropyron smithii),* slender wheatgrass *(Agropyron trachycaulum)* and prairie cordgrass *(Spartina pectinata).* Reeds and sedges predominate on the poorly drained sites. On areas of solonetz soils major species include western wheatgrass, inland saltgrass *(Distichlis stricta)* and buffalograss *(Buchloë dactyloides).*

CHARACTERISTICS OF CHERNOZEMS AND ASSOCIATED SOILS[5]

The northern Chernozem soil zone in eastern North Dakota contains extensive acreages of soils classified in several great soil groups. Besides Chernozems the more extensive of these are the Calcium Carbonate Solonchaks, Humic-Gley soils, chernozemic Regosols and solonetzic soils. All of these soils have some characteristics in common. They have developed under grass or grass-like vegetation. They have black[6] or very dark gray A horizons that are high in organic matter (> 3%), have low C/N ratios (< 13.5) and contain abundant roots. The A horizons are friable and granular with a high degree of base saturation. The principal bases present are Ca and Mg. With the exception of a few chernozemic Regosols all groups have distinct horizons of lime accumulation in their profiles underlying the A horizon or the B horizon if present, However, the thickness of the A horizon and depth to the C_{ca} horizon vary markedly among great soil groups.

1. Northern Chernozem Soils

These are well-drained soils on convex slopes or moderately well-drained soils on very gentle concave or plane slopes. They have black, granular A horizons that normally range in thickness from 5 to 14 inches. The pH generally ranges from 6.5 to 7.5. Sand grains are unstained and some are free of any adhering organic particles. The B horizon varies from brown to very dark grayish brown in color. Usually it is a color B with higher chroma than either the A or C horizons but it may be a textural B with clay films on ped faces that range from thin and patchy to thin and continuous. It is usually moderately prismatic in structure, breaking to blocky. Consistence varies from friable to firm. pH ranges from 6.5 to 8.0 or greater if lime occurs in the lower portion of the horizon. Most of the sand grains are lightly stained with brown. Thickness of the B horizon varies from 5 to 14 inches, usually having about the same thickness as the A horizon. The C_{ca} horizon underlies the B_2 or B_3 when present. It varies in color from light olive brown to

---

[5] Based on results of over 100 profile analyses, many less complete analyses and a great many recorded field observations.

[6] Moist colors are given unless stated otherwise.

pale yellow, is usually friable and has weak structure. It is strongly calcareous. Thickness ranges from 8 to over 20 inches. Gypsum is occasionally present in or just below this horizon. The C horizon consists of olive brown to olive calcareous glacial deposits that usually are somewhat mottled and may contain appreciable quantities of soluble salts. Where appreciable salts are present they tend to increase (with depth) below the B although a secondary maximum may be present in the C_{ca} horizon. Earthworms and burrowing rodents are active throught the sola. Associated soils include chernozemic Regosols, Calcium Carbonate Solonchaks, Humic-Gley and solonetzic soils.

2. Calcium Carbonate Solonchaks (3)

These soils vary in drainage from moderate to poor. They have formed under the influence of a high or intermittently high water table in nearly level to depressional areas. Most of them are calcareous throughout their profiles but in some moderately well-drained members the upper part of the A horizon is free of lime. They have black or very dark gray, friable, granular A horizons that are 6 to 15 inches thick with a range in pH of 7.5 to 8.0. Particularly where the water table is permanently high the A abruptly overlies a strongly calcareous grayish brown to pale olive or white C_{ca} horizon. The C_{ca} horizon ranges in thickness from 10 to 25 inches with a pH range of 7.5 to 8.5. The parent material is calcarous and may be gleyed. The pH ranges from 7.8 to 8.2. Moderate amounts of salts and gypsum may occur in the C_{ca} or C horizons. In general, where the water table is close to the surface most of the time, the A horizon is thin and strongly calcareous and the C_{ca} horizon is most prominent. Burrowing rodents and earthworms are active in better drained profiles. Calcium Carbonate Solonchaks are frequently associated with moderately well-drained Chernozems and Humic-Gley soils. In these instances they usually occupy small rises (1 to 2 feet) above the surrounding soils.

3. Humic-Gley Soils

These are imperfectly and poorly drained soils that occur in nearly level or depressional areas with restricted internal drainage. They have thick (12 to 24 inches) black granular and friable A horizons with pH ranging from about 6.0 to 7.5. These horizons overlie gleyed textural B horizons which are usually massive and firm when moist but may be prismatic or blocky when dry. pH ranges from 7.0 to 8.0 and thickness from 8 to about 20 inches. Colors range from very dark gray to dark grayish brown. The C_{ca} horizon is gleyed and the lime content varies from little more than the C_g horizon to an excess of over 10 percent. The pH ranges from 7.5 to 8.5. The C_g horizon is coarser in texture than the B, is light gray to olive in color and may be mottled. It is usually moderately calcareous with pH ranging around 8.0. In a few instances some sandy Humic-Gley soils have no lime within 5 feet and the A horizon directly overlies a gleyed C horizon. Many of the imperfectly drained Humic-Gley soils have distinct A_2 horizons that abruptly overlie textural B horizons. These soils probably belong to another great soil group although in many respects they resemble the Humic-Gley soils. Closely associated soils include Calcium Carbonate Solonchaks, Chernozems, and solonetzic soils.

4. Chernozemic Regosols

These soils occur in areas with excessive surface drainage or with excessive internal drainage. Slopes are usually convex. Where surface drainage is excessive water is removed rapidly by runoff and little leaching occurs. The A horizon is black, or very dark gray, granular and friable and 4 to 7 inches thick. Commonly it is leached free of lime in the upper portion. It usually overlies a weak C_{ca} horizon which in turn overlies calcareous parent material. Soils with excessive internal drainage occur on slopes ranging from nearly level to steep. Profiles are not dissimilar to those developed under excessive surface drainage but the lime may be leached to considerable depth. Profiles are coarse textured and have an A-C_{ca} (weak)-C horizon sequence. Burrowing rodents and earthworms are active in these soils. Associated soils are usually Chernozems.

5. Solonetzic Soils

These soils are not extensive. They are associated with Chernozems, Calcium Carbonate Solonchaks, and Humic-Gley soils on nearly level to gently sloping areas. They are imperfectly drained. The degree of development varies considerably. Some profiles (Solonetz) have A-B-C_{ca}-C_g horizons with weak textural B horizons that are coarse columnar in structure and have gray coatings (dry) on the tops of the columns. Lime may be present in the interiors of the columns. These soils have more than 15 percent Na saturation particularly in the B and C_{ca} horizons. Profiles with A_1-A_2-B_2-$C_{ca\ cs}$-C_g horizon sequence (Solodized Solonetz) are more common. They have distinct textural B horizons that are strong fine to medium columnar in structure with considerable exchangeable Na present below the upper B_2. Westin (5) has discussed some of these soils in eastern South Dakota and Mogen et al. (2) and Kellogg (1) in western North Dakota.

MORPHOLOGICAL, CHEMICAL, AND PHYSICAL DATA FOR CHERNOZEM AND CALCIUM CARBONATE SOLONCHAK SOILS IN EASTERN NORTH DAKOTA

Topographic and general morphological characteristics of Chernozems and associated soils are illustrated in figure 2. Descriptions are given below of three well-drained Chernozem profiles (Barnes loam), a moderately well-drained Chernozem (Aastad loam), and a moderately well-drained Calcium Carbonate Solonchak (Hamerly loam) developed in friable, calcareous glacial till. At least two profiles were analyzed in each area and the analyses presented seem to be representative of each soil in that area. Chemical and physical data are included in tables 1 and 2. In figure 2 the Cavour is a Solodized Solonetz soil and the Parnell is a Humic-Gley soil.

Table 1—Analytical data of representative profiles of Barnes, Aastad, and Hamerly soils developed in calcareous friable loam till in eastern North Dakota.*†

Depth	Horizon	pH, paste	CaCO₃ equivalent	Gypsum	Organic carbon	Total nitrogen	C/N ratio	Particle size distribution				Saturation extract		CEC	NH₄OAc extractable cations				Moisture tensions	
								Sand 2.0-0.5 mm.	Silt 0.5-0.002 mm.	Clay <0.002†† mm.	Fine clay <0.0001†† mm.	Conductivity	Soluble Na		Ca	Mg	Na	K	1/3 atm.	15 atm.
in.			%	me./100 g.	%	%	ratio	%	%	%	%	mmhos/cm.	me./liter	me./100 g.	—— me./100 g. soil ——				%	%
								Barnes loam, S53ND-2-1 (Well-drained Chernozem from type location in Barnes County in central-eastern North Dakota)												
0-6	A₁ₚ	7.7	—		2.87	0.212	13.5	44.2	34.3	21.5	5.0	0.7	Tr.	28.2	21.6	4.8	0.1	0.5	25.6	12.2
6-8	A₁₂	7.8	—		2.46	0.188	13.1	37.2	39.3	23.5	10.9	0.7	Tr.	26.3	18.7	5.9	0.1	0.4	26.1	13.4
8-16	B₂	7.8	—		0.93	0.099	9.4	39.1	37.8	23.1	8.1	0.7	Tr.	21.0	13.5	7.2	0.1	0.2	22.1	11.4
16-24	C_ca	7.9	25	—	0.56	0.060	9.3	34.0	39.9	26.1	1.9	1.2	0.1						23.3	10.7
24-31	C_cs1	7.8	19	57	0.39	0.040	9.8	31.7	45.1	23.2	3.4	3.5	0.3						25.9	12.2
31-39	C_cs2	7.9	15	10	0.20	0.026	7.7	29.0	45.1	25.9	3.4	4.7	0.7						27.9	12.4
39-47	C₁	7.9	16	—	0.16	0.020	8.0	38.2	39.0	22.8	3.4	5.5	0.9						24.1	10.8
47-60	C₂	8.0	16	3	0.14	0.015	9.3	47.7	33.1	19.2	3.4	6.5	1.2						17.5	7.9
								Barnes loam, S53ND-11-1 (Well-drained Chernozem from Dickey County in southeastern North Dakota)												
0-2	A₁₁	6.9	—		5.23	0.475	11.0	25.7	48.1	26.2	5.8	0.8	Tr.	31.1	25.4	6.8	0.2	1.5	37.5	18.9
2-4	A₁₂	6.0	—		3.60	0.341	10.6	29.4	43.9	26.7	8.8	0.4	Tr.	28.8	19.1	5.6	0.1	1.0	30.6	15.4
4-7	AB	6.1	—		2.61	0.243	10.7	27.7	43.2	29.1	10.2	0.4	Tr.	27.2	18.6	6.1	0.1	0.8	27.2	14.1
7-14	B₂	6.6	—		1.37	0.154	9.0	18.1	49.2	32.7	9.8	0.4	Tr.	26.3	18.4	7.6	0.1	0.8	26.9	13.6
14-29	C_ca1	7.6	13	—	0.54			22.5	46.4	31.1	3.8	0.6	Tr.	20.1			0.1	0.4	26.0	10.9
29-39	C_ca2	7.9	16	—	0.21			32.7	36.9	30.4	4.5	0.6	0.1	18.8			0.5	0.3	24.5	11.6
39-48	C₂₁	8.1	11	—	0.12			31.5	40.9	27.6	3.7	0.7	0.2	17.2			1.1	0.3	26.7	11.2
48-60	C₂₂	8.2	13	—	0.09			30.4	42.2	27.4	3.5	0.8	0.3	17.4			1.3	0.4	29.1	11.7

(continued on page 89)

Barnes loam, S54ND-10-2 (Well-drained Chernozem from Cavalier County in northeastern North Dakota)

Depth	Horizon	pH	$CaCO_3$	Gyp	O.C.	N	1	2	3	4	5	6	7	8	9	10	11	12	13	14
0-5	A$_{1p}$	7.6	—		3.21	0.274	11.7	40.2	40.5	19.3	5.5	0.7	0.1	28.5	26.0	5.1	0.4	0.9	36.0	15.2
5-10	B$_{21}$	7.5	—		1.06	0.118	9.0	30.7	37.8	31.5	10.5	0.7	0.2	27.9	20.4	7.0	1.3	0.3	36.8	17.5
10-14	B$_{22}$	7.4	1		1.00	0.118	8.5	32.9	36.5	30.6	9.0	0.9	0.2	29.6			2.0	0.3	38.5	19.7
14-27	C$_{cacs}$	7.7	13	76	0.29			33.7	40.2	26.1		4.9	1.4	17.5			4.1	0.2	35.3	15.6
27-34	C$_{ca}$	7.8	13		0.21			32.8	43.2	24.0	2.5	7.5	2.9	18.7			7.4	0.4	34.1	15.9
34-60	C	7.8	8		0.19			38.2	42.0	19.8	2.7	7.5	3.4	19.3			9.2	0.6	33.1	15.5

Aastad loam, S53ND-2-3 (Moderately well-drained Chernozem from Barnes County in central-eastern North Dakota)

Depth	Horizon	pH	$CaCO_3$	O.C.	N	1	2	3	4	5	6	7	8	9	10	11	12	13	14
0-6	A$_{1p}$	6.4	—	3.46	0.259	13.4	42.8	36.9	20.3	6.6	0.4	—	30.8	18.4	5.7	0.9	0.1	31.6	13.5
6-10	A$_{12}$	6.5	—	2.65	0.206	12.9	38.9	39.0	22.1	8.8	0.4	Tr.	27.2	16.6	5.7	0.4	0.2	26.0	12.4
10-17	AB	6.6	—	0.81	0.087	9.3	37.6	39.2	23.2	8.8	0.4	Tr.	20.5	11.1	7.0	0.4	0.2	21.3	10.2
17-23	B$_2$	7.0	—	0.49	0.056	8.8	40.4	32.2	27.4	8.2	0.5	Tr.	22.0	11.3	9.0	0.5	0.2	23.2	11.4
23-30	B$_{3ca}$	7.6	12	0.38	0.050	7.6	34.9	36.6	28.5	4.9	0.6	Tr.						24.0	13.1
30-46	C$_{ca}$	8.0	24	0.29	0.036	8.0	24.9	40.9	34.2	2.4	1.1	0.1						25.4	12.9
46-60	C	7.8	16	0.12	0.017	7.0	40.2	41.6	18.2	1.2	3.0	0.2						23.8	9.9

Hamerly clay loam, S53ND-32-1 (Moderately well-drained Calcium Carbonate Solonchak from Nelson County in central-eastern North Dakota)

Depth	Horizon	pH	$CaCO_3$	O.C.	N	1	2	3	4	5	6	7	8	9	10	11	12	13	14
0-7	A$_p$	8.0	2	3.21	0.270	11.9	24.6	45.0	30.4	0.7	Tr.		31.9	25.6	5.2	0.1	0.6	36.5	17.2
7-16	C$_{ca1}$	8.5	19	0.76	0.086	8.8	27.0	42.4	30.6	0.6	Tr.		45.5	20.7	24.4	0.1	0.3	32.0	15.6
16-24	C$_{ca2}$	8.4	25	0.53	0.060	8.8	28.1	41.3	30.6	0.8	0.1		43.6	22.7	20.5	0.2	0.3	33.1	17.0
24-34	C$_1$	8.2	18	0.20	0.029	6.9	36.1	38.3	25.6	0.8	Tr.		38.8	24.9	13.4	0.2	0.3	27.6	14.0
34-45	C$_{21}$	8.0	15	0.14	0.024	5.8	38.1	38.7	23.2	0.7	Tr.		37.2	26.7	10.0	0.2	0.3	27.0	13.3
45-60	C$_{22}$	7.9	14	0.09	0.021	4.3	39.9	38.5	21.6	0.6	Tr.		35.8	27.4	7.9	0.2	0.3	27.1	13.3

*All fine clay analyses and nitrogen on Barnes loam (S53ND-11-1) by North Dakota Agr. Exp. Sta., Fargo, North Dakota; CEC, extractable cations, organic carbon, and particle size distribution by Soil Survey Laboratory, SCS, Beltsville, Maryland, for Barnes loam (S53ND-2-1), Aastad loam (S53ND-2-3) and Hamerly clay loam (S53ND-32-1). All other analyses by Soil Survey Laboratory, SCS, Mandan, North Dakota.

†pH by glass electrode, $CaCO_3$ equivalent by CO_2 evolution, gypsum by precipitation with acetone, organic carbon by wet combustion, total nitrogen by Kjeldahl, mechanical analyses by pipette, fine clay centrifuged and pipetted, conductivity on saturation extract, exchange capacity—summation of NH_4OAc extractable cations and hydrogen except Barnes loam from Dickey and Cavalier Counties determined by NH_4OAc distillation, calcium as oxalate, magnesium as $MgNH_4PO_4$, sodium and potassium by flame photometer, moisture tensions using pressure plates and pressure membrane apparatus.

‡Equivalent diameter.

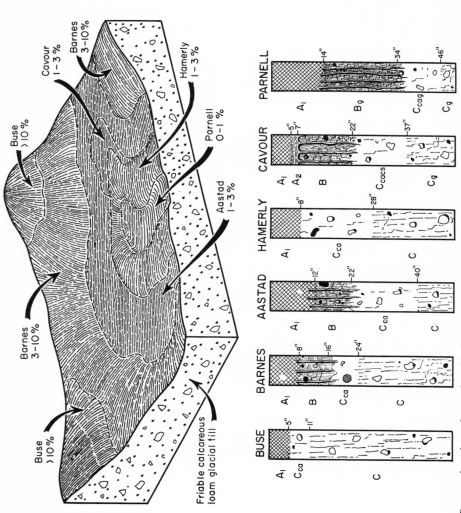

Fig. 2—Topographic relationships and profile characteristics of Barnes and associated soils developed on glacial till with moderate relief.

Table 2—Bulk density, porosity, and permeability of two Barnes profiles.[*]

Depth	Horizon	Bulk density	Pores		Permeability
			Noncapillary (60 cm. tension)	Capillary	
in.		g./ml.	%	%	in./hr.
		Barnes loam, S53ND-11-1			
1-4	A	0.89	14.2	52.1	11.8
10-13	B_2	1.18	16.3	39.2	10.5
23-26	C_{ca}	1.45	10.4	34.7	252
45-48	C	1.55	5.5	35.8	0.06
		Barnes loam, S54ND-10-2			
1-4	A	1.04	14.3	46.4	5.3
6-9	B_2	1.19	12.5	42.7	3.2
17-20	C_{cacs}	1.11	14.5	43.7	4.2
42-45	C	1.30	6.5	44.5	0.005

[*]Analyses by North Dakota Agr. Exp. Sta., Fargo, North Dakota. Results are averages for 3 cores, 3 inches high and 3 inches in diameter.

Barnes Loam

Barnes loam (S53-ND-2-1), Barnes County (central eastern North Dakota) is a well-drained Chernozem developed in friable calcareous loam till on a 3 percent northeast facing slope of a gently rolling till plain. Associated soils are Buse, Aastad, Hamerly, and Parnell. Mean annual precipitation is 19 inches and temperature 39 F. The field is cultivated.

Horizon	Depth, inches	Description
A_{1p}	0- 6	Black (10YR 2/1) loam, very dark gray (10YR 3/1) when dry; moderate very fine granular structure; friable; sand grains are unstained and some are free of adhering particles; abrupt, smooth lower boundary.
A_{12}	6- 8	Similar to above but tends to be blocky breaking to granular. Lower boundary is clear and wavy; it tongues down to the base of the B_2 horizon. A_1 horizon is 6 to 10 inches thick.[7]
B_2	8-16	Very dark grayish brown (10YR 3.5/2.5) loam; moderate medium prismatic structure which breaks readily to moderate medium and fine subangular blocky; prism faces have some black coatings; friable; few thin patchy clay films on some peds; most of the sand grains are lightly stained with brown; non-calcareous; clear slightly wavy lower boundary. B_2 is 4 to 10 inches thick.
C_{ca}	16-24	Brown (1Y 5.5/3) loam with a few fine white specks; very weak fine subangular blocky structure; nearly massive; friable; very

[7]Range in thickness includes normal variation.

strongly calcareous with disseminated lime; gradual wavy lower boundary. C_{ca} is 8 to 15 inches thick.

C_{cs1} 24-31   Olive brown (2.5Y 4/3) loam with prominent white masses of gypsum crystals; weak very fine angular blocky structure; friable; strongly calcareous; diffuse and slightly wavy lower boundary.

C_{cs2} 31-39   Olive brown (2.5Y 4/4) loam with a few medium and fine gray, white and reddish brown mottles; weak coarse blocky structure; friable; numerous small nests of gypsum crystals; diffuse, slightly wavy lower boundary. C_{cs} is 10 to 20 inches thick.

C_1 39-47   Mottled dark grayish brown and olive brown (2.5Y 4/2 and 4/3) loam till; weak very coarse blocky structure; friable; moderately calcareous, few fine white flecks of segregated lime; clear wavy lower boundary.

C_2 47-60+   Mottled olive brown and very dark grayish brown (2.5Y 4/3 and 3/2) till which is mixed and weakly layered with sandy loam, clay loam and silt; few fine mottles of red and yellowish red; massive; friable; moderately calcareous; sand grains not stained but appear dirty because of adhering silt and clay; some gypsum crystals in bottom 1½ inches. Many feet thick.

Barnes loam (S53-ND-11-1), Dickey County (southeastern North Dakota) is on an 8 percent northwest facing, slightly convex slope along the edge of a glacial outwash channel. The parent material is friable calcareous clay loam till. Associated soils include Aastad and Buse. It is a virgin profile with native grass vegetation. Mean annual precipitation is about 20 inches, and temperature about 41 F. This profile differs from the one described above in but a few minor respects. It has developed on somewhat finer and less calcareous till and lacks gypsum in the upper 60 inches at least. However, of 11 representative Barnes profiles studied in eastern North Dakota, 7 did not contain gypsum. The A horizon is only 4 inches thick and rests on a very dark gray AB horizon. The lower A_1 and AB horizons have strong, medium to fine, prismatic structure. In this respect this soil resembles the Chestnut soils.

Barnes loam (S54-ND-10-2), Cavalier County (northeastern North Dakota) was obtained on a 7 percent north-northeast facing plane slope of a gently rolling till plain. The parent material is friable, shaly, moderately calcareous loam till. Associated soils include Buse, Aastad, Hamerly and Parnell. Mean annual precipitation is about 18 inches and temperature about 36 F. The field is cultivated. This profile differs from the Barnes County Barnes profile in that the A horizon is thinner and the B_2 is browner (10YR 4/3 in B_{21} and 1 Y 4/4 in B_{22}). The B_2 has very dark brown (10YR 3/2 and 1Y 2.5/2) thin continuous colloidal films on ped faces. Probably due to the high shale content of the till the lime content is lower and the exchangeable Na in the profile is higher. The shale in this area is generally not very dense and probably also accounts for the bulk density of the C horizon being lower (table 2) than is normal (1.50 to 1.67) for the parent till. There is a distinct textural B which may be due either to the higher Na status, the presence of a greater amount of more easily weatherable minerals, or to the lower lime content of the parent material. This soil is being considered as a separate series from Barnes.

Aastad Loam

Aastad loam (S53-ND-2-3), Barnes County (central eastern North Dakota), is a moderately well-drained Chernozem developed in calcareous, friable loam till on a 2 percent southwest facing slope in a concave position with Barnes soils on steeper slopes nearby. Mean annual precipitation is 19 inches and temperature 39 F. The field is cultivated.

Horizon	*Depth, inches*	*Description*
A_{1p}	0-6	Black (10YR 2/1) loam, dark gray (10YR 4/1) when dry; moderate to strong very fine granular structure; friable; clear smooth lower boundary.
A_{12}	6-10	Black (10YR 2/1) loam; compound structure of moderate coarse prisms and medium subangular blocks; friable; gradual smooth lower boundary. A_1 is 10 to 14 inches thick.
AB	10-17	Very dark brown loam crushing to very dark grayish brown (10YR 2/2 to 3/2); compound structure of moderate medium and coarse prisms separating to moderate fine blocks; friable; gradual, smooth lower boundary. AB is 3 to 7 inches thick.
B_2	17-23	Brown (10YR 4/3) clay loam; compound structure of strong fine and medium prisms separating to moderate fine blocks; prisms are coated very dark grayish brown (10YR 3/2) friable; clear smooth lower boundary. B_2 is 6 to 10 inches thick.
B_3	23-30	Light olive brown (2.5Y 5/3) clay loam; compound structure of moderate to strong fine and medium prisms separating to moderate fine blocks; friable; faces of prisms have very dark grayish brown coatings (10YR 3/2); moderately calcareous with a slight amount of segregated lime; clear wavy lower boundary. B_3 is 2 to 8 inches thick.
C_{ca}	30-46	Light yellowish brown (2.5Y 6/4) clay loam; moderate fine blocky structure; friable; strongly calcareous with a large amount of segregated lime in white seams, films and soft round concretions; gradual smooth lower boundary. C_{ca} is 10 to 20 inches thick.
C	46-60	Light yellowish brown loam mottled with light gray (2.5Y 6/4 with 7/2); moderate fine blocky structure; friable; strongly calcareous with a slight amount of segregated lime.

Hamerly Clay Loam

Hamerly clay loam (S53-ND-32-1), Nelson County (in central eastern North Dakota) is a moderately, well-drained Calcium Carbonate Solonchak developed in friable, calcareous loam till. Topography is very gently undulating with Aastad on the upper slopes and Hamerly on slight rises (1 to 2 feet) above depressions containing imperfectly drained soils. The sample site is on a slight rise (1½ feet) above the edge of a depression. Mean annual precipitation is 18.5 inches and temperature is 37 F. The field is cultivated.

Horizon	Depth, inches	Description
A_{1p}	0- 7	Black (10 YR 2/1) clay loam, very dark gray (10YR 3/0.5) when dry; moderate very fine granular structure; friable; moderately calcareous. (Some light-colored C_{ca} horizon has been brought up and mixed by cultivation). Abrupt smooth lower boundary. A_1 is 5 to 16 inches thick.
C_{ca1}	7-16	Light brownish gray (2.5Y 6/2.5) clay loam with numerous vertical tongues of dark grayish brown; moderate medium prismatic structure breaking easily to weak medium blocks; friable; very strongly calcareous with disseminated lime; porous; gradual smooth lower boundary.
C_{ca2}	16-24	Grayish brown (2.5Y 5/2.5) clay loam similar to above horizon except no prisms observed; clear wavy lower boundary. C_{ca} horizon is 10 to 25 inches thick.
C_1	24-34	Olive brown (2.5Y 4/3) loam till with few to common, faint, medium and fine light gray mottles; very weak, very fine angular blocky structure; friable; strongly calcareous; porous; gradual, slightly wavy lower boundary.
C_{21}	34-45	Olive brown (2.5Y 4/3.5) loam till with common fine and medium mottles of gray and a few of red; moderate, medium and very coarse platy structure; friable; strongly calcareous; porous; diffuse smooth lower boundary.
C_{22}	45-60 +	Similar to C_{21} but contains a considerable number of weathered shale chips and some lime is segregated along cracks.

LITERATURE CITED

1. Kellogg, C. E. Morphology and genesis of Solonetz soils of western North Dakota. Soil Sci. 38:483-500. 1934.
2. Mogen, C. A., McClelland, J. E., Allen, J. S., and Schroer, F. W. Chestnut, Chernozem, and associated soils of western North Dakota. Soil Sci. Soc. Am. Proc. 23:56-60. 1959.
3. Redmond, C. E., and McClelland, J. E. The occurrence and distribution of lime in Calcium Carbonate Solonchak and associated soils of eastern North Dakota. Soil Sci. Soc. Am. Proc. 23: 61-65. 1959.
4. Ruhe, R. V., and Scholtes, W. H. Ages and development of soil landscapes in relation to climatic and vegetational changes in Iowa. Soil Sci. Soc. Am. Proc. 20:264-273. 1956.
5. Westin, F. C. Solonetz Soils of eastern South Dakota, their properties and genesis. Soil Sci. Soc. Am. Proc. 17:287-293. 1953.

MORPHOLOGY AND GENESIS
OF NONCALCIC BROWN SOILS IN CALIFORNIA

Frank Harradine

University of California, Davis [1]
Received for publication March 18, 1963

In North America, noncalcic brown soils occur almost exclusively in the interior valleys and foothill regions of northern California and in the coastal plain and valleys of southern California, excluding the desert region. This great soil group comprises approximately 17 percent, or 4.5 million acres. of the 26 million acres of valley and foothill lands in the State which support intensive agricultural and range pasture programs.

An important concern is the fact that these noncalcic brown soils have inherent characteristics that are both beneficial and troublesome to agricultural use. Many of them are uniquely and consistently associated with management problems involving surface soil crusting, slow water penetration, and compaction of subsoil horizons.

The nature and severity of these problems depends upon whether they have been induced temporarily by improper management practices or whether they are pedologic in origin and too far advanced to be economically amended. In most cases, management difficulties are less severe when the noncalcic brown soils have some brunizemic or reddish brown lateritic characteristics. These and related aspects of noncalcic brown soils will be discussed in a subsequent report.

REGIONAL CHARACTERISTICS

The areal distribution of noncalcic brown soils in California is closely associated with a rather definite combination of soil-forming factors. For the purpose of orienting this great soil group into its unique regional environment, the pedogenic factors are described and evaluated.

Climate

An important feature of the climatic environment is that essentially a two-season cycle prevails. Spring and fall can be considered as mild transition periods between the two dominant seasons of hot dry summer and cool moist winter. This climatic pattern can be broadly classified as a mesothermal, semiarid to subhumid Mediterranean type.

The mean annual precipitation varies within the limits of 10 to 25 inches, with

---

[1] Contribution from the Department of Soils and Plant Nutrition.

Reproduced with permission from *Soil Science,* Vol. 96, 1963, p. 277-287. Copyright ©
1963, The Williams and Wilkins Company, Baltimore, Maryland 21202, USA.

a dominant range between 12 and 20 inches. More than 90 percent of the precipitation falls during the seven months of October through April. The mean January temperature varies between 45 and 52 F with occasional periods of frost. About 230 or more days of the year are frost-free and seldom is more than an inch of the surface soil frozen. A July average temperature will vary between 62 and 82 F with many days during July, August, and September having a maximum temperature as high as 103 or 110 F. The mean annual temperature is 56 to 63 F.

From extensive field observations and correlation of laboratory analyses, typical noncalcic brown soils, as defined in this report, only occur in regions having the climatic environment outlined. It seems reasonable to conclude therefore, that the genesis of a noncalcic brown soil is fundamentally dependent upon a unique two-season climatic pattern within prescribed limits of annual amounts of precipitation and degrees of temperature. Other opinions concerning the genetic role of this particular climate will be expressed when the chemical and physical data are discussed.

Soil Material

A complex geologic pattern in California associated with numerous combinations of the other soil-forming factors has given rise to more than 600 soil series, which represent 26 or more great soil groups (5).

Noncalcic brown soils originate from many kinds of soil materials, with the exception of highly calcareous deposits and formations that are strongly acidic. Variations in the composition and fabric of soil material, in a given climatic environment, will be reflected proportionately in the chemical and physical properties of profiles about as expected.

From a practical consideration, the nature of soil material is important, because management problems are found to be more consistently associated with soils derived from sedimentary and metamorphic formations than with soils derived from igneous materials of plutonic or intrusive origin. The most troublesome problems of subsoil compaction and water penetration usually arise in soils that have a relatively high silt content and a low Ca/Mg ratio, often less than one, in the subsoil. These and other correlations are being studied in order to properly evaluate the cause and effect aspects.

Physiography

A diagrammatic cross-section of a large valley in California will show a slightly raised river flood plain near the center with a lower-lying flat basin on either side. Outward from the edge of the basin area gently sloping alluvial fans extend to the base of terrace deposits which, in turn, give way to rolling foothills and steeper mountains. Physiography or topography, as a factor of soil formation, includes the variables of degree, length, and shape of slope; compass exposure; and depth from land surface to permanent or intermittent water table.

Representative noncalcic brown soils occur predominantly in stabilized areas of well-drained alluvial fans, terrace deposits, and lower foothill regions. The slope gradient of these physiographic land forms will usually not be less than 2 percent nor more than 25 or 30 percent. When the relief is nearly level, and depending upon the presence or absence of groundwater influence, the soils are classified as intrazonal hydromorphic, halomorphic, or planosols. On relief steeper than 30 percent, where erosion activity is favored, the soils become progressively shallower and have profile depths associated with azonal lithosols.

Vegetation

The dominant classes of native vegetation presently existing in the alluvial fan and terrace regions are grasses, forbs, and shrubs. At slightly higher elevations along the lower foothill region it is principally a grass-woodland vegetation with scattered blue oak and a few other deciduous trees. Most of the grass and small herbaceous plants mature during spring or early summer, leaving much of the land practically barren until the following winter rainy season.

It is difficult to sort out and satisfactorily demonstrate the influence of natural vegetation on soil properties. One of the complications is that under different climatic environments, vegetation can play a dual role as a dependent and an independent variable. In any event, the low organic matter content of noncalcic brown soils is consistent with their relatively sparse native vegetative cover. Other associated properties include weak surface soil structures, and pale, yellowish, or brown-colored surface horizons.

Time (Age of Soil Material)

Time, or age of soil material, has long been recognized as an important factor in the development of distinctive soil profiles. In a key for the identification and classification of soils in California developed by Storie and Weir (6), five stages of profile development are defined. The alluvial soils are separated at the series level according to their degree of profile development and are placed into five profile groups ranging from undeveloped profiles to profiles containing a cemented hardpan. This scheme is particularly well adapted to the great variability in geologic age and physiographic position of land forms existing in the valleys and coastal plain areas of California (5).

Noncalcic brown soils are forming in a climatic environment which induces a very low and essentially uniform rate of leaching. The differences observed in profile development must therefore be related to age of deposition.

DESCRIPTION OF REPRESENTATIVE SOILS

Four representative soil series with profiles exhibiting different stages of development have been selected for a characterization of their morphology and associated environment. Horizon designations and descriptive terminology conform essentially with the nomenclature in the Soil Survey Manual (4). Some of their chemical and physical properties not included in the descriptions are presented in tables 1 and 2.

The stage or degree of profile development of the selected profiles is designated as minimal, medial, maximal, and maximal with a hardpan. These commonly used terms correspond to the terms young, immature, semimature, and mature as defined by Shaw (3), and to four of the profile groups defined by Storie and Weir (6).

Descriptions of other noncalcic brown soils are to be found in California soil survey reports of the Madera area (7), Merced area (1), and Stockton area (2). This report also includes data from unpublished manuscripts of the recently completed soil surveys of Tehama County by Ken Gowans, and Glenn County by Gene Begg.

Greenfield Fine Sandy Loam—Minimal Development

Soils of the Greenfield series are forming on well-drained gently sloping alluvial fans at elevations usually less than 700 feet. The soil material is medium-coarse- to medium-textured granitic alluvium. Vegetation is mainly herbaceous plants, annual grasses, and occasional shrubs and oaks.

Annual rainfall varies from 12 to 17 inches during the moist half of the year, and an average January temperature is 48 F. The dry season has an average July temperature of from 70 to 80 F and has many summer days with temperatures over 100 F. Usually about 200 or 250 days a year are frost-free and only during a few brief periods is the surface inch of soil frozen.

The profile described was obtained in the Salinas Valley approximately 3 miles west of the town of Greenfield near where the series was established in 1925. At this site, beans, lettuce, peas, and other irrigated truck crops are grown annually.

Ap1 horizon, 0-10 inches

Brown (10YR 5/3, dry; 10YR 4/3, moist) fine sandy loam; rather massive and hard when dry; very weak fine granular and friable when moist; nonplastic, nonsticky; numerous roots. Gradual, smooth lower boundary.

A12 horizon, 10-20 inches

Yellowish brown (10YR 5/4, dry; 10YR 4/4, moist) fine sandy loam; very weak fine granular structure; slightly hard when dry, friable when moist; nonplastic, nonsticky; some medium and fine roots. Smooth lower boundary.

B2 horizon, 20-30 inches

Loam of same color as A12 horizon; weak medium subangular blocky; slightly hard, friable; nonplastic, nonsticky; thin patchy clay coatings. Clear, smooth lower boundary.

B3 horizon, 30-36 inches

Light yellowish brown (10YR 6/4, dry; 10YR 5/4, moist) fine sandy loam; weak medium subangular blocky; slightly hard, friable; nonplastic, nonsticky; few thin clay coatings. Gradual, smooth lower boundary.

C horizon, 36-60 inches

Sandy loam of same color as B3; often stratified with sandy loam or fine sandy loam; massive; soft when dry, very friable when moist; nonplastic, nonsticky. Essentially the same at lower depths with textural variations.

Tehama Loam—Medial Development

The Tehama soils have formed on well-drained, medium-textured, valley-filling materials transported from sedimentary rock formations. They occur on stabilized lower terraces or older alluvial fans, with a nearly level relief at elevations ranging from 100 to 500 feet. Vegetation is mainly annual grasses with an open to very open stand of oaks.

Mean annual rainfall varies from 15 to 25 inches, with more than 75 percent occurring during the winter months. An average January temperature is 45 F; an average July temperature is 80 F with prolonged hot spells over 105 F during the summer months. About 270 days are frost-free and rarely is more than an inch of the surface soil frozen.

The selected profile was sampled in Tehama County, about 1 mile northwest of the railroad depot of Corning, which is 2 miles north of the type location for the Tehama series. At this site, barley is usually planted in the fall about 2 years out of 5 and dry-farmed.

Ap1 horizon, 0-8 inches

Pale brown (10YR 6/3, dry; 10YR 4/2, moist) loam; massive; hard when dry, friable when moist; slightly sticky and slightly plastic; many fine roots. Abrupt, smooth lower boundary.

B2 horizon, 19-31 inches

Brown (10YR 5/3, dry; 10YR 4/3, moist) clay loam; massive but breaks to angular blocks; extremely hard when dry, very sticky and very plastic; very few fine roots. Diffuse, irregular lower boundary.

B31 horizon, 31-42 inches

Light yellowish brown (10YR 6/4, dry; 10YR 5/4, moist) clay loam; massive; extremely hard when dry, very firm when moist; very sticky and very plastic; few dark coatings on sand particles; thin clay films in seams; very few fine roots. Clear, irregular lower boundary.

B32 horizon, 42-56 inches

Loam of same color as B31; massive; very hard when dry, firm when moist; sticky and plastic; few thin clay films between sand grains; very few fine roots. Gradual, irregular lower boundary between variable C1 horizon which may contain some lime.

Kimball Loam—Maximal Development

The soils of the Kimball series are well drained and have formed in alluvium composed mainly of sedimentary rock materials mixed with lesser amounts of acid and basic igneous materials. They occur on very old terrace land forms with a smooth, very gently undulating topography at elevations ranging from 100 to 400 feet. Native vegetation consists of annual grasses and forbs. Trees and other deep-rooted plants cannot grow successfully because of the strongly developed clay pan condition in these soils.

The mean annual rainfall is about 18 inches during the moist half of the year and an average January temperature is 46 F. An average July temperature is 80 F. and, during the long, dry half of the year, there are prolonged hot spells with day-time temperatures of 105 F and higher. The frost-free season is about 230 to 280 days and rarely is more than an inch of the surface soil frozen.

The profile chosen for illustration was sampled at the type location for the Kimball series which is near the west edge of the Western Pacific railroad right of way, 0.3 miles south of Central House Road about 2 miles northwest of Honcut in Butte County. At this site, the soil is used as range pasture and occasionally a dry-farmed barley crop is raised.

Ap1 horizon, 0-4 inches

Brown (7.5YR 4/5, dry; 7.5YR 3/5, moist) loam; massive; hard when dry, friable when moist; many very fine pores; abundant fine roots. Abrupt, slightly wavy lower boundary.

A3 horizon, 4-10 inches

Loam of same color as Ap1; massive; hard when dry, friable when moist; slightly sticky and slightly plastic; many very fine pores; many very fine roots. Clear, smooth lower boundary.

B1 horizon, 10-17 inches

Reddish brown (5YR 4/5, dry; 7.5YR 4/5, moist) loam; massive breaking to coarse angular blocks; very hard when dry, friable when moist; slightly sticky and slightly plastic; many very fine, few fine pores; thin, nearly continuous clay films in pores; many very fine roots. Abrupt, slightly wavy lower boundary.

B2 horizon, 17-34 inches

Reddish brown (5YR 4/5, dry; 5YR 4/4, moist) clay; moderate prismatic structure breaking to strong coarse angular blocks; extremely hard when dry; very firm when moist; sticky and very plastic; common very fine tubular pores; few fine shot; moderately thick, continuous clay films on ped faces, colloid mainly in bridges; many very fine roots along ped faces. Gradual, slightly wavy lower boundary.

B31 horizon 34-46 inches

Brown (7.5YR, dry; 5YR 4/4, moist) sandy clay loam; massive, breaking to irregular blocks; very hard when dry, firm when moist; slightly sticky and plastic; clay films moderately thick and nearly continuous in very fine pores; some black stains in pores; few very fine roots. Diffuse, irregular lower boundary.

B32 horizon, 46-64 inches

Sandy clay loam of same color as B31; massive; hard when dry, firm when moist; slightly sticky and plastic; common, thin discontinuous clay films in many very fine pores, mainly interstitial; very few fine roots. The depth of sola range from 36 inches to more than 60 inches.

San Joaquin Loam—Maximal Development with a Hardpan

The San Joaquin series comprises well-drained soils with hardpans that have formed in moderately coarse-textured alluvium that is dominantly granitic in composition. They occur at elevations between 50 and 500 feet on old terrace land forms that are very gently sloping or undulating and have a pronounced hummocky microrelief. Native vegetation is a moderate to thin stand of annual grasses and herbs. A dense clayey subsoil horizon overlying an indurated hardpan severely restricts the growth of trees and other plants that require deep rooting.

Mean annual precipitation varies from 10 to 20 inches during the moist season, and the average January temperature is 45 F. More than 250 days a year are frost-free and only occasionally is the surface soil frozen to a depth of one inch. The dry season has an average July temperature of 80 F with many daytime temperatures of 105 F and higher.

The selected profile was obtained about a mile south of Woodbridge in San Joaquin County, along old U.S. Highway 99 from Stockton to Sacramento. A pit was dug in the fenced-off and uncultivated edge of the right of way. From this site northward into Sacramento County, more than 180,000 acres of San Joaquin soils have been mapped.

A1 horizon, 0-6 inches

Brown (7.5YR 5/3, dry; 7.5YR 4/4, moist) loam; massive to weak fine granular; hard when dry and friable when moist; nonsticky and nonplastic; many fine pores; abundant grass roots. Clear, smooth lower boundary.

A3 horizon, 6-15 inches

Yellowish brown (10YR 5/4, dry; 10YR 4/3, moist) loam; weak fine blocky structure; hard when dry and friable when moist; nonsticky and nonplastic; many fine pores; abundant grass roots. Clear, smooth lower boundary.

B1 horizon, 15-24 inches

Reddish yellow (7.5YR 6/6, dry; 7.5YR 4/4, moist) loam; moderate fine blocky structure; very hard when dry and friable when moist; nonsticky and nonplastic; thin clay films on ped faces and in the fine pores, with some clay bridging between sand grains; many fine roots. Clear, smooth lower boundary.

B2 horizon, 24-30 inches

Reddish brown (5YR 4/4, dry; 5YR 3/3, moist) clay loam; strong fine and medium blocky structure; extremely hard when dry and firm when moist; slightly sticky and slightly plastic; continuous clay films on ped faces; few fine pores; very few roots. Abrupt, slightly wavy lower boundary.

Cm horizon, 30-38 inches

Strong brown (7.5YR 5/6, dry; 7.5YR 4/4, moist) indurated iron-silica hardpan; smooth on upper surface and very dense, with a few manganese stains in fissures; lower portion is less strongly cemented and occasionally contains a few lime seams. Abrupt, smooth lower boundary.

C horizon, 38-72 inches

Light yellowish brown (10YR 6/4, dry; 10YR 4/4, moist) gritty loam; massive; very weakly consolidated; hard when dry and firm when moist, becoming softer with increasing depth; nonsticky and nonplastic. This horizon is quite variable as to firmness or degree of consolidation.

FIELD AND ANALYTICAL PROCEDURES

The information presented in this paper was obtained from the regions of California where noncalcic brown soils predominate. In some of the regions, cooperative soil surveys by the University of California and the United States Department of Agriculture, either recently completed or in progress, provided an appreciable amount of data. This was supplemented in other regions with field examinations from auger borings, pits, and bank cuts. The intensity of field investigation varied from just looking around in a reconnaissance manner to detailed mapping procedures.

From more than 200 sites, 86 profiles representing 31 soil series were chosen for a detailed examination of their genesis, morphology, field environment, and chemical and physical properties. Figures 1-4 show the trend and variation with depth of four selected properties of these 86 profiles. For practical reasons, only four of the many profiles examined could be described in detail in this report and some of their important properties are presented in tables 1 and 2.

All laboratory measurements were made according to the standard methods and procedures as outlined in numerous articles of scientific journals. Descriptions of these standard methods will be omitted in order to conserve space and reading time.

Most of the analyses were made in the University of California Soil Morphology Laboratories either at Berkeley or Davis. Selected data for about 10 profiles were extracted from analyses made in the U.S. Dep. Agr. Soil Survey Laboratory at Riverside, California.

DISCUSSION

As previously indicated, noncalcic brown soils in California have characteristic properties that are largely the result of a definite range of annual precipitation and temperature, which is distributed in accordance with a prevailing two-season climatic pattern. The summer half of the year is hot and dry and the winter half is cool; annual precipitation is between 10 and 25 inches.

In regions of California where the summer season is cool or the winter season humid and cold, the soils have properties that are characteristic of other zonal great soil groups. For example, soils with brunizemic characteristics usually occur in regions where the precipitation during the moist season is greater than 25 inches and the dry summers are relatively cool. Reddish brown lateritic soils are commonly found in regions with a moist season of 35 inches or more precipitation and summers which are warm to hot and winters not extremely cold. Intrazonal and azonal soils, however, can be expected to occur in any of the zonal soil climatic environments, because their origin is largely dependent upon such factors as drainage conditions, topography, and composition of soil material.

Only the noncalcic brown great soil group seems to be confined essentially to a moist-dry two seasonal climate with a prescribed annual minimum and maximum range of precipitation and temperature. In contrast, all the other great soil groups in California are found in other parts of the United States and elsewhere under a variety of climatic patterns. Their specific requirement as to annual precipitation and temperature is not dependent upon any particular seasonal distribution.

The chemical and physical data in tables 1 and 2 will point up the dominating influence of a contrasting two-season annual climate on the genesis and morphology of noncalcic brown soils. Table 1 shows that, in the A horizons of all four selected profiles, the organic carbon content is less than 1.5 percent, and it decreases rapidly with depth. The low organic matter content, as indicated by the organic percentages, must be attributed to the limited amount of grass and shrub vegetation that can grow during the warmer months of the moist season. This inherent or consequent low organic matter content is considered to be largely responsible for the massive or very weak surface soil structures that are characteristic of noncalcic brown soils.

Other data in table 1 show that, regardless of age or stage of profile development, the percent of base saturation is high in all parts of the profile, and usually highest in the lower subsoil horizons. These values are fairly consistent with the reaction trend in the profiles at all stages of development. Surface horizons have pH values ranging from near neutral to slightly acid, which remain relatively uniform or increase about 1 pH unit to neutral or slightly basic in the lower subsoil horizons. Under the prevailing climate, the soils are leached with respect to carbon-

Table 1—Chemical properties of representative noncalcic brown soils

Horizon	Depth	pH of Soil Paste	Extractable Cations				Cation-Exchange Capacity	Base Satu-ration	Organic Carbon
			Ca	Mg	Na	K			
	in.		——————— *me./100 g. soil* ———————					%	%

GREENFIELD fine sandy loam—Minimal development

Horizon	Depth	pH of Soil Paste	Ca	Mg	Na	K	Cation-Exchange Capacity	Base Saturation	Organic Carbon
Ap1	0-10	6.5	7.4	1.7	0.16	0.69	13.0	77	1.36
A12	10-20	6.4	6.6	2.2	0.19	0.24	11.0	85	0.57
B2	20-30	6.3	8.9	3.9	0.24	0.16	15.3	87	0.13
B3	30-36	7.0	8.2	4.8	0.21	0.11	14.3	94	0.23
C	36-60	7.2	6.0	3.9	0.18	0.09	11.2	91	0.11

TEHAMA loam—Medial development

Ap1	0-8	5.5	3.8	2.3	0.1	0.1	9.5	66	0.86
A3	8-19	5.9	5.3	4.4	0.1	0.1	13.4	74	0.33
B2	19-31	6.5	6.8	11.9	0.1	0.2	23.0	83	0.25
B31	31-42	7.0	6.1	10.7	0.1	0.2	23.0	74	0.12
B32	42-56	7.1	6.2	10.6	0.1	0.1	23.5	72	0.14

KIMBALL loam—Maximal development

Ap1	0-4	6.4	6.0	2.7	0.1	0.3	11.4	80	1.01
A3	4-10	6.0	3.7	2.2	0.1	0.2	8.7	71	0.38
B1	10-17	6.1	4.6	3.4	0.1	0.1	11.8	69	0.20
B2	17-34	6.6	11.2	8.6	0.2	0.2	22.0	92	0.19
B31	34-46	7.1	11.6	8.4	0.2	0.2	21.0	97	0.09
B32	46-64	7.0	10.6	7.0	0.2	0.1	18.8	95	0.07

SAN JOAQUIN loam—Maximal development with hardpan

A1	0-6	5.6	3.6	1.6	0.08	0.54	8.3	70	1.41
A3	6-15	5.7	3.3	1.6	0.36	0.35	6.7	84	1.02
B1	15-24	6.1	3.6	2.4	0.14	0.16	7.3	86	0.76
B2	24-30	6.0	4.0	11.6	0.45	0.18	16.5	99	0.25
Cm	30-38	—	—	*	*	*	—	—	—
C	38-72	6.8	8.1	4.3	0.20	0.20	13.7	93	0.22

*Iron-silica-cemented hardpan.

ates and soluble salts. Yet even after a long period of time, the overall leaching effectiveness can be considered only as moderate in the upper horizons and slight in the lower horizons.

The cation-exchange capacity (table 1) for loam or fine sandy loam textured surface horizons is in the order of 12 me. per 100 g. for young soils and 8 me. for very old soils. The maximum cation-exchange capacity is about 30 in the finer-textured surface horizons of young soils. In any given profile, the textural B2 horizon usually will have the highest cation-exchange capacity. The magnitude of difference between the surface and the B2 horizon is greatest in profiles with maximal development. Calcium and magnesium are by far the dominant exchange cations and they

Table 2—Physical properties of representative noncalcic brown soils

Horizon	Depth	Particle Size Distribution				Bulk Density	Moisture Tensions		
		Sand 50μ	Silt 50-2μ	Clay			Moisture equivalent	1/3 atm.	1/15 atm.
				Total 2.0μ	Fine 1.0μ				
	in.	%				*g./cc.*	%		
GREENFIELD *fine sandy loam—Minimal development*									
Ap1	0–10	60.9	28.8	10.3	8.7	1.5	13.3	13.4	5.8
A12	10–20	63.0	26.7	10.3	9.1	1.5	11.6	11.8	4.7
B2	20–30	56.6	26.8	16.6	12.8	1.7	13.8	14.4	5.6
B3	30–36	63.9	23.7	12.4	10.7	1.6	12.2	12.2	5.2
C	36–60	77.6	14.1	8.3	7.7	1.5	8.4	8.2	3.9
TEHAMA *loam—Medial development*									
Ap1	0–8	33.9	52.1	14.0	10.1	1.5	19.5	23.7	5.0
A3	8–19	32.4	51.1	16.5	12.6	1.7	17.8	20.1	6.2
B2	19–31	22.7	46.9	30.4	25.7	2.0	21.8	23.1	11.3
B31	31–42	27.5	44.4	28.1	24.0	2.0	20.8	23.6	10.0
B32	42–56	32.2	43.7	24.1	21.8	1.8	20.3	23.5	9.4
KIMBALL *loam—Maximal development*									
Ap1	0–4	46.3	35.1	18.6	14.5	1.7	17.9	19.8	7.4
A3	4–10	44.3	37.9	17.8	14.4	1.7	15.6	17.4	6.5
B1	10–17	39.1	37.1	23.8	19.8	1.8	17.6	19.7	8.6
B2	17–34	32.1	30.1	37.8	34.2	2.0	26.1	29.6	16.6
B31	34–46	46.0	25.0	29.0	25.2	1.8	23.7	26.1	13.4
B32	46–64	51.2	23.0	25.8	22.4	1.8	22.2	25.0	12.1
SAN JOAQUIN *loam—Maximal development with hardpan*									
A1	0–6	46.5	39.8	13.7	11.5	1.3	18.5	—	5.9
A3	6–15	38.0	45.4	16.6	13.7	1.6	15.6	—	5.1
B1	15–24	45.6	37.0	17.4	14.2	1.6	15.5	—	5.6
B2	24–30	34.3	32.6	33.1	30.1	1.8	21.2	—	11.8
Cm	30–38	—	—	*	*	*	—	—	—
C	38–72	47.5	35.8	16.7	12.8	1.6	19.9	—	10.2

* Iron-silica-cemented hardpan.

increase in content with profile depth. The exchange calcium content varies from 2 or less me. per 100 g. in surface horizons to about 15 me. in lower subsoil horizons. Ca/Mg ratios are greater than one, but quite variable in surface horizons, and narrower or with magnesium in excess of calcium in the subsoils of older profiles.

Considering all members of the noncalcic brown group of soils, there is a rather wide range in cation-exchange capacity and content of exchange calcium and magnesium. This variance is initiated by the nature of their soil materials, which are developed through progressive stages of weathering in a unique climate and are characterized by the composition of their clay mineral fraction.

Young soils derived from basic igneous materials are usually finer-textured; they have the highest cation-exchange capacity and the highest content of exchange calcium and magnesium. Coarse-textured soils formed from acid igneous materials have the lowest cation-exchange capacity at all stages of profile development, while soils derived from sedimentary and metamorphic materials have a wide intermediate range.

From the limited number of x-ray analyses at hand, it is indicated that the clay fractions of young soils are predominantly 2:1 lattice clays and that montmorillonite is the dominant clay mineral. In some of the strongly weathered soils with hardpans, up to 60 percent of the clay is kaolinite and 40 percent an assortment of 2:1 lattice clay minerals. Most of the clays analyzed, however, had a range in the order of 25 to 30 percent kaolinite in young soils and about 45 percent in old soils.

The production of clay and the solution of mineral materials is very slow in noncalcic brown soils. Chemical weathering processes and microbial activity are confined essentially to the few late spring months when the soils are warming up and are still moist. Effective leaching occurs only during the winter season when there is sufficient rainfall from a concentrated storm to penetrate the deep subsoil horizons. Nevertheless, the physical data in table 2 show that increasingly dense B2 horizons and iron-silica-cemented hardpans eventually can be formed.

At all stages of profile development, the proportion of clay relative to silt plus clay (table 2), increases with depth and the ratio becomes progressively wider for older soils. In addition to the four profiles in table 2, analyses for a number of representative profiles show that young soils have an actual clay increase in B2 horizons ranging from about 5 to 10 percent. Soils with maximal development have an actual clay increase in B2 horizons ranging from 20 to 40 percent.

This characteristic range of clay increase in B2 horizons is believed to be largely due to inherent differences in the many kinds of soil materials from which noncalcic brown soils are formed. Variations in the matrix of soil materials associated with fabric, mafic mineral content, and the proportion of stable and unstable minerals must surely be reflected in weathered soil profiles. There is also the effect of stratification during the deposition of soil materials. Yet one cannot always be certain about the existence of stratification particularly when a finer-textured layer happens to have been deposited at a depth from the surface, and of a thickness which coincides with pedogenic B2 horizons of the region.

The genesis of iron-silica cemented hardpans in noncalcic brown soils is a debatable subject and several explanations have been proposed. This perhaps can be expected because a long period of time is involved and certain environmental assumptions are necessary. The most reasonable explanations, in the writer's opinion, are oriented around a thesis that these hardpans have formed under present climatic conditions.

During the early spring months chemical and biological activity is favored by a warming soil and the moisture from late rains. This promotes the release of bases, the solution of silica and sesquioxides, and their general movement downward in the profile. As the soil is rapidly dried during late spring, iron and silica are irreversibly precipitated and a small increment of the less permeable subsoil gradually becomes cemented. Quite frequently, subsoil stratification induces a perched moisture condition and thereby determines the depth of hardpan formation.

The variation and trend with profile depth of percent organic carbon, clay content, reaction, and percent base saturation is illustrated in figures 1-4. This is a composite image of 86 representative profiles comprising 31 soil series. Only occasionally will the limits of range indicated be exceeded in a profile that is con-

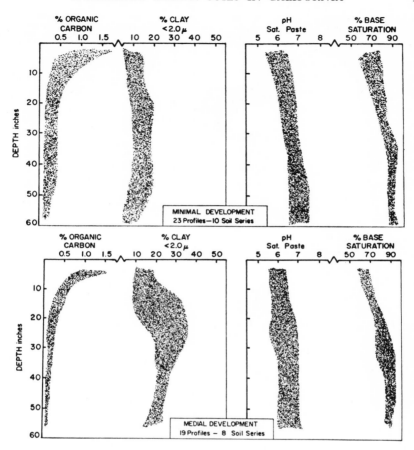

Fig. 1—*(Upper)*. Range of per cent organic carbon, clay content, pH, and per cent base saturation with profile depth in 10 soil series having minimal noncalcic brown characteristics.

Fig. 2—*(Lower)*. Range of per cent organic carbon, clay content, pH, and per cent base saturation with profile depth in eight soil series having medial noncalcic brown characteristics.

sidered to be a typical noncalcic brown soil at a designated stage of profile development.

One of the distinguishing characteristics of these soils is their low percent of organic carbon as shown in figures 1-4. Maximum values of 1.5 percent in surface horizons were usually obtained in profiles taken at uncultivated sites. The organic matter content, as indicated by the organic carbon values, decreases rapidly with depth in older soils, which are the least suitable for plant growth.

The distribution of clay with depth (figs. 1-4) clearly indicates the justification for a minimal, medial, and maximal separation of noncalcic brown soils on the basis of their stage of profile development. The range of clay content, particularly in the B2 horizons of these soils, is considered to be normal in view of the fact that their soil matrices are quite variable.

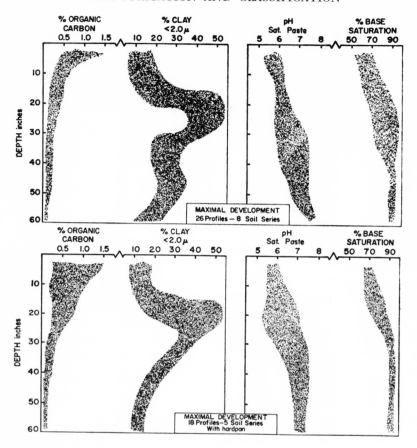

Fig. 3—*(Upper)*. Range of per cent organic carbon, clay content, pH, and per cent base saturation with profile depth in eight soil series having maximal noncalcic brown characteristics.

Fig. 4—*(Lower)*. Range of per cent organic carbon, clay content, pH, and per cent base saturation with profile depth in five soil series having maximal with hardpan noncalcic brown characteristics.

There is a consistent increase in pH values with depth (figs. 1-4) and this is another distinguishing characteristic of noncalcic brown soils. The increase is usually less in young soils regardless of whether the reaction at the surface is near neutral or slightly acid. The oldest soils, being the most leached, generally have surface horizon pH values between 5.5 and 6 and near neutral to slightly basic in the deep subsoil.

The percent of base saturation, as indicated in figures 1-4, is high in all soils, being consistently higher than 50 percent in surface horizons and increasing with depth to values higher than 80 or 90 percent. There is also a fairly consistent and proportional increase of pH values accompanying the accumulation of bases in subsoil horizons. Leaching has been slow over the years and it has taken a long time to impress its mild to moderate effectiveness.

A discussion of the morphology and genesis of noncalcic brown soils would seem incomplete without the important role of climate being mentioned again. Previous statements have implied that noncalcic brown soils, as defined in this report, can originate and develop only in regions where essentially a two-season climate prevails. The annual rainfall is limited to a range between 15 and 25 inches and most of it falls during a cool winter season. After a transition period, there follows a long dry and hot season. Under this mesothermal, semiarid to subhumid Mediterranean type of climate, soil distinctions at the series classification level are primarily the result of differences in the nature of soil materials and degree of profile development with time.

SUMMARY

The distinguishing characteristics of noncalcic brown soils are:

1. Very weak surface soil structures when moist, or essentially massive and hard to very hard when dry.

2. Low organic carbon content with maximum values of 1.5 percent in surface horizons, decreasing rapidly to amounts less than 0.5 percent in subsoils.

3. The color of soils will vary in accordance with the mafic mineral content of their soil material. As a general range, surface soils (moist and dry) are between 7.5YR and 10YR in hue, 4 to 6 in value, and 3 to 6 in chroma, with little change in the subsoils of young soils. In older soils, the subsoils become browner, yellowish red, or redder with age.

4. At all stages of profile development, the proportion of clay relative to silt plus clay increases with depth, and the ratio becomes progressively wider the older the soils.

5. pH values increase with profile depth. Surface soil reactions are near neutral to slightly acid. Deep subsoils, with some exceptions, are near neutral to slightly basic in reaction.

6. The percent of base saturation is consistently higher than 50 in surface horizons and it increases in subsoils to values that often are higher than 80 or 90.

7. Calcium and magnesium are by far the dominant exchange cations with the exchange-calcium content ranging from 2 me. per 100 g. or less in surface horizons to about 15 in lower subsoils. Ca/Mg ratios are greater than one, but variable in surface horizons and narrow, or with magnesium in excess of calcium in the subsoils of older profiles.

8. All stages of profile development, including the maximum with an iron-silica cemented hardpan, are attained within the noncalcic brown group of soils in California.

REFERENCES

1. Arkley, R. J., et al. 1962. Soil survey of the Merced Area, California. U.S. Dep. Agr. Series 1950, No. 7.
2. Retzer, J. L., et al. 1951. Soil survey of the Stockton Area, California. U.S. Dept. Agr. Series 1959, No. 10.

3. Shaw, C. F. 1928. Profile development and the relationship of soils in California. Proc. Intern. Congr. Soil Sci. 1st Congr. 4:291-397.
4. Soil Survey Staff. 1951. Soil survey manual. U.S. Dep. Agr. Handbook, No. 18.
5. Storie, R. E., and Harradine, F. F. 1958. Soils of California. Soil Sci. 85:207-227.
6. ...., and Weir, W. W. 1953. Soil Series of California. Assoc. Students Store, University of California, Berkeley, California.
7. Stromberg, L. K., et al. 1962. Soil survey of the Madera Area, California. U.S. Dep. Agr. Series 1951, No. 11.

SOILS OF THE BERYL-ENTERPRISE AREA, UTAH:
THEIR ORIGIN, PROPERTIES, AND CLASSIFICATION[1]

Rudolph Ulrich[2]

ABSTRACT

Because of low average rainfall, sparse vegetative cover, and relatively gentle slopes, soil differences in the Beryl-Enterprise area strongly reflect parent material and time factors of soil development. In the better drained, more recent, and somewhat older alluvial fan and terrace positions free of excess soluble salts, carbonates, and exchangeable sodium, soil development appears to progress from the Alluvial great soil group through various stages of the Sierozems, called minimal, medial, and maximal. Removal of lime from the A_1 and B_2 horizons, increasing clay formation and concentration in the B_2 horizon, increasing lime in the C_{ca}, and decreasing reaction in the A_1 and B_2 accompany these stages. In areas relatively high in carbonates, profile development has been dominated by lime movement and concentration in the C_{ca} horizon. The soils are calcareous to the surface and show little evidence of clay formation, movement, or concentration. These soils are classified as Calcisols. Where excessive soluble salts, exchangeable sodium, or both have been an important factor, Solonetz development has resulted. Such soils are confined to the basin area and to minimal and medial stages of development.

Soils of the deserts have been studied far less than those of humid regions, mainly because of their low agricultural potentialities. Interest in possible use of arid lands for additional food production has increased in recent years. Successful efforts to use such lands more intensively will require more complete understanding of their soils. Further studies of the origin, properties, and behavior of soils of desert regions are therefore essential. It is the purpose of this paper to present findings on soils of an area in southwestern Utah, a small but typical sample of desert regions.

DESCRIPTION OF STUDY AREA

The Beryl-Enterprise area consists of approximately 595 square miles in the southern end of Escalante Valley, principally in Iron County. Roughly triangular

---

[1]Contribution from the Soil Survey, Soil Conservation Service, USDA. Presented before Div. V, Soil Science Society of America, Davis, Calif., Aug. 17, 1955. Received Jan. 14, 1956.

[2]Soil Correlator (Interpretations), Far Western States, Soil Survey, Soil Conservation Service, USDA. Grateful acknowledgment is made to Roy W. Simonson for advice and assistance in the preparation of this paper.

Reproduced with permission from *Soil Science Society of America Proceedings,* Vol. 20, 1956, p. 570-574. Published by the Soil Science Society of America, Madison, Wisconsin, USA.

in shape, the area is bounded by mountain ranges. It can be divided into two main parts: (a) an outer rim of gently sloping alluvial fans or terraces. and (b) a central nearly level old lake basin considered by Gilbert (2) to have been part of ancient Lake Bonneville. Most of the area lies at elevations between 5,000 and 5,500 feet, with the highest portions of the alluvial fans approaching 6,000 feet.

The climate is continental and semi-arid with relatively wide ranges in seasonal and daily temperatures, low humidity, much sunshine, a short growing season, and low rainfall. Total annual rainfall ranges from about 9 inches in the central basin to about 15 inches on the highest parts of the fans.

Predominant natural vegetation is sagebrush *(Artemisia tridentata)* and galleta grass *(Hilaria jamesii)* on alluvial fans, big rabbitbrush *(Chrysothamnus nauseosus)* and sagebrush in the higher part of the basin, and greasewood *(Sarcobatus vermiculatus)* and shadscale *(Atriplex confertifolia)* in the lower basin (5).

Parent materials are mostly water-transported sediments originating in the surrounding mountains. Rock sources for these sediments are predominantly rhyolites with some latite, andesite, basalt, and obsidian. These extrusive acid igneous rocks overlie older reddish Cretaceous and Tertiary sedimentary formations. In the lower basin, the original sediments were apparently more calcareous and contained larger quantities of soluble salts than in the fans.

The soils of the Beryl-Enterprise area have a number of features in common. The solum is never thick, the depth of leaching is limited, and the accumulation of organic matter in the A horizon is small. These characteristics reflect the arid climate, sparse vegetation, and gentle topography.

Differences among the soils in the area are commonly due to factors of time and parent material. For example, the Alluvial soils in the more recent alluvial fans have very little horizon differentiation. On the other hand, soils occupying the old alluvial fans have distinct horizons. Soils that are intermediate in degree of horizon differentiation occur on land surfaces that are intermediate in age. Thus, a number of differences among soils in the area can be attributed to differences in the time during which profile development has been possible. Furthermore, the relationships between soil morphology and topographic position of the soils suggest that at least a number of the soils have progressed in horizon differentiation from Alluvial soils to Sierozems.

The rate and direction of horizon differentiation have been affected by the kinds of parent materials. If the parent materials were not high in alkaline earth carbonates or soluble salts containing sodium, the profiles seem to have changed from Alluvial soils to Sierozems. On the other hand, if the parent materials were unusually high in carbonates or sodium salts, profile development has progressed to Calcisols (3) and Solonetz, respectively. Textures and colors of horizons in many of the soils reflect textures and colors of the original sediments.

DESCRIPTION OF SOILS

Seven soils from the Beryl-Enterprise area are described in this paper on the basis of field observations and laboratory analyses. Profiles are described in the text whereas laboratory data are given in table 1. Horizon designations and descriptive terminology generally follow the Soil Survey Manual (6). Laboratory methods are indicated by footnote in table 1.

The seven soils were selected to represent the Alluvial, Sierozem, Calcisol, and Solonetz groups. Three of the profiles are considered to reflect as many stages of horizon differentiation for the Sierozem group, whereas two profiles are thought to represent stages in development of Solonetz soils. One profile is described for each of the Alluvial and Calcisol groups. The general framework of soil classification is that outlined by Baldwin, Kellogg, and Thorp (1) as modified by Thorp and Smith (4). Recognition of Calcisols as a great soil group (3) was proposed subsequent to 1949 and would constitute a modification of the general framework. Restriction of Sierozems to soils with some evidence of a textural B horizon would also be a modification of earlier concepts of that group.

Alluvial Soils

The earliest stage in the evolution of soil profiles can be illustrated by a profile of Redfield loam. This profile was described in a barren area 200 feet west of the SE corner, sec. 23. T. 36.. R. 16 W.

Horizon	Depth inches	Description
A_1	0-6	Reddish brown (5YR 5/4, dry) to dark reddish brown (5YR 3/4 to 4/4, moist) loam; weak very fine granular; soft, very friable; moderately to strongly calcareous; pH 7.9. The half inch surface layer may be a very fine vesicular horizon, incipient A_v[3] with weak very thin platy structure.
C_{11}	6-15	Reddish brown (5YR 5/4, dry) to reddish brown (5YR 4/4, moist) loam; very weak coarse granular crushing to medium and fine granules; slightly hard, friable; strongly calcareous; pH 7.9, contains many tubules and root channels (some up to 3 mm. in diameter).
C_{12}	15-19	Similar to C_{11} above but containing visible thin lime seams and flecks; pH 7.9.
C_2	19-60	Yellowish red (5YR 5/6, dry) to yellowish red (5YR 4/6, moist) loam; very weak coarse granular peds crushing to medium and fine granules; slightly hard, friable, strongly calcareous; pH 8.0.

The Redfield soils show a minimum of horizon differentiation since the deposition of their parent materials. The reddish colors are quite uniform throughout the soil and are largely an inherited characteristic due to the influence of contributing reddish Cretaceous and Tertiary sandstones. Only a slight darkening of the A_1 horizon has resulted from the vegetation, and the platy and vesicular horizon at the surface is very thin, but slightly developed, and discontinuously present. Structural development is essentially very weak to almost massive. Soil reaction is uniform, and a few thin

---

[3] A surface horizon characterized by vesicular (spheroidal or honeycomblike) porosity, massive or platy structure, low organic matter content, light color, commonly with thin crust that is slightly harder when dry than rest of horizon.

Table 1—Mechanical analyses, pH, CaCO₃ equivalent, organic carbon, total nitrogen and C:N ratios of representative soil series of the Beryl-Enterprise Area, Utah.*

Depth	Horizon	Size class and diameter of particles (mm.)									pH		CaCO₃ equivalent	Organic carbon	Total nitrogen	C:N ratio
		Very coarse sand 2–1	Coarse sand 1–0.5	Medium sand 0.5–0.25	Fine sand 0.25–0.1	Very fine sand 0.1–0.05	Silt 0.05–0.002	Clay <0.002	Other classes 0.02–0.002	>2	Paste	1:5				
inches		%	%	%	%	%	%	%	%	%			%	%	%	
Redfield loam (Alluvial soil)																
0–6	A₁	0.1	3.1	2.9	13.3	17.3	43.5	19.8	22.7	5	7.9	9.0	10.3	0.47	0.051	9.2
6–15	C₁₁	0.3	1.5	2.0	9.2	17.8	50.2	19.0	23.9	1	7.9	8.9	16.6	0.37	0.041	9.0
15–19	C₁₂	2.7	3.9	3.8	15.3	17.1	40.7	16.5	18.6	3	7.9	9.0	11.2	0.27	—	—
19–60	C₂	4.5	8.5	8.5	20.2	14.1	30.2	14.0	15.3	10	8.0	8.8	8.3	0.22	—	—
Zane clay loam (Minimal Sierozem)																
0–1†	Aᵥ	—	—	—	—	—	—	—	—	5.7	8.0	—	<0.5	0.71	0.069	10.3
1–8	A₁	2.8	5.9	3.3	8.4	7.5	38.2	33.9	26.0	0.6	7.7	—	<0.5	0.39	0.041	9.5
8–13	B₂	1.3	2.6	1.4	3.6	3.9	38.5	48.7	24.9	0.8	7.6	—	<0.5	0.41	0.044	9.3
13–20	B₃	4.9	4.5	4.9	5.7	5.6	53.2	21.2	34.5	5.0	8.0	—	2.8	0.41	—	—
20–40	C	6.0	6.4	3.8	10.0	9.8	47.1	16.9	28.1	7.9	7.6	—	1.5	0.34	—	—
Sevy sandy clay loam (Medial Sierozem)																
0–1†	Aᵥ	—	—	—	—	—	—	—	—	6.8	7.3	8.2	0.0	0.28	0.029	9.7
1–4	A₁	4.4	11.7	8.9	18.8	11.2	23.0	22.0	11.9	1.7	7.0	8.0	0.0	0.39	0.047	8.3
4–13	B₂	4.5	7.8	6.2	15.4	15.4	22.8	27.9	7.3	1.7	7.1	7.8	0.0	0.28	0.044	6.4
13–16	B₃	3.6	8.2	7.3	17.6	13.6	23.1	26.6	9.9	3.4	8.0	8.9	5.5	0.36	—	—
16–34	Cca	3.2	6.1	5.0	11.7	10.4	28.2	35.4	15.1	4.1	8.2	9.1	27.5	0.42	—	—
34–60	C	8.1	8.2	5.9	17.9	16.3	32.2	11.4	13.1	6.5	8.3	9.2	12.0	0.22	—	—
13–16†	B₃	3.5	9.1	8.4	17.6	15.2	23.6	22.6	6.9	—	—	—	—	—	—	—
16–34	Cca	3.7	7.5	7.5	17.7	14.8	27.1	21.7	10.4	—	—	·	—	—	—	—
34–60	C	5.8	8.7	6.9	22.3	21.3	33.4	1.6	10.5	—	—	—	—	—	—	—

Table 1—Continued

Timpahute sandy loam (Maximal Sierozem)

Depth	Horizon															
0–2	Av	3.4	14.2	13.0	21.3	9.0	33.9	5.2	17.8	2.8	7.5	7.6	0.0	0.25	0.029	8.9
2–6	A1	2.3	13.8	16.7	25.5	7.7	24.7	9.3	16.3	1.1	7.6	7.8	0.0	0.35	0.050	7.0
6–15	B2	1.4	8.0	11.0	19.8	7.0	10.4	42.4	5.0	3.9	7.3	8.3	0.0	0.52	0.063	8.3
15–24	B3	4.0	10.2	12.2	23.2	9.0	13.2	28.2	7.0	6.7	8.1	9.3	2.0	0.38	—	—
24–52	Cca	—	—	—	—	—	—	—	—	—	8.6	9.2	20.7	0.41	—	—
					Strongly cemented caliche											
52–60	C	1.0	3.3	5.3	26.8	21.5	34.3	7.8	13.5	1.8	8.2	9.0	3.6	0.09	—	—

Escalante fine sandy loam (Calcisol)

Depth	Horizon															
0–1†	Av	—	—	—	—	—	—	—	—	0.0	8.2	9.2	9.5	1.04	0.123	8.5
1–12	A1	5.4	5.0	6.6	13.6	16.7	41.7	11.0	36.0	6.0	8.3	9.5	10.8	0.71	0.078	9.1
12–27	Cca	1.6	4.9	3.9	10.2	22.7	46.7	10.0	24.2	6.6	8.5	9.8	22.9	0.37	0.035	10.6
27–39	C	5.2	12.0	8.2	13.8	18.7	37.6	4.5	12.7	10.9	8.3	9.7	2.0	0.13	—	—
					Beds of sand and gravel, unconforming											
39–112	D															

Antelope Springs silt loam (Minimal Solonetz)

Depth	Horizon															
0–3	Av	0.6	1.0	0.9	4.7	10.1	67.3	15.4	40.5	0.0	8.3	9.0	5.5	0.60	0.068	8.8
3–6	A1	0.2	0.6	0.6	2.2	4.7	59.4	32.3	46.0	0.0	7.9	8.9	1.8	0.43	0.051	8.4
6–13	B2	0.9	4.0	3.6	8.0	9.1	43.0	31.4	29.0	0.0	7.9	8.7	21.5	0.74	0.077	9.6
13–18	B3	0.3	1.5	1.8	7.5	10.1	35.5	43.3	20.4	0.0	8.0	8.6	36.2	0.59	—	—
18–48	C	0.2	1.1	1.2	4.7	7.5	36.1	49.2	19.7	0.0	7.9	9.1	37.8	0.36	—	—

Uvada loam (Medial Solonetz)

Depth	Horizon															
0–1	Av	0.8	1.8	2.0	4.1	31.8	53.8	5.7	27.1	0.1	8.4	9.2	3.4	0.69	0.068	10.1
1–5	A1	0.1	1.0	1.6	12.6	18.6	55.2	10.9	32.4	0.0	8.4	9.3	3.4	0.41	0.053	7.7
5–10	B2	0.1	0.3	0.5	4.1	6.4	48.8	39.8	35.2	0.0	8.5	9.5	9.5	0.56	—	—
10–18	B3	0.1	0.7	0.7	2.7	7.5	50.0	38.3	32.8	0.0	8.6	9.5	14.3	0.38	—	—
18–48	C	1.0	4.6	4.4	9.7	9.2	32.2	38.9	28.9	0.0	8.2	8.8	28.4	0.24	—	—

*Analyses by Soil Survey Laboratory, Riverside, Calif. Mechanical analyses by pipette, pH by glass electrode, CaCO$_3$ equivalent by CO$_2$ evolution, organic carbon by wet combustion, and total nitrogen by Kjeldahl procedure.
†First two horizons mixed in equal parts and subsample taken for particle size distribution.
‡Same as respective horizons above but treated with HCl to remove excess carbonates before mechanical analysis.

lime seams and flecks occur at 15 to 19 inches. Although this slight lime concentration is neither present nor visible uniformly, its depth of occurrence is quite significant in terms of probable future profile development and horizon differentiation. Other soils developing from recent alluvial materials, as well as slightly more differentiated profiles in the area, have thin lime seams and flecks at about the same depth. This indicates the approximate depth at which lime begins to accumulate in the soils of the area, particularly those of intermediate textures.

Sierozem Soils

In parent materials that are not high in alkaline earth carbonates or soluble salts containing sodium, profile development seems to proceed in stages from Alluvial soils to Sierozems in the Beryl-Enterprise area. Furthermore, there are several stages or degrees of horizonation that can be recognized in the Sierozems. Three stages or degrees of horizon differentiation are recognized in this paper under the names minimal, medial, and maximal. These terms are relative and are based on changes in morphology such as: (a) textural, structural, and color modification to distinguish the B horizon from the C horizon, (b) leaching of carbonates and relative prominence of the C_{ca} horizon, (c) the degree of expression of the vesicular surface horizon, and (d) changes in reaction from the C horizon.

Minimal

This stage of horizon differentiation is illustrated by a profile of Zane clay loam taken in a barren area 700 feet west of the NE corner of sec. 35, T. 33 S., R. 17 W.:

Horizon	Depth inches	Description
A_v	0-1	Pinkish gray (7.5YR 7/2, dry) to Brown (7.5YR 5/4, moist) clay loam; very weak, very thin platy; weak, very fine vesicular, slightly hard, friable, noncalcareous; pH 8.0.
A_1	1-8	Reddish brown (5YR 5/4, dry) to dark reddish brown (5YR 3/4, moist) clay loam; moderate fine granular; slightly hard, friable; noncalcareous; pH 7.7.
B_2	8-13	Reddish brown (5YR 5/4, dry) to reddish brown (5YR 4/4, moist) light clay; weak medium prismatic and weak very fine subangular blocky; slightly hard, friable; thin patchy clayskins; noncalcareous; pH 7.6.
B_3	13-20	Brown (7.5YR 5/4, dry) to dark brown (7.5YR 4/2 to 4/4, moist) silt loam; weak medium subangular blocky; slightly hard, friable; thin very patchy clayskins; moderately to strongly calcareous with fine lime seams; pH 8.0.
C	20-60 +	Light brown (7.5YR 6/4, dry) to brown (7.5YR 5/4, moist) fine sandy loam to light loam; massive; slightly hard, friable; strongly calcareous; pH 7.6.

Compared with Redfield loam, this profile has considerably more development or horizon differentiation. The platy and vesicular A_v horizon is thicker, more strongly developed, leached of lime, and continuous. The A_1 horizon also shows color modification, stronger structural development, and a loss of free lime. A lime-free, weak color, and weak structural B_2 horizon is also present. The B_3 indicates somewhat less development, but it has weak structure, some increase in clay content, and fine lime seams in the lower part.

These soil properties indicate that the leaching of lime in the A_1 and B_2 horizons has occurred more or less concurrently with an increase in clay formation and concentration. The reddish color in these horizons is probably due to an increase in free iron-oxide content accompanying secondary clay formation from the primary minerals in the parent alluvial deposit.

Medial

This stage in profile development is basically an intensification of the processes outlined in the minimal stage. A profile of Sevy sandy clay loam taken in a barren area 1/4 mile south of the W1/4 corner, sec. 22, T. 36 S., R. 16 W, illustrates this stage:

Horizon	Depth inches	Description
A_v	0-1	Light brown (7.5YR 6/4, dry) to dark brown (7.5YR 4/2, moist) sandy clay loam; weak very thin platy; weak to moderate very fine vesicular; soft, very friable; noncalcareous; pH 7.3.
A_1	1-4	Reddish brown (5YR 5/3, dry) to reddish brown (5YR 4/3, moist) sandy clay loam; moderate to strong very fine granular; slightly hard, friable; noncalcareous; pH 7.0.
B_2	4-13	Reddish brown (5YR 4/4, dry or moist) sandy clay loam; moderate coarse subangular blocky; hard, friable; thin nearly continuous clayskins; noncalcareous; pH 7.1.
B_3	13-16	Light brown (7.5YR 6/4, dry) to brown (7.5YR 5/4, moist) sandy clay loam; moderate to weak coarse subangular blocky; hard, friable; thin patchy clayskins; strongly calcareous; pH 8.0.
C_{ca}	16-34	Pinkish white (7.5YR 8/2, dry) to pink (7.5YR 7/4, moist) clay loam; weak medium subangular blocky to massive; hard to weakly cemented, friable; very strongly calcareous; pH 8.2.
C	34-60 +	Pink (7.5YR 7/4, dry) to brown (7.5YR 5/4, moist) fine sandy loam; massive; soft, very friable; very strongly calcareous; pH 8.3.

As compared with Zane soils the Sevy profile shows intensification of the same process of lime removal and concentration as well as color, textural, and structural horizon differentiation. Lime has concentrated in large quantities in the C_{ca} horizon and is hardened to weakly cemented in the dry condition in some places. Dense lime incrustations and lenses also occur, but the material is soft and not uniformly hardened into a massive caliche-like deposit. The mechanical analysis with and without the presence of lime indicates that much of the lime in the C_{ca} horizon may be in the clay-size fraction. In addition to the loss of lime, the A_1 and B_2 horizons are now neutral in reaction.

Maximal

This stage in profile development is a still further intensification of processes outlined in step two. A profile of Timpahute sandy loam collected in a barren area 1/4 mile south of NW corner of sec. 6, T. 35 S., R. 18 W., illustrates this stage:

Horizon	Depth inches	Description
A_v	0-2	Light gray (10YR 7/2, dry) to light brownish gray (10YR 6/2, moist) sandy loam; very weak very thick platy; strong very fine vesicular; soft, very friable; noncalcareous; pH 7.5. The immediate surface ¼ to ½ inch is a loose mulch containing numerous gravel.
A_1	2-6	Very pale brown (10YR 7/3, dry) to brown (10YR 5/3, moist) sandy loam; moderate very fine granular; soft, very friable; noncalcareous; pH 7.6.
B_2	6-15	Brown to dark brown (7.5YR 5/4 and 4/4, dry or moist) sandy clay; strong medium to coarse prismatic and strong medium angular blocky; very hard, firm; thick continuous clayskins; noncalcareous; pH 7.3.
B_3	15-24	Brown to dark brown (7.5YR 5/4 and 4/4, dry or moist) sandy clay loam; weak coarse subangular blocky; very hard, firm; thin patchy clayskins; weakly to strongly calcareous; pH 8.1.
C_{ca}	24-52	Pinkish white (7.5YR 8/2, dry) to pink (7.5YR 7/4, moist) massive; strongly cemented caliche; very strongly calcareous; pH 8.6.
C	52-60+	Very pale brown (10YR 7/3, dry) to brown (7.5YR 5/3, moist) sandy loam; massive; soft, very friable; very strongly calcareous; pH 8.2. With increasing depth, this material becomes chiefly coarse sand, gravel, and cobbles.

As compared with the Sevy soils, the Timpahute profile reveals a much thicker and more strongly cemented caliche lime zone. The clay concentration horizon in the B_2 is also greater. In addition, whitish sprinklings and a paper thin but discontinuous A_2 horizon can be found occasionally just above the horizon of maximum clay concentration. Some variation in color and thickness of the respective horizons occurs. The soil is browner in the vicinity of Modena and more reddish in the vicinity of Enterprise, and has a thinner A_1 and a thicker B_2 horizon than the soil near Modena. These variations indicate somewhat more clay formation and concentration and may be a reflection of the somewhat greater rainfall, over 15 inches at Enterprise and less than 11 at Modena.

Calcisols

In parent materials that are exceptionally high in carbonates, profile development appears to take another course. Clay formation and movement is inhibited or retarded and a horizon of lime rather than clay enrichment is the conspicuous feature of the profile. These soils are called Calcisols and their morphology and genesis has recently been discussed by Harper (3). A profile of Escalante fine sandy loam located in a barren area at the NW corner of sec. 2, T. 35 S., R. 16 W., is illustrative of this kind of soil:

Horizon	Depth inches	Description
A_v	0-1	Pink (7.5YR 7/4, dry) to brown (7.5YR 5/4, moist) fine sandy loam; very weak thin platy; very fine vesicular; soft, very friable; very strongly calcareous; pH 8.2.
A_1	1-12	Pink (7.5YR 7/4, dry) to brown (7.5YR 5/4, moist) fine sandy loam; very weak very fine granular to massive; soft, very friable; very strongly calcareous; pH 8.3.
C_{ca}	12-27	Pinkish white (7.5YR 8/2, dry) to pink (7.5YR 7/4, moist) fine sandy loam; massive; weakly cemented, caliche-like; very strongly calcareous; pH 8.5.
C	27-39	Pink (7.5YR 7/4, dry) to brown (7.5YR 5/4, moist) sandy loam with some gravel; massive; slightly hard, very friable; very strongly calcareous; pH 8.3.
D	39-112+	Unconforming beds of sand and gravel of variable size and composition but all highly siliceous; single grained; very weak to noncalcareous; moderately alkaline.

Other than the concentration of lime in the C_{ca} horizon, the Escalante profile indicates very little horizon differentation. Although this lime zone hardens appreciably on drying and appears to be caliche-like, it moistens quite rapidly under irrigation. Strongly alkaline reactions and some soluble salts are typically associated with the lime concentration zone, but the reaction quickly drops to moderately alkaline upon deep moistening under irrigation. Unconforming gravelly beds occur in places at variable depths in excess of 3 feet but usually in excess of 5 feet.

Solonetz Soils

In parent materials high in soluble salts containing sodium, profile development appears to proceed in stages from Alluvial soils to Solonetz in this area. As in the case with the Sierozems, several stages of development can be recognized. Two stages are recognized in this paper under the names minimal and medial.

Minimal

A profile of Antelope Springs silt loam located at the N 1/4 corner of sec. 29, T. 35 S., R. 15 W., illustrates the initial effects of excess exchangeable sodium on soils of this area. The following profile was located in a barren area between greasewood plants. Under greasewood and shadscale plants, the pH is considerably higher and the soil is more strongly affected by alkali.

Horizon	Depth inches	Description
A_v	0-3	Pink (7.5YR 7/4, dry) to brown (7.5YR 5/4, moist) silt loam; moderate medium platy; moderate very fine and fine vesicular; soft, very friable; moderately calcareous; pH 8.3.
A_1	3-6	Reddish brown (5YR 4/4, dry) to dark reddish brown (5YR 3/4, moist) silty clay loam; moderate very fine to fine granular; slightly hard, friable; strongly calcareous; pH 7.9.
B_2	6-13	Reddish brown (5YR 5/4, dry) to reddish brown (5YR 4/4, moist) clay loam; weak medium subangular blocky; hard, firm; thin patchy clayskins; strongly calcareous; pH 7.9.
B_3	13-18	Brown (7.5YR 5/4, dry or moist) clay; massive to weak medium subangular blocky; hard, firm; few thin patchy clayskins; strongly calcareous; pH 8.0.
C	18-60	Pinkish white (7.5YR 8/2, dry) to light brown (7.5YR 6/4, moist) clay; massive to very weak fine subangular blocky; hard, firm; moderately calcareous; pH 7.9.

The Antelope Springs soil appears to be developing from more recent medium- to fine-textured alluvial deposits overlying older basin materials. Although influenced by exchangeable sodium, only weakly differentiated profiles are evident. The differentiation is mainly in structure of the A_1 and B_2 horizons with some accompanying color changes but little textural change. In places, buried dark-colored soil materials of variable thickness occur in the subsoils and substrata of those soils.

Medial

The most advanced stage of horizon differentiation under the influence of strong concentrations of soluble salts and excess exchangeable sodium in this area is illustrated by a profile of Uvada loam located in a barren area at the E 1/4 corner of sect. 9, T. 35 S., R. 15 W.:

Horizon	Depth inches	Description
A_v	0-1	Pinkish white (7.5YR 8/2, dry) to light brown (7.5YR 6/4, moist) loam; weak medium platy; strong very fine to large vesicular; soft; very friable; strongly calcareous; pH 8.4.

A₁   1-5   Pink (7.5YR 7/4, dry) to brown (7.5YR 5/4, moist) loam; weak very thin platy; very fine vesicular; soft to slightly hard, very friable to friable; strongly calcareous; pH 8.4.

B₂   5-10   Strong brown (7.5YR 5/6, dry) to dark brown (7.5YR 4/4, moist) heavy silty clay loam; strong medium prismatic and fine and very fine subangular blocky; surfaces of prisms covered with thin nearly continuous clayskins and stained with organic matter; hard, firm to friable; weakly calcareous and moderately alkaline on the outside of prisms but brownish to whitish and strongly calcareous and strongly alkaline on the inside; pH 8.5.

B₃   10-18   Light brown (7.5YR 6/4, dry) to brown (7.5YR 5/4, moist) heavy silty clay loam; weak fine to medium subangular blocky; hard, firm to friable; thin patchy clayskins; very strongly calcareous; pH 8.6.

C   18-60   Pink (7.5YR 8/4, dry) to pink (7.5YR 7/4, moist) clay loam; massive; hard, friable; very strongly calcareous; pH 8.2.

Compared with Antelope Springs soils, this profile exhibits pronounced horizon differentiation, but the morphology is not everywhere so well developed. Neither has it progressed so far as to have the rounded columnar type of structure in the B horizon. A few whitish sprinklings are occasionally present in the lower A horizon.

LITERATURE CITED

1. Baldwin, M., Kellogg, C. E. and Thorp, J. Soil classification in Soils and Men. Yearbook of Agriculture, USDA. p. 979-1001. 1938.
2. Gilbert, G. K. Lake Bonneville. U.S. Geol. Sur. Mon. No. 1. 1920.
3. Harper, W. G. Morphology and genesis of Calcisols. Soil Sci. Soc. Amer. Proc. In press.
4. Thorp, J., and Smith, G. D. Higher categories of soil classification: Order, suborder, and great soil groups. Soil Sci. 67:117-126. 1949.
5. Shantz, W. L., and Premeisel, R. L. Types of vegetation in Escalante Valley, Utah, as indicators of soil conditions. USDA Tech. Bul 713. 1940.
6. Soil Survey Staff. Soil Survey Manual. USDA. Handbook No. 18. 1951.

PLANOSOLIC PIEDMONT SOILS OF NORTH CAROLINA:
I. MORPHOLOGY AND COMPOSITION

R. J. McCracken, S. B. Weed, and E. F. Goldston

North Carolina State [1]

Received for publication August 16, 1963

Iredell and White Store are planosolic soil series common in the Piedmont physiographic region of North Carolina, South Carolina, and Virginia. These are problem soils because of their physical characteristics of high contents of plastic clay in B horizons under thin A horizons, with restricted internal drainage. They represent extremes with respect to clay accumulation in B horizons. The Iredell soil series is estimated to occupy 370,000 acres and the White Store 200,000 acres in North Carolina (8). The location of these soils in central North Carolina is shown in figure 1.

Properties of Iredell soils were described by Marbut (11) and by Cobb (5). Obenshain and others (15-18) reported the characteristics of Iredell soils in Virginia, chiefly their chemical properties. Lutz (9) reported free-iron percentages of an Iredell soil in North Carolina. Detailed studies of the Iredell and White Store soils were undertaken because of the scarcity of information on these extensive soils with respect to their genesis, composition, and management problems.

The Iredell soils formed from diorite, gabbro, or similar dark-colored ferromagnesian (mafic) rocks. White Store soils formed from mudstones and shales in an area of level-bedded unconsolidated to slightly consolidated sedimentary rocks in the eastern Piedmont known as the Deep River Basin or Triassic Basin. These sediments originated from the surrounding Piedmont soils and saprolite and are believed to have been deposited in shallow lakes in the Triassic period (22).

Environmental factors for these soils are similar. The mean annual temperature is approximately 61 F., and mean annual rainfall is 45 to 50 inches. The excess of rainfall over evapotranspiration is about 8 inches per year, chiefly in the fall and winter months (10). The soils are on side slopes, ordinarily gently concave downward, on Piedmont ground surfaces of uncertain geomorphic age. They receive runoff and seepage water from the convex, well-drained soils upslope; during the winter season, they may have a high water table. The vegetation is oak-hickory (though there are early settler reports of natural grasslands on Iredell soils).

---

[1] Of University of North Carolina at Raleigh. Journal Series Paper No. 1657, North Carolina Agricultural Experiment Station, Raleigh, North Carolina. Appreciation is expressed to the Soil Testing Division (E. J. Kamprath, Director) of the North Carolina Department of Agriculture for assistance with the exchangeable-basic-cation determinations.

Reproduced with permission from *Soil Science,* Vol. 98, 1964, p. 22-32. Copyright©
1964, The Williams and Wilkins Company, Baltimore, Maryland 21202, USA.

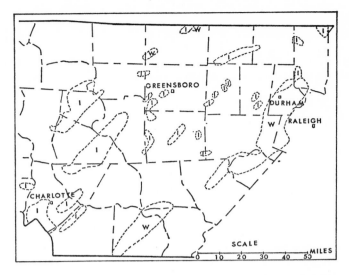

Fig. 1—Location of Iredell (I) and White Store (W) soils in the Piedmont of North Carolina.

SOILS

Iredell Profile I (Alamance County, N.C., near Burlington)

A1 Horizon, 0 to 4 inches

Gray (10YR 5/1), sandy loam; weak medium and fine granular; friable; gradual smooth boundary.

A2 Horizon, 4 to 7 inches

Grayish brown (10YR 5/2), sandy loam; weak fine to medium granular; few medium and fine ferromanganese nodules and concretions in upper part, numerous in lower part; friable; abrupt wavy boundary.

B1 Horizon, 7 to 13 inches

Light olive brown (2.5Y 5/4), with few coarse red mottles (2.5YR 4/8), clay; strong medium to coarse subangular blocky; few large ferromanganese nodules and concretions; firm; gradual smooth boundary.

B2t Horizon, 13 to 17 inches

Light olive brown (2.5Y 5/4), clay; strong medium to fine subangular blocky; very firm; common discontinuous cutans; gradual smooth boundary.

B3 Horizon, 17 to 24 inches

Olive gray (5Y 5/2), clay; strong medium to coarse subangular blocky; firm; common discontinuous cutans; gradual wavy boundary.

C1 Horizon, 24 to 36 inches

Gray and olive brown clay loam; firm; common fragments of diorite which can be crushed with the fingers.

Iredell Profile II (Iredell County, N.C., near Elmwood)

0 Horizon, 1 to 0 inches

Leaves of oak and hickory.

A1 Horizon, 0 to 1.5 inches

Very dark gray (10YR 3/1), loam, weak medium granular; very friable.

A2 Horizon, 1.5 to 5 inches

Light yellowish brown (2.5Y 6/4), sandy loam, weak medium granular; few fine ferromanganese nodules; very friable; abrupt wavy boundary.

B1 Horizon, 5 to 9 inches

Light olive brown (2.5Y 5/4), clay loam, moderate medium and fine subangular blocky structure, slightly firm; common hard concretions 0.5 to 1 mm. in diameter; clear smooth boundary.

B21t Horizon, 9 to 13 inches

Yellowish brown (10YR 5/6) with coatings of light gray (10YR 6/2) on aggregate faces; clay; moderate medium subangular blocky; common nearly continuous cutans; clear smooth boundary.

B22t Horizon, 13 to 17 inches

Yellowish brown (10YR 5/6) and light olive brown (2.5Y 5/4) with a few seams of light gray (10YR 7/2) clay; strong medium subangular blocky; extremely firm; common nearly continuous cutans; gradual smooth boundary.

B3t Horizon, 17 to 21 inches

Light olive brown (2.5Y 5/4) and yellowish brown (10YR 5/5), clay; moderate medium subangular blocky; very firm; common dark green spots of partially weathered ferromagnesian minerals; common discontinuous cutans; gradual irregular boundary.

C1 Horizon, 21 to 32 inches

Soft apparently weathered diorite with few seams and pockets of clay; a few clay films.

C2 Horizon, 32 to 55 inches

Diorite with common local soft areas; few clay films in vertical channels.

R Horizon, 55 to 60+ inches

Hard dark green and gray diorite.

White Store Profile I (Durham County, N.C., south of Durham)

A1 Horizon, 0 to 1 inches

Dark grayish brown (10YR 4/2), sandy loam, fragmental, breaking to a weak coarse granular; very friable.

A2 Horizon, 1 to 5 inches

Yellowish brown (10YR 5/4), sandy loam; fragmental crushing to a weak medium granular; very friable; clear wavy boundary.

B1 Horizon, 5 to 11 inches

Brownish yellow (10YR 6/6) and light yellowish brown (2.5Y 6/4) with a few coatings of yellowish red (5YR 5/6), clay; moderate medium subangular blocky; very firm; thin discontinuous cutans; clear wavy boundary.

B21t Horizon, 11 to 16 inches

Brownish yellow (10YR 6/6) with a few aggregate mottlings of light gray (10YR 7/2) and a few fine spots of red (2.5YR 4/6), clay; moderate medium angular and subangular blocky, very firm, few discontinuous cutans; clear wavy boundary.

B22t Horizon, 16 to 23 inches

Brownish yellow (10YR 7/6) and strong brown (7.5YR 5/6) with common gray (10YR 7/2) mottlings, seams and spots, and few red (2.5YR 5/6) streaks, clay; weak medium subangular blocky; extremely firm; common discontinuous cutans; gradual irregular boundary.

B3 Horizon, 23 to 36 inches

Yellow (10YR 7/8) and light gray (10YR 7/2) with common spots of yellowish red (5YR 4/6), clay; very weak medium subangular blocky; very firm gray clay lines, voids, and root channels; gradual wavy boundary.

C1 Horizon, 36 to 45 inches

Pale yellow (5Y 7/3) with common spots of reddish brown (5YR 4/3), clay; massive to fragmental; very firm; gradual irregular boundary.

R1 Horizon, 45 to 60 inches

Pale yellow (5Y 7/3) and light gray (5Y 7/2), clay loam; massive.

R2 Horizon, 60 to 80+ inches

Partially oxidized and weathered micaceous weakly consolidated sandy shale and mudstone.

White Store Profile II (Chatham County, North Carolina)

0 Horizon, 2 to 0 inches

Leaf litter of white oak, post oak, red oak with a few loblolly pine needles.

A1 Horizon, 0 to 1.5 inches

Dark grayish brown (10YR 4/2), coarse sandy loam; very weak coarse granular; very friable; smooth clear boundary.

A2 Horizon, 1.5 to 6 inches

Pale brown (10YR 6/3), coarse sandy loam; fragmental breaking to weak granular; very friable; abrupt wavy boundary.

B1 Horizon, 6 to 9 inches

Pale brown (10YR 6/3) and strong brown (7.5YR 5/6), sandy clay loam; weak medium subangular blocky; friable; few cutans on peds in lower part; clear wavy boundary.

B21t Horizon, 9 to 15 inches

Yellowish red (5YR 5/6) with common coatings and spots of brownish yellow (7.5YR 6/6) clay; moderate medium subangular blocky; very firm; common nearly continuous cutans on peds; gradual wavy boundary.

B22t Horizon, 15 to 21 inches

Yellowish red (5YR 5/6) and brownish yellow (7.5YR 6/6) with common coatings and spots of very pale brown (10YR 6/3), clay; moderate medium and coarse subangular blocky; extremely firm; numerous nearly continuous cutans on peds; few fine mica flakes; gradual wavy boundary.

B23t Horizon, 21 to 29 inches

Brownish yellow (10YR 6/6) and very pale brown (10YR 6/3) with a few spots of yellowish red (5YR 5/6) sandy clay; weak coarse subangular blocky; very firm; common discontinuous cutans on peds; common mica flakes; gradual wavy boundary.

B3 Horizon, 29 to 35 inches

Olive brown (2.5Y 6/6) with common coarse streaks of light gray (5Y 7/1) and a few coarse streaks of brownish yellow (7.5YR 6/6); stratified clay, sandy clay, and sandy clay loam; very weak coarse subangular blocky; few cutans on peds; common mica flakes; diffuse wavy boundary.

C Horizon, 35 to 42 inches

Light gray (5Y 7/2) and gray (5Y 7/1) with common coarse streaks of brownish yellow (10YR 6/6); sandy clay loam; numerous mica flakes; diffuse irregular boundary.

R1 Horizon, 42 to 54 inches

Partially consolidated brownish yellow and gray sandy shale; numerous mica flakes.

R2 Horizon, 54 to 66 inches

Partially consolidated sandstone with numerous mica flakes and a few feldspar fragments.

METHODS

Particle-size-distribution analyses were made by dry-sieving and by a modified Day (7) hydrometer procedure, using sodium hexametaphosphate solution as a dispersant. Bulk-density determinations were made by a coated-clod technique, employing Dow Saran F-120 resin in methyl ethyl ketone as coating material.[2]

Exchangeable basic cations were determined on N NH$_4$OAc leachates, using mod-

---

[2] Unpublished procedure, U.S. Dep. Agr. Soil Survey Laboratory.

Table 1—Particle-size distribution and bulk density.

Horizon	Depth	Sand 2000-50 μ.	Silt 50-2 μ.	Clay <2 μ.		Horizon	Depth	Sand 2000-50 μ.	Silt 50-2 μ.	Clay <2 μ.	
	in.	% weight			g./cm.³		in.	% weight			g./cm.³
Iredell I, Alamance County, N. C. (N. C. Profile 79-13)						White Store I, Durham County, N. C. (N. C. Profile 174-6)					
A1	0–3	68.6	25.5	5.9	1.4	Ap	0–5	66.8	19.1	14.1	1.7
A2	3–7	68.3	25.1	6.6	1.8	B1	5–11	29.0	17.9	53.1	1.8
B1t	7–14	24.9	21.9	53.2	1.9	B21t	11–16	23.7	16.3	62.0	1.8
B2t	14–18	23.1	24.5	52.4	2.1	B22t	16–23	16.9	23.9	59.2	1.8
B3t	18–23	18.8	22.0	59.2	1.9	B3t	23–30	28.7	21.8	49.5	1.7
C	23–36	21.8	44.6	33.6	2.0	C1	30–36	19.0	43.1	37.9	1.7
						C2	36–45	38.2	42.6	19.2	1.7
						R1	45–60	67.4	27.7	4.9	1.8
						R2	60–80+	66.7	29.5	3.8	1.9
Iredell II, Iredell County, N. C. (N. C. Profile 79-14)						White Store II, Chatham County, N. C. (N. C. Profile 174-7)					
A1	0–15	51.3	41.2	7.5	1.5	A1	0–1.5	75.2	19.5	5.3	1.5
A2	1.5–5	52.3	38.5	9.3	1.7	A2	1.5–6	76.2	19.6	4.2	1.7
A3/B1	5–9	50.3	34.9	14.8	—	A3/B1	6–9	67.0	20.5	12.5	1.8
B1t	9–13	17.9	16.4	65.7	1.7	B1t	9–15	32.8	15.3	51.9	1.7
B2t	13–17	20.9	17.3	61.8	1.7	B2t	15–21	30.3	16.8	52.9	1.7
B3	17–21	34.6	24.6	40.8	1.9	B31t	21–29	40.2	21.7	38.1	1.7
C1	21–32	61.7	26.7	11.6	1.9	B32t	29–35	47.0	21.0	32.0	—
C2	32–55	70.8	22.7	6.5	2.0	C	35–42	57.5	24.8	17.7	1.8
						R1	42–54	65.2	20.6	14.2	1.8
						R2	54–66+	66.2	20.0	13.8	1.8

ifications of the method of Peech et al. (19). Exchange acidity was determined by the method of Mehlich (12), using $BaCl_2$-triethanolamine buffered at pH 8.2 as displacing solution. Exchangeable Al was determined by titration of N KCl leachate with standard base, as described by Coleman et al. (6). Measurements of pH were on 1:1 soil water suspensions. Total nitrogen was determined by a Kjeldahl method. Free iron was determined by a dithionite-citrate bicarbonate buffered extraction (13). Thin sections were prepared by impregnating selected blocks with a Laminac (American Cyanamid Laminac 4116 resin)-styrene mixture under vacuum followed by sawing and grinding to desired thickness. The sections mounted on glass slides were then examined with a polarizing microscope.

RESULTS

Physical Composition

All four of the profiles studied have high clay concentrations in B2 horizons (table 1). B/A clay ratios range from about 4 to 10. Clay concentration increases rapidly over a narrow increment of depth in the A to B horizon transition. These are criteria which have previously been associated with "clay pan planosols" (23). Also, clay percentages decrease sharply from B to C horizons. Bulk-density values of B horizons are relatively high, indicating low porosity and permeability in B horizons. These data suggest strong similarity in the physical characteristics of Iredell and White Store soils.

Chemical Composition

Marked differences in certain chemical characteristics of the soils are indicated by the data of tables 2 and 3. Of particular importance are the high exchangeable Al levels and relatively low exchangeable basic cation populations of the White Store soil in contrast to the high "base saturation" of the Iredell soil. This is apparently due to the high content of weatherable minerals in the parent material of the Iredell (and which also persist in the solum), in contrast to the clayey, weathered sediments comprising the White Store parent material[3]. The Al saturation of the White Store solum exceeds the 60 per cent level suggested by Nye et al. (14) as that level at which significant concentration of Al appears in solution. Thus Al toxicity can be expected in White Store soils.

Exchangeable Mg exceeds Ca in B horizons of the four profiles studied in detail. A possible explanation is the release of Mg from octahedral layers of montmorillonite present in these soils[4], according to the mechanism suggested by Barshad (2). This cyclic, successive decomposition of the octahedral layers would also provide a source for the high amounts of exchangeable Al in the White Store B horizons. As previously indicated, fragments of weatherable minerals releasing bases, plus slow rate of leaching, apparently preserve the high base status in the Iredell soils.

Exchangeable Na levels exceeding 1 me./100 g. in the Iredell profile I apparently originate from the sodium hornblende minerals common in the parent material. Increases in exchangeable Na with depth were also found in the Iredell II and White Store I profiles. Since the maximum amount is less than 5 per cent of exchange capacity, it would not be expected to be a major factor in these soils, though it might perhaps contribute to dispersion of the clay. Cobb (5) noted higher content of total sodium in the Iredell soil in comparison to redder more friable associated soils, and suggested this as a possible contributor to deflocculation.

Free-iron percentages (table 3) of the Iredell soils reflect the deliberate attempt to sample profiles representing a range in color and concentration of iron-rich nodules and concretions in the A2 to B1 transition. Likewise, White Store profile I was selected as a grayer member, and profile II as a redder member, of the range of this series. The free-iron maximum in the A2 horizon of Iredell profile I, coupled with the lower percentage in the B and the concentration of diffuse (poorly organized) nodules in the A2 and B1, suggest a periodic "perching" of a water-saturated zone above the plastic and relatively impermeable B2 horizon. Thus, this type of profile could be classed as "somewhat poorly drained." The browner colors and higher free-iron percentages in Iredell profile II B horizon suggest that this profile should be classed as "moderately well drained." The relatively low concentration of free iron in parent material and solum of White Store profile I apparently stems from low iron content in the sediment plus lack of appreciable iron concentration during

---

[3] S. B. Weed and R. J. McCracken (manuscript, North Carolina State at UNC, Raleigh).
[4] *Ibid.*

Table 2—Exchangeable cation populations.

Horizon	Depth.	Exchangeable Basic Cations				Exchange Acidity	Exchangeable Al	Bases + Exchange Acidity
		Ca	Mg	K	Na			
	in.	me./100 g.						

Iredell I, Alamance Co.

Horizon	Depth.	Ca	Mg	K	Na	Exchange Acidity	Exchangeable Al	Bases + Exchange Acidity
A1	0–3	0.28	0.20	0.06	0.14	7.5	0.17	8.2
A2	3–7	0.28	0.20	0.02	0.21	6.1	0.05	6.8
B1t	7–14	6.0	9.0	0.06	0.64	0.7	0.25	16.4
B2t	14–18	8.8	9.6	0.08	0.92	4.6	0.06	24.0
B3t	18–23	13.0	13.7	0.15	1.3	1.3	0.02	29.5
C	23–36	18.2	10.4	0.12	2.0	0	0	30.7

Iredell II, Iredell Co.

Horizon	Depth.	Ca	Mg	K	Na	Exchange Acidity	Exchangeable Al	Bases + Exchange Acidity
A1	0–1.5	4.8	2.4	0.14	0.01	6.5	0.21	13.9
A2	1.5–5	0.70	0.38	0.04	0.01	3.9	0.59	5.0
A3/B1	5–9	1.45	1.8	0.03	0.03	3.7	0.50	7.0
B1t	9–13	10.1	11.2	0.07	0.34	8.6	0.91	30.3
B2t	13–17	10.7	12.3	0.07	0.40	7.2	0.39	30.7
B3	17–21	11.4	12.8	0.07	0.42	1.1	0.03	25.8
C1	21–32	11.2	8.0	0.08	0.49	0.58	0	20.4
C2	32–55	10.3	7.0	0.09	0.60	0	0	18.0

White Store I, Durham Co.

Horizon	Depth.	Ca	Mg	K	Na	Exchange Acidity	Exchangeable Al	Bases + Exchange Acidity
Ap	0–5	5.0	1.2	0.08	0.10	1.2	0.17	7.6
B1	5–11	7.0	3.1	0.22	0.14	15.4	11.8	25.9
B21t	11–16	4.1	3.9	0.29	0.25	24.8	21.5	33.3
B22t	16–23	5.1	4.0	0.34	0.37	26.4	20.7	36.2
B31t	23–30	4.0	4.0	0.29	0.42	22.5	17.3	31.2
B32t	30–36	5.9	6.5	0.41	0.62	28.6	22.6	42.0
C1	36–45	6.2	6.2	0.25	0.65	22.4	18.8	25.7
R1	45–60	8.4	4.0	0.10	0.71	10.8	7.5	24.0
R2	60–80+	13.5	7.0	0.13	1.23	10.0	6.9	31.9

White Store II, Chatham Co.

Horizon	Depth.	Ca	Mg	K	Na	Exchange Acidity	Exchangeable Al	Bases + Exchange Acidity
A1	0–1.5	0.32	0.24	0.10	0.04	6.5	1.2	7.2
A2	1.5–6	0.20	0.06	0.07	0.03	6.4	1.2	6.8
A3/B1	6–9	0.12	0.35	0.10	0.02	6.3	4.5	6.9
B1t	9–15	0.20	2.7	0.31	0.04	22.6	17.7	25.9
B2t	15–21	0.25	3.0	0.28	0.15	25.8	20.1	29.5
B31t	21–29	0.12	1.9	0.18	0.15	20.9	15.1	23.3
B32t	29–35	0.20	1.5	0.15	0.21	17.5	13.6	19.6
C	35–42	0.60	0.73	0.11	0.24	10.7	8.5	12.4
R1	42–54	0.50	0.30	0.11	0.18	9.0	7.2	10.1
R2	54–66+	0.40	0.18	0.09	0.16	8.4	6.4	9.2

soil formation, possibly due to hydration and reducing conditions. This profile could also be classed as "somewhat poorly drained." White Store profile II has evidence of free-iron concentration in the solum during soil formation. The free iron is not, however, concentrated in the clay, but is segregated into local concentrations, suggesting occasional water saturation, especially in the lower solum. This profile could thus be classed as "moderately well drained."

Table 3—Free iron, nitrogen, and pH in Iredell and White Store Profiles.

Iredell, Profile I

Horizon	Depth (in.)	Free Iron Whole soil (%)	Free Iron Clay (%)	Total N (%)	pH (1:1 H_2O)
A1	0–3	1.8	0.74	0.056	4.7
A2	3–7	3.9	0.88	0.034	5.2
B1t	7–14	1.1	—	0.042	4.9
B2t	14–18	0.75	1.7	0.022	6.0
B3t	18–23	0.19	1.2	0.008	7.0
C	23–36	1.7	0.58	0.011	7.5
R	36–48+	0.90	—	—	

White Store, Profile I

Horizon	Depth (in.)	Free Iron Whole soil (%)	Free Iron Clay (%)	Total N (%)	pH (1:1 H_2O)
Ap	0–5	0.30	—	0.050	5.7
B1	5–11	0.80	—	0.031	4.6
B21t	11–16	0.60	—	0.022	4.5
B22t	16–23	0.2	—	0.022	4.3
C1	23–36	1.1	—	0.017	4.4
C2	36–45	0.56	—	0.014	4.7
R1	45–60	0.93	—	0.011	5.2
R2	60–80+	0.88	—	0.008	5.4

Iredell, Profile II

Horizon	Depth (in.)	Free Iron Whole soil (%)	Free Iron Clay (%)	Total N (%)	pH (1:1 H_2O)
A1	0–1.5	0.84	—	0.148	4.6
A2	1.5–5	1.1	—	0.031	4.9
A3/B1	5–9	3.7	—	0.014	4.9
B1t	9–13	10.1	—	0.034	4.8
B2t	13–17	9.0	—	0.022	5.2
B3	17–21	3.3	—	0.017	6.0
C1	21–32	3.5	—	0.006	6.5
C2	32–55	3.3	—	—	7.2
R	55–66+	4.4	—	—	

White Store, Profile II

Horizon	Depth (in.)	Free Iron Whole soil (%)	Free Iron Clay (%)	Total N (%)	pH (1:1 H_2O)
A1	0–1.5	0.57	1.5	0.067	4.5
A2	1.5–6	0.42	0.65	0.020	4.4
A3/B1	6–9	1.2	1.3	0.014	4.3
B1t	9–15	4.8	0.91	0.020	4.1
B2t	15–21	3.4	0.61	0.017	4.1
B31t	21–29	3.2	0.82	0.011	4.2
B32t	29–35	1.7	—	0.012	4.3
C	35–42	0.95	0.33	0.010	4.8
R1	42–54	0.97	0.32	0.014	4.9
R2	54–66+	2.1	—	0.009	5.0

Nitrogen contents (table 3) are presented as a measure of organic matter distribution. No significant differences in the N content between the two soil series are indicated, except for the slight concentration in the B1 horizons of the Iredell, possibly due to a sieving effect by this clay-rich zone.

Micromorphology

A tabulation of micromorphological characteristics of the four soil profiles studied in detail is presented in table 4. A striking characteristic is the scarcity of illuviation argillans ("clay films") in these B horizons of high concentrations of clay, together with the common occurrence of stress cutans ("pressure faces") (figs. 2 and 3). Absence of extensive illuviation argillans suggests either (a) that the evidence for clay illuviation which may have taken place has been obliterated by the swelling of the montmorillonite-bearing clay, this latter marked by the stress cutans, or (b) that clay movement has not taken place to a significant extent in these soils, the coarser textures of A horizons thus being due to concentration of quartz (and other minerals) by a residue effect.

Another prominent feature of these soils is the presence of strongly developed plasma fabric with prominent plasma separations [local areas showing moderate to strong orientation of clay particles within the matrix (4) in B horizons (figs. 2

Table 4—Micromorphological characteristics of Iredell and White Store profiles.

Horizon; and Depth (*in.*)	Micromorphological Characteristics*			
	Voids	Glaebules	Cutans	Plasma Fabric
Iredell Profile I				
B1; 10–12	Common joint and skew planes, few channels and vesicles	Sparse large normal Fe-Mn(?) concretions; common diffuse Fe nodules; common reddish brown papules (lithorelicts?)	Few illuviation argillans (0.2% cross-sectional area) common stress cutans	Skelattisepic
B2t; 15–17	Common joint planes; common vugs and vesicles	Common diffuse irregular Fe nodules; sparse reddish brown papules (lithorelicts?)	Very few illuviation argillans 0.1% of cross-sectional area) common stress cutans	Lattisepic
C; 34–36	Common joint and skew planes; few large vugs	Common diffuse irregular Fe nodules	Very few thin discontinuous vug and vesicle argillans	(Insufficient plasma for fabric description)
Iredell Profile II				
A2; 4–5	Abundant vugs and channels	Sparse normal nodules 0.5–2 mm. dia., opaque or very dark, Fe-rich, possibly with Mn; quartz grains occluded	None	(Insufficient plasma for fabric description)
B1t; 9–11	Common vugs, skew planes; few joint plants, channels	Sparse normal nodules 1–2 mm. dia., Fe-rich, a few concretionary in form, quartz grains occluded	Few illuviation argillans (1.6% cross-sectional area) common stress cutans	Lattisepic
B2t; 14–16	Common vugs, skew planes, few channels	Sparse normal nodules 1–2 mm. dia., Fe-rich,	Very few illuviation argillans (0.4% of cross-sectional area), common stress cutans; B3 has 0.3% cross-sectional area illuviation argillans	Lattisepic
White Store Profile I				
B1, 8–10	Few joint planes, skew plants, channels; very few vugs	Common yellowish red and red papules (litho or pedorelicts?)	Few illuviation argillans in some channels, (3.1% cross-sectional area); few stress cutans	Lattimosepic
B22t, 16–18	Common vugs, few joint planes	Sparse red papules randomly distributed (sedimentary relicts?), sparse dark irregular nodules (both Fe-Mn and carbonaceous)	Thick but discontinuous illuviation argillans in vugs vesicles (0.8% of cross-sectional area) papules in matrix may be relict argillans; common stress cutans	Mosepic
C	Few large vugs; very few channels	Common dark brown papules (lithorelicts from biotite or chlorite?); sparse red papules	None	(Plasma in thin bands of interstitial material, fabric not recognizable)
D, 42–44	Few vugs; very few channels	Sparse small normal opaque nodules; very sparse red papules	None	None
White Store Profile II				
B1, 7–8	Common vugs and packing voids	Few yellowish red papules	None	Asepic—small amount of fabric
B21t, 10–12	Abundant joint skew planes, vesicles and vugs	Common red-yellow red papules 0.05–0.1 mm.; sparse normal Fe nodules	Common discontinuous argillans in vesicles, vugs (1.9% cross-sectional area); few stress cutans	Mosepic
B2t	Numerous joint, skew planes; common vugs	Sparse red papules, common diffuse irregular Fe nodules	Few illuviation argillans (1.2% of cross-sectional area, 0.1% in B3); common stress cutans	Mosepic
C, 38–40	Common vugs, joint planes; few vesicles	Common reddish brown papules	Few illuviation argillans	Mosepic

* Nomenclature used is that of Brewer (3), Brewer and Sleeman (4), and unpublished work of Brewer and Sleeman presented by Brewer at the Soil Clay Mineralogy Seminar, held at Blacksburg, Va., July, 1962. Glaebules are 3-dimensional units within the soil material, recognizable either because of greater concentration of some constituent and/or fabric difference compared with enclosing soil material, or because they have a distinct boundary with the enclosing soil material. Concretions, nodules, and papules are types of glaebules. Papules are composed mostly of clay minerals; they have sharp boundaries with enclosing soil material, continuous internal fabric, and, commonly, strong continuous orientation (the "clay galls" of the sedimentary petrographer are a type of papule). Plasma fabric refers to the spatial arrangement of solid particles and associated voids in the plasma or fine-grained mobile portion of the soil. Specific types are recognized according to the number and arrangement of plasma aggregates [domains (1) and larger plasma separations (patches with flecked and striated orientation of clay particles, without sharp boundaries)]. The suffix "sepic" indicates that a significant number of large plasma separations are present. The prefixes indicate the type of orientation: Mo = mosaic, latti = lattice, skel = around skelton grains.

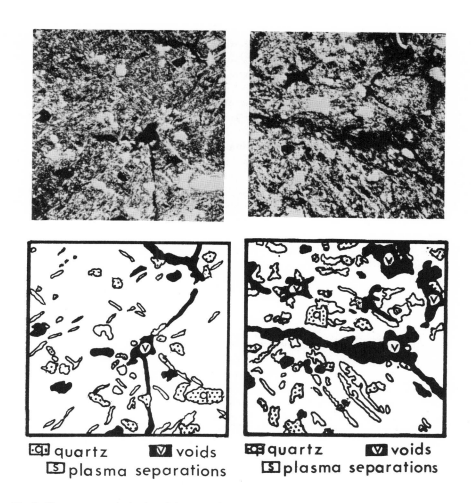

Fig. 2—Photomicrograph *(top)* and diagram of photomicrograph *(bottom)* of White Store B2t horizon, showing absence of illuviation argillans in void *(dark spot in matrix)* and mosaic fabric of plasma separations *(light streaks in matrix).*

Fig. 3—Photomicrograph *(top)* and diagram of photomicrograph *(bottom)* of Iredell B2t horizon, showing lattisepic pattern of plasma separations in matrix (polarized light, 50 x).

and 3)]. Iredell soils exhibit lineation of these plasma orientations in two general directions; White Store plasma separations tend to occur in a scattered mosaic pattern. It is suggested that this lattisepic fabric pattern in the Iredell soils may result from clay minerals forming in place from primary mineral grains followed by extrusion of this clay into linear form by swelling forces. The White Store soils, however, inherited randomly distributed clay from the sedimentary parent material with few weatherable mineral grains. Thus segregated clay is not available for development of linear fabric patterns. Clay domains (1) of large size are a prominent feature of both soils, which may be a factor in the "strength" and water relations of these soils.

The reddish papules in the White Store soils are thought to be sedimentary relicts, inherited from the sediments serving as parent materials of these soils. Since these sediments were derived from the Piedmont, these reddish clayey segregations may be relicts from previous Piedmont soils.

Occurrence of iron-manganese nodules and concretions in the A2 and B1 horizons of the Iredell soil suggests seasonal "perching" of a water-saturated zone above the B2 horizon. This results in movement of the relatively high content of iron and manganese in these soils from "basic" (mafic) rocks into segregation centers in the wetting-drying cycles of this part of the soil profile. Absence of such concretions and nodules in the White Store profile apparently is a result of much lower content of iron and manganese in the original sedimentary parent material. Redden and Porter (20) reported abundant concretions containing iron and manganese in certain horizons of Iredell and similar soils formed from greenstone in Virginia. They suggested that the iron and manganese must have been derived from the underlying greenstone, with concentration due to local waterlogging characteristic after each rain. They also reported that the concretions tend to form most abundantly in the lower A horizon and are softer in the lower solum.

Classification

Placement of these soils in the newly devised soil classification system (21) is:

Iredell—Albaqualfic Normudalf. The relatively high saturation of the exchange capacity with exchangeable basic cations and the high pH (tables 2 and 3) of the B horizon, together with clay accumulation in the B, places this soil series in the Alfisol order. The presence of the light-colored A2 horizon, the gray colors and mottles in lower B horizons, and the abrupt textural change are the basis for placement in the Albaqualfic subgroup of this order.

White Store—Aquic Normochrult. Low content of exchangeable basic cations and high exchangeable Al content relative to exchange capacity of the B horizon, together with clay accumulation in the B, is the basis for placement in the Ultisol order. The gray mottles and other characteristics indicating seasonal wetness are the basis for placement in the Aquic subgroup of this order.

SUMMARY AND CONCLUSIONS

Iredell and White Store soils are rather similar in physical characteristics, such as sandy surface soils and high content of clay in B horizons. but differ markedly in chemical properties. Iredell soils have high "base status," whereas White Store soils have high exchangeable Al saturation.

Both Iredell and White Store soils were found to have exchangeable Mg contents higher than exchangeable Ca. This is thought to result from release of Mg from the octahedral layers of the montmorillonite clays present in these soils. The high content of weatherable minerals in the solum maintains high exchangeable basic cation populations in the Iredell soils.

Both Iredell and White Store soil series were found to possess only a few illuviation argillans in B horizons despite the high B/A clay ratios and the field description of clay films. Stress cutans ("pressure faces") were found to be common in both soils, reflecting swelling activity of B horizon clays.

Iredell is placed in the Albaqualfic Normudalf subgroup and White Store in the Aquic Normochrult subgroup in the newly proposed (7th Approximation) classification system.

REFERENCES

1. Aylmore, L. A. G., and Quirk, J. D. 1959 Swelling of clay-water systems. Nature 183:1752-1753.
2. Barshad, I. 1960 Significance of the presence of exchangeable magnesium ions in acidified clays. Science 131:988-990.
3. Brewer, R. 1960 Cutans: their definition, recognition and classification. J. Soil Sci. 11:280-292.
4. Brewer, R., and Sleeman, J. R. 1960 Soil structure and fabric: their definition and description. J. Soil Sci. 11:172-185.
5. Cobb, W. B. 1928 A comparison of the development of soils from acidic and basic rocks. Trans. Intern. Congr. Soil Sci., 1st. Congr. 4:456-465.
6. Coleman, N. T., Weed, S. B., and McCracken, R. J. 1959 Cation exchange capacity and exchangeable cations in Piedmont soils of North Carolina. Soil Sci. Soc. Am. Proc. 23:146-149.
7. Day, P. R. 1956 Report of the Committee on Physical Analyses, 1954-1955. Soil Sci. Soc. Am. Proc. 21:16-20.
8. Lee, W. D. 1955 The soils of North Carolina, N.C. Agr. Expt. Sta. Tech. Bull. 115.
9. Lutz, J. F. 1936 The relation of free iron in soil to aggregation. Soil Sci. Soc. Am. Proc. 1:43-45.
10. McCaleb, S. B., and Lee, W. D. 1956 Soils of North Carolina: 1. Soil Sci. 82:419-431.
11. Marbut, C. F. 1935 Soils of the United States. (In Atlas of American Agriculture, part III. O. E. Baker, editor.)
12. Mehlich, A. 1953 Rapid determination of cation and anion exchange properties and pH of soils. J. Assoc. Offic. Agr. Chemists 36:445-457.
13. Mehra, O. P., and Jackson, M. L. 1960 Iron oxide removal from soils and clays by a dithionite-citrate system buffered with sodium bicarbonate. Clays and Clay Minerals, 7th. Nat. Conf. on Clay Minerals Proc., pp. 317-327.
14. Nye, P., et al. 1961 Ion exchange equilibria involving aluminum. Soil Sci. Soc. Am. Proc. 25:14-17.
15. Obenshain, S. S., and Porter, H. C. 1959 Chemical characteristics of important Loudoun County soils. Virginia Agr. Expt. Sta. Research Rept. 31.
16. ...., and Petro, J. H. 1960 Chemical characteristics of Fauquier County Soils. Virginia Agr. Expt. Sta. Research Rept. 40.
17. ...., and Porter, H. C. 1960 Chemical and Physical Properties of Fairfax County Soils. Virginia Agr. Expt. Sta., Virginia Polytechnic Institute, Blacksburg, Virginia.
18. ...., and Coleman, C. S. 1960 Virginia Agr. Expt. Sta. Research Rept. 43.
19. Peech, M., et al. 1947 Methods of soil analysis for soil-fertility investigations. U.S. Dep. Agr. Circ. 757.
20. Redden, J. A., and Porter, H. C. 1962 Preliminary note on some soil concretions in the Virginia Piedmont. Mineral Ind. J. IX:1-4.
21. Soil Survey Staff. 1960 Soil Classification, A Comprehensive System—7th Approximation. U.S. Dep. Agr., Washington, D.C.
22. Stuckey, J. L., and Conrad, S. G. 1958 Explanatory text for geologic map of North Carolina. N. Carolina Div. Mineral Resources Bull. 71.
23. Thorp, J., and Smith, G. D. 1949 Higher categories of soil classification: order, suborder, and great soil groups. Soil Sci. 67:117-126.

DARK-CLAY SOILS OF WARM REGIONS VARIOUSLY CALLED RENDZINA, BLACK COTTON SOILS, REGUR, AND TIRS[1]

Harvey Oakes and James Thorp [2]

Deep dark clays of warm-temperate and tropical regions have many fundamental properties in common and appear to require a separate major group in a natural classification. Various local names, most of which appear to be nearly synonymous, have been used for these soils, but none of them has become generally used for the entire group and none appears to be appropriate. This paper comprises (1) a summary and partial review of the literature in English on Rendzina, Black Cotton Soils, Regur, Tirs, Black Earths of warm regions, and other local names for these soils and (2) a proposal and tentative definition of a general name, *Grumusol,* for the group.

Deep dark clays characterized by much shrinkage and swelling with changes in moisture have been described from many parts of the world. They are developed mainly in clayey calcareous sediments or residuum from certain basic rocks, mainly basalt, gneiss, and argillaceous limestones. Generally they are high in calcium and have surface horizons either calcareous or neutral to only slightly acid, but strongly acid forms occur in some areas with more than 40 inches of rainfall. They are most extensive in warm-temperate to tropical regions but also occur in cool regions. They are found on every continent, but largely in regions with well-defined rainy and dry seasons and rainfall of less than 50 inches. The most extensive areas seemingly are in Africa, India, the southern United States, Australia, South America, the Philippines, Mexico, Cuba, and various islands in the South Pacific. Although sometimes designated as humic-carbonate, humic-lime, or calcium soils, they have generally been called Rendzina in the United States, Regur or Black Cotton Soils in India, Black Earths in Australia and South America, and Tirs in Morocco.[3]

RENDZINA

In all countries except the United States, the name Rendzina is used primarily for shallow to very shallow, gray to black soils developed in limestone or chalk. Typically, the A_1 horizon is dark grayish brown to black and medium textured,

---

[1] Contribution from the Division of Soil Survey, B.P.I.S.A.E., USDA.

[2] Soil Scientist, and Principal Soil Scientist, respectively, Division of Soil Survey.

[3] Various other descriptive names such as blackland, black prairie, adobe clay, hog-wallow, gilgai, crab-holey, self-mulching, self-swallowing, buffalo-wallow, devil-devil, Bay of Biscay, melon-hole, puffs and depressions, mbuga, and others have been used to indicate certain obvious characteristics. Some of the soils have good surface drainage, but others are flat and water collects in the microdepressions during rainy periods.

Reproduced with permission from *Soil Science Society of America Proceedings.* vol. 15, 1951, p. 347-354. Published by the Soil Science Society of America, Madison, Wisconsin, USA.

contains many fragments of limestone or chalk, ranges from strongly calcareous to about neutral, and grades through a lighter colored calcareous transition into parent rock of limestone or chalk within 18 inches of the surface. A few deep clayey Rendzinas have been recognized in Europe and Asia, but these are on transported material and are distinctly atypical, according to the prevailing concepts of Rendzinas. Natural vegetation is usually forest, although shrubby vegetation, or a mixture of forest and grass, is not uncommon. In the United States the principal soils called Rendzinas are dark soils developed in calcareous parent materials, with profiles ranging from about 15 to 60 inches thick. The shallower of these soils, as well as the very shallow ones now included with the Lithosols, are essentially like the Rendzinas of other countries; but the deeper and darker soils are more like the Black Cotton Soils (Regur) of India, the black clays of Africa, and the black earths of Australia than the Rendzinas of European countries.

The term Rendzina was first used by the agrarian people of Poland (16) for soils formed from calcareous parent rocks. The conditions essential for the development of Rendzinas, as given by 'Sigmond (23), are parent rock rich in calcium carbonate, or gypsum, which has the fineness of structure and solubility necessary to neutralize the podsolizing effect of the humid climate under which they are developed, and a forest vegetation. He states also that Rendzinas are azonal soils. Stebutt (24) and Kellogg (19) give similar explanations for the development of Rendzinas. Morphologically (23), Rendzinas are characterized by humiferous surface horizons that contrast sharply with the parent rock and contain much coarse calcareous debris of rock fragments, gravel, and sand. The silt and clay fractions are usually small. 'Sigmond gives mechanical analyses of the humiferous, or A, horizon of Rendzinas from four locations which show that the combined clay and silt ranged from 13 to 24 percent, the clays, less than .002 mm, being less than 10 percent in any of the samples. Rendzinas (23) are suitable for calcicole species of trees, but as arable soils they are usually poor in plant nutrients and plants often suffer from drought.

Glinka (7) classes Rendzinas as endodynamomorphic soils. To this group he assigns all those soils partly of fine earth and partly of undecomposed rock, whose development has been more strongly influenced by the character of the parent rock than by external conditions. Glinka states that these humus carbonate soils usually contain considerable undecomposed rock which decreases with soil development. It appears that it was from this interpretation that the concept of plastic sticky clay soils was derived. However, all the Rendzina profiles given by Glinka and Stebutt are of shallow soils similar to that described by 'Sigmond. The A horizon is 6 to 12 inches thick, contains varying amounts of fragmental limestone, and grades through a thin transition of lighter-colored material into fragmental limestone, at about 18 inches or less. This is presumed to be the modal Rendzina profile as recognized by the Russians and Poles.

Robinson (21) divides the soils developed from calcareous parent materials in Great Britain into two groups. The soils with undeveloped profiles in which the character of the parent material is strongly impressed on the soil, he groups with the Rendzinas; those that are leached and have texture profiles are excluded. These Rendzinas are calcareous and base-saturated. The mineral color is grayish or brownish gray, the surface horizon is rich in organic matter, and the clay complex is highly siliceous. Most profiles are shallow, but deep profiles may occur in col-

Fig. 1—Rendzina from escarpment of the Chiltern Hills near Rothamsted, England. Regarded by the English as a good Rendzina. A_1, 0-9 inches: Dark grayish brown silt loam; D, 9 inches plus: Nearly white, brittle chalk.

luvium. Muir[4] describes the Rendzina of England as a shallow soil over chalk or chalky marl. (Fig. 1) The Icknield and Upton series are modal representatives. The typical Rendzinas of Greece, as described by Catacouzinos,[5] are also shallow soils over limestone or marl. The Rendzinas of Hungary, according to Kotzmann (14), are shallow soils, 12 to 15 inches deep, over limestone or dolomite, and the soils are similar to Rendzinas described by the Russians and other European scientists. The proportion of organic matter in the A horizon varies but ranges up to about 25 percent. The humus is saturated with Ca, or partly with Mg, and is completely stable. Rendzinas are of slight extent in Morocco, but they are mentioned by Del Villar (4) as very shallow black soils resting on parent rock with frequent rock outcrops. Stephens (25, 26) emphasizes the characteristic morphology of the Rendzina of Australia as a shallow, black, medium to heavy textured soil resting on calcareous parent material. The Rendzina and degraded Rendzina soils of Manitoba described by Ellis (5) are developed under forest. They are very shallow, mostly less than 12 inches deep, over marly calcareous carbonate accumulation underlain by limestone drift, or by limestone and dolomite.

As defined by Kellogg and Baldwin, et al., (11) and Marbut (15), "Rendzina soils are an intrazonal group of soils, usually with brown or black friable surface horizons underlain by light-gray or whitish calcareous material. They have developed under grass vegetation or mixed grasses and forest, in humid and semiarid regions from relatively soft, highly calcareous parent materials of chalk, soft limestone, or marl, and may be regarded as immature. The most extensive soils of this group are in the blacklands of northern and central Texas, and in the black prairies of Alabama and Mississippi."

---

[4] Private communication from Dr. Alex Muir, Head of the Soil Survey of England and Wales, Rothamsted, England.

[5] Private communication from Dr. Dem. S. Catacouzinos, Director of the Central Soil Laboratory, Ministry of Agriculture, Athens, Greece.

Fig. 2—Houston Black clay, Milan County, Tex. A typical example of what has been called Rendzina in the United States.

The principal soils now classed as Rendzinas in the United States are deep, dark, heavy clays, mostly calcareous, in which contrasting eluvial and illuvial horizons are very weak or lacking, over parent materials of chalk, limestone, or calcareous clays. Some medium depth and shallow strongly calcareous soils (solum 10 to 30 inches thick) with granular, crumbly subsurface layers are also classed as Rendzinas, but comprise only a minor portion of this group. Houston Black clay (Fig. 2) and Denton clay probably are the most extensive series of the group in the United States. Houston Black clay is a deep, dark calcareous clay with granular surface horizon and subsurface soil of dark gray, very weak blocky clay over chalky limestone or highly calcareous clay at 40 to 60 inches below the surface. It is characteristically free of limestone fragments to a depth of 40 to 60 inches, swells, shrinks, and cracks on wetting and drying, and develops the "hog-wallow" or "gilgai" microrelief.[6] Natural vegetation is tall grasses; average annual rainfall is 30 to 40 inches. The shallow phases of these calcareous soils and the associated calcareous Lithosols of the prairies of the Southern United States conform more nearly to the Rendzina of other countries than do the medium depth and deep soils. Some writers

---

[6]Consisting of microdepressions and humps and designated by many different local names, including gilgai, hog-wallowed, melon-hole, Bay of Biscay, devil-devil, hush-a-by, and crab-holey.

have construed the term Rendzina to mean sticky plastic clay, but there is little supporting evidence in the European literature to indicate that the heavy clays, such as the Houston Black of Texas and the Diablo series of California, are Rendzinas as currently recognized in other countries.

The term Rendzina is used for dark calcareous or alkaline soils, in both the older countries and in the United States, but we have applied the term to a wider variety of soils than have most of the European scientists. There appears to be a need for re-examination and revision of our classification of these soils.

BLACK COTTON SOILS, REGUR, AND BLACK EARTHS

The Black Cotton Soils, or Regur, of India are described by Kossovich (13) as black sticky heavy clays. Some have a grayish or brownish tinge. The soils are mostly 3 to 6 feet deep and underlain by a loess-like parent material which rests on gneiss or trap rock. Some rest directly on weathered basalt. Leaching is confined to the calcium carbonate, which accumulates in the lower layers in the form of concretions, known locally as "Kunkar", or "kunkur". Natural vegetation is grass and shrubs. The annual precipitation is about 47 inches. 'Sigmond (23) suggests that the black color of these soils is due principally to organic matter, as in the case of Chernozems, but the high clay content and frequent deep cracks indicate that their structure is different from the Chernozem. Actually, the content of organic matter is low, less than 1 percent in many of these soils, especially in cultivated areas. Hilgard (8) concludes that the physical character, chemical composition, and cultural characteristics of Black Cotton Soils, or Regur, are very similar to those of the "black adobe" of California and the "prairie soils" of the cotton states (i.e., Houston Black clay and close relatives).

A typical Black Cotton Soil was described by Nagelschmidt, et al., (18) as follows: "The soil is a dark grayish clay loam which is hard and compact to the lowest depth of sampling, 48 inches. The fine material contains little calcium carbonate but some nodules and concretions are distributed throughout the profile; there is no pronounced horizon of calcium carbonate accumulation. The pH increases with depth from 8.0 to 8.4 and the soluble salt content varies between 0.05 and 0.07 percent. The soil is derived from colluvium over gneiss. Total annual rainfall ranges between 37 and 40 inches." The mechanical analyses of this soil show very little variation in texture within the profile, the percentage of clay being about 40 in all horizons.

In a study of the structure in the Black Cotton soils of the Nizamsagar Project Area, Hyderabad State, India, Krishna and Perumal (12) found that these deep clays crack and swell on drying and wetting and some have a distinct structure pattern which they term "lentil". Soils with lentil structure have the water table at 14 or more feet, but those in which the lentil structure is weak or indistinct have impeded drainage with water table at about 5 to 7 feet below the ground level. The vegetation is grass in both types.

Bal (2) describes the Black Cotton Soils of the Central Province of India as developed on Deccan trap or basalt, sandstone, and gneissic rocks. They show considerable variations in depth and clay content, depending on their position. Those situated at lower levels are generally deep and heavy and contain 40 to 50 percent clay. In general, the lime content varies inversely with the rainfall. The soils derived from trap are black heavy clays. Where climatologically suited to the growth of cotton, they are known as Black Cotton Soils. They ordinarily show no marked soil horizons, but the subsoil has a slightly higher percentage of clay than the surface soil. Some calcium and silica have been leached from the surface. Depth to semi-weathered rock generally is about 4½ feet, but may be 10 to 15 feet. He states that the soils contain a very low percentage of organic matter, due to a high temperature throughout the year.

Aubert (1) describes heavy clays of French West Africa as of two kinds: (1) those that shrink and crack when dry, called "Dian Pere" by the natives; and (2) those that do not crack, called "Boi" soils. Some of these soils have as much as 70 percent clay. These appear similar to the black and gray clays of East Africa.

Robinson (20) suggests that the "Grey and Black Soils" of Kenya, locally called Black Cotton Soils, may represent tropical Chernozems. His discussion, however, indicates that they are similar to the soils of East Africa described by Milne and some of the glei Tirs of Morocco.

Prescott (19) relates his black earths of Australia to the Regur of India, Tirs of Morocco, and other lime humus soils. He states that they develop only on heavy materials, mainly of basaltic origin, and have mostly neutral to alkaline subsoils. Eluvial and illuvial horizons are not present. Organic matter decreases gradually with depth. Visible calcium carbonate occurs as streaks and small concretions within the black horizon. Nitrogen is very low, about 0.07 percent. Stephens (25) states that the organic matter in the surface horizon of these soils is usually below 4 percent. These soils swell, shrink, and crack on wetting and drying and develop the gilgai microrelief, characteristic of many heavy dark clays.

The soils of Australia with gilgai microrelief were studied in detail by Howard (9). He found that this phenomenon occurs mainly in deep soils with clay subsoils of poor permeability that occupy flat areas where water tends to accumulate. Howard mentions a variant that occurs under periodic flooding and saturation of the soil, followed by hot dry periods when the soil is dried out. The calcareous B horizon has become intimately mixed with the surface soil and the entire surface is covered with a gray calcareous self-mulching soil. He attributes the formation of the mounds and depressions, which he calls "puffs", to the swelling of the heavy B horizon in a solonetsic soil having a thin A horizon and impermeable B.

In a study of the soils of the Red River Valley, Manitoba, developed under grass, Ellis and Shafer (5) observed that the dark clay soils have tongued intrusions of dark surface material which penetrates into the lower horizons to a depth of 1 to 4 feet or more below the surface. For the most part, the surface has a distinct micro-relief of hummocks, irregular in outline, 3 to 5 feet in diameter and 4 to 6 inches high. They attribute these deep intrusions to shrinking, cracking, swelling, and heaving which produces the hump or hummock. These soils are very high in nitrogen, 0.5 to 1.0 percent, and the tongued intrusion, which is the depression, contains a much higher percentage of nitrogen to a greater depth than the hump or level between the depressions. These soils are about neutral to a depth of 10 to 18 inches and calcareous below this depth. Similar phenomena occur on the lacustrine clay plains of Saskatchewan and Alberta under semiarid climates.

Milne's (17) "black or grey clays" of East Africa appear similar to the Black Cotton Soils, Regur, and some of the Tirs. He distinguishes between calcareous and noncalcareous subgroups, stating that the former are pedocals and the latter are glei soils, but places them together in one major group described as "dark-coloured ill-drained soils having a siliceous clay fraction, plastic when wet and cracking deeply when dry." Both subgroups are further subdivided into soils of: (a) low ground, developed in alluvium in sumps or depressions; and (b) high ground but seasonally saturated—sedentary soils associated with lime-yielding or shaly rocks. The calcareous black clays are very extensive in the drier and flatter regions, which have alternating short rainy seasons and prolonged drouths. A horizon of lime accumulation, varying from a distinct layer 6 inches thick to only an occasional pellet (kunkar), occurs in the transition from the black soil to the weathering parent material. Large continuous areas of such soils occur in some areas. In others, as in Kenya, where they are derived from gneiss, the distribution is catenary, with red soils (latosols?) occupying the more elevated positions. "There is no sharp division between the calcareous and noncalcareous black clays, and the latter in turn pass insensibly through greyish-black and grey types to those that have podzolic characteristics. The differentiation into horizons and the acidity both increase through this range, . . . increased wetness making for degradation of the black clays."

Plastic clays with nearly black layers 30 to 34 inches thick, which seem essentially like some of Milne's "black or grey" clays are reported by Van Der Merwe (31, 32, 33, 34) from subtropical semiarid to subhumid parts of South Africa with 22 to 32 inches rainfall. "They crack deeply, have very high clay (52 to 74 percent) and moderate silt contents . . . with little variation throughout the soil profiles. The sand fractions are very low." He lists nine differences from and seven similarities to Chernozem, concludes (a) they are more like the Regur of India and Black Cotton Soils of Kenya than like Chernozems and (b) they are not solonetsic, and recommends they be classified as "Black Soils of Sub-Tropics".

Dark-colored shrinking and swelling of clays of slow permeability are extensive in nearly level areas of subhumid Shantung Province, China, where summers are wet and winters are dry. Those of the undrained slight depressions, called "Lakeland Shachiang soils" (22, 29), are nearly black clayey soils that are wet except near the close of the long dry season. Those of the slightly higher areas, called "Upland Shachiang soils", are wet only during and immediately after the wet summer season. Most of the soils are calcareous, but some of the wet ones are slightly acid. Nearly all have the shachiang (calcareous concretions) sometimes called "kanku".

Black and dark-gray granular shrinking clays were observed by the junior author in the Philippines just south of Manila. The black clay persists to about 18 inches and grades through lighter-colored blocky clay into weathered dacitic or andesitic tuff. Depth to rock ranges from 18 inches to several feet. Similar soils were found southeast of Manila, developed from a tuff-bearing hard limestone. These black soils appear to be essentially the same as the "margalite soils" of Indonesia, described by Dames (3). Most of them are now used for paddy rice.

The dark-clay soils of prairies in the southern United States are now classed as Rendzinas. They are typified by Houston Black clay (described below), Bell clay, and Denton clay, which are deep dark calcareous crumbly clays developed in highly calcareous argillaceous sediments (15, 27, 28). In the group as a whole the surface soils are calcareous, but some are neutral, and a few are acid. The organic matter

Fig. 3—Gilgai microrelief on Bell clay, a strongly calcareous deep dark clay of Texas. (Photo courtesy, E. H. Templin.)

is less than 3 percent in virgin areas; there is no horizon of eluviation. Where undisturbed, most of them have pronounced gilgai microrelief (Fig. 3). On nearly level areas this consists of a succession of microbasin and microknolls with relief of 6 to 24 inches; on slopes it consists of microvalleys and microridges that run with the slope. The thickness of the dark soil varies in relation to the microrelief (Figs. 4 and 5) as does that described as tongued intrusion by Ellis and Shafer (5), and is attributed to the same cause—shrinking and cracking on drying, soil falling and washing into the cracks, and expansion on wetting. The mechanical analysis of Houston Black clay shows a nearly uniform texture throughout the profile, the percentage of clay being about 58 in all horizons.

Profile Description of Houston Black Clay

Location: Ellis County, Tex.
Surface: Plane; 1 percent gradient.
Surface drainage: Moderately slow; water does not stand.
Vegetation: Originally tall prairie grass.
Parent material: Taylor marl.

Horizon	Depth inches	Description
A_{11}	0-18	Dark-gray (2.5Y 4/1; 3/1, moist) clay extremely sticky and plastic; strongly calcareous. Moderate fine to medium granular, crumbly. On moistening and drying the soil mass crumbles naturally to fine granules.
A_{12}	18-38	Dark-gray (2.5Y 4/1; 3/1, moist) clay; strongly calcareous; weak very coarse blocky; extremely sticky and plastic; extremely firm; very slowly permeable.
A_3	38-54	Dark-gray (2.5Y 4/1; 2/1, moist) clay coarsely mottled with

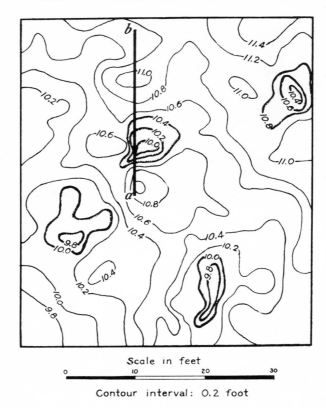

Scale in feet

0   10   20   30

Contour interval: 0.2 foot

Fig. 4—Contour map of gilgai microrelief of Houston Black clay. Kaufman County, Tex. (Drawing by E. H. Templin.)

		light olive brown (2.5Y 5/4; 4/4, moist); contains numerous concretions of $CaCO_3$; very strongly calcareous; very slowly permeable.
C_1	54-84	Brownish-yellow (10YR 6/6; 5/6, moist) clay strongly mottled with light brownish gray (2.5Y 6/2; 5/2, moist); very strongly calcareous; no concretions; weakly laminated or shaly.
C (collected at 10 feet)	84-180	Light brownish gray strongly calcareous clay strongly mottled with brownish yellow and some white; this is slightly weathered Taylor marl.
C (collected at 25 feet)	15-35 feet	Light gray (2.5Y 7/1; 6/1, moist) strongly calcareous clay with concoidal breakage.

Comparison of mechanical analysis of Houston Black clay with that of a typical Black Cotton Soil of India (18) shows the similarity in particle-size distribution and lack of a distinct eluvial horizon. Both are developed under grass in areas having pronounced hot-dry seasons and cool-wet seasons with average annual rainfall of about 30 to 40 inches.

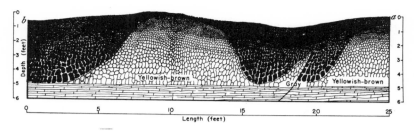

Fig. 5—Profile of Houston Black clay with gilgai microrelief. Kaufman County, Tex. (Drawing by E. H. Templin.)

Fig. 6—Gilgai microrelief on Irving clay, a deep acid clay developed in clayey alluvium. Burleson County, Tex. (Photo courtesy E. H. Templin.)

Gilgai microrelief (Fig. 6) occurs on a variety of heavy clay soils of the United States that lack texture profiles. They range from highly calcareous to medium and even strongly acid. They occur under subhumid to humid climate and tall grass to forest vegetation, on level flats to droughty slopes.

The foregoing indicates a close relationship between the Black Cotton Soils, or Regur, of India, the Black Earths of Australia, the Black and Gray soils of Kenya, and the deep dark-clay soils of the Southern United States, now classed as Rendzinas.

TIRS OF MOROCCO

According to Del Villar (4), "Tirs" is a Berberian term which in Tashelhit dialect signifies soil and in Tamazirt, humus. The name is also known in Algeria where it signifies a heavy clay soil. He divides the Tirs into several types of which glei Tirs, deep Tirs, and crust Tirs are the most important. The typical glei Tirs of which there are two types, black and gray, occupy large depressed areas between rivers bordered by slightly higher strips of Alluvial soils. The black and gray Tirs apparently occur together, the black occupying the microdepressions and the gray, slightly higher levels in the large depressed areas. Many areas are waterlogged under heavy rains and occasional floods. In many cases, the high water table prevails so much of the year that the land becomes a sort of permanent marsh. Depth to the water table varies from about 6 feet during extremely dry periods to at or near the surface during rainy seasons.

According to Del Villar, the glei Tirs have developed from different parent materials, but differ only in degree of development. The gray Tirs have a rather uniform profile and, as a rule, the water table is at a greater depth than under the black Tirs. Both are calcareous. He explains that the lime in the profile of the gray Tirs is due to the upward movement of salts and to presence of mollusk shells and calcareous parent material. In the black Tirs, developed in noncalcareous red sands, it is attributed to upward movements of salts. The surface layers are high (73 to 75 percent) in clay, neutral to weakly alkaline, and low in organic matter (0.6 to 2.7 percent). On drying, they crack to a depth of several feet and the fissures are marked at the surface by a polygonal network. The mass breaks into clods and lumps and these into platy chips which, in turn, break into irregular granules. These glei Tirs are almost impervious, poorly drained, flooded during the rainy season, very difficult to till, and unsuitable for agricultural use unless drained.

Another type, deep Tirs, occurs on level or gently sloping areas in high broken country above the glei Tirs. The deep Tirs on lower slopes are similar to the glei Tirs. The deep Tirs in valleys or level areas have much thicker dark clay layers, which may be 6 to 10 feet thick, and are higher in organic matter, as much as 5.5 percent, than the glei Tirs. They are derived from a variety of materials ranging from sandy earths to calcareous rock. The water table is at a greater depth than that of the glei Tirs, and the soils are cultivated without drainage.

The crust Tirs are very different soils. They are relatively shallow, range from sandy to clayey, and have a calcareous hardpan or crust. The crust Tirs differ from the glei Tirs mainly in having more loamy upper horizons without columnar structure, higher content of organic matter, one or more indurated horizons or crusts, and water table at more than 7 feet below the surface. The A horizons range from neutral to calcareous. They occur on level to undulating surfaces with an annual rainfall of 8 to 16 inches.

The term Tirs appears to be used rather loosely to include soils having the common characteristics of one or more "glei" horizons but differing considerably in morphological and genetic characteristics. It appears to include members of at least two and possibly three great soil groups as they would be defined in the United States.

CONCLUSIONS AND PROPOSALS

The review indicates that: (1) collectively, the names used include two major classes of soils that need separation at one of the higher categories in a natural classification; (2) usage of Rendzina in the United States conflicts and is unreconcilable with prevailing usage elsewhere; (3) the prevailing usage of Rendzina overlaps two orders, azonal and intrazonal, in the American classification; and (4) Black Cotton Soils, or Regur, Tirs, and most of the soils that have been called Rendzina in the United States, as well as various other deep clays, belong in a separate Great Soil Group or Suborder.

The term Grumusol is proposed for these dark clay soils developed under widely varying climatic conditions but usually with alternating wet and dry seasons. The name is coined from the Latin word *grumus,* which means little heap or hillock, and which is also akin to the English word crumb, and *sol* for soil. Clayey soils that have the crumbly structure of the surface layer or gilgai microrelief, or both, would be included in Grumusols. The group is typified by Houston Black clay and consists of soils that have all or most of the following characteristics in combination:

(a) Clay texture in the typical form.

(b) No eluvial and illuvial horizons.

(c) Moderate to strong granular structure in the upper 6 to 20 inches, becoming blocky or massive below.

(d) Calcareous reaction in the type form, with acid to neutral intergrades to other groups.

(e) High coefficient of expansion and contraction on wetting and drying.

(f) Gilgai microrelief.

(g) Extremely plastic consistence.

(h) Exchange complex nearly saturated with calcium, or calcium and magnesium.

(i) Clay minerals dominantly of the Montmorillonite group.

(j) Parent material mostly calcareous, high in clay, and nearly impervious.

(k) Sola more than 10 inches deep, typically more than 30.

(l) Dark color of low chroma.

(m) Medium to low content of organic matter, usually 1 to 3 percent in surface soil; the organic matter gradually decreasing with depth.

(n) Stage of weathering, relatively unadvanced or minimal.

(o) Tall grass or savannah vegetation.

This characterization is tentative and will require modification as more information accumulates. At present, it seems to the authors that the greatest emphasis should be placed on the dark color and granular surface-soil structure, in combination with the swelling and shrinking characteristics, and that less emphasis should be given to the proportion of calcium carbonate present in the soil. For instance, some gray to light-gray clays that are medium to strongly acid in the A horizon but alkaline to calcareous below 2 to 4 feet and that have developed under forest and have the gilgai microrelief, e.g., the Garner series of eastern Texas, and the Vaiden and Eutaw clays of Alabama and Mississippi, might be included. Whether the division between calcareous soils and noncalcareous soils of this general morphology should be made at the level of great soil group or at a lower level is a matter for further study. The ultimate place of Grumusols in the classification scheme will depend to a considerable degree on the extent to which the whole system may be rearranged. A subsequent paper, giving a more exact definition of the group and specific limits of the range with suggestion for the place of Grumusols in the classification system, is planned as a further study by the authors.

SUMMARY

A summary of the characteristics of the dark-clay soils of warm regions is made from a partial review of the literature.

The term Rendzina is used in countries outside the United States mainly for shallow to very shallow dark soils of medium texture containing a high percentage of coarse fragmental calcareous material over calcareous parent rock at depths averaging less than 18 inches. Vegetation is forest, and the soils are of very low agricultural value. In the United States, the term Rendzina is used mostly for dark, deep, heavy clay soils developed under grass and typified by Houston Black clay, but it also includes some moderately shallow soils similar to the deeper part of the Rendzinas of Europe. The Rendzina of this country is more like the Black Cotton Soils, or Regur, of India, Milne's "Black or Grey clays" of East Africa, Van Der Merwe's Black Soils of the Sub-Tropics, and Prescott's Black Earths of Australia than like the Rendzina of other countries.

The Black Cotton Soils, or Regur, of India have thick black or dark gray clayey upper horizons over calcareous or at least calcium-rich parent materials, at depths of 4 feet or more. The dark clay soils of Southern United States, the Black and Gray clays of East Africa, and the Black Earths of Australia have practically all the characteristics of the Regur of India.

The Tirs of North Africa include soils with varying characteristics, but all have in common one or more "glei" horizons and most of them are black or dark gray. The glei Tirs and deep Tirs appear to be closely related but the crust Tirs probably are not. None of the Tirs, except perhaps the Deep Tirs, appear closely related to the Regur Soils.

A new name, "Grumusol", is proposed as a general term for those dark clay soils and is tentatively defined.

LITERATURE CITED

1. Aubert, George S. Note on the Vernacular Names of the Soils of the Sudan and Senegal. Tech. Comm. No. 46; Proc. First Commonwealth Conference on Tropical and Sub-Tropical Soils. 1948. (pp. 107-108)

2. Bal, D. V. Some aspects of the Black Cotton soils of Central Provinces, India. London: Thomas Murby and Co.: Trans. Third Int. Cong. of Soil Sci., 3:154-157. 1935.

3. Dames, T. W. G. Margalite soils in Indonesia. Trans. Fourth Int. Cong. Soil Sci., II:180-182. 1950.

4. Del Villar, Emile H. The Tirs of Morocco, Rabat, Morocco. Soil Sci., 57:313-339. 1944.

5. Ellis, J. H., and Shafer, W. The nitrogen content of the Red River Valley soils. Sci. Agr., 9 (4):231-248. 1928.

6. .... The soils of Manitoba. Soils Dept., Univ. of Manitoba, Economic Survey Board, Winnipeg, Province of Manitoba. 1938. (pp. 57, 58, and 62)

7. Glinka, K. D. The Great Soil Groups of the World and Their Development. (Translated from the German by C. F. Marbut, USDA) 1927. (pp. 146-149)

8. Hilgard, E. W. Soils. London: The McMillan Co. 1921. (pp. 414-415)

9. Howard, A. Crab-Hole, Gilgai, and Self-Mulching soils of the Murrumbridge Irrigation Area. Pochvovedenie, Moscow, USSR, Part 2, pp. 14-18. 1939.

10. Kellogg, C. E. Development and significance of the Great Soil Groups of the United States. USDA, Misc. Pub. 229:19 and 35. June 1936.

11. ...., et al. Soils and Men. Yearbook of Agr., USDA June 1936. (pp. 19 and 35)

12. Kossovitch, P. "Die Schwarzerde", "(Tschernosion)". Verl. f. Fachliteratur, GMBH, Berlin. 1912. (pp. 137-139)

13. Kotzmann, L. G. Genetic and chemical characteristics of Rendzina Soils. London: Thomas Murby and Co. Trans. Third Int. Cong. Soil Sci., 1:296-97. 1935.

14. Krishna, P. G., and Permul, S. Structure in Black Cotton Soils of the Nizamsagar Project Area, Hyderabad State, India. Soil Sci., 66 (1):29-38. 1948.

15. Marbut, C. F. Soils of the United States. Atlas Amer. Agric., USDA 1935. (pp. 15 and 75)

16. Miklashewski, Slow. Compte Rend. de la II Conf. Intern. Agropedologique a Prague. 1922. (pp. 312-317)

17. Milne, G. A provisional soil map of East Africa. East African Agr. Res. Sta., Amani. 1936.

18. Nagelschmidt, G., Desai, A. D., and Muir, Alex. The minerals in the clay fraction of a Black Cotton Soil and a Red Earth from Hyderabad, Deccan State, India. Jour. Agr. Sci., 30:639-653. 1940.

19. Prescott, J. A. The soils of Australia in relation to vegetation and climate. Commonwealth of Australia; Council for Scientific and Industrial Research, Bul. 52:65-67. 1931.

20. Robinson, G. W. Soils, Their Origin, Constitution, and Classification. London: Thomas Murby and Co. Ed. 2. 1931. (pp. 266-267)

21. .... Soils of Great Britain. London: Thomas Murby and Co. Third Int. Cong. Soil Sci., 2:19-20. 1935.

22. Shaw, C. F. Soils of China. Nat. Geol. Survey of China, Bul. No. 1:38. 1931.

23. 'Sigmond, A. A. J. de. The Principles of Soil Science. London: Thomas Murby and Co. (Translation by Yolland, A. B.) 1936. (pp. 161, 236-244)

24. Stebutt, A. "Lehrb. d allg. Bodenkunde". Berlin. 1931. (pp. 387-9)

25. Stephens, C. G. Comparative morphology and genetic relationships of certain Australian, North American, and European soils. Jour. Soil Sci., Vol. 1 (2):123-149. 1949.

26. .... A review of recent work on Australian tropical and sub-tropical soils. Tech. Comm. No. 46. Proc. First Commonwealth Conf. on Tropical and Sub-Tropical Soils. 1948. (pp. 1-8)

27. Templin, E. H., and Huckabee, J. W., Jr. Soil Survey of Kaufman County, Texas. USDA, Series 1936, No. 3, pp. 71-75. 1940.

28. ...., et al. Soil Survey of Fannin County. USDA, Series 1938, No. 10, pp. 103-105.

29. Thorp, James. Geography of the Soils of China. Nat. Geol. Survey of China. 1936. (552 pages, illus.)

30. ...., and Tschau, T. Y. Notes on Shantung Soils. Nat. Geol. Survey of China, Soil Bul. 14:130 (illus.) 1936.

31. Van Der Merwe, C. R. Morphology of the South African Black Clays. London: Thomas Murby and Co. Tran. Third Int. Cong. Soil Science, 1:301-303. 1935.

32. .... The Sub-Tropical Black Clay Soils. Tech. Comm. No. 46, Proc. First Commonwealth Conf. on Tropical and Sub-Tropical Soils, Commonwealth Bureau of Soil Science, Harpenden, England. 1948. (pp. 43-45)

33. .... South African soil types. Tech. Comm. No. 46, Proc. First Commonwealth Conf. on Tropical and Sub-Tropical Soils, Commonwealth Bureau of Soil Science, Harpenden, England. 1948. (pp. 8-15)

34. .... Sub-Tropical Black Clays. Trans. Fourth Int. Cong. Soil Sci., II:191-193. 1950.

35. .... Glei soils. Trans. Fourth Int. Cong. Soil Sci., II:178-180. 1950.

A PEDOLOGICAL INVESTIGATION
OF JAPANESE VOLCANIC-ASH SOILS

by

Ichiro Kanno

Kyushu Agr. Expt. Sta., Chikugo, Fukuoka Pref. (Japan)

Japanese volcanic-ash soils are widely distributed on terraces, hills, and mountains in Japan from Hokkaido in the north to Kyushu in the south. The area with slopes below about 22 degrees covered with deposits of volcanic ash, extends over 3 100 000 ha corresponding to about 8.4 percent of the total area (1). The soils, however, cover a considerable portion of the mountain area with slopes above 22 degrees, so that the above figure will become larger considerably. The soils have already been introduced into soil literatures through works of Thorp (2) and others who have designated them as Ando soils. The clay mineral of some volcanic-ash soils has been reported by Aomine and Yoshinaga (3).

The purpose of this investigation was to obtain fundamental information for establishing an appropriate taxonomic position of Japanese volcanic-ash soils and to characterize different subgroups of the soils on the basis of their morphological and analytical characteristics.

MORPHOLOGY

Morphological characteristics of a representative profile found on the uncultivated terrace land are as follows:

A_0 layer (3-5 cm in thickness): Thin leaf litters with partially-decomposed, dark grayish brown organic matter.

A_{11} horizon (15-40 cm in thickness): Brownish black to black, fine sandy loam to silt loam rich in humus. Very loose, soft and mellow; weakly-developed fine granular or crumb structure. In grasslands the horizon is heavily matted with grass rootlets that form a sod. In some places where volcano is inactive, the uppermost layer has often been supplied with fresh volcanic sands or dusts.

A_{12} horizon (20-50 cm in thickness): It closely resembles the upper horizon although the former is more compact and blackish than the latter. Fine sandy loam to clay loam rich in humus; weakly-to moderately-developed, coarse to very coarse subangular blocky structure; and very friable. It does not show any evidence of bleaching, and gradually merges into the lower horizon.

Several types of the A horizon can be recognized owing to the difference of modes of deposition. For example, an aeolian or normal type found on nearly flat terraces

Reproduced with permission from *Transactions of the 6th International Congress of Soil Science,* Vol. E, 1956, p. 105-109. Published by the International Society of Soil Science, c/o Royal Tropical Institute, Amsterdam, Netherlands.

150

has a character mentioned above. A colluvial type found at the base of slopes has a thick, dark-coloured surface horizon that is more than 1 m deep, while a truncated type found on steep and convex slopes has lost a majority of its A horizon by erosion. A reworked type with varying amounts of gravels shows broken horizon-boundaries. In southern Kyushu and Hokkaido there can be seen numerous buried profiles in the ash deposit; a majority of the buried soils is two- or three-storied.

B_1 horizon (15-30 cm in thickness): It is a transitional horizon. Dark brown loam to clay loam with some humus that has come down from above. Moderately-developed, coarse to very coarse angular blocky structure; fine porus and friable.

B_2 or C horizon: Very light yellowish brown, yellowish brown to brown fine sandy loam, silt loam, clay loam to clay; moderately- to strongly-developed angular blocky structure.

The older members of the soils have distinct B horizons with more clay than A horizons, but the younger members are essentially "AC soils", as has been pointed out by Thorp (2). The C horizon of glassy-ash soils, being regarded as the younger member, has been called "Akahoya, Imogo, or Akaonji" by natives. It is characterized by saw dust-like appearance, moderately-developed angular blocky structure, high porosity that is more than 80 percent, and the presence of small bean-like pumices in the lower part. Many fragments of colourless volcanic glass have so firmly touched to one another that plant roots cannot penetrate into the horizon. The thin pumice layer, and the firmness are a remarkable feature of the aeolian glassy-ash soils.

It is obvious that colour by itself cannot be used as a criterion in soil classification, but when considered in connection with other characteristics such as mineralogical composition, the difference in colour of the B horizon is of great importance for subdividing Japanese volcanic-ash soils. From the result of field examination, Japanese volcanic-ash soils could be grouped into at least three kinds as follows:

1. Brown type distributing in the southern part of the Kanto Plain, that has a characteristic brown-coloured subsoil with a relatively finer texture.

2. Onji type or the glassy-ash soil distributing in the southern part of Kyushu, that has a characteristic bright yellowish brown C horizon with abundant volcanic glasses.

3. Others, excluding two subgroups mentioned above, that have a light yellowish or a yellowish-brown subsoil, and are widely distributed throughout Japan. This subgroup may be subdivided into two kinds based on its mineralogical characteristics, as described later.

Furthermore, there were some volcanogenous soils that could not be placed in the same great soil group with Japanese volcanic-ash soils. They involve regosols consisting of recent volcanic sands, gravels, or pumices; in which no profile development has appeared; podzolic soils with a bleached horizon; and imperfectly drained or poorly drained soils with a gleyed horizon.

ANALYTICAL CHARACTERISTICS

Mineralogical characteristics: The microscopic examination of the fine sand fraction separated from soil materials of 17 profiles may indicate that there are four mineral-associations, namely, 1) those with some olivine, 2) those with abundant acid glasses (n=1.50 and 1.450), 3) those where hornblende predominates among heavy minerals, and 4) those where pyroxene predominates among heavy minerals. Since the four mineral-associations are closely connected with morphology and origin of the soils, Japanese volcanic-ash soils can be divided into four subgroups, namely, 1) Brown type (basaltic ash soils, Fuji origin), 2) Onji type (glassy ash soils, Kirishima origin?), 3) Light yellowish brown type (hornblende-andesitic ash soils, miscellaneous origins), and 4) yellowish brown type (pyroxene-andesitic ash soils, miscellaneous origins).

The fact that the amount of volcanic glass decreased with increasing weathering, indicated that glass was considerably unstable. Differential thermograms of the silt fraction consisting mainly of glass and plagioclase feldspar, gave an indication of the presence of allophane.

Mechanical composition: Mechanical analysis was carried out by the writer's method (4) in which dilute HCl was used as a dispersing agent, and amounts of silica and sesquioxides dissolved by H_2O_2- and HCl-treatments, were added to the percentage of the clay fraction. Analytical data showed that the evidence of mechanical eluviation of clay particles was obscure, and that there was a marked shift in mechanical composition between fresh ash (5) and ash soils, that is, the fine sand fraction decreased as weathering progresses, while the silt and clay fractions increased greatly. The Onji type had a relatively coarser texture than other subgroups.

Chemical characteristics: The soils are characterized by the abundant accumulation of humus with a high C/N ratio (15-30) in the surface horizon. The contents of humus in the A and the B horizons were 8-30 and 1-6 percent, respectively. The A horizons with few exceptions showed such low pH value as 4.5. The Brown type and the C horizon of the Onji type, however, showed a rather high pH value of about 6. It may be explained by the facts that the former contains a relatively higher exchangeable Ca than others, and the high reaction of the latter with a low base-status is due to the influence of a high isoelectric point of allophane.

Cation exchange capacities of the A and the B or C horizons were 30-60 and 10-40 m.e. per 100g., respectively. The amount of exchangeable bases in uncultivated lands was up to 20 m.e., mostly below 5 m.e. per 100g. The degrees of base-saturation were up to 40 percent, mostly below 20 percent while in arable lands they have increased to 50-60 percent. Of the exchangeable bases Ca predominates, Mg is of the next. From amounts of Al dissolved by neutral, normal salt solutions or by dilute HCl solutions, with varying pH values, it was considered that the soils contained a considerable amount of exchangeable Al ions. The fact that fresh ash has a relatively high base content (5), while their weathering products show a low base-status, indicates that the intensive leaching process has taken place in the ash deposit.

Clay minerals: The silica-alumina ratios of the clay fractions (below 2 microns) ranged from 0.7 to 2.1. The younger member was not always higher in ratio than the older member. Differential thermograms, X-ray diffraction patterns, and chemical composition of the clay fractions indicated that the clay minerals in every subgroup consisted mainly of allophane with varying amounts of gibbsite, crystalline hydrous oxides of iron (2.69-2.70 A), and the kaolin mineral, usually hydrated halloysite. There is a very small amount of a mineral with the 14 A line in some soils. Since the 14 A line was not affected by dilute HCl- or glycol-treatment, the mineral may be regarded as vermiculite. Allophane was predominant in the surface horizons, while gibbsite and hydrated halloysite considerably increased with depth.

From works of Sudo (6), Fieldes and Swindale (7), and Aomine (personal communication), and the data obtained here, it may be suggested that there are two transformation stages for the formation of clay minerals of the soils, that is, in the early stage allophane is formed from glass particles, and in the advanced stage the crystallization from allophane to hydrated halloysite is caused by the influence of percolating water containing silica.

The pedogenesis of Japanese volcanic-ash soils, belonging to the intrazonal order, is neither podzolization nor laterization, but it is a peculiar one subjecting to the intensive leaching process of silica and bases accompanied with the abundant accumulation of humus in the surface horizon. The soils, therefore, should be distinguished from Brown Forest soils, Black Tropical soils, and Prairie soils. Japanese volcanic-ash soils should be regarded as a new great soil group.

SUMMARY

This paper deals mainly with morphological and analytical characteristics of Japanese volcanic-ash soils. In the writer's opinion the soils could be divided into four subgroups, namely, 1) Brown type (basaltic ash soils, Fuji origin), 2) Onji type (glassy ash soils, Kirishima origin?), 3) Light yellowish brown type (hornblende-andesitic ash soils, miscellaneous origins), and 4) yellowish brown type (pyroxene-andesitic ash soils, miscellaneous origins). The soils with few exceptions are characterized by a strongly acid reaction and a very low base-status. The dominant clay mineral consisted of allophane with varying amounts of gibbsite, hydrous oxides of iron, and hydrated halloysite. The pedogenesis of the soils is a peculiar one subjecting to the intensive leaching process of silica and bases accompanied with the abundant accumulation of humus in the surface horizon. They should be regarded as a new great soil group.

REFERENCES

1. Ritchie, T.E. Reconnaissance soil survey of Japan (summary). SCAP, GHQ, NRS, Report No. 110-I (1951).
2. Thorp, J. and Smith, G.D. Soil Sci., 69, 117-126 (1949).
3. Aomine, S. and Yoshinaga, N. Soil Sci., 79, 349-358 (1955).
4. Kanno, I. Bull. Kyushu Agr. Expt. Sta., 2, 235-249 (1954). (J.e.)
5. ...., Nagai, M. and Arimura, S. Soil and Plant Food, 1, 77-80 (1955).
6. Sudo, T. Clay Min. Bull., 2, 96-106 (1954).
7. Fieldes, M. and Swindale, L.D. New Zealand J. Sci. Tech., Sec. B, 36, 140-154 (1954).

SOME CHARACTERISTICS OF THE SOILS OF THE DISMAL SWAMP SECTION OF PASQUOTANK COUNTY, NORTH CAROLINA[1]

Arthur E. Shearin[2]

The great Dismal Swamp is one of the best known swamps in this country, and literature concerning it is extensive. This paper describes the general location and extent of the swamp, its vegetation, previous soil investigations in the area, and results obtained in investigations made of the Dismal Swamp section of Pasquotank County, N. C., made by the author between 1946 and 1949 in connection with the soil survey of that county.

LOCATION AND EXTENT

The Dismal Swamp lies partly in northeastern North Carolina and partly in southeastern Virginia (Fig. 1). It comprises portions of Camden, Currituck, Pasquotank, Gates, and Perquimans Counties in North Carolina and Nansemond and Norfolk Counties in Virginia. This region is the northern extension of the characteristic swamp country of the southern Atlantic Coast. According to Shaler (9) it belongs to that group of inundated lands in which the lack of drainage is due to the original deficiency of slope combined with the flow-retarding influence of the vegetation on the movement of water from the land.

Most writers estimate the swamp area as about 750 square miles. Fairly accurate acreage figures of the swamp proper[3] are available from published and unpublished soil survey reports (1, 2, 6, 8) of all the counties in which the swamp occurs except Norfolk County, Va. Based on information from soil survey reports, the total acreage is calculated to be between 375 and 400 square miles distributed among the various counties as follows:

Camden and Currituck Counties, N. C.[4]	135 square miles
Gates County, N. C.	55 " "
Perquimans County, N. C.	8 " "
Pasquotank County, N. C.[5]	55 " "
Nansemond County, Va.	73 " "
Norfolk County, Va.[6]	60 " "

---

[1] Contribution of Division of Soil Survey, B. P. I. S. A. E. USDA.

[2] Soil Scientist, Division of Soil Survey. Grateful acknowledgment is made of the assistance in the field work by J. P. Covington, Soil Scientist, Soil Conservation Service. USDA.

[3] Permanently wet areas consisting mainly of organic soils.

[4] Does not include an area of about 35 miles in the Great Swamp which is not considered a part of the Dismal Swamp.

[5] Field work has been completed, but report has not been published.

[6] Acreage estimated.

Reproduced with permission from *Soil Science Society of America Proceedings*, Vol. 15, p. 343-347. Published by the Soil Science Society of America, Madison, Wisconsin, U.S.A.

154

PHYSIOGRAPHY

The Dismal Swamp occupies a smooth, low-lying marine terrace at an elevation below 25 feet, known as the Pamlico terrace in North Carolina or the Dismal Swamp terrace in Virginia. The western boundary is marked by a well-defined sea-facing scarp known as the Pamlico-Chowan scarp in North Carolina and the Suffolk scarp in Virginia. Lake Drummond, a shallow fresh water lake in the southeast corner of Nansemond County, Va., is reported to be 22 feet above sea level and the highest point in the swamp.

VEGETATION

The Dismal Swamp region lies in the northern extension of the Southern Pine region of the southeastern United States. Kearney (4) reports that the Dismal Swamp originally was occupied mainly by three species, southern white cedar *(Chamaecyparis thyoides)*, cypress *(Taxodium distichum)* and swamp black gum *(Nyssa biflora)*. Of these, southern white cedar was by far the most important. Indications are that large portions of the swamp were occupied originally by nearly pure stands, called cedar glades or juniper glades. Korstian and Brush (5) report that the heaviest commercial stands of southern white cedar occurred originally in Virginia and North Carolina, especially in the Dismal Swamp and in the swamps draining into Albemarle and Pamlico sounds in North Carolina. According to Mattoon (7) the commercial range of cypress commenced at southeastern North Carolina and continued south, so this species was probably of minor importance in the Dismal Swamp.

Lumbering and fires have greatly modified the forest stands in and surrounding the swamp. In Pasquotank County, N. C., where the detailed studies were made, it is estimated that more than half the area of the Dismal Swamp section has been severly burned within recent years. These severely burned areas support a thick growth of large cane or reed *(Arundinaria macrosperma)*; small cane or reed *(Arundinaria tecta)*; sprouts of red maple *(Acer rubrum)*, sprouts of swamp black gum *(Nyssa biflora)*, and sprouts of black willow *(Salix nigra)*; a scattering of pond pine *(Pinus rigida* var. *serotina* (Michx.) Loud.); and various shrubs and grasses such as sweet pepper bush *(Clethra almifolia)*, gallberry *(Ilex galbra)*, greenbrier *(Smilax glauca)*, bamboo vine *(Smilax lauriafolia)*, swamp huckleberry *(Vaccinium corymbosum)* and wool grass *(Scirpus criiphorum)*. A few pond pine *(Pinus rigida* var. *serotina* (Michx.) Loud.) seed trees are scattered over most of the severely burned areas and young seedlings are present in most places. Areas that have not been so severely burned support a cover of hardwoods mainly, including swamp black gum *(Nyssa biflora)*, yellow poplar (*Liriodendron Tulipifera)*, red maple *(Acer rubrum)*, swamp bay *(Persea pubescens)*, Carolina ash *(Fraxinus Carolinana)*, and a few pond pine. In Pasquotank County, N. C., southern white cedar *(Chamaecyparis thyoides)* is confined almost exclusively to the northern part of the swamp on mucky-peat more than 5 feet deep. Here it is mixed with hardwoods. Fires and clean cutting no doubt have been contributing factors to the decline in stands and range of this valuable tree.

SOILS

Except for Norfolk County, Va., soil surveys have been made of all the counties in which the swamp occurs. The Soil Survey of Pasquotank County, N. C., was completed in 1949. In the survey of Gates County, N. C., (1) the soils in the swamp were classified as peat, which ranges up to 12 feet in depth. In the survey of Camden—Currituck Counties, N. C. (8) they were classified as shallow phase peat, and peaty muck. Peat was described as being 3 to 12 feet deep and shallow peat 20 to 30 inches deep. Peaty muck was described as being well decayed vegetable matter more than 3 feet deep. In the old survey of Perquimans and Pasquotank Counties (6) the portion of the swamp in Perquimans County was classified as swamp. In the survey of Nansemond County, Va. (2), the soils in the swamp were classified as shallow phase peat and peat, the shallow phase being less than 3 feet deep. The late Dr. A. P. Dachnowski—Stokes of the Bureau of Chemistry and Soils studied some peat profiles in the Dismal Swamp section of Nansemond County, Va. A very detailed description of deep peat, which he observed in the southeast corner of the county, appears in the section on Morphology and Genesis of Soils in the Nansemond Co., Va. soil survey report.

During the survey of Pasquotank County considerable thought was given to the type of survey to be made in the Dismal Swamp section, an area of about 55 square miles. Some people feel that the swamp, or part of it offers possibilities for agricultural development. It was decided that a detailed survey of the area would not be feasible due to the difficulty of getting over it and the time that would be involved. The area is very difficult to traverse due to the thick growth of cane or reeds, vines, briars, and fallen trees. Soft places in the peat, where a person can sink in to his waist, and the fact that the area is covered with water most of the time also hinder coverage of the area.

Though a detailed survey did not seem advisable, it was decided that more information should be obtained on the character and depth of the organic material and also on the texture of the underlying mineral soil than had been obtained in the surrounding counties. Therefore, the soils were examined carefully to a 5-foot depth along the two roads that cross the swamp and along all passable foot trails and old railroad grades in the area. In addition, two trails were brushed at right angles to each other across the main body of the swamp (Fig. 1). The northeast-southwest trail is 24,540 feet long and the northwest-southeast trail is 41,780 feet long.

SOIL UNITS

Listed below are the units used in the classification of the soils in the swamp and in the area bordering the swamp in Pasquotank County:[7]

Mucky peat, less than 3 feet thick over light to moderate textured material.

Mucky peat, less than 3 feet thick over moderate to heavy textured material.

Mucky peat, 3 to 5 feet thick over light to moderate textured material.

---

[7] No series name is given the units of mucky-peat pending final correlation of the area.

Mucky peat, 3 to 5 feet thick over moderate to heavy textured material.
Mucky peat, more than 5 feet thick.
Bayboro mucky loam.
Pocomoke mucky loam.
The separations based on thickness of the mucky peat are more or less arbitrary. It is felt, however, that this type of information would be very helpful in the event any drainage operations are considered for the area. Likewise, information on the texture of the underlying mineral soil would be very helpful in planning drainage operations.

DESCRIPTION OF SOIL UNITS

Mucky peat, less than 3 feet deep over light to moderate textured material.—This separation consists of mucky peat ranging in thickness from 18 to 36 inches but generally 24 to 36 inches. The mineral soil is mainly light fine sandy loam underlain by loamy fine sand or sand; in places the fine sandy loam grades into light loam which is underlain by loamy fine sand.

Mucky peat, less than 3 feet thick over moderate to heavy textured material.— This separation differs from the one described directly above in the texture of the underlying mineral soil, which is mainly a fine sandy loam underlain by clay loam, sandy clay loam, or silty clay loam. Loamy sand is present in places in the lower part of the 5-foot section. A description of a representative profile is given below:

0 to 2 inches, raw and partially decomposed leaf litter and twigs.
2 to 16 inches, very dark brown partially and well decomposed plant remains with a tangled mass of roots and underground woody shoots; open, loose, and spongy; well developed granular structure when moderately dry; extremely to very strongly acid.
16 to 30 inches, black fairly well decomposed material; some well preserved plant remains and woody fragments are evident; soft and very friable; slightly sticky.
30 to 40 inches, dark grayish-brown fine sandy loam; very friable.
40 to 60 inches, gray silty clay loam or silty clay; firm; plastic.

Mucky peat, 3 to 5 feet thick over light to moderate textured material.—The thickness of the mucky peat ranges from 3 to 5 feet. Where the mucky peat is less than 5 feet deep the upper part of the mineral soil is mainly light fine sandy loam, which continues in some places to a depth of 5 feet. In other places the fine sandy loam grades into loamy fine sand or sand and in others into light loam.

Mucky peat, 3 to 5 feet thick over moderate to heavy textured material.—This differs from the soil above in being underlain by heavier textured mineral soil. The mineral soil is generally heavy fine sandy loam or silt loam 6 to 12 inches thick over clay loam, silty clay loam, or silty clay. A description of a representative profile is given below:

0 to 2 inches, raw and partially decomposed leaf litter.
2 to 18 inches, very dark brown partially and well decomposed plant remains

with a tangled mass of roots and underground woody shoots; loose and spongy; well developed granular structure when moderately dry; extremely acid.

18 to 46 inches, black, fairly well decomposed material with some well preserved plant remains and woody fragments evident; soft and smooth; slightly sticky in places; stumps and buried tree trunks are numerous in this horizon.

46 to 52 inches, dark grayish-brown silt loam; very friable.

52 to 60 inches, gray silty clay loam or silty clay; firm; plastic.

Mucky peat, more than 5 feet thick. — The mucky peat ranges from 5 to 10 feet or more in thickness. The upper 16 inches consists of partially decomposed material matted with roots and underground shoots. Below 16 inches the material is more highly decomposed and varies in color from dark brown to black. Stumps and fallen tree trunks are numerous. It is extremely to very strongly acid.

Bayboro mucky loam. — The surface layer is black or very dark brown loam with a well developed granular structure and ranges in thickness from about 6 to 18 inches. This is underlain by a dark grayish-brown or gray silt loam 6 to 10 inches thick, overlying a gray to dark gray silty clay or clay with brownish-yellow mottles. About 60 acres of this soil has been cleared and drained, and is under cultivation or used for pasture.

Pocomoke mucky loam. — The surface layer is 6 to 16 inches thick. It is black or very dark brown, very friable loam with well developed granular structure. This is underlain by light gray fine sandy loam or loam mottled with brownish-yellow which grades into gray loamy fine sand or sand at 24 to 36 inches.

Bayboro mucky loam and Pocomoke mucky loam are essentially phases of Bayboro loam and Pocomoke loam, respectively. The content of organic matter in the surface layers ranges from about 20 to 45 or 50 percent. These soils occur around the borders of the swamp and are considered to be transitional between the mucky peat (Bog soils) and the mineral soils (Humic Gley and Low Humic Gley soils) surrounding the swamp. Both soils are extremely to very strongly acid in the surface layers.

ACREAGE OF SOIL UNITS

The soil units listed below were made a l o n g the traverses in and bordering the swamp but were not delineated by boundaries. The total length of all traverses is about 31 miles. The acreage estimates were obtained by using the formula $(c/b)a$, in which a represents the total acreage of the swamp, b the total length of traverse within the area, and c the total length of traverse for each soil unit. These results show the acreage of mucky peat less than 3 feet deep. Mucky peat 3 to 5 feet deep, and mucky peat more than 5 feet deep, are more extensive than any of the other units.

Listed below is a rough estimate of the acreage of each soil unit described.

Mucky peat, less than 3 feet deep over light to
    moderate textured material . . . . 1,956 acres
Mucky peat, less than 3 feet deep over moderate
    and heavy textured material 2,680   ”

Mucky peat, 3 to 5 feet deep over light to moderate
    textured material 5,592   "
Mucky peat, 3 to 5 feet deep over moderate to
    heavy textured material 10,100   "
Mucky peat, more than 5 feet deep 9,337   "
Bayboro mucky loam 4,051   "
Pocomoke mucky loam 1,529   "

        Total . . . . 35,245 acres

CHARACTERISTICS OF THE MUCKY PEAT
SOIL PROFILES

Along the two brushed trails shown in Fig. 1, soil profile descriptions were taken at 300-foot intervals. Along other traverses in the swamp, the soils were examined at 500- to 800-foot intervals. In Fig. 2, profile sections show the depth of the mucky peat and the texture of the underlying material along these trails. The upper section is the northwest-southeast trail and the lower section the northeast-southwest trail.

It will be noted that the mucky peat varies in depth from about 2 to more than 5 feet, and that the underlying mineral soil is variable in texture. Where the mucky peat is more than 5 feet deep no attempt was made to classify the underlying mineral soil.

Further study of Fig. 2 suggests that the mucky peat has formed in a depressed or trough-like position. This is strongly expressed in the prolife along the northeast-southwest trail as the line is sharp between Pocomoke mucky loam and peat on the south end and between Bayboro loam and peat on the north end. Observations indicate that this is also true in other places. The west end of the northwest-southeast trail begins on an island near the border of the swamp and the east end is in the swamp.

The pattern of the underlying mineral soil suggests that the same type of texture profiles exists under the peat as in the mineral soils surrounding the swamp. In places the fine sandy loam overlies loamy fine sand; in others the fine sandy loam grades into light loam which overlies loamy fine sand, and in places it grades into clay loam or heavier material. Where the upper part of the mineral soil is silt loam it is invariably underlain by clay loam or heavier material. This is essentially the same type of pattern that exists in the mineral soil series in this region.

ORGANIC MATTER CONTENT OF MUCKY
PEAT SOILS

Twelve samples of mucky peat were collected along the trails shown in Fig. 1 for organic matter determinations. The locations for most of these samples are shown in Fig. 2. Loss on ignition was the method used for making the determinations.[8] The results are as follows:

[8] Determinations made by the North Carolina Agricultural Experiment Station, Raleigh, N. C.

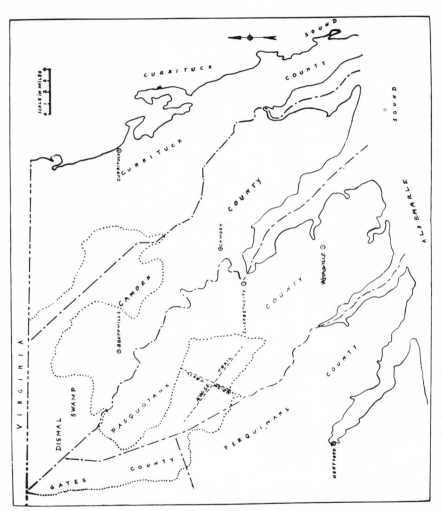

Fig. 1—Sketch map of northeastern North Carolina showing location of the Dismal Swamp and location of the two trails where detail studies of the organic soils were made.

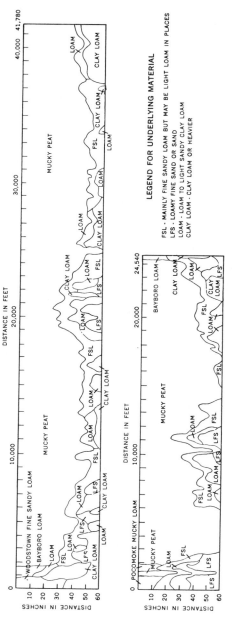

Fig. 2—Profile sections along the two trails shown in Fig. 1. The upper section is the northwest-southeast trail and the lower section the northeast-southwest trail.

Sample No.	Per cent organic matter
1	87.95
2	89.83
3	86.58
4	86.95
5	87.16
6	80.04
7	89.95
8	83.08
9	84.54
10	79.75
11	89.41
12	36.21

These results indicate that the organic matter content is rather uniform regardless of the thickness of the mucky peat, since the samples represent all the mucky peat soil units. Sample 12 alone is out of line with the others for some unknown reason.

LAND USE

No attempt has been made to drain and reclaim any of the mucky peat soils and Pocomoke mucky loam for agricultural purposes. Areas of these soils support cut-over and burned-over forest growth. Severely burned areas support only a brushy forest growth and a thick cover of reeds or cane. About 60 acres of Bayboro mucky loam has been cleared and drained, and is under cultivation or in pasture.

SUMMARY

The Dismal Swamp occupies an area of 375 to 400 square miles in five counties in northeastern North Carolina and two counties in southeastern Virginia. The original vegetation consisted mainly of southern white cedar, cypress, and swamp black gum.

In Pasquotank County, N. C., the swamp is occupied mainly by mucky peat, ranging in depth from about 2 to more than 10 feet. The material is fairly well decomposed and appears to be quite uniform in physical characteristics and content of organic matter, irrespective of its thickness. The underlying mineral soil varies from light to heavy textured. Soils with relatively shallow dark surface layers, ranging in content of organic matter from about 20 to 50 percent, occur around the borders of the swamp.

Results of rough estimates show that about 14 percent of the area of the swamp in Pasquotank County, N. C., is occupied by mucky peat less than 3 feet deep, 45 percent by mucky peat 3 to 5 feet deep, 24 percent by mucky peat more than 5 feet deep, and 15 percent by Bayboro and Pocomoke mucky loams.

LITERATURE CITED

1. Davis, W. A., and Devereux, R. E. Soil survey of Gates County, North Carolina, Bur. Chemistry and Soils, USDA Bul. No. 1, Series 1929.

2. Devereux, R. E., Shulkcum, Edward, and Patterson, G. W. Soil Survey of Nansemond County, Virginia. Bur. Chemistry and Soils, USDA Bul. No. 6, Series 1932.

3. Federal Writers Project, North Carolina. A Guide to the Old North State. American Guide Series. 1939. (601 pages)

4. Kearney, Thomas H. Report on a botanical survey of the Dismal Swamp region. U. S. D. A., Div. of Botany, Vol. 5, No. 6. 1901.

5. Korstian, C. F., and Brush, W. D. Southern white cedar. U. S. Dept. of Agr. Tech. Bul. No. 251. 1931.

6. Lapham, J. E., and Lyman, W. S. Soil survey of Perquimans and Pasquotank Counties, North Carolina. U. S. D. A. Bur. of Soils. 1905.

7. Mattoon, W. R. The southern cypress. U. S. D. A. Bul. No. 272. 1915.

8. Perkins, S. O., Lee, W. D., Shivery, G. B., and Davidson, S. F. Soil survey of Camden and Currituck Counties, North Carolina. U. S. D. A., Bur. of Chemistry and Soils, Bul. No. 2. Series 1923.

9. Shaler, N. S. General account of the fresh water morasses of the United States with a description of the Dismal Swamp region of Virginia and North Carolina. U. S. Geol. Survey, Annual Report, Part 2, 10:313—339. 1890.

MAJOR GENETIC SOILS OF THE ARCTIC SLOPE OF ALASKA[1]

J. C. F. Tedrow, J. V. Drew, D. E. Hill, and L. A. Douglas

(Rutgers University, New Jersey, U.S.A.)

SUMMARY

The genetic soils of Arctic Alaska can be arranged in a drainage catena. The mature soils on well-drained sites are Arctic Brown and related soils. The Tundra profile is an imperfectly- to poorly-drained catena member. The Bogs, with permafrost, occupy many of the broad, flat, very wet areas. No evidence of a qualitative soil-forming process unique to the Arctic areas is found. Instead, the Arctic Tundra is primarily a northern extension of the hydormorphic soils of the forested regions, whereas the Arctic Brown and related soils represent the northern extensions of the podzolic process. The term Tundra, when used in connection with zonal great soil groups along with Podzols, Chernozems, Laterites and related soils, is an erroneous one and its use, except for a hydromorphic soil, should be discouraged. The podzolic process on the stable, well-drained sites weakens northward, resulting in the successive development of Podzols, Minimal Podzols, Arctic Browns, Arctic Browns shallow phase, and finally, no soil formation.

INTRODUCTION

A somewhat arbitrary line drawn by soil scientists marks the northern extremity of the podzol region in America. North of this line the soils are referred to, at the Great Soil Group level, as Tundra and Bog (with permafrost). Although the soils of the Arctic Tundra of North America are largely unexplored, recent investigations in northern Alaska by the authors indicate the presence of a number of genetic soils in this region. Our first objective was to describe the major genetic soils of the Alaskan Arctic Slope. From these studies it was found possible to offer some hypotheses concerning the soil-forming processes operating in this Arctic environment.

It has been generally implied that the podzolic process gives way to a type of Tundra soil-forming process, the Podzols 'grading' into Tundra soils in the direction of the pole. A climatic optimum exists for podzolization, northward from which the

---

[1] Journal series paper of the New Jersey Agricultural Experiment Station, Rutgers, the State University of New Jersey, department of soils.

These studies were aided by a contract between the O.N.R., Department of the Navy, and the Arctic Institute of North America. Reproduction in whole or in part permitted for any purpose of the United States Government.

Reproduced with permission from *Journal of Soil Science*, Vol. 9, 1958, p. 33-45.
Published by the British Society of Soil Science, England.

process weakens. The qualitative process of podzolization does not, however, grade into a special type of soil formation unique to the Tundra areas. Instead it grades into one giving rise to soils that are weakly podzolic in character. These have been termed Arctic Brown (Drew and Tedrow, 1957; Tedrow and Hill, 1955) and related soils (Kellogg and Nygard, 1951). Therefore, a second objective—to follow the weakening podzolic process along a theoretical transect from the northern forested areas to the polar deserts—was added to the study.

CLIMATE

The climate of northern Alaska is truly Arctic, the mean temperature for July, the warmest month, approximating 50 F, and that of February, the coldest month, approximating − 27 F (Conover, 1953). Precipitation averages 4 to 8 in. a year, with much of it in the form of snow. Relative humidity is very high. The low value for precipitation is somewhat misleading because evaporation is low and moisture may accumulate in the soil directly by condensation. Apparently this condensation does not provide sufficient moisture to cause much leaching in the profile, the effect being primarily that of maintaining the soil in a somewhat more moist state than would be expected in an area of low precipitation. The entire area is underlain by continuous permafrost, the maximum measured thickness near Point Barrow being 1,030 ft. (MacCarthy, 1952).

SOIL CONDITIONS

As a result of low soil temperatures and a short growing season, organic matter synthesis and decomposition are very slow. Silt loam textural classes dominate, but considerable variations exist. At one extreme, coarse-textured material is present, as in some of the dune and beach ridge areas of the Arctic Coastal Plain. But the bentonite deposits of the Arctic Foothills consist largely of clay, with only small quantities of silt and fine sand. Soils of the Arctic regions are reported to be predominantly medium-textured, with a large percentage of silt. This suggests the possibility that the rocks and minerals have been weathered mainly through physical processes to silt, at which size-range they reach a somewhat static state, further reduction of size being of only minor significance. Grigorijev (1945), Taber (1943), Tsyplenkin (1946), and others discussed the question of weathering under Arctic conditions, but their findings and opinions are inconclusive. Sigafoos and Hopkins (1952) state that 'grain size of Arctic soils . . . is largely a function of the grain size of parent rock'.

Topography is of major importance in soil formation in the Arctic regions. As the slow seasonal thaw of the active layer progresses considerable water is released. Since the underlying frozen layer in the soil is impervious, drainage water moves sluggishly across and through the active layer. Ridges and narrow watershed divides tend to be better drained than the surrounding flat areas. The latter areas, having little or no runoff, tend to accumulate organic matter and to develop organic soils. Low rates of evaporation, coupled with condensation of atmospheric moisture, contribute to the wet conditions so prevalent in the Tundra (Gorodkov, 1939).

The few descriptions of Tundra soils generally describe conditions only above the frozen layer. In our northern Alaskan investigations mechanical drills and explosives were employed to open up the soil so that the upper portion of the permafrost as well as the active layer could be examined.

SOILS OF PREDOMINATLY WET ENVIRONMENT

Tundra soils

The most widespread soil of the Arctic Slope of Alaska is the wet mineral soil known as Tundra. This Great Soil Group tends to mantle the undulating and sloping landscape from ridge top to valley bottom, and the flat costal plain areas as well. Silt loam textures predominate. The profiles show little if any textural change among the several horizons that are related to soil-forming processes. Profile characteristics vary in relation to parent material, relief, and time.

Tundra profiles show considerable variation. Local factors, such as the complex pattern of ground ice in the form of ice wedges, veins, lenses, and stems, and the amount and character of the organic material at the surface, leave their marks on the profile morphology. Application of conventional horizon designations in Tundra profiles has little meaning. To avoid misunderstanding, a numerical system is used.

While the idealized Tundra profile is acid in reaction, especially in the upper horizons, recent field investigations revealed extensive areas of highly calcareous soils in Arctic Alaska. Little is known about the influence of the high calcium content on the soil processes.

Fig. 1 shows an idealized profile thought to typify in general terms the Tundra soils in northern Alaska. Three master horizons are present: (*a*) the active layer (horizons 1,2, and 3 of Fig. 1), (*b*) the upper portion of the permanently frozen layer (horizon 4), containing considerable organic staining and pieces of organic matter,[2] and (*c*) and the permanently frozen parent material without organic staining (horizon 5). The active layer is the only portion of the soil that is subject to seasonal thaw. The appearance of this layer varies at different sites, depending upon such factors as relative wetness, parent material, plant cover, organic matter, and topography. Colours range from yellows and browns, with various intensities of mottling, in the drier areas, to dark greys in the wetter sites. Near the top of the active layer the mottling consists of a spectrum of yellow, orange, and grey but the colours near the bottom are darker. The soil is nearly always saturated, and excavations, with few exceptions, fill with water.

The soil-forming process associated with the Tundra profile is primarily one of gleization in a low-temperature environment. There is no evidence to indicate that

---

[2] The processes by which the organic matter becomes dispersed through the ice in the upper part of the permafrost are unknown. Some possibilities are suggested: (1) Some of the organic matter may have been displaced downward by frost action during a warmer period of the Pleistocene. The dispersion of organic matter and organic staining throughout the ice in this layer indicates that the depth of thaw may have been greater at some time than at present. That there were warmer periods in this region during the past is fairly well established (Grigorijev, 1945). (2) Some of the organic matter may have been translocated slowly downward in the form of a colloidal suspension during a warmer period of the Pleistocene. (3) The present permanently frozen organic stained ice and frozen pieces of peaty material may be profile remnants buried by aeolian and other processes.

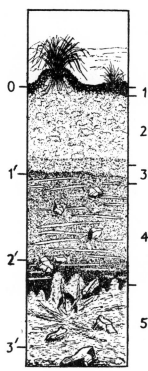

1. Organic matter, dark brown to black, consisting of partially decomposed sedges, sphagnum, and heaths. This horizon may vary from a thin discontinuous one to an organic mat some six inches thick. Usually very loose, fibrous, wet, and strongly acid.

2. Light olive-brown (2·5Y 5/4) silt loam, usually very wet but, upon drying, is loose and friable. Mottling is nearly always present but in varying degrees. Strongly acid.

3. Dark grey (2·5Y 4/0) silt loam, mottled, very wet. The bottom of this layer approximates to the permafrost table.

4. Very dark grey (2·5Y 3/0) silt loam, permanently frozen. Considerable organic staining in the ice and shreds of organic matter are intermixed throughout the horizon. The bottom of the layer is very uneven and has a much darker colour than the central portion of the horizon. The upper part of the horizon also may have a darker colour than the central portion. The horizon varies from frozen mineral soil to ground ice. Pieces of peaty material are commonly present.

5. Frozen, grey mineral matter interspersed with ground ice. No evidence of organic staining. In many instances the material is virtually clear ice. Weakly acid to calcareous, depending upon parent material.

Fig. 1. Idealized description of a Tundra profile. Soil colours based on field conditions using Munsell colour chips, Munsell Color Co., Baltimore, Md.

moisture moves downward into the permafrost. Frost action and solifluction operate simultaneously with soil formation. Frost action tends to disrupt the acquired morphology in some locations. Organic matter is commonly present to depths exceeding several feet. The 'frost churning' discussed in the literature is thought to take place in northern Alaska at an exceedingly slow rate. Cores of finely ground garnet 1 in. in diameter were inserted in a few places to depths approximating 3 ft. After two years no detectable displacement was noted. On the steeper land, however, solifluction processes are active, causing major profile disturbances.

Thickness of the horizons, colour, intensity of mottling, organic matter content, topographic position, relative wetness, and related criteria were used to separate the Tundra soils into two units. Tentatively, they have been called Upland Tundra and Meadow Tundra. These two units are somewhat analogous in drainage to Low Humic Gley and the Humic Gley soils of the temperate climates. Upland Tundra occupies the relatively drier sites on sloping land and rounded hilltops that afford better drainage than the lower areas. On these Upland Tundra sites the upper horizons tend to show slightly greater oxidation, more brown and yellow coloration, and less organic-matter accumulation than do those of the Meadow Tundra. Meadow Tundra occupies the lower positions, the flatter areas, and similiar situations of poor drainage. Relative wetness of the Meadow Tundra profile is greater, colours are darker grey, the thickness of the surface organic matter is greater, and related conditions of poor drainage increase in intensity, in comparison with the Upland Tundra.

Organic Soils

Wide areas of flat terrain provide little opportunity for surface runoff. The frozen soil layer serves as an impermeable stratum. Under these conditions the soils are saturated with water throughout most of the summer months and frequently have water standing on the surface to depths exceeding 1 ft. The waterlogged condition of the soil prevents much organic-matter decomposition, and peaty material tends to accumulate (Fig. 2). Peat thicknesses exceeding 4-6 ft. do not appear to be extensive, but thicknesses exceeding 20 ft. have been observed in isolated cases along swales. The organic soils are usually sedge-sphagnum-grass mixtures, much of the organic material retaining its fibrous condition.

The organic soils are subdivided into Half-Bogs with organic matter accumulations approximately 6 to 12 and, in some instances, 18 in. in thickness, and Bog soils with an organic layer at times exceeding 4 ft.

Because of polygonal development, stream cutting, and related processes, some of the organic deposits are in a comparatively dry environment. The majority, however, remain very wet. On the 'dry' peat areas plant species common to well-drained sites are usually present.

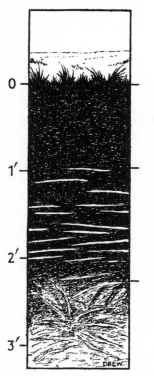

1. Reddish brown sphagnum and sedge peat. Fibrous and very wet, usually moderately to strongly acid.

2. Black sphagnum and sedge peat with ice lenses, strongly acid.

3. Frozen black peat and mineral matter with considerable ground ice.

Fig. 2. Idealized profile of a Bog soil formed on a river terrace.

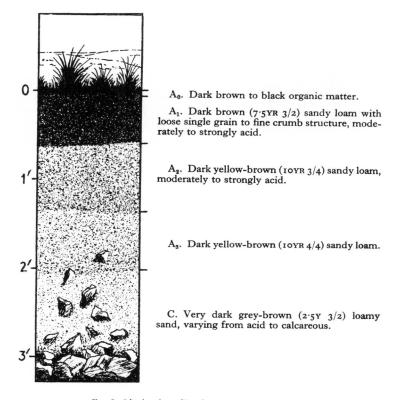

A₀. Dark brown to black organic matter.

A₁. Dark brown (7·5YR 3/2) sandy loam with loose single grain to fine crumb structure, moderately to strongly acid.

A₂. Dark yellow-brown (10YR 3/4) sandy loam, moderately to strongly acid.

A₃. Dark yellow-brown (10YR 4/4) sandy loam.

C. Very dark grey-brown (2·5Y 3/2) loamy sand, varying from acid to calcareous.

Fig. 3. Idealized profile of an Arctic Brown soil.

SOILS OF PREDOMINANTLY DRY ENVIRONMENT

On escarpments, shoulders, ridges, terrace edges, stabilized dunes, and similar locations, the active layer may have a thickness of as much as 3 to 5 ft. By virtue of their positions, these sites are well drained. The thickness of the active layer is greater where sand and gravel are present, but well-drained sites of silt loams are found in isolated cases. The mature soil on these well-drained, stable areas has been designated as Arctic Brown (Fig. 3).

The Arctic Brown soil (Drew and Tedrow, 1957; Tedrow and Hill, 1955) is interpreted as a segment of what Russian workers (Filatov, 1945) have designated as dry Tundra in the Siberian Arctic and Subarctic. Where bedrock is within 12 to 18 in. of the surface and drainage is good the Arctic Brown shallow phase (Fig. 4) is commonly present. Shallow, well-drained soils are more likely to be found in the higher elevations in the Southern Arctic Foothills, but they have also been observed on unconsolidated deposits as far north as the coastal areas.

Some of the soils are gradational between the Arctic Brown and Tundra. They tend to have most of the features of the Arctic Brown, especially in the upper horizons, but the lower horizons have a gley appearance at a depth of 12-24 in. Permafrost is nearer the surface than in the typical Arctic Brown soil, being usually 18

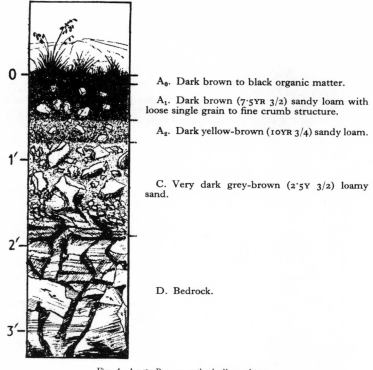

A$_0$. Dark brown to black organic matter.

A$_1$. Dark brown (7·5YR 3/2) sandy loam with loose single grain to fine crumb structure.

A$_2$. Dark yellow-brown (10YR 3/4) sandy loam.

C. Very dark grey-brown (2·5Y 3/2) loamy sand.

D. Bedrock.

Fig. 4. Arctic Brown soil, shallow phase.

to 30 in. deep. The drainage of this soil is somewhat analogous to that of a 'moderately well-drained' soil of the temperate climates. An interesting feature of these soils is the presence of a black organic colour immediately above the permafrost. This appears to result from the slow, downward migration of the organic matter which, on reaching the bottom of the active layer, becomes trapped immediately above the permafrost. This soil is referred to as Arctic Brown moderately well-drained phase.

The Arctic Brown profiles can, therefore, be subdivided into Arctic Brown normal phase, Arctic Brown shallow phase, and Arctic Brown moderately well-drained phase.

Lithosols

The rugged terrain of the mountains is characterized primarily by rock land, generally with no soil cover but occasionally covered with shallow 'dry' soil having a brown surface horizon that may attain a thickness of 1-6 in. Topography is so steep and erosion so rapid that the soil-forming processes cannot keep pace with processes of mass wasting.

Regosols

Certain alluvial, aeolian, marine, outwash, and talus deposits are well drained to depths exceeding 2 to 3 ft. Because of the youthfulness of the area, many of the soils of these sites have developed little or no semblance of a genetic profile. Permafrost is unusually deep, often as much as 4 to 6 ft. These areas have been included with the Regosols.

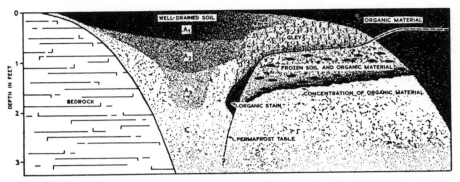

Fig. 5. Major genetic (drainage) sequences in the soils of the Arctic Slope of Alaska (diagrammatic).

SCHEMATIC ARRANGEMENT OF THE GENETIC SOILS

A drainage sequence of profiles in the Arctic regions has long been broadly implied by many investigators. Filatov (1945) recognized a dry Tundra associated with sandy or stony, coarse soils with a dry turfy layer and many kinds of Tundras with impeded drainage. Sheludyakova (1938) describes Lichen Tundra formed under good drainage conditions, grassy cotton-grass Tundras formed under poor drainage, and marshy lake-plain littoral Tundra formed in the wet Tundra marshes. Dansereau (1954) implies drainage sequences in Baffinland, and information and samples furnished by him indicate the presence of drainage sequences. Smith (1956) describes a series of soils in Spitzbergen which falls into a drainage catena. Retzer (1956) recently described a somewhat similar drainage sequence in the Alpine Tundra regions of the Rocky Mountains.

The major soil profiles of the Alaskan Arctic Slope can be arranged in the form of a drainage catena, the Arctic Brown representing the mature, well-drained soil of the region (Fig. 5). In grading from the deep, well-drained to shallow, well-drained condition, there is no change in the type of soil-forming processes, but only a diminution of profile thickness. In the shallow soils the A_3 horizon is no longer evident. Continuing through more shallow conditions, the A_1 horizon maintains about the same thickness, but there is a marked decrease in the thickness of the A_2. With very shallow soils only dry organic matter overlying coarse matter is evident. Finally a point is reached where there are no acquired soil features, only scattered crustose lichens over rock or rock debris. The shallow Arctic Brown profile is commonly present at higher altitudes and elevations where bedrock is near the surface as well as under the more severe Arctic climates where the rate of soil formation is exceedingly slow. The shallow Arctic Brown profile is also present on the more recent deposits, the shallowness of the profile being due to insufficient time having elapsed for a deep profile to develop.

In grading from the Arctic Brown normal phase to the moderately well-drained phase (Fig. 5), permafrost is present at depths approximating 18 to 30 in., and a gley appearance is apparent 1 to 6 in. immediately above the permafrost table. Where the permafrost table occurs near the surface, the gley appearance is intensified, and the Tundra profile becomes evident. Complete saturation of the profile gives rise to organic-matter accumulation and the formation of Bog soils.

Fig. 5 diagrams the four major soils—Lithosols, Arctic Brown, Tundra, and Bog. The mature or zonal soil is considered the Arctic Brown, while the Tundra and Bog soils are definitely considered intra-zonal soils.

PODZOLIC PROCESS IN THE ARCTIC ENVIRONMENT

Statements and inferences that the podzolic process 'grades' into a completely different soil-forming process in Arctic regions as one proceeds northward are without foundation. The vast wet expanses of the Arctic are primarily Tundra soils, but they are forming under a wet environment and cannot be thought of in terms of mature soils such as Podzols and Chernozems. The concept that the Tundra process is qualitatively inseparable from the gley process has been carefully analysed and presented by Gorodkov (1939), a seasoned Arctic pedologist, who states:

The differences between the gleyey and podzolic-gleyey soils of the northern forest zone and the Tundra and polar-desert soils is not qualitative but quantitative. . . . Only Liverovskii tries to find special soil-forming processes in the Arctic, and he sometimes classifies the soils as 'a special variant of the gley-marsh processes' sometimes as 'a special type of soils of the gleyey-marshy series'. In confirming his opinion, he draws on data from Zaitsev and Afanas'ev which is analogous to his own, forgetting both their works relate to soils of the forest zone, and not to the Arctic. Therefore his reference to them merely confirms the lack of special Arctic soil formation. . . . . Such (Tundra) soils are commonly included in the classification schemes along with Podzols, Marshy-gleyey, Chernozem, and others although there are no serious foundations in principle or in fact for such a classification. There was some excuse for a special classification of Tundra soils in Dokuchaev's and Sibertsev's time, when information on the natural conditions of the tundra zone was scarce and often completely incorrect; at present we have no basis for considering the Arctic as something special by way of soils.

Numerous workers have described the weakening of the podzolic process in the direction of the pole (Filatov, 1945; Gorodkov, 1939; Meinardus, 1930; Sheludyakova, 1938; Sochava, 1933). This weakening of the process is due primarily to climatic conditions in that there is a smaller amount of total precipitation and temperatures are lower than farther south in the well-defined Podzol areas. Biologic activity and chemical weathering are weak in the far-north areas. Traces of mineral elements brought into solution in the northernmost regions move downward in barely measurable quantities. In some cases no downward movement is apparent.

If the summer precipitation were greater in the areas of Arctic Brown soil and if the soils had sufficient permeability and drainage, Podzols would probably dominate the well-drained sites. The degree of this podzolic development would be in proportion to the increase in rainfall.

The diagrammatic presentation commonly employed to show the relation of great soil groups to climate indicates that Tundra soils form under conditions varying from 'dry-cold' to 'wet-cold'. This concept can be quite misleading because Tundra soils in Alaska form under conditions of high humidity but low precipitation. During the summer months relative humidity seldom drops below 70-80, and most of the time it exceeds 90 percent. On the other hand, precipitation in the Arctic is very limited and leaching potential is correspondingly low.

The change from the Podzols to the brown surface soils of the Arctic and Sub-arctic regions is one of gradual transition. The qualitative process expresses itself in varying intensities that tend to diminish northward. The results of the varying intensities of podzolization are idealized in a sequence of profiles in Fig. 6. Considerable interfingering of Arctic Brown and Minimal Podzol profiles occurs, depending upon the nature of the parent material (Fig. 7), age, relief, altitudinal limits, and related factors. Signs of a feeble podzolic process are manifested in Arctic Brown, Subarctic Brown Forest, and related profiles. Kellogg and Nygard (1951) regard what is designated as Subarctic Brown Forest soil of Central Alaska as representing a stage of immaturity before Podzol. This concept has merit and the nomenclature is one of semantics. A very weak podzolic process is operating in the area but at an exceedingly slow rate. If the process operated on a stable land surface for very long periods of time a soil with distinct Podzol features could possibly develop. The brown surface soils are present, however, on many kinds of material of diverse ages, and they appear to be in reasonably good equilibrium with their environment. If the Subarctic Brown Forest soil is considered transitory, then the Grey-Brown Pod-

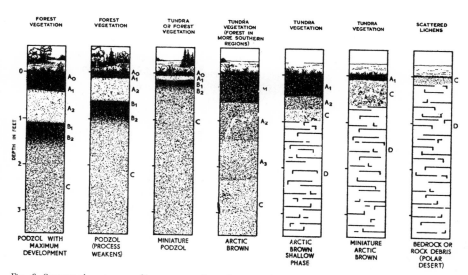

Fig. 6. Suggested mature profile sequences from the zone of maximum podzolization (*left*) northward to the zone of polar deserts(*right*).

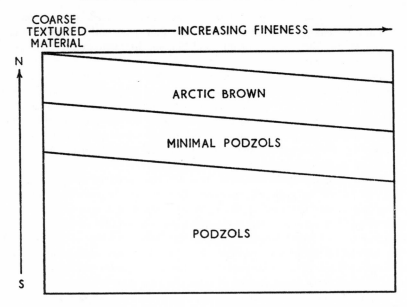

Fig. 7—Influence of textural composition on the degree of podzolization of the well-drained sites at northern latitudes.

zolic, and related soils are likewise transitory and, in time, will develop into Podzols. If the Grey-Brown Podzolic, Brown Podzolic, and related soils are considered mature, then the Subarctic Brown Forest and Arctic Brown soils are also mature, regional soils.

Minimal Podzols have been detected on the sandy Coastal Plain of northern Alaska within a few tens of miles of the Arctic Ocean. In the same general areas Arctic Brown profiles without any visible signs of podzolization are found. Podzol formation has been reported by the Russian workers on the dry sands of the Siberian Tundra. Sochava (1933), reporting on the Anabar drainage basin west of the lower Lena River, states: 'One may almost always detect a podzol-formation process on the sands and subsands.' Gorodkov (1939) describes the weakening of both the podzolic and gley processes in the direction of the pole. He states that the podzolic process weakens first, whereas the gleys are preserved up to the extreme limits of the land that is free of ice. In discussing the podzolic process in the Tundra area Gorodkov states:

In the Gydan tundra we observed not only podzolized spots and interlayers in the sands under the lichen and moss-lichen cover as far north as the 71st parallel but also some manifestation of an accumulation horizon. Liverovskii describes well-developed podzolic soils on sands of the Bol'shezemelskaya tundra. On the Kola Peninsula up to the very coast one may find podzols, but with a weak podzolic horizon.

The weakening of the podzolic process eastward leads to the fact that generally we do not find podzolic soils even in sandy grounds in the tundra zone of the far east.

Theoretically, as one proceeds northward, on similar parent material the Arctic Brown soil grades into a weakly developed profile until a point is reached where it is quite primitive and the developed features of the profile consist mainly of a brown surface 1 to 2 in. in thickness. Finally, a climatic condition is reached where on dry sites sparse dry lichens do not produce any discernible changes in the parent material, and there is no evidence of soil. This condition corresponds to the polar deserts described by Russian workers (Gorodkov, 1939).

The weakening podzolic process in a northerly direction is well illustrated by Gorodkov's map showing a northern zone adjoining the Arctic Ocean in Siberia with soils having *scarcely perceptible podzolic features*. To the south of this zone is a second zone of *weakly podzolic features* and farther to the south a third zone of *podzolic soils*. This principle has been described by other Russian investigators. Gorodkov states that 'the difference between the gleyey and Podzolic-gleyey soils of the northern forest zone (Siberia) and the tundra and polar desert soils is not qualitative but quanititative. They lead only to varied intensity of the podzolic and gleyey processes.'

The misconceptions about the soils of the Tundra are largely a result of a confusion of processes of soil formation with areal distribution. In proceeding from the Podzol zone to the Arctic regions the podzolic process continues to operate on well-drained sites, but with a marked decrease in intensity. In the far northern Arctic regions the podzolic process is near the zero point, representing only a potential.

Northward from the forested areas the proportion of well-drained soils diminishes greatly (excluding the areas where consolidated bedrock is at or near the surface). The deep, well-drained soils of the north give way to an overwhelming increase in poorly drained land. The major factors causing this great shift to poorly drained soils include: presence of permafrost, low evaporation, low temperatures, and poorly developed drainage patterns.

ACKNOWLEDGEMENTS

Appreciation is expressed to F. C. Erickson and C. M. Matthews, of Boston University Physical Research Laboratories, for help and encouragement during the earlier phases of this investigation. Some of the concepts presented in this paper were developed in the field while two of the authors, Tedrow and Hill, were with the Boston University field party in northern Alaska in 1953. The authors also wish to thank F. C. Erickson for making important Russian translations available. Firman E. Bear offered many important suggestions during the preparation of the manuscript, and for his advice and assistance the authors are very grateful.

REFERENCES

Conover, J. H. 1953. A preliminary report on climatology of the Arctic Slope of Alaska. Boston Univ. Phys. Res. Lab. Tech. Note 100

Dansereau, P. 1954. Studies of Central Baffin vegetation. I. Bray Island. Vegetatio, 5-6, 329-39.

Drew, J. V., and Tedrow, J. C. F. 1957. Pedology of an Arctic Brown profile near Point Barrow, Alaska. Soil Sci. Soc. Amer. Proc. 21, 336-9.

Filatov, M. 1945. Geography of the Soils of the U.S.S.R. Moscow, p. 334.

Gorodkov, B. N. 1939. Peculiarities of the Arctic top soil. Izv. Gosud. Geogr. Obshch. 71, 1516-32.

Grigorijev, A. A. 1945. Subarctica Ann. SSSR.

Kellogg, C. E., and Nygard, I. J. 1951. Exploratory study of the principal soil groups of Alaska. U.S. Dept. Agr. Agric. Monograph 7.

MacCarthy, G. R. 1952. Geothermal investigations on the Arctic Slope of Alaska. Trans. Amer. Geophys. Un. 33, 589-93.

Meinardus, W. 1930. Boden der kalten Region. Blancks Handbuch der Bodenlehre, 3. Springer, Berlin.

Retzer, J. L. 1956. Alpine soils of the Rocky Mountains. J. Soil Sci. 7, 22-32.

Sheludyakova, V. A. 1938. The vegetation of the Indigirka River Basin. Sovet. Bot. (4-5), 42-79.

Sigafoos, R. S., and Hopkins, D. M. 1952. Soil instability on slopes in regions of perennially-frozen ground. Frost Action in Soils. Highway Research Board, Washington, D.C., p. 176-92.

Smith J. 1956. Some moving soils in Spitsbergen. J. Soil Sci. 7, 10-21.

Sochava, V. B. 1933. Tundras of the Anabar River Basin. Izv. Gosud. Geogr. Obshch. 65, 340-64.

Taber, S. 1943. Perennially-frozen ground in Alaska, its origin and history. Bull. Geol. Soc. Amer. 54, 1433-1558.

Tedrow, J. C. F., and Hill D. E. 1955. Arctic Brown soil. Soil Sci. 80, 265-75.

Tsyplenkin, E. I. 1946. Perennially-frozen ground and soil formation. Pedology, No. 12, 709-18.

(Received 28 January 1957)

Part III

SOIL FORMING FACTORS---
CONCEPTS AND INTERPRETATION

THE PLANT FACTOR IN SOIL FORMATION

R. L. Crocker

University of Sydney, N.S.A., Australia

INTRODUCTION

Ever since the days of Dokuchaev, the founder of modern pedology, it has been recognised that plants are an important factor in the genesis of soils. Despite this it has proved very difficult to study the plant factor in soil formation largely because of the climate-vegetation-soil interaction. Partly to overcome such difficulties and in attempting to make pedology a more quantitative science, Jenny (1) formalized the relationship between soils and the factors in their formation in a functional equation

$$s = f(o, p, r, cl, t)$$

where s = any soil property, o = organism, p = parent material, cl = climate, and t = age of the system. The equation can be written

$$s = Soil = f(o, p, r, cl, t)$$

Jenny attempted to define these factors in such a way that they could be considered independent variables. The approach has proved valuable even though there are theoretical difficulties with these definitions which we need not go into. For our purposes, all we need to state is that the organism factor was recognised as having a micro-organism, fauna, and vegetation component, and the vegetation component was identified as the incidence of plant disseminules. This, in general terms, is very closely akin to the ecologists' concept of *flora*.

Despite the long interest in plants as soil-forming factors and Jenny's moves towards a quantitative pedology, there is still very little reliable information on the role of plants in soil formation.

It is proposed in this talk to indicate how this role of vegetation might be investigated and to give some examples of investigations which have been carried out.

METHODS OF APPROACH

Broadly speaking, there are three methods of approach which are likely to prove useful. Each of these attempts to isolate the effect of plants from that of the other soil-forming factors.

Reproduced with permission from *Proceedings of the Ninth Pacific Science Congress,* Vol. 18, 1960, p. 84-90. Published by the Secretariat, 9th Pacific Science Congress, Dept. of Science, Bangkok, Thailand.

The first is the *experimental* method. Simple soil system models might be set up where the environmental factors other than plants could be kept uniform. Treatments could include different plants and plant combinations and controls. After a time, the differences in soil properties as a function of plants could then be measured. This is a very straightforward approach using a very simplified system. It is a method however which has been very little employed, chiefly because time studies have indicated that soil genesis takes a very long time. Except in properties of the system which are very rapidly changed, therefore, it is not likely to be a very rewarding approach.

The second method is to seek out simple systems in nature and follow *soil development with time* in relation to the *vegetation.* This is a more complex situation, and the measurements cannot be made directly because again one does not live long enough. However, if different time-states of the system can be found existing in nature, then the broad plant effects can be readily determined for particular time-states. Such systems are found in fact amongst the more reliable succession studies of the ecologists.

The third method is to make a *comparative study* of the soils of *different floral regions,* where the other environmental factors can be restricted within narrow limits of variation, and where similar time-states can be identified. For example, as a beginning, we might look at soils developed on surfaces of equivalent age and from similar parent materials, in similar climates, on different land masses.

Unfortunately none of the foregoing methods are easily applied. The type of ideal systems we seek in nature are very restricted, and we will probably often have to settle for something falling considerably short of the ideal. Nevertheless by investigating even sufficient approximate situations we are likely to formulate some significant scientific generalizations. Indeed natural systems lending themselves to studies of this type are well worth seeking for there seems no other way in which we can evaluate the full effects of plants in soil genesis.

EFFECTS OF PLANTS ON SOIL PROPERTIES

From theoretical considerations it might be anticipated that the soil properties most directly and immediately influenced by plants would be the organic carbon profiles and the nitrogen profiles because plants are the agents of fixing both carbon and nitrogen from the atmosphere. It might also be anticipated that soil pH would be another property rapidly influenced by the nature of plant residues. Investigations of time sequences in relation to vegetation, the second method mentioned, has in fact indicated that in soil development, organic carbon, nitrogen, and pH profiles develop quite rapidly. Another soil property, bulk density, has also been shown to be rapidly changed by the developing vegetation. A summary of some of these effects is outlined below. Soil development was investigated on a succession of mudflows of known ages in the Shasta region of California, coastal dune sequences of broadly determinable age in northern California, and glacial morasses of known age, southeast Alaska.

Soil Development Relative to Vegetation Succession

The general features of these natural systems are briefly outlined below.

Mt. Shasta Sequence, California (Dickson and Crocker, 1953, 1954).

A series of old mudflows of ages ranging from 27-12,000 years. Over this period vegetation succession proceeds from a pioneer young pine *(P. ponderosa)*-shrub stage, through a thick pine dominant young forest to an open pine forest, and finally, after about 500 years to a pine-fir (Pseudo Douglasii) forest.
The parent material is andesitic volcanic material.

Fort Bragg Dune Sequence, California (Crocker and Zuike, 1955).

A sequence of coastal dunes of various ages from very young (0-75 years) to probably more than 1,500 years. The youngest dunes are bare or covered with grass, and with age (and distance from the coast), this is replaced by shrubs or stunted trees and then by a pine *(Pinus contorta)* and spruce *(Picea Sitchensis)* dominated community. The oldest dunes, of unknown age, carry a redwood *(Sequoia sempervirens)* forest.

Glacier Bay Sequence, Alaska.

Deglaciation, over the last 200 years in the Glacier Bay region of Alaska, has resulted in the exposure of considerable areas of bare ground. Plant succession over this period proceeds through a pioneer stage to a shrub-thicket stage (mainly older) to a spruce *(Picea sitchensis)* dominated forest.

Organic Carbon

(1) Mt. Shasta Region.

There is a very rapid build-up of organic carbon over the first 60 years and an apparent decreasing rate of accumulation after that with a tendency to approach steady state conditions.

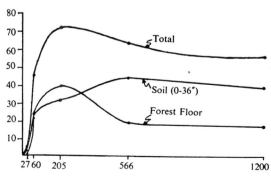

TIME (years)

The figures for the forest floor and perhaps for the mineral soil for the 566 and 1,200 year stage are likely to be low on account of fires.

(2) Fort Bragg Sequence.

The variability within the general surface age groups investigated was wider than expected. This was probably due to a variable fire history.

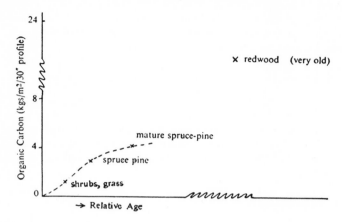

(3) Glacier Bay Sequence.

Organic carbon accumulates in the upper 18″ of mineral soil at a fairly regular rate of about 15gr/sq.m./annum. About 60 percent of the carbon is in the uppermost 6″ even in the oldest soils of the sequence.

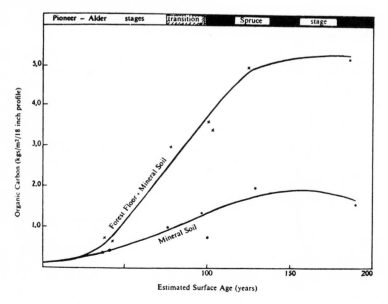

Total Nitrogen

(1) Mt. Shasta Sequence.

The accumulation of nitrogen, like that of carbon, was especially rapid in the early stages, but was relatively more rapid in the mineral soil than in the forest floor. Over the first 60 years, the average rate of nitrogen build-up was about 55 lbs/acre/annum.

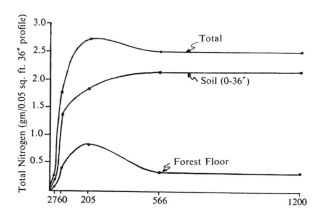

(2) Fort Bragg Dune Sequence.

The nitrogen profiles, so like the organic carbon profiles, are very erratic. They show, however, a very rapid build-up during the initial shrub-grass stage which is followed by a fairly stable period during the dominance of spruce and pine. The redwood-forest soils, whose age is probably of a quite different order of magnitude, contain several times as much nitrogen as the early stages.

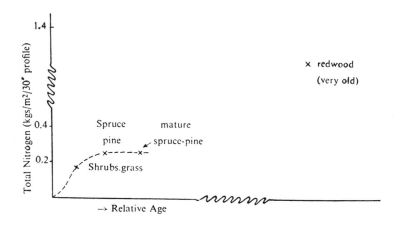

(3) Glacier Bay Sequence.

During the older thicket stage, nitrogen accumulates in the mineral soil profile at about the rate of 1.5gm/sq.m./annum and 4.9gm/sq.m./annum (55 lbs/acre/annum) in the mineral soil and forest floor. There is a fall of nitrogen in the upper part of the profile during the early stages of spruce dominance.

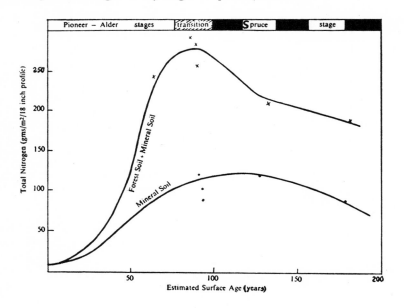

pH Changes

(1) Mt. Shasta Sequence.

pH changes were rather variable. The soil increased in acidity during the earlier sequence, with the greatest effect being shown during the first 200 years.

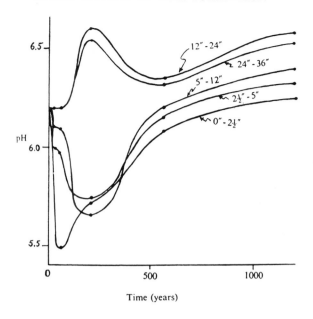

Time (years)

(2) Fort Bragg Dune Sequence.

The most coasterly and youngest dunes are alkaline. Those of the spruce-pine are moderately acid. The oldest (redwood) soils have a fairly uniform pH of about 5.5, tending to be more acid with depth.

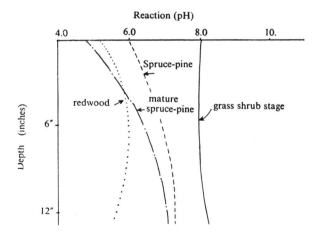

(3) Glacier Bay Sequence, Alaska.

During the earlier stages of succession at Glacier Bay, it was possible to compare the change in pH at different time states under different kinds of plants with the effect of leaching in the absence of macroscopic vegetation altogether. These effects were most pronounced in surface soil and are summarized below:

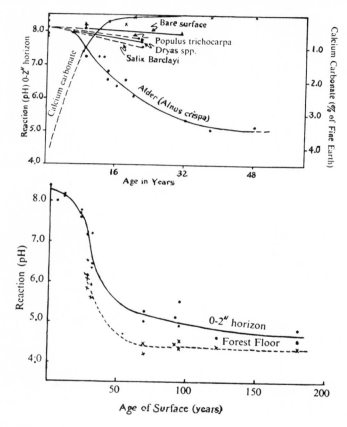

It is to be noted that in the Glacier Bay region pH fairly rapidly approaches apparent steady state conditions.

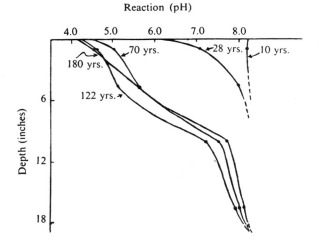

Bulk Density

(1) Mt. Shasta Sequence.

The bulk density of the soil parent material at initiation of soil formation was 1.6 gm/cc. In the surface horizons of the soil, bulk density fell to about half this value throughout the sequence. Most of this change occurred in the first 500 years.

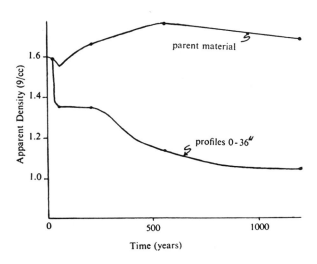

(2) Fort Bragg Dune Sequence.

The bulk density changes of upper soil horizons from the very young (shrub-grass) to the mature (pine-spruce) and old (redwood) profiles is most striking. Initially the sand had a bulk density of about 1.6 gm/cc., but this had fallen to about 1.0-1.2 gm/cc. during the pine-spruce dominance and to 0.7 gm/cc. in the redwood soils. Examples of depth functions typical of the various stages are given below.

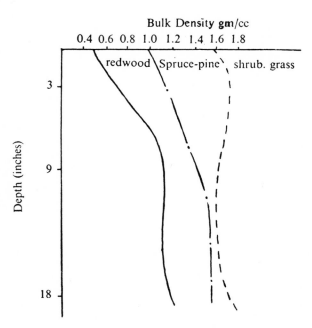

(3) Glacier Bay Sequence.

The general effects of bulk density changes in relation to vegetation stage are shown in the depth functions below. Five to ten years is the Pioneer stage; 70 years, the Alder thicket stage; and the 122- and 182 years profiles, the Spruce forest stage.

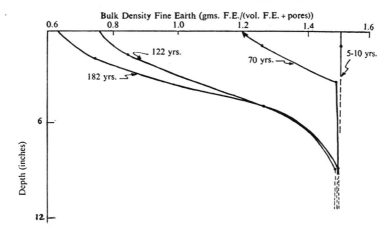

Soil Development as a Function of Floral Regions

The third method of evaluating some of the influences of vegetation—the comparative method between different floral regions—offers a great number of possibilities, but has been neglected. The main care to be taken in this type of investigation is to determine that the differences being measured truly relate to plant differences, and not to other soil-forming factors. Stephens (6), using a not very rigorous approach of this type, has ascribed many of the differences between Australian, American, and European Great Soil Groups to differences in the biotic factor.

SUMMARY AND CONCLUSIONS

It is very difficult to isolate the role of plants in soil genesis. However, some of these difficulties can be overcome, at least in broad manner, to show some of the major plant effects. From the studies that have already been made, it is apparent that plants affect most directly and rapidly the properties of organic carbon, total nitrogen, pH, and bulk density. All of these properties may be very rapidly changed during the early stages of plant colonization and development.

Organic carbon increases rapidly in the early stages of all the sequences studied. In all probability, it continues to do so throughout, and the apparent decline or approach to steady-state conditions in some of our systems is probably due to fire history or investigational errors. One would logically expect continued accumulation and a progressive downward extension of carbon in the soil over the relatively short time ranges of all these investigations.

The total nitrogen accumulation is especially interesting. In all of the systems investigated there is a very rapid build-up during the pioneer and early stages of the succession. This probably means that a number of species characteristic of these stages has some micro-organism associations leading to nitrogen fixation (supported by the occurrence of nodules on *Dryas, Sheperdis, Alnus,* etc.). This feature may well be a characteristic of pioneer communities. As the successions develop, there is a decline in the rate of nitrogen accumulation, indeed during subsequent stages there may even be a loss from the mineral soil-forest floor subsystems.

Soil reaction changes were pronounced in all the sequences. Here again the changes were very rapid during the early stages and were clearly shown to be related to the presence of vegetation. Indeed the purely leaching effect, as demonstrated by bare surfaces, was very slight. The effect of alder in reducing the pH of the surface soil from 8.0 to 5.0 in 30 years is truly remarkable. After the very rapid early changes of pH, further change is fairly slow.

Bulk density is a property that is very markedly modified by the presence of plants. In all our investigations there has been a very rapid change from initial values of about 1.5-1.6 gm/cc. to final values as low as 0.5 gm/cc. in the surface horizons. Undoubtedly the major factor in this process is the presence of plant roots and residues and their associated microfloras. It is because these are concentrated in the upper horizons that the most pronounced effects are in the surface zones. The overall result is a loosening up of the surface soil—a process which then extends downwards towards the B horizon.

The general results from the investigations outlined, and their consistency, show the value of one method approach to studying the plant factor in pedogenesis. Both of the other methods suggested, the experimental method and that of a comparison of the effects of different floras, must also be employed if we are to get much of an understanding of the role of plants in soil genesis.

Unfortunately no methods can be suggested which can be used with older polygenetic soils, and we are beginning to believe that most soils are polygenetic.

REFERENCES

1. Jenny, H. 1939, Factors in Soil Formation. McGraw Book Co.
2. Dickson, B. A., and Crocker, R. L. 1953. A chronosequence of soils and vegetation near Mt. Shasta, California. Jour. Soil Sci. 4(2):142-154.
3. .... 1954. A chronosequence of soils and vegetation near Mt. Shasta, California. II. Jour. Soil Sci. 5(2):173-191.
4. Crocker, R. L., and Major, J., 1955, Soil Development in relation to Vegetation and Surface Age at Glacier Bay, Alaska. Jour. of Ecol. 43(2):427-448.
5. .... and Zinke, P., 1955, A Soil and Vegetation Sequence in the Fort Bragg Area, California, unpublished.
6. Stephens, C. G., 1946, Comparative Morphology and Genetic Relationships of certain Australian, North American and European Soils. Jour. Soil Sci. 1(2):123-149.

EFFECTS OF CERTAIN ANIMALS THAT LIVE IN SOILS

James Thorp

Located at the University of Nebraska, Professor Thorp is Regional Inspector of Soil Surveys for the Great Plains, Division of Soils, USDA. He has taught in Puerto Rico, in China (at Nanking University), and at Earlham College, his alma mater.

In discussing the biologic factor of soil formation, textbook authors are accustomed to lay great emphasis on vegetation as it affects soil profile development and to give less space to the influence of animal populations in soils. During many years of field work I have been repeatedly impressed by the extent and magnitude of the modifications of soil profiles accomplished by animals that live in the soil. The effects superficially most noticeable are those brought about by the larger animals, such as burrowing rodents and carnivores; but in many places the smaller animals, such as worms, insects, spiders, crustaceans, and myriapods have made very marked changes in soils and have affected their characteristics more fundamentally than have the larger animals. Animals that live in the soil range in size from minute protozoa, visible only under the microscope, to burrowing mammals of quite large size (wolves, badgers, and large rodents). No attempt will be made to discuss in detail the effects of protozoa on the conversion of raw organic matter into humus, and, of course, effects of these animals on the microstructure of soils. Some conception of the importance of the microbial population (both protozoa and microscopic plants) may be seen in F. Garbrecht's note entitled *¿Cuanto pesan los microbios de la tierra?* ("How much do the soil microbes weigh?") He estimates a total weight of 2,000 grams per square meter of cultivated soil to a depth of 20 centimeters, or a little less than 18,000 pounds (9 tons) per acre in the topmost 8 inches. Of course, the weight of the microbial population will vary greatly with the kind of soil and other factors.

The importance of microscopic life is also brought out by A. G. Norman, who states that a substantial portion of the humified organic matter in soils is composed of the dead remains of microorganisms that feed on the residues of higher forms of life.

Among the most important visible animals that affect soil profile development are very small insects, such as springtails, mites, and celaphids that are abundant in the raw humus of the podzol soils; ants and termites, very active in many soils of the world; many small crustaceans, such as wood lice, or sow bugs; and millipedes, centipedes, and various kinds of spiders. Springtails and other minute insects consume the raw humus of the forests and convert it into new types of humus, the details of which have been covered by other workers (T. H. Eaton, Jr., and R. F. Chandler, Jr.) and need not be discussed here.

Reproduced with permission from *The Scientific Monthly,* Vol. 68, 1949, p. 180-191. Published by the American Association for the Advancement of Science, Washington, D. C. 20005, USA.

EARTHWORMS

In forested and cultivated soils, especially in soils of medium to heavy texture and where vegetation is of a type that is appetizing to them, earthworms are very active in converting raw vegetable matter to humus and in mixing the humus with the mineral portion of the soil. In many forested areas, and also in some grasslands, the superficial several inches of the soil consist almost entirely of earthworm castings that have given the soil a characteristic granular or crumb structure sometimes called "earthworm mull." This does not imply that all granular and crumb structures are due to the action of earthworms or other animals, but it is true that much soil structure originates in this way. In forested soils of some areas, especially in those of medium to clayey textures, it is conservatively estimated that 500-2,500 tons per acre of soil have been modified in structure and organic content by earthworms alone. Darwin estimated deposits of earthworm castings at rates of 7.5-18 tons per acre per year. A. C. Evans and W. J. Guild found up to 11.5 tons of castings per acre per year in pasture land, clay-with-flints soils, at Rothamsted Experimental Station, England. The same authors quote C. Beaugé as finding 107 tons of castings per acre deposited in the valley of the White Nile during one six-month rainy season.

In the spring of 1919, the earthworms were so abundant in the rendzina soils of the military parade grounds at Dôle du Jura in eastern France that the ground was almost covered with fresh castings. When soils were saturated following heavy rains, the worms were forced to the surface by the water and could be heard withdrawing hastily into their burrows as one walked across the field.

Earthworms not only mix mineral matter with humus at the surface, but they also carry organic matter deep into the subsoil horizons and parent material when they retreat downward with the moisture during dry weather. Incidental to carrying organic matter to deep horizons and fresh minerals to surface horizons, they leave tunnels behind them that facilitate movement of water through the soils. In the course of studying cross sections of soils, I have seen water drip from earthworm burrows 2-3 feet below the surface when a pit was dug in Miami loam in southern Michigan soon after a rainstorm. Earthworm tunnels become coated with organic and mineral colloids and in many places provide passage space for roots through soil materials that are otherwise rather dense.

Earthworms have interesting methods of collecting food in forested areas. Apparently, Darwin was the first of recent times to discuss this subject in detail, and considerable work has been done still more recently on the Harvard and Yale forests in New England, in Ohio State University, and in England and other parts of Europe. These studies show that earthworms like to concentrate their activities in areas where plants are to their liking. For example, they like especially well the fallen leaves of ash, hickory, tulip tree, dogwood, large-toothed aspen, and several other species. Some kinds of earthworms go out during the night to gather up their favorite kinds of leaves and drag them to the mouths of their tunnels. They pull the leaves partially into the tunnels or heap them up around the tunnel mouths to form "earthworm middens" composed of petioles and other leaf fragments mixed with the feces of the earthworms (Fig. 1). In the early stages of development, middens comprise chiefly mounds of entire leaves and other plant remains.

Fig. 1—*Left:* Earthworm middens on stony brown forest soil in the Yale Forest. Note tangled petioles heaped around burrows between rocks. Pencil, lower right, gives the scale. *Right:* Middens composed of earthworm feces and petioles of sugar maple, ash, tulip poplar, and linden leaves. Wawaka silt loam, a gray-brown podzolic soil, at Earlham College, Richmond, Ind.

Marked differences in organic content and structure of upper horizons of soils developed under hardwood cover versus those developed under coniferous forest are ascribed in part by P. R. Gast to differences in kind and degree of activity of the soil fauna. Referring to J. W. Johnston, he makes this statement relative to the preferences of earthworms for different kinds of leaves:

"Of importance here are the observations by Johnston on the food preferences of the angleworm. He found that of six species studied in laboratory feeding experiments, the large-toothed aspen, white ash, and basswood were accepted immediately in that order. Sugar maple and red maple were taken less avidly; the latter was not entirely consumed. Red oak was not eaten."

It is indicated further that white-pine needles, in the field tests, were only 30 percent decomposed two seasons after falling, the assumption being that the earthworms probably refused them as food, and that other biotic factors were responsible for their slow disappearance.

B. G. Griffith and others found earthworms were always associated with soils of good tilth under hardwood forest cover and were generally absent in the soils of pine forests. Exception noted was in a twenty-year-old forest where the soil was formerly well cultivated.

Abundant earthworm middens were observed at Quaker Hill and at Earlham College (Fig. 1), Richmond, Indiana, in the autumn of 1941 and again in June 1947. They were especially plentiful under ash and sugar-maple trees on Fox silt loam, deep phase, that had once been cultivated. Under one large maple tree, at Quaker Hill in June 1947, my nephew and I counted 27-35 middens per square yard, or roughly 145,000 per acre. The middens were about 3/4 by weight of worm feces and about 1/4 by weight of maple-leaf petioles and grass stems. The total moist material in the middens from one square yard weighed 3.25 pounds—a rate of more than 15,500 pounds per acre. This material represented the work of the worms in late fall 1946 and spring 1947. In this period of about eight months the worms could have been active for no more than five months.

In Lewis Woods, a remnant of virgin hardwood forest in Wayne County, Indiana, I. C. Brown and I noted in 1939 that the Miami silt loam there has a crumb-mull horizon, 1-4 inches thick, made up largely of earthworm castings and feces of other small invertebrates. Organic matter was high in this layer (6.2 percent), and the reaction was only slightly acid. Assuming an average thickness of 2 inches, this mull horizon represents about 56,000 pounds (28 tons) per acre total, of which about 3,500 pounds (1.75 tons) is humified organic matter, totally reworked by earthworms and their associates. This topmost 2 inches is only a fraction of the total soil in the profile that has been permeated and mixed by earthworms.

It is not necessary to assume that the worms have added any new material to the soil in this instance; but it is obvious that they have facilitated the conversion of raw organic matter to humus and have been instrumental in mixing the humus with soil minerals. Homer Hopp and H. T. Hopkins have demonstrated that earthworms add little or no new plant nutrients to the soil in which they live and grow; but their dead bodies, if added in large quantities to infertile soils, will nourish the plants in these soils.

In an oak-hickory forest of northern Indiana I once noticed that the earthworms had selected hickory leaves to the almost complete exclusion of oak leaves. In June or early July practically all the dead leaves remaining scattered evenly over the surface in this forest were of oak; the earthworm middens were made up almost entirely of petioles and other remnants of hickory leaves mixed with worm feces. The worms have a similar appetite for ash, dogwood, and some other species. Certain earthworms will eat oak, pine, and other leaves, but generally are not very abundant in the dense oak and pine forests of eastern United States.

There is evidence, not yet fully conclusive, that the palatability of vegetation to earthworms depends somewhat on the mineralogical composition of the soils. Well-nourished trees seem to have more palatable leaves than undernourished ones of the same species.

Earthworms are also very active in some prairie and chernozem soils, where they play an important part in mixing organic and mineral soil constituents and in the development of granular or crumb structure. Even in desert regions they soon become abundant when moisture conditions and food supply are improved by irrigation.

Earthworms do not always improve the structure of soils they inhabit, however. For example, A. Leahey, Head of the Dominion Soil Survey Staff of Canada, told me that soils of Alberta and Manitoba were damaged by earthworms that were introduced. Under virgin conditions, the highly fertile chernozem soils of Alberta, Saskatchewan, and Manitoba had no indigenous earthworms. Dr. Leahey made the following statement on the subject in a letter dated November 22, 1948:

"About 1931 I visited a farm north of Edmonton with J. D. Newton. While there, the lady of the house asked us how to get rid of earthworms, as they had ruined one garden for her in a matter of two years and were rapidly ruining a second one. Her story was that the earthworms had turned the soil into a sticky, plastic mess. The soil was a Chernozem clay which normally had a good (granular) structure. Earthworms had a deleterious effect on the physical condition of the Chernozem clay soils. Instead of being improved, the granular friable clay broke down into a sticky mass that was extremely difficult to manage after the earthworms had multiplied sufficiently to have a noticeable effect."

R. L. Pendleton has made some observations on the activities of earthworms in certain tropical areas. In Siam, for example, earthworms attain a length of a foot or two and seem to prefer to live in imperfectly drained soils that have been highly leached and are very infertile. In contrast, dense colonization by earthworms in the United States usually is interpreted to be a fair indication of medium to high soil fertility. Pendleton states that the earthworm mounds of Siam, composed mainly of the feces of these animals, are as much as a foot high and a yard across. Fresh earthworm mounds may be chimneylike in form, similar to those built by crawfish and crabs in the United States and the West Indies.

W. M. Johnson writes (October 21, 1948) from Colombia, South America:

" . . . you will be interested in the macro-fauna of these soils . . ., especially the earthworms. There are at least two species in the region, some relatively small that build towers up to about three inches high, with their casts—like miniature crawfish deposits; the other worms are big, up to a half inch in diameter and at least 18 inches long. Photos show the earth's surface to a depth of 3/4 inch completely covered with casts from these big worms."

He goes on to say that, in spite of their hardness, the casts break down rapidly when the rains come, and he infers that the fresh castings are all of the current season. With two wet and two dry seasons each year, one may assume that the worms till the soil to a depth of at least 1.5 inches each year.

INFLUENCE OF ANTS

Estimates of insect and other invertebrate fauna populations at Rothamsted by H. M. Morris gave a total invertebrate fauna of 15,100,000 per acre of land that received 14 tons of manure per year for about seventy-eight years. Of this population, 7,720,000 were insects. A plot that had been unfertilized for eighty-two years had an invertebrate fauna population of 4,950,000, including 2,470,000 insects. Observations on a pasture plot in Cheshire by the same author revealed an insect population of 3,586,088. These figures give an idea of the order of magnitude of animal populations in soils. Most soil invertebrates are short-lived; a large proportion of them die and return the organic matter of their bodies to the soil within a year and in some instances in much less than a year. It takes a large number of most insects or of the other very small invertebrates to make a weight equal to one field mouse, but the vast numbers and rapid turnover of population among the invertebrates probably more than offset the differences in weight of individuals.

The ants are among the most interesting of the insects, so far as soil formation is concerned. They are of many different species, each of which has its characteristic habits and habitats. W. P. Taylor and W. G. McGinnies state:

"Everyone is familiar with the earthworm's outstanding reputation as a soil maker. That other animals play an important role is doubtless not so widely appreciated. Yet Shaler in his paper on "The Origin and Nature of Soils" says that ants produce a far greater effect on soils than earthworms. Shaler thinks the vertebrates exercise an influence on the soil perhaps as great as that of all their lower kindred."

The leaf-cutting ants march for long distances, cut out fragments of leaves and stems of plants that are to be used directly or indirectly for food, carry them back home, and store them in underground chambers. Here they are used to produce fungus that is in turn used for food. In this way organic matter, both in the forests of Central America and in the brushlands of northern Mexico and Texas, is incorporated in the soil and converted to humus through the activities of fungi (planted by the ants) and by the deposition of fecal matter by the ants themselves. In a private communication, R. L. Pendleton reports that mounds of these leaf-cutter ants in Central America frequently are as much as 15 feet across and 3 feet high. I have seen smaller ones in the brushy lands of south Texas. The mere tunneling operations of these ants have the effect of moving mineral material from one horizon of the soil to another, and after the anthills are abandoned the chambers provide channels for rapid water penetration to the deeper subsoil horizons.

Throughout the greater part of the subhumid and semiarid portions of the United States there is a large red ant (perhaps of more than one species) which builds a chambered nest beneath the surface of the ground and a conical mound of excavated material above the surface. The mound is riddled by chambers used for the storage of food and the rearing of the young. Many who read this doubtless are familiar

Fig. 2— *Top, left:* Anthill and cleared space in desert soil of southwestern Utah. Plants on rim of 12-foot cleared circle are slightly larger than those beyond because of reduced competition for water. *Right:* In the ponderosa pine forests of the West, ants sometimes build their nests almost entirely of pine needles, with a minimum of mineral material. When these are abandoned, they leave a concentrated supply of organic matter on the soil.

Center, left: Anthill on sierozem soil in Sevier County, Utah. *Right:* Close-up of same anthill, showing fine-gravel roof with which the ants protect their homes. The fine gravel is eventually incorporated into the A soil horizon.

Bottom, left: Geologist's hammer near center shows, by comparison, small size of one kind of anthill scattered through the United States. (Anthills outlined in black for clarity.) It was estimated that small ants piled 500 pounds per acre of sandy material on the surface at Archer, Wyo., within a few days' time. *Right:* Melting snow reveals "roll" of earth made by small burrowing mammals in the Medicine Bow Mountains, Wyo. Rolls soon break down and are incorporated in the A horizon.

with the anthills scattered over tremendous areas of the Great Plains and in the deserts and intermountain valleys of the United States. Somewhat similar anthills occur in the humid sections of the country. I have made conservative estimates of the amount of soil material in the anthills of representative areas of the Western plains. The figures for the amount of material affected are based on a conservative estimate of the average-sized anthill and of the number of anthills per acre in some parts of the country. The anthill in the photograph (Fig. 2) has a volume of approximately 1.9 cubic feet of fine earth mixed with coarse sand and fine gravel brought up from subsoil horizons. Some of the fine gravel may have been gathered from the surface in near-by areas. It is used by the ants to form a sort of pavement or roof over the hill. If we estimate that one cubic foot of earth will weigh approxi-

Fig 3—Vertical aerial. photo of ant-infested grassland area southeast of Denver. Minute light-gray specks represent circular bare spots where ants have harvested all vegetation. The 40 acres with cross lines are estimated to have about 400 anthills.

mately 90 pounds, then the individual anthill will probably contain about 170 pounds of soil material. If, as is not uncommon, there are 20 anthills per acre, about 3,400 pounds of earth will have been piled up on the surface by the ants. This material is removed largely from subsoil horizons, with the net effect of rejuvenating the soil by bringing up fresh material to the surface from beneath. To be sure, the number of large anthills in much of the Great Plains is less than 20 per acre, but it is also true that some anthills are destroyed every year and new ones are built on different sites so that the effects over a long period of years are very great. In addition, many small anthills built by other species, are not counted in this estimate (Fig. 2).

An aerial photograph (Fig. 3) taken in Kiowa County, Colorado, shows about 400 anthills on a selected 40 acres of land. Doubtless many exist that do not show on the photograph. An oblique aerial photograph (Fig. 4) taken northeast of Den-

Fig. 4—Oblique aerial photo shows circular anthill clearings, 6-20 feet in diameter, on brown soils northeast of Denver.

ver, gives a closer view of clearings made by ants. The hills are visible on aerial photographs because the ants have cut all vegetation from around each hill in a circle, the diameter of which varies ordinarily from hill to hill from about 6 to 20 feet. The bare earth reflects the light and makes a whitish spot on the picture in each case. In some instances the hills are so close together that the bare spots merge and it is impossible to distinguish one hill from the next on small-scale aerial photographs. The largest mound I have observed so far was seen in the semidesert country of Duchesne County, Utah, where an anthill estimated to contain 300 pounds of earth was surrounded by a cleared area 40 feet in diameter.

Ants seem to prefer somewhat sandy and fine gravelly soil materials, probably because they can find suitable gravel for roofing their hills. I have seen anthills on the Houston and Wilson soils of Texas, however, where practically no satisfactory grit is available. There, the ants bring up balls of limy material from below ground and deposit them at the surface in lieu of fine gravel, thus tending to maintain a neutral or alkaline reaction in the surface soil.

Fragments of vegetation cut from the surface and removed to the anthills are eaten by the ants or stored in bins or granaries for future use. Commonly, great masses of seeds are stored in some of the bins of these anthills, presumably for use during the season of the year when vegetation is scarce. These materials are converted gradually to humus in the soil through the action of fungi and digestion by ants. The earth in anthills built on fine-textured soils frequently has a fine-granular structure induced by the activity of earthworms that feed on the organic material stored by the ants.

Clearings made by ants leave the soil exposed to erosive effects of wind and rain. On the older anthills one finds a slight depression around the mound itself where wind and water have removed the soil material; and small mounds of earth have collected around clumps of vegetation in the vicinity (Fig. 2). In this way soils are truncated and rejuvenated, little by little.

TERMITES

Termites have been studied to a limited extent by various soil scientists, especially in the tropics. G. Milne, of Africa (now deceased), Pendleton, formerly of Thailand, and G. Aubert have done some work on this problem. Some of the termite mounds are as much as 6-10 feet high and perhaps as much as 20-40 feet across. The termites gather vegetation from the soils of the neighborhood and carry it to their nests, where it is used for food either directly or for the cultivation of edible fungus. On some of the old strongly leached and weathered soils of East Africa, Milne found that soils on certain plains where termites were active contained only a small trace of calcium, but that the soils in the termite mounds were very high in calcium; in fact, some of the mounds were calcareous throughout and had great masses of impure limestone *(caliche)* at the centers, which may possibly have formed through the hardening of lime left as a deposit from the waste matter from plants. It seems a reasonable hypothesis that over periods of centuries, and perhaps hundreds of centuries, the termites have gradually accumulated in their mounds practically all the calcium from the soils of the neighborhood by harvesting nearly all the vegetation that came up and carrying the calcium to the mounds in the form of organic matter. Milne suggests a few alternative hypotheses for the accumulation of lime carbonate, one of which is that the termites bring it up from deep substrata to use as cement.

Pendleton has raised the question, without solving it, as to why the termite mounds contain such a large amount of calcium without any apparent similar accumulation of phosphates. He reports that in Thailand a practical advantage was taken of the work of termites in accumulating calcium in the soils. Over a large area on the plains of Thailand most soils have been so highly leached and weathered that crop production on them is almost out of the question without heavy fertilization. The soil supports only a scrubby growth of forest trees except in the vicinity of these ancient termite mounds. Here the pH is higher and the fertility is sufficient for the people to use the earth in the mounds as soil, and they can raise various food crops and tobacco with little fertilization. The termite mounds are partially leveled and used for farming, whereas the ancient soils between them are used only when heavy fertilization is possible. The process of leveling must be spread over a period of years in order to incorporate organic matter in the material of the lower horizons of the mounds. One could mention further that termites in the Temperate Zone of the United States perform the function of converting wood into humus in the forests and, unfortunately, in our homes also if we are not watchful.

Milne noted that native farmers in East Africa took similar advantage of fertility stored in termite mounds. He calculated that the mounds contain enough calcium carbonate to make a heavy lime application to the leached soils between them and recommended this as an agronomic amendment for some of the infertile soils of the region.

In a personal communication Aubert described termite mounds of several types in the French Sudan, French West Africa, and along the Ivory Coast. He states that some mounds contain concentrated lime carbonate, like those described by Milne, and some do not. All representatives from Africa at the 1948 Commonwealth Conference on tropical soils at Rothamsted mentioned the activities of termites in soils of Africa.

Wood lice, millipedes, centipedes, and spiders all affect soil profile development, especially to the extent that they consume organic matter of various sorts and convert it into other forms of humus. In forest soils the A_1 horizon in many places consists almost entirely of feces of these small animals mixed with those of earthworms. Some of this material retains its original form for a long time and imparts to the soil a characteristic and persistent very fine granular structure.

CRUSTACEANS

Large crustaceans, including crabs and crawfish, are very active in soils where the water table is within a few inches or a few feet of the surface. I have observed the activity of land crabs, especially in the West Indies, where they inhabit low swampy and marshy areas adjacent to the sea and build tunnels from the surface down to the water table. At night they bring up balls of earth tunneled from beneath and deposit them in the form of chimneys at the surface. In sugar-cane fields cultivation breaks down the chimneys and partially refills the burrows, which are cleared out again the night after the land is cultivated. An enormous amount of earth is thus kept in circulation. The crabs feed on vegetation, and possibly on carrion, and of course mix this organic matter with the soils. Incidentally, they are a great pest in cane fields and are poisoned systematically by agriculturists, or are trapped and used as food by the people.

Crawfish range in size from very small up to perhaps as much as one foot long. They are active in poorly and imperfectly drained soils from the Gulf Coast north to the Canadian border. They are especially active in the southern part of the gray-brown podzolic soils zone and throughout the zone of red and yellow podzolic soils, but they confine their activities largely to soils of the planosol, wiesenboden, and half bog groups. They build chimneys on the surface much like those made by the crabs. Chimneys on planosols in southern Indiana measure as much as 8 inches in height and about 4-8 inches in diameter (Fig. 5). The crawfish work at night, bringing mud from deep underground. Some of the vertical tunnels beneath the chimneys are as much as 15 feet deep, because the crawfish must have contact with the water table at all times. Their tunnels penetrate the clay pans of the planosols, facilitating upward and downward movement of water, and they bring fresh soil material to the surface from great depths. The importance of their activities can be estimated from the photographs in Figure 5.

In one area studied in southern Indiana, a large chimney occurred about every 5-10 feet in each direction; all the chimneys had been built by the crawfish after the corn had been planted (Fig. 5). At the time this area was studied the corn was just ready for its first cultivation. Tunnels to the water table were about 10 feet deep. If one examines a field in which all chimneys have been destroyed by cultivation,

Fig. 5—*Upper left:* Crawfish chimneys in fields of very young corn, on Robinson silt loam, a planosol of southern Indiana. (Photo retouched to accentuate three of the chimneys.) *Upper right:* Close-up of two crawfish chimneys.

Lower left: Abundant small crawfish chimneys on poorly drained Plummer fine sandy loam, Beauregard Parish, La. Scale is 7 inches long. *Lower right:* Single crawfish chimney on Caddo fine sandy loam, same Parish.

one will find that a whole crop of new chimneys will have been built up a few days after the field is cultivated, as in this instance. The activity is especially great during the spring when there is plenty of moisture in the soil. Where crawfish chimneys weigh 3 pounds each and 625 of them occur per acre (1 every 8 feet in each direction), the total weight of earth heaped on the surface would be a little less than one ton per acre. If chimneys occur every 5 feet in each direction, the total weight would be a little less than 2.5 tons per acre. Perhaps the chimneys would be destroyed and rebuilt three or four times in one season, and 3-10 tons of earth would be moved. In 1946 E. Templin, H. Oakes, and I noted small crawfish chimneys on Beaumont clay in east Texas spaced so closely that there were 20,000-50,000 of them per acre in areas of greatest concentration. The water table was only a foot or two below the surface.

One lasting effect of the activities of crawfish and crabs can be seen in very old soil profiles in certain red podzolic soils of southern Alabama. At Grand Bay, in Mobile County, a group of us studied a railroad cut through a low ridge on which there was a red podzolic soil with an incipient lateritic hardpan 2 or 3 feet below the surface. In this cut were several "fossilized" crawfish tunnels which extended from approximately the surface to a depth of 6 or 8 feet in the cut. The tunnels were lined with hard limonite to a thickness of about 0.5 inch, and the interiors were filled with clayey material. Each tunnel terminated at the bottom in an ovate chamber about 6 x 10 inches. It must have been thousands of years since this particular set of tunnels was made by the crawfish, because the water table has long since retreated many feet below the bottoms of the chambers. The fossil crawfish tunnels are in a remnant of a former ground-water laterite soil which formerly extended over a considerably greater area than it now does. In recent times it has been converted to a red podzolic soil following a lowering of the water table brought about by dissection of the land. The soil occurs on the highest Pleistocene terrace remnant.

OTHER ANIMALS

Burrowing mammals and, in some instances, amphibia and lizards are important factors in the rejuvenation of soils in many parts of the world. Their activities are especially noticeable in grassland areas of the Great Plains and in the deserts and semideserts where prairie dogs, gophers, and other rodents are very abundant and active; but the total effects are probably just as great, though less noticeable, in forested areas. These animals burrow through the entire *solum* and well into the parent material or substrata beneath the soil, and parts of all horizons and underlying materials are brought to the surface and there thrown out as a heterogeneous mixture. In some prairie-dog towns almost the entire soil has been completely churned and rejuvenated by the activities of the animals. Prairie dogs frequently build their towns in places where subsoil horizons are clayey, and in some instances they select areas of solonetz or solodized solonetz for their homes. Their activities tend to destroy parts of the clayey layers and to heap fresh limy or salty material on the surface.

Fig. 6—Profile of Marshall silt loam, a prairie soil of southwestern Iowa, shows dark blotches in deep subsoil where a gopher burrow has been filled by dark earth from the A horizon.

Figure 6 shows how rodent burrows in deep subsoils become filled with dark soil from surface soils of the prairie, chernozem, and chestnut soils zones. J. E. Weaver, of the Botany Department, University of Nebraska, tells me that he always finds burrow fillings in excavations made for studying grass roots in soils of the Great Plains. This checks with the experience of soil scientists in the same region. Some of the small burrowing mammals bring soil material to the surface and use it as back-fill when they burrow in deep snow. These peculiar "rolls" of material are exposed when the snow melts, and break down to form "ribbons" of light-colored subsoil material on the darker surface soils (Fig. 2).

In May 1947, L. T. Alexander and I estimated roughly the amount of earth that burrowing animals had piled on the surface or mixed with the surface soil of Rago silt loam at the Dry Land Experiment Farm, Akron, Colorado. We measured off a 4-acre plot of land in a virgin pasture where sandy and gravelly mounds marked the former dwellings of prairie dogs and badgers (Fig. 7). Sixty-nine mounds were counted in the 4 acres, an average of about 17 per acre. A deep excavation showed the original soil to be developed from calcareous loess, of silt loam texture, that overlies strata of gravel and sand at depths ranging approximately 6-10 feet. In the course of soil formation the lime carbonate has been leached out to depths ranging from about 14 to 20 inches. That all the burrows had reached down as far as the sand and gravel layers is proved by the preponderance of sand and gravel in the mounds. The undisturbed soil contains no gravel or medium- or coarse-grained sand.

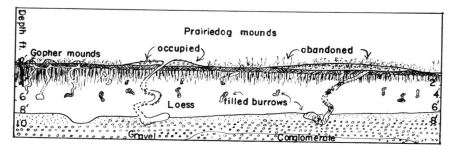

Fig. 7—Diagram of Rago soils on virgin pasture land of the Dry Land Experimental Station, Akron, Colo. Rago silt loam occurs between the mounds built by small mammals. Soils on the mounds contain a mixture of silt loam with sand and gravel brought up from deep substrata. In adjacent cultivated fields most of the mounds and intervening soils have been mixed to form Rago loam. Note dark earth in vacated burrows.

Two of the several large mounds measured proved to have a maximum thickness of 18-19 inches and a diameter of 24 feet. For convenience in estimating the volume it was assumed that the mounds were conical in shape, an assumption that will give a conservative estimate of the volume of the mound. The volume of a cone is calculated as follows:

$$V = \pi \frac{r^2 \times h}{3}$$

where r is the radius of the base and h is the altitude of the cone; substituting measured values for r and h,

$$V = \frac{\frac{22}{7} \times 12^2 \times 1.5}{3} = 226.3 \text{ cubic feet.}$$

One cubic foot of dry loam or sandy loam, with some gravel, will weigh about 100 pounds. The weight of the mound is therefore about 22,630 pounds, or 11.3 tons. By similar methods, weights of mounds of several different sizes were estimated to range from a minimum of 210 to the maximum of 22,630 pounds given above.

Estimating the average size at 3,770 pounds, we obtain a total weight of 130 tons for 4 acres, or 32.5 tons for 1 acre. By another method of estimating we get a higher figure (Table 1). This is equivalent to 156 tons on 4 acres, or 39 tons on 1 acre. Thus we may say conservatively that the burrowing animals have brought

Table 1

No. of Mounds of Given Size	Weight of Each Mound	Total Weight in Pounds
10	22,600	226,000
15	3,850	57,750
24	1,000	24,000
20	210	4,200
		311,950

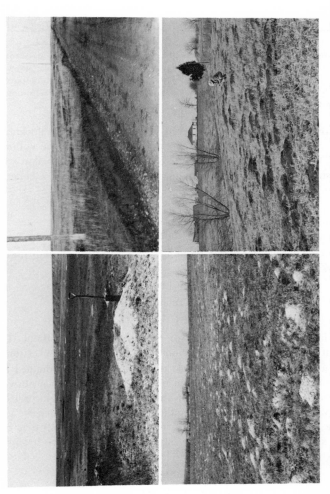

Fig. 8—*Upper left:* Prairie-dog mound, Akron, Colo., about 8 feet in diameter and 10 inches high. Mound contains much sand and gravel, whereas surrounding soils do not. *Upper right:* Low, broad mounds on chestnut soils on a high terrace, 10 miles west of Wisdom, Beaverhead Co., Mont. An intimate mixture of silt loam, gravel, and organic material, the mounds resemble the lower of the Mima mounds of western Washington. Burrowing rodents are very active in them.

Lower right: Small gopher mounds southeast of Lincoln, Nebr., made in autumn 1947. Total earth piled on surface is about 56,000 pounds (28 tons) per acre. (Photo by W. M. Johnson.) *Lower left:* Gopher mounds in deep sandy soils of Cherokee County, Texas, tentatively correlated as Eustis loamy fine sand. About one third of surface soil has been "plowed" in one season (fall-winter, 1947-48).

30-40 tons of mixed sand, gravel, and subsoil material to the surface. Much of this came from a depth of 8-10 feet underground.

Near the same place, we counted 50 fresh mounds in a prairie-dog town on one measured acre of land (Fig. 8). The mounds ranged from 2 feet in diameter, 6 inches high, to 18 feet in diameter, 18 inches high. Some of these mounds were largely gravel and sand; others, where the loess is thicker, were almost entirely of yellowish calcareous loess of silt loam texture. On this acre of land a calculation based on the weight of an average mound gives a total of about 22.5 tons of earth piled on the surface.

On this field the prairie dogs were keeping the grass, largely western wheat (*Agropyron smithii*) and blue grama (*Bouteloua gracilis*), cut close to the ground. Heaps of rodent manure were piled around the borders of the mounds; and these, with the urine from the animals, were serving to fertilize the next crop of grass. One of the characteristic phenomena around old mounds is the dark-green color of the vegetation—evidence of abundant nitrogen.

Surface soils on about one third of the experimental plots at the Akron Station have been converted from silt loam to loam through the activities of rodents and badgers. Apparently a colony of these animals lived here before the station was established. Subsequent tillage operations have thoroughly mixed the gravelly and sandy materials of the mounds with the original silt loam surface soil. The thickness of loess and soil over stratified sand and gravel on the plots, where measured, ranged from about 6 to about 10 feet.

The common pocket gophers and ground squirrels of the Great Plains appear in large colonies from time to time. In 1947 Earl D. Fowler and I made some measurements of earth moved in a few weeks by a colony of gophers at Lincoln, Nebraska (Fig. 8). We calculated that 56,000 pounds, or 28 tons, of earth had been piled up by these animals on one acre. The smaller mounds weighed about 15-20 pounds each, and the largest was estimated to weigh 400 pounds.

This brings to mind the paper by V. B. Scheffer on the Mima mounds of western Washington. Scheffer suggests that these phenomenal mounds, and possibly the famous San Joaquin soil mounds of California, are the work of gophers. R. C. Roberts and W. J. Leighty, of the Division of Soil Survey, and L. C. Wheeting, of Washington State College, visited the mounds with me in September 1948, and we found it difficult to suggest any other satisfactory explanation for their development. The soils on these mounds are very gravelly and contain a high percentage of black humified organic matter. The black horizon is more than 30 inches thick on many of the mounds, which is much thicker than in most prairie soils of normal development, and lends weight to Scheffer's hypothesis. Figure 8 shows some mounds in Montana that are similar to the lower of the Mima mounds.

Where rodent colonies become too dense, most of the vegetation is destroyed and erosion may be accelerated. A particularly noteworthy example of this was seen on the Tibetan borderland and reported to me by a Chinese scientist, C. C. Ku, who traveled in that region. In this area certain burrowing rodents had become so abundant that all the soil was honeycombed by their burrows. Yaks and other domesticated animals, pastured in these areas, broke through the tunnels and exposed the soils to wind and water erosion. In some places all the soil was swept from large areas of hillsides in this region.

With reference to burrowing animals, Taylor states:

Mice and other burrowing species, notably the pocket gopher, in many of the forests of the West are continually cultivating the soil, letting in water and air, carrying down vegetation, bringing up earth, in general helping the great soil complex to function. There is little doubt that all these creatures have their place in maintaining the natural equilibrium between soil, climate, plants, and animals.

Field and woods mice, moles, and shrews have intricate systems of tunnels in the soils of forests and grasslands. Ground squirrels and gophers are so abundant in some places (e.g., south Texas) as to turn over 15-20 percent of the surface soils in a single season. Kangaroo rats and other burrowing mammals in desert and semi-desert regions either build mounds 6-10 feet in diameter and 1-3 feet in height, or build their homes in sandy mounds developed by wind action. In some places the colonies of the kangaroo rats make up fully 30 percent of the land surface. Taylor records as much as 12.5 pounds of sections, crowns, and seeds of grasses stored by kangaroo rats in one burrow.

One might go on to enumerate many other kinds of animals that burrow in the soils and bequeath their waste materials and dead bodies to the organic component. Suffice it to say that the animals that live in the soil in many places are almost as important in the development of soil profiles as the vegetation of the region. If we consider the effects of all land animals on soils, we may say that animals as a whole probably are as important in soil profile development as vegetation, except, of course, that animals cannot exist without vegetation. Doubtless we should have soils if there were no animals, but we could not have soils without plants. It is to be hoped that in the future more soil research will be directed toward the investigation of the influences of animals on soil character. Truly, the biological factor of soil formation *is* a *biological* one, involving symbiotic and antipathetic relationships among animals and animals, plants and plants, and among plants and animals.

CLIMATES PREVAILING IN THE YELLOW-GRAY EARTH
AND YELLOW-BROWN EARTH ZONES IN NEW ZEALAND

F. B. Hurst [1]

New Zealand Department of Scientific and Industrial Research

Received for publication January 8, 1951

A knowledge of the relative importance of all five soil-forming factors, parent rock, biotic conditions, climate, topography, and time, is necessary to understand the processes operating in a soil (3). For two important New Zealand soil groups, yellow-gray earths and yellow-brown earths,[2] four soil-forming factors can be nearly similar, but climate appears to differ significantly, yellow-gray earths and associated soils being found under much drier conditions than yellow-brown soils. Substantial areas of soils transitional between the groups made it desirable to give a more quantitative expression to climate in the yellow-gray and yellow-brown earth zones than that indicated above. In this paper methods of evaluating climate are discussed and applied to the problem.

CHARACTERISTICS OF THE SOIL GROUPS

Chemical properties of four typical profiles are set out in tables 1 and 2. Profiles of these soil types have been described by Vucetich[3] as follows:

1. *Yellow-gray earth from "loess"* (fig. 1)
    6 inches brown-gray silt loam, soft crumb structure.
    3 inches transitional, with worm casts.
    6 inches light gray yellow-brown silt loam, grading into
    5 inches very compact matrix of deeply stained orange blotches in a light gray yellow-brown heavy silt loam.
    12 inch blocks of drab gray yellow-brown fine sandy loam with diffuse orange mottling, separated by light gray cracks lined with brown humus staining ON massive compacted drab gray yellow-brown fine sandy loam.

---

[1] Soil Bureau Publication No. 22 of New Zealand Department of Scientific and Industrial Research. The writer is indebted to fellow workers at the Soil Bureau, and particularly to J. K. Dixon, chief chemist, for helpful criticism and advice in the preparation of this paper; to H. S. Gibbs, senior pedologist, for help in the classification of stations; to C. G. Vucetich, pedologist, for profile descriptions; and to N. G. Robertson of the New Zealand Meteorological Office for climatic data.

[2] As defined by Taylor, N. H. A genetic classification of New Zealand soils. New Zeal. Dept. Sci. and Indus. Res. Soil Bur. Bul. 3 (unpublished).

[3] C. G. Vucetich, private communication.

Reproduced with permission from *Soil Science,* Vol. 72, 1951, p. 1-19. Copyright © 1951, The Williams and Wilkins Company, Baltimore, Maryland 21202, USA.

Fig. 1—*(left)*. Profile of a yellow-gray earth developed on "loess" Location 1. Scale marked in feet. Photo by C. S. Harris

Fig. 2—*(right)*. Profile of a yellow-brown earth developed on "loess" Location 2. Scale marked in feet. Photo by C. S. Harris

2. *Yellow-brown earth from "loess"* (fig. 2)
    6 inches dark gray silt loam, fairly good crumb structure.
    2 inches transitional
    8 inches brownish yellow silt loam, no mottling,
    ON brownish light gray silt loam.
3. *Skeletal yellow-gray earth from graywacke*
    6 inches dark gray stony silt loam.
    2—5 inches transitional.
    10 inches gritty stony silt loam, light gray yellow-brown.
    ON weathering graywacke.
4. *Skeletal yellow-brown earth from graywacke*
    4-6 inches gray-brown loam, loose and powdery when dry.
    12-18 inches yellow-brown silt loam, with fragments of graywacke.
    ON weathering graywacke.

Tussock vegetation is common to all the profiles quoted. Graywacke is a fairly uniform sedimentary rock which forms the basement rock of New Zealand; "loess" is a sediment derived from graywacke possibly by glacial erosion, which mantles large areas, particularly in the South Island.

The base saturation and pH values of yellow-brown earths are lower than those of yellow-gray earths (table 1), showing that the former are more leached and more acid. With depth, the base saturation of yellow-gray earths increases, whereas that

Table 1—Chemical analyses of typical yellow-gray and yellow-brown earth profiles*

LAB. NO.	DEPTH	pH	1% CITRIC-SOLUBLE P_2O_5	OR-GANIC C	TOTAL N	C/N	BASE EXCHANGE						CLASSIFICATION	LOCALITY
							Ex-change Capacity	Total Bases	Base Satn.	Ca	Mg	K		
	in.		%	%	%		me./100 gm.	me./100 gm.	%	me./100 gm.	me./100 gm.	me./100 gm.		
4394A	0–5	5.6	0.021	3.8	0.30	12	15.2	8.2	54	4.8	3.4	0.75	Moderately leached	Banks Peninsula 1 on figure 4
4394B	8–13	5.7	0.008		0.10		9.6	5.1	54	2.9	2.4	0.45	Moderately gammate†	
4394C	16–22	6.0	0.008		0.06		9.7	6.4	66	3.6	3.0	0.35	Tussock melanized	Derived from "loess," under tussock
4394D	22–27	6.2	0.009		0.05		9.6	6.9	72	4.1	3.1	0.30	Yellow-gray earth	
4394E	34–38	6.2	0.009		0.05		9.8	7.4	75	4.3	3.4	0.30		
5008A	0–5	5.3	0.035	8.1	0.49	16	24.5	5.6	23	2.9	2.2	0.70	Strongly leached	Banks Peninsula 2 on figure 4
5008B	10–14	5.4	0.025	2.1	0.15	13	11.7	0.6	5	0.4	0.3	0.20	Moderately weathered	
5008C	23–27	5.3	0.014	0.4	0.05	11	6.8	0.5	8	0.3	0.2	0.20	Yellow-brown earth	Derived from "loess," under tussock
5006A	0–5½	5.9	0.020	3.5	0.27	13	21.1	13.8	67	9.9	3.2	1.45	Skeletal yellow-gray earth	N. Canterbury, 3 on figure 4
5006B	13–19	6.0	0.010	1.1	0.11	10	14.7	11.8	78	8.8	2.9	0.44		Derived from graywacke, under tussock
1675A	0–6	5.3	0.008	3.9	0.27	15	23.7	7.3	31	4.7	2.2	0.90	Skeletal yellow-brown earth	Marlborough, 4 on figure 4
1675B	7–12	5.2	0.008		0.15		20.5	3.4	17	2.2	1.0	0.10	Moderately weathered	Derived from graywacke, under tussock

* Analyses based on soil oven-dried at 105°C. Chemical analysis of 4394A–E by T. W. Collie and of 1675A–B by A. J. Metson.

† Gammation is a term used by Taylor to describe the uneven weathering.

Table 2—Mechanical analyses of typical yellow-brown earth profiles on ignited basis by International method

LAB. NO.	DEPTH	COARSE SAND	FINE SAND	SILT	CLAY	SOLU-TION LOSS	AIR-DRY MOIS-TURE	IGNI-TION LOSS	TEXTURE
	in.	*per cent*	*per cent*	*per cent*	*per cent*	*per cent*	*per cent*	*per cent*	
4394A	0–5	0.5	53.1	18.9	15.4	1.8	2.5	8.0	Loamy fine sand
4394B	8–13	0.2	57.3	20.5	14.8	1.1	1.7	3.0	Fine sandy loam
4394C	16–22	0.3	58.2	19.1	16.4	1.0	1.9	2.6	Fine sandy loam
4394D	22–27	0.3	59.6	19.5	15.0	0.9	1.8	2.5	Fine sandy loam
4394E	34–38	0.3	59.1	17.5	16.8	1.0	1.7	2.1	Fine sandy loam
5008A	0–5	0.2	38.9	18.3	16.8	3.0	5.8	16.9	Loam
5008B	10–14	0.2	47.6	21.3	17.8	2.7	2.7	7.3	Loam
5008C	23–27	0.3	59.8	20.3	12.1	1.7	2.1	3.6	Fine sandy loam

of yellow-brown earth decreases. Calcium/magnesium ratios remain wide in yellow-brown earths as the C horizon is approached, but narrow in yellow-gray earths. Yellow-brown earths are usually richer in organic matter (see carbon and nitrogen figures in table 1) than the corresponding yellow-gray earths. Mechanical analyses (table 2) do not show striking differences in degrees of weathering. Differences in mode of weathering are shown by the subsoil colors used for naming the soil groups. Except for skeletal members, yellow-gray earths show in the field a characteristic uneven subsoil weathering resulting in the block and crack structure described above for the yellow-gray profile over loess. Yellow-brown earths do not show this.

ASSESSMENT OF CLIMATE

Briefly, yellow-gray earths are found under annual rainfalls of 23 to 35 inches on 100 to 150 days, with dry summers; and yellow-brown earths, under rainfalls from 45 to about 85 inches on 100 to 200 days a year. Figure 3 shows the frequency distribution of rainfall in the soil zones. The soil properties suggest that a climatic index which illustrates seasonal variations would be valuable. Four classifications were tried: Meyer's (4), Prescott's (5), and Thornthwaite's (7,8) two classifications.

Meyer Ratio

Meyer's N-S quotient is based on the relation of rainfall (P) to the *saturation deficit (sd), P/sd.* The saturation deficit is the difference between the vapor pressure of the air when saturated with water and the vapor pressure found. It is calculated from the average relative humidity and temperature for each month. This system has the merit of being a logical rather than an empirical expression of the ratio of precipitation to evaporation. The saturation deficit has been related to evaporation from a 36-inch standard tank (5). Unfortunately, relative humidities in New Zealand are based on measurements taken at 9:30 a.m. and, according to Robertson,[4] differ

---

[4] N. G. Robertson, verbal communication.

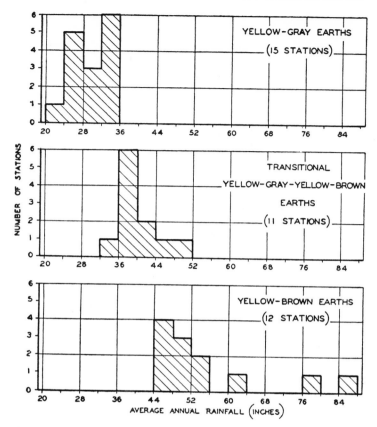

Fig. 3—Frequency distribution of annual rainfall of stations within the soil zones

appreciably from the average for the whole day. Although values for saturation deficit are thereby open to question, the quotients have been calculated.

Prescott (5) says that the monthly quotient must be greater than 13.2 for optimum biological conditions. This figure was used as a criterion for "dry" months.

Prescott's Climatic Index

Prescott has separated Australian soil groups on a logarithmic-scaled graph in which annual precipitation is plotted against saturation deficit. The lines separating the groups have an approximate slope of 0.7, and from this and other data he proposed a climatic index of the form:

$$\text{Climatic index} = K = \frac{P}{E^m}$$

where P = annual precipitation in inches, and E = evaporation from a free water surface, taken at 258 sd where sd is calculated in inches of mercury from annual averages of temperature and relative humidity; m is likely to lie between 0.67 and 0.80. By use of Prescott's value of $m = 0.7$, which is based directly on soil boundaries, the index was calculated from the approximate values of relative humidity available.

Thornthwaite's Empirical Classification

Thornthwaite's early classification of climate is based on the empirical equaitons,

$$\text{The precipitation-evaporation index, } P - E = \int_{n=1}^{n=12} 115\left[\frac{P}{T-10}\right]_n$$

$$\text{The thermal efficiency index, } T - E = \int_{n=1}^{n=12}\left[\frac{T-32}{4}\right]_n$$

where $P =$ monthly rainfall in inches; $T =$ monthly average temperature in Fahrenheit; $n =$ number of months.

This will be called *Thornthwaite's empirical classification.* P-E and T-E indexes for 25 stations have been calculated by Garnier (2) and are quoted in table 7. The number of subhumid months [that is, months in which $P\text{-}E = (63/12) = 5.3$] has been used to indicate dry spells. The classification is based on temperature and rainfall alone, and does not take into account relative humidity or day length in the regulation of transpiration.

Thornthwaite's Rational Classification

Thornthwaite's rational classification is based on *water need,* that is, the amount of water lost by evaporation and transpiration from a soil covered with vegetation under ample moisture conditions. *Potential evapo-transpiration* is another term used by Thornthwaite to denote this. It is assessed by a relation between temperature and day length. Water need is then balanced against water supply (rainfall). When rainfall is equal to water need, the soil is maintained at field capacity, and no leaching takes place. When the supply is greater than the need, there is a *surplus* for leaching the soil. When it is less, the soil moisture in the root zone is drawn upon until wilting point is reached. After this there is a water *deficiency.* At the end of the dry season the reservoir of soil moisture must be filled up to field capacity before there can again be a surplus. According to Thornthwaite (8):

Although a water surplus in one season cannot prevent a deficiency in another except as moisture may be stored in the soil, to a certain extent one may compensate for the other. Water surplus means annual additions to subsoil moisture and ground water. Deeply rooted perennials may make use of this subsoil moisture and thus minimize the effect of drought. Transpiration proceeds, but at reduced rates. For this reason a surplus of only 6 inches in one season may counteract a deficiency of 10 inches in another. Thus in an over-all moisture index the humidity index has more weight than the aridity index.

The relation between water surplus s, deficiency d, need n, and the *moisture index* (I_m) is:

$$\frac{100s - 60d}{n} = I_m$$

The *humidity factor and the aridity factor,* which are the surplus and the deficiency respectively expressed as percentages of the water need, give an indication of seasonal variations. *Potential evapo-transpiration* is the index of thermal efficiency. *(Continentality* is expressed by a relation between the total annual potential evapo-transpiration and the percentage of it which is concentrated in the summer months.) *Monthly runoff* to the drainage system is calculated from the water surplus on the assumption that half the surplus from one month is available for the next.

Since all the stations studied were found to be of summer concentration type a' (summer concentration of thermal efficiency less than 48 percent), Thornthwaite's table for these indexes are not quoted. The appendix shows his allotment of indexes to obtain the other climatic types. Instructions for the calculation of P-E are given in his paper (8). Examples of the calculations for three stations are shown in tables 3, 4, and 5.

Thornthwaite's relation between the moisture indexes of his two classifications, $P\text{-}E = 0.8I_m + 48$, did not hold exactly for the New Zealand stations studied. The equation relating them was found to be $P\text{-}E = 0.6I_m + 46$. Two discrepancies were rectified by recalculating P-E index from 1945 averages (for I_m) rather than the 1940 averages used by Garnier (2).

A disadvantage of the rational classification is that saturation deficit is not taken into account.

An assumption which appears important in dry climates is that the storage capacity of the soil (the difference between moisture content at field capacity and wilting point) averages 4 inches, provided the soil is not shallow. It must vary with the texture of the soil; in sandy soils it may be about 3 inches. To find out whether a difference in storage capacity alters the results appreciably, Woodbourne, a yellow-gray station, was taken, climate factors being worked out on the basis of 3-inch and 4-inch storage capacity. Table 6 shows that variations in storage capacity do not make drastic changes in the indexes.

The perhumid climate type covers a wide range of moisture status. Other work has shown that both podzols and yellow-brown earths are found in the perhumid type, although there is a large difference in moisture index. This emphasizes that the boundaries between the humid climatic types are arbitrary and that index values are more illuminating than types in comparison of stations.

Dry months are taken as those with runoff less than 0.5 inch. Thornthwaite assumes that 50 percent of the month's water is held over until the following month and says that for watersheds of less than 100 square miles the percentage is probably smaller. In other words, it takes time for water to reach the drainage system of a watershed from the place where it falls. The time for water to percolate through the solum will be much less. If it is inappreciable, "dry" months, so far as the soil is concerned, will be those in which the surplus rather than the runoff is low. The number of dry months calculated on the basis of the runoff is one less than the number of "low surplus" dry months at nearly every station, so that the over-all picture of dry seasons remains practically the same. The average "low runoff" months is 8.2 for yellow-gray earths and 1.0 for yellow-brown earths, as compared with

Table 3—Climatic indexes according to Thornthwaite's rational classification, Golden Downs (41°33'S., 172°53'E.) yellow-brown earth station

		JAN.	FEB.	MARCH	APRIL	MAY	JUNE	JULY	AUG.	SEPT.	OCT.	NOV.	DEC.	YEAR
Mean temperature	°F.	59.7	59.4	56.8	52.2	45.6	41.3	39.5	42.8	46.4	50.6	54.3	57.8	50.5
	°C.	15.4	15.2	13.75	11.2	7.55	5.15	4.2	6.0	8.0	10.3	12.4	14.3	
i		5.49	5.38	4.62	3.39	1.87	1.05	0.77	1.32	2.04	2.99	3.96	4.91	37.79 = I
Unadjusted P-E	cm.	7.4	7.3	6.5	5.2	3.4	2.25	1.8	2.65	3.65	4.8	5.9	6.8	
Adjusted P-E	in.	3.74	3.07	2.74	1.89	1.14	0.67	0.58	0.96	1.44	2.19	2.84	3.50	24.76
Rainfall	in.	3.83	4.24	2.70	4.02	3.78	4.83	4.17	4.80	4.06	4.12	3.74	3.72	48.01
Storage change	in.	0	0	−0.04	+0.04	0	0	0	0	0	0	0	0	0
Storage	in.	4.0	4.0	3.96	4.0	4.0	4.0	4.0	4.0	4.0	4.0	4.0	4.0	
Actual evaporation	in.	3.74	3.07	2.74	1.89	1.14	0.67	0.58	0.96	1.44	2.19	2.84	3.50	24.76
Water deficiency	in.	0	0	0	0	0	0	0	0	0	0	0	0	0
Surplus water	in.	0.09	1.17	0	2.09	2.64	4.16	3.59	3.84	2.62	1.93	0.90	0.22	23.25
Runoff	in.	0.53	0.85	0.42	1.26	1.95	3.06	3.33	3.59	3.09	2.51	1.70	0.96	23.25

P-E = 24.76 inches.

Aridity index = 0

Hmidity index = $\dfrac{23.25}{24.76}$ = 94 per cent.

Moisture index = 94 per cent.

Summer concentration of thermal efficiency = 42 per cent.

Climatic type = $B_4B_1'a'r$.

Table 4—Climatic indexes according to Thornthwaite's rational classification, Taihape (30°39'S, 172°49'E.) transitional yellow-gray-yellow-brown earth station

		JAN.	FEB.	MARCH	APRIL	MAY	JUNE	JULY	AUG.	SEPT.	OCT.	NOV.	DEC.	YEAR
Mean temperature	°F.	59.2	58.9	56.6	52.5	46.5	42.8	41.4	42.9	45.7	49.8	52.5	56.3	50.4
	°C.	15.1	14.9	13.65	11.4	8.05	6.0	5.2	6.05	7.6	9.9	11.4	13.5	
i	cm.	5.33	5.22	4.57	3.48	2.06	1.32	1.06	1.34	1.89	2.81	3.48	4.50	37.06
Unadjusted P-E	cm.	7.3	7.2	6.6	5.4	3.7	2.7	2.3	2.7	3.5	4.65	5.4	6.5	
Adjusted P-E	in.	3.64	2.99	2.77	1.98	1.26	0.83	0.76	0.98	1.38	2.10	2.54	3.28	24.51
Rainfall	in.	3.31	2.87	2.43	2.80	3.33	3.28	3.07	2.71	3.16	3.36	3.32	3.27	36.91
Storage change	in.	−0.33	−0.12	−0.34	+0.80	0	0	0	0	0	0	0	−0.01	
Storage	in.	3.66	3.54	3.20	4.0	4.0	4.0	4.0	4.0	4.0	4.0	4.0	3.99	
Actual evaporation	in.	3.64	2.99	2.77	1.98	1.26	0.83	0.76	0.98	1.38	2.10	2.54	3.28	24.51
Water deficiency	in.	0	0	0	0	0	0	0	0	0	0	0	0	0
Water surplus	in.	0	0	0	0.02	2.07	2.45	2.31	1.73	1.78	1.26	0.78	0	12.40
Runoff	in.	0.29	0.15	0.07	0.05	1.06	1.76	2.04	1.88	1.83	1.55	1.16	0.58	

P-E = 24.51 inches.

Aridity index = 0

Humidity index = $\dfrac{12.40}{24.51}$ = 50.5 per cent.

Moisture index = 50.5 per cent.

Summer concentration of thermal efficiency = 38.5 per cent.

Climatic type $B_2B_1'a'r$.

Table 5—Climatic indexes according to Thornthwaite's rational classification, Napier (39°29'S., 17°55'E.) yellow-gray earth station

		JAN.	FEB.	MARCH	APRIL	MAY	JUNE	JULY	AUG.	SEPT.	OCT.	NOV.	DEC.	YEAR
Mean temperature	°F.	65.5	65.4	62.3	58.6	52.4	48.4	46.8	48.9	51.8	56.4	59.8	63.1	56.6
	°C.	18.6	18.5	16.8	14.7	11.3	9.1	8.2	9.4	11.0	13.5	15.4	17.2	
i		7.31	7.25	6.84	5.12	3.44	2.48	2.12	2.60	3.30	4.50	5.49	6.49	56.94 = I
Unadjusted P-E.	cm.	8.2	8.2	7.1	5.9	4.1	3.0	2.6	3.25	3.95	5.25	6.3	7.4	
Adjusted P-E.	in.	4.08	3.41	2.97	2.16	1.39	0.93	0.86	1.18	1.55	2.36	3.01	3.74	27.64
Rainfall	in.	2.66	2.72	2.67	2.61	3.21	3.04	3.55	2.99	2.01	1.92	2.05	2.05	31.48
Storage change	in.	−0.91	0	0	+0.45	+1.82	+1.73	0	0	0	−0.44	−0.96	−1.69	
Storage	in.	0.0	0	0	0.45	2.27	4.00	4.0	4.0	4.0	3.56	2.60	0.91	
Actual evaporation	in.	3.57	2.72	2.67	2.16	1.39	0.93	0.86	1.18	1.55	2.36	3.01	3.74	26.14
Water deficiency	in.	0.51	0.69	0.30	0	0	0	0	0	0.46	0	0	0	1.50
Water surplus	in.	0	0	0	0	0	0.38	2.69	1.81	0.46	0	0	0	5.34
Runoff	in.	0.07	0.03	0.02	0.01	0.0	0.19	1.44	1.63	1.04	0.52	0.26	0.13	

P-E = 27.64 inches.

Aridity index $= \dfrac{1.50}{27.64} = 5.4$ per cent.

Humidity index $= \dfrac{5.34}{27.64} = 19.3$ per cent.

Moisture index $= \dfrac{534-(60 \times 1.5)}{27.64} = 16.1$ per cent.

Summer concentration of thermal efficiency = 38 per cent.

Climatic type = $C_2B'_1a'r$.

Table 6—Effect of storage capacity on climatic indexes

WOODBOURNE	STORAGE CAPACITY ASSUMED TO BE 3 INCHES	STORAGE CAPACITY ASSUMED TO BE 4 INCHES
Moisture index....................per cent	11.1	9.6
Humidity index....................per cent	20.2	16.5
Aridity index.....................per cent	15.1	11.4
Water surplus.........................in.	5.54	4.54
Climatic type............................	$C_2B_1'a'r$	$C_2B_1'a'r$

8.9 and 2.0, respectively, on the low surplus basis. Since runoff is useful from the hydrological point of view, the dry months were assessed on that basis.

In soil formation the important part of runoff is the ground water fraction that percolates through the soil. On flat slopes this will be all the water surplus. The greater the slope, the greater will be the proportion of surface runoff. To keep this proportion constant, only soils on similar slopes can be compared. Absolute values for water surplus apply only to soils on zero slope.

It is of interest to compare this classification with Crowther's leaching factor (1). From the data of Robinson and Holmes, Crowther calculated that a rise of 4.04 cm. rainfall per year for every degree centigrade rise in mean annual temperature is required to maintain a constant SiO/Al_2O_3 ratio. For constant CaO content of the clay, the rainfall figure was found to be 3.78 cm. By an application of Thornthwaite's classification of climate, this can be assessed. The potential evapo-transpiration is the water needed to keep the soil in the stable condition of field capacity moisture content without leaching. By plotting annual potential evapo-transpiration against mean annual temperature, it was found that the water needed for each degree centigrade rise is 2.15 cm.

Crowther's leaching factor ($R+24-\frac{3}{4}T$, where R = annual rainfall in inches, T = mean annual temperature) has been calculated.

Application to Yellow-Gray and Yellow-Brown Earth Zones

Indexes of these climate classifications for stations in the yellow-gray and yellow-brown earth zones are given in table 7. Localities of the stations are shown in figure 4. Averages are given in table 8.

The problem now is to choose the most suitable classification of climate for differentiation of the soil groups.

The moisture index and related P-E index show no overlapping in the ranges of values for yellow-gray and yellow-brown earths. Except for Wellington and Onawe, which have values within the yellow-brown soil range, transitional soil stations have indexes between those of the main groups. The Meyer ratio is more variable than are the Thornthwaite indexes, as shown by Ohakea, Taihape, and East Gore, which have quotients that seem too high for their groups. Three stations which have no period of reduced biological activity by the Meyer ratio have 6, 8, and 12 months of low runoff, according to Thornthwaite's rational classification. Prescott's modification of this ratio gives a clearer differentiation between the groups. Based on

Table 7—Summary of climate indexes for 38 New Zealand stations arranged in soil groups Calculated from average climatic data up to 1945

STATION	LOCATION	Climatic type	THORNTHWAITE'S RATIONAL CLASSIFICATION*						THORNTHWAITE'S EMPIRICAL CLASSIFICATION*			MEYER		PRESCOTT'S INDEX	CROWTHER'S LEACHING FACTOR	RAIN DAYS	AVERAGE ANNUAL RAINFALL	NUMBER OF YEARS AVERAGED†
			Water need (in.)	Humidity index (%)	Aridity index (%)	Moisture index (%)	Surplus water (in.)	Months with runoff less than *f*	P-E index	T-E index	Subhumid months (P-E 5.03)	Meyer ratio	Months P/sd less than 13.2				(in.)	
Yellow-Gray Earth																		
Napier	39°29'S 176°55'E	$C_1B_1'a'r$	27.6	19.3	5.4	16.1	5.3	8						1.35	12	114	31.5	21
Hastings	39°39'S 176°51'E	$C_1B_2'a'r$	27.95	22.6	6.3	18.7	6.3	7						1.35	15	128	32.5	17
Tanginoana	40°18'S 175°15'E	$B_1B_1'a'r'$	26.8	29	0	29	8.0	6	61.2	70.2	6	286	3	1.67	18	149	34.8	21
Ohakea	40°12'S 175°23'E	$B_1B_1'a'r$	26.9	29.5	0	29.5	8.0	6				389	0	1.80	18	148	34.8	5
Blenheim	41°33'S 173°57'E	$C_1B_1'a's$	26.9	10.7	18	-0.15	2.9	10	47.7	67.8	9	235	6	1.04	8.5	98	24.9	13
Woodbourne	41°31'S 173°52'E	$C_2B_1'a'r$	27.5	16.5	11.4	9.3	4.5	8							12		28.8	4
Waihopai	41°40'S 173°34'E	$B_1B_1'a'r$	26.1	29.5	0	29.5	7.8	6				255	3	1.41	18	117	33.9	14
Balmoral	42°50'S 172°41'E	$C_2B_1'a'r$	25.7	14	2.8	12.3	3.6	9	51.5	59.0	9	215	6	1.11	12.5	112	26.6	18
Lake Coleridge	43°21'S 171°32'E	$B_1B_1'a'r$	25.2	29.9	0.1	29.8	7.6	6	68.2	57.3	5	264	5	1.35	19	109	32.5	28
Darfield	43°29'S 172°07'E	$C_2B_1'a'r$	25.5	19.9	0	19.9	5.1	8						1.64	17	100	30.6	6
Christ-church	43°32'S 172°37'E	$C_2B_1'a'r$	25.15	8.7	8.8	0.35	2.2	10	51.8	61.3	9			1.35	11	126	26.1	56
Lincoln	43°38'S 172°30'E	$C_2B_1'a'r$	25.1	11.5	6.2	7.8	2.9	9				328	5	1.34	12	121	25.9	64
Ashburton	43°55'S 171°46'E	$C_2B_1'a'r$	25.4	16.1	2.7	14.5	4.1	8	61.1	57.9	7	316	0	1.43	16	126	29.7	18
Timaru	44°24'S 171°14'E	$C_2B_1'a'd$	25.4	1.7	7.5	-2.5	0.4	12	45.5	59.4	12			1.20	8	115	23.2	36
Waimate	44°44'S 171°03'E	$C_2B_1'a'd$	26.5	0.1	0.6	-0.2	0.0	12				289	0	1.31	19.5	130	25.5	37
Transitional Yellow-Gray-Yellow-Brown Earth																		
Gisborne	38°39'S 178°02'E	$B_2B_1'a'r$	27.9	41	0	41	11.4	6	72.7	73.9	6	377	2	1.64	19	153	38.3	8

Station	Lat.	Long.	Soil																
Taihape	39°39'S	175°49'E	$B_2B_1'a'r$	24.5	50.5	0	50.5	12.4	4	78.7	55.4	2	516	0	2.14	23	36.9	170	34
Palmerston North	40°23'S	175°37'E	$B_3B_1'a'r$	26.6	38	0	38	10.1	5	73.5	69.1	4			1.96	20	36.7	169	33
Kapiti Is.	40°52'S	174°55'E	$B_3B_1'a'r$	27.3	50	0	50	13.7	4				451	0	2.12	24	41.0	149	37
Waingawa	40°59'S	175°37'E	$B_2B_1'a'r$	26.45	43	0.3	43	11.3	6	87.9	66.1	3	447	2	1.76	21.5	37.7	149	21
Wellington	41°17'S	174°46'E	$B_2B_1'a'r$	26.6	69	0	69	18.3	4						2.49	28.5	44.9	156	83
Appleby	41°17'S	173°06'E	$B_1B_1'a'r$	26.9	34.8	0	35	9.4	6	82.4	57.3	0	350	0	1.56	19.5	36.4	113	13
Methven	43°33'S	171°42'E	$B_3B_1'a'r$	25.8	50	0	50	13.0	2	89.3	67.0	6	328	0	1.78	26	40.1	132	17
Akaroa (Onawe)	43°46'S	172°56'E	$B_3B_1'a'r$	26.45	91	0	91	24.2	4				499	6	2.25	34	50.6	137	8
Dunedin	45°52'S	170°29'E	$B_2B_1'a'r$	25.5	54	0	54	13.8	3				388	0	1.89	24	39.3	161	3
E. Gore	46°05'S	168°58'E	$B_2B_1'a'r$	24.65	41	0	41	10.2	4				697	0	2.56	31	34.9	180	37
Yellow-Brown Earth																			
Auckland	36°51'S	174°46'E	$B_1B_1'a'r$	29.25	68	0	68	19.9	4	91.9	81.1	3	485	0	2.18	29	49.1	184	36
Waihi	37°23'S	175°51'E	$A\ B_1'a'r$	27.5	208	0	208	57.2	0	180.1	72.8	0			4.35	67	84.6	181	35
Tauranga	37°42'S	176°10'E	$B_1B_1'a'r$	27.5	92	0	92	25.4	0	104.8	74.1	0	534	0	2.54	34.5	52.9	149	32
Hamilton	37°46'S	175°20'E	$B_2B_1'a'r$	27.1	79	0	79	21.5	3	92.1	73.2	2			2.50	31	48.6	159	31
Rotorua	38°09'S	176°15'E	$A\ B_1'a'r$	26.9	106	0	106	28.5	0	123.9	68.9	0	619	0	2.66	38	55.4	145	59
Lake Waikaremoana	38°48'S	177°08'E	$A\ B_1'a'r$	24.8	206	0	206	51.4	0	176.4	58.7	0			5.05	62	76.3	199	10
New Plymouth	39°04'S	174°04'E	$A\ B_1'a'r$	26.9	126	0	126	33.7	0	122.9	72.5	0	761	0	3.50	43	60.6	187	24
Karioi	39°27'S	175°31'E	$A\ B_1'a'r$	23.4	101	0	101	23.6	0	114.2	49.3	1	594	0	2.72	35	47.0	166	18
Pahiatua	40°27'S	175°50'E	$A\ B_1'a'r$	26.3	96	0	96	25.3	2	108.3	65.5	1	702	0	3.11	35.5	51.6	176	18
Golden Downs	41°33'S	172°53'E	$B_2B_1'a'r$	24.8	94	0	94	23.2	0	109.9	56.6	1	575	0	2.64	34	48.0	108	16
Hanner Springs	42°33'S	172°47'E	$B_4B_1'a'r$	24.4	88	0	88	21.4	1	102.8	54.2	0	475	0	2.20	32	45.8	145	24
Invercargill	46°26'S	168°21'E	$B_2B_1'a'r$	24.1	85	0	85	20.6	0	100.5	54.1	0	703	0	2.96	31	44.7	199	40

* Quoted from Garnier (2), based on data up to 1940.
† Years averaged for mean temperatures up to 1945. Many stations have had rainfalls averaged for much longer; for example, rainfalls have been measured at Waimate since 1898 and at Hanmer since 1905.

Table 8—Average climatic indexes

	YELLOW-GRAY SOILS		TRANSITIONAL		YELLOW-BROWN SOILS	
Temperature criteria						
Potential evapo-transpiration*.............	26.2	(*15*)†	26.1	(*11*)	25.8	(*12*)
T-E index‡................................	61.85	(*7*)	64.78	(*6*)	65.08	(*12*)
Moisture criteria						
Moisture index*..........................	14.2	(*15*)	51.1	(*11*)	112.7	(*12*)
P-E index‡...............................	55.28	(*7*)	80.76	(*6*)	119.0	(*12*)
Meyer ratio..............................	286	(*9*)	450	(*9*)	605	(*9*)
Prescott's index..........................	1.38	(*14*)	2.01	(*11*)	3.03	(*12*)
Aridity index*...........................	4.7	(*15*)	0	(*11*)	0	(*12*)
Humidity index*..........................	17.3	(*15*)	51.1	(*11*)	112.7	(*12*)
Water surplus*...........................	4.58	(*15*)	13.44	(*11*)	29.35	(*12*)
Crowther's leaching factor................	14.4	(*15*)	24.7	(*11*)	39.3	(*12*)
Seasonal variation criteria						
Months with runoff less than ½ inch*.......	8.2	(*15*)	4.4	(*11*)	1.0	(*12*)
Subhumid months (P-E 5.3)‡..............	8.1	(*7*)	4.2	(*6*)	0.7	(*12*)
Months of low biological activity (Meyer)..	3.1	(*9*)	0.2	(*9*)	0	(*9*)
Number of rain days......................	121	(*14*)	153	(*11*)	165	(*12*)

* Thornthwaite's rational classification.

† Italic figures in parentheses indicate the number of stations averaged.

‡ Thornthwaite's empirical classification [from Garnier (2)].

annual values of temperature and rainfall, this index gives a fairly rapid estimation of moisture conditions, but it does not take account of seasonal variation. Prescott (6) reported that values of the index between 1.1 and 1.5 correspond to conditions where rainfall balances transpiration and evaporation, so that on this basis most yellow-gray earths should have no leaching at all.

Crowther's leaching factor does not appear to be related closely to water surplus; for example, Timaru and Waimate have leaching factors of 8 and 19.5 respectively, although they have virtually no water surplus. Crowther's factor appears to be the most variable, particularly for the transitional soils.

In Thornthwaite's two classifications there seems to be a close relation severally between the indexes for thermal efficiency, moisture status, and length of droughts as given by the "dry" months, but the rational classification supplies more information than is given by the empirical classification. By using humidity and aridity indexes to divide the year into wet and dry seasons, and by furnishing "water surplus" as a measure of leaching, the rational classification becomes a valuable means of distinguishing climate from the pedological viewpoint, from which seasonal variation and leaching are very important. For these reasons Thornthwaite's rational classification was adopted for studying the climatic environments of yellow-gray and yellow-brown earths.

Climatic Environments According to Thornthwaite's Rational Classification

The essential differences between climates prevailing at the yellow-gray and yellow-brown earth stations are shown graphically in figure 5. At Golden Downs, where

Fig. 4—Climatic stations in New Zealand

yellow-brown earths are developed, only for an insignificant period in March is the water supply less than the water need. Surplus is available for leaching virtually all year. At Taihape (a transitional earth station) water need exceeds rainfall for 3½ months, necessitating a withdrawal of nearly an inch of water from the reservoir of soil moisture. Before the reservoir is empty, rainfall exceeds water need, and after the soil moisture is replaced, there is a surplus over the last 7 months of 12.4 inches. Napier is an example of a yellow-gray earth station. For 6 months the water need

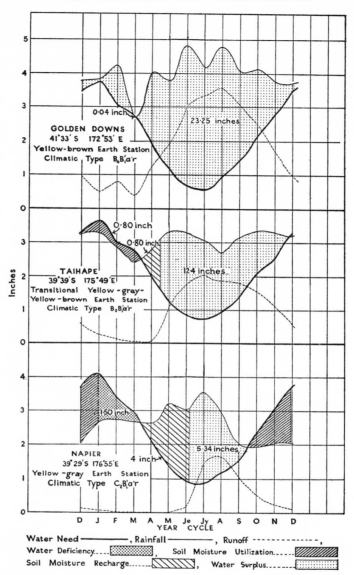

Fig. 5—Essential differences of climates prevailing at Yellow-Gray, Yellow-Brown, and transitional earth stations

is greater than the rainfall. Available soil moisture is exhausted and there is a period of deficiency. By the time the soil is recharged with moisture, only 5.3 inches of surplus water is left for leaching the soil.

Temperature. There is no appreciable difference in average thermal efficiency (as shown by potential evapo-transpiration) between the soil groups. Yellow-brown earths are found under a wider temperature range (*P-E* = 23.4 to 29.3 inches) than are the yellow-gray earths (25.1 to 28.0 inches).

Moisture. The moisture index shows values between –2.5 and 29.5 (average 14.2) for yellow-gray soils, between 35 and 91 (average 51) for transitional soils, and between 68 and 208 (average 113) for yellow-brown soils. Onawe, on Banks Peninsula, is a station which does not fit well. Its I_m of 91 is typical of a yellow-brown soil. So far as moisture index is concerned, Wellington approaches a yellow-brown climate. Water deficiency occurs only in the yellow-gray soils.

Surplus water. Provided soils on the same slope are compared, the annual surplus gives an indication of the relative leaching. It would seem that the amount of leaching in a yellow-brown earth is between five and six times that in a yellow-gray earth if both are on very slight slopes. This may explain the lower base status of yellow-brown earths, both in the solum and beyond the influence of the organic cycle in the C horizon. Wet conditions may inhibit the oxidation of organic matter in yellow-brown earths.

Seasonal variation. The distribution of runoff throughout the year shows which are the dry months (see fig. 5). Yellow-gray earths average 8 months when the runoff is less than half an inch. Yellow-brown earths average 1 month of low runoff. Aridity indexes also give an indication of dry periods: yellow-gray earths average 4.7, whereas transitional and yellow-brown earths have nil values. Taylor considers that droughty seasons are important in the formation of yellow-gray earths. During these periods the subsoil may crack, allowing easy penetration of water to the cracks in the wet season, although the intervening blocks may not be wetted to the same degree, so bringing about the uneven subsoil weathering characteristic of these soils.

To sum up, the prevailing climates for yellow-gray earths are not colder than those of yellow-brown earths, but they give drier conditions with less leaching and longer spells of droughty weather than are found with yellow-brown soils.

SUMMARY

The profile characteristics and properties of New Zealand yellow-gray earths and yellow-brown earths are described.

Four classifications of climate, namely, the Meyer ratio, Prescott's index, and Thornthwaite's "empirical" and "rational" classifications, are discussed. Besides giving the best differentiation between the soil groups on the basis of moisture status, Thornthwaite's "rational" classification, by the number of months with low runoff and the aridity index, provides the best indication of seasonal variation. Water surplus gives a leaching factor that is as significant as Crowther's leaching factor. For these reasons, Thornthwaite's "rational" classification is judged to be the most useful in dealing with the problem.

According to Thornthwaite's "rational" classification, thermal efficiency is similar for both soil groups. Moisture differences can be stated generally by the moisture index, which shows quantitatively that yellow-gray earths are found under much drier conditions than are yellow-brown earths. Pedologically important aspects of soil moisture are demonstrated by values for water surplus, which show that effective leaching is lower for yellow-gray earths, whereas the aridity index and distribution of surplus water throughout a season show that yellow-gray earths have much longer droughty seasons then do yellow-brown earths.

REFERENCES

1. Crowther, E. M. 1930 The relationship of climatic and geological factors to the composition of soil clay and the distribution of soil types. Roy. Soc. London Proc., Ser. B. 107: 1-30.
2. Garnier, B. J. 1946 The climates of New Zealand: according to Thornthwaite's classification. Ann. Assoc. Amer. Geogr. 36: 151-177.
3. Jenny, H. 1946 Arrangement of soil series and types according to functions of soil-forming factors. Soil Sci. 61: 375-392.
4. Meyer, A. 1926 Some relations between climate and soils in Europe. Chem. der Erde 2: 209-347.
5. Prescott, J. A. 1938 Indices in agricultural climatology. Jour. Aust. Inst. Agr. Sci. 4: 33-40.
6. .... 1949 A climatic index for the leaching factor in soil formation. Jour. Soil Sci. 1: 9-19.
7. Thornthwaite, C. W. 1931 The climates of North America according to a new classification. Geogr. Rev. 21: 633-655.
8. .... 1948 An approach toward a rational classification of climate. Geogr. Rev. 38: 55-94.

APPENDIX. CLIMATIC SUBDIVISIONS ACCORDING TO THORNWAITE'S RATIONAL CLASSIFICATION

Table 1—Moisture criteria

MOISTURE INDEX Im	CLIMATIC TYPE
$\geqq$ 100	A perhumid
80–100	B_4 humid
60–80	B_3 humid
40–60	B_2 humid
20–40	B_1 humid
0–20	C_2 subhumid
−20 to 0	C_1 dry subhumid
−40 to −20	D semiarid
−60 to −40	E arid

Table 2—Temperature criteria

P-E	THERMAL EFFICIENCY TYPE	
inches		
>44.8	A'	Megathermal
39.27–44.8	B_4'	
33.66–39–27	B_3'	
28.05–33.66	B_2'	Mesothermal
22.44–28.05	B_1'	
16.83–22.44	C_2'	
11.22–16.83	C_1'	Microthermal
5.61–11.22	D'	Tundra
<5.61	E'	Frost

Table 3—Seasonal variations

MOIST CLIMATES	ARIDITY INDEX	DRY CLIMATES	HUMIDITY INDEX
r, little or no deficiency	0–16.7	d, little or no surplus	0–10
s, moderate summer deficiency	16.7–13.3	s, moderate winter surplus	10–20
w, moderate winter deficiency	16.7–13.3	w, moderate summer surplus	10–20
S_2, W_2, large summer and winter deficiency	33.3+	S_2, W_2, large winter and summer surplus	20+

INFLUENCE OF THE COMPOSITION OF PARENT MATERIALS ON SOIL FORMATION IN MANITOBA[1]

W. A. Ehrlich[2], H. M. Rice and J. H. Ellis

Received for publication April 27, 1955

ABSTRACT

The analysis of the major horizons of ten soil profiles was undertaken in an attempt to ascertain the effect of the composition of parent material on soil formation in well-drained Mankato till sediments, under various environmental conditions. The results showed that the composition of parent materials had a profound effect on the type of profile formed. Increasing amounts of inorganic carbonates restricted profile development and inhibited the decomposition of non-calcareous rock fragments. The amount of inorganic carbonates in the parent material has been a major factor in determining and differentiating certain great soil groups; furthermore, the mineralogical composition of the parent material also has been a determining factor in the formation of Brown Podzolic and Podzol soils. Weathering of non-calcareous minerals and rocks (except shale) was found to be comparatively slight; examination of the clay fraction revealed approximately equal percentages of the dominant types in each horizon.

INTRODUCTION

The effect of the composition of soil parent materials on pedogenic processes has long been recognized. It was recorded in the well-known writings of the earlier Russian soil scientists, and it has been the subject of later researches by Polynov (7), Jenny (4), Stobbe (9), and others. Thus, the significance of parent material on soil morphological characteristics has been observed by many workers in various regions, but the extent of the influences of this factor on soil formation in Mankato till sediments that occur in the northern portion of the Central Plains Region does not appear to have been given the study which it deserves. Furthermore, owing to the fact that other soil-forming factors and processes are variables, their effect also is variable; hence, the influence of parent material in its entirety is extremely difficult to determine or to enunciate. Nevertheless, some approximations may be made from

---

[1]Part of thesis submitted by senior author in partial fulfilment of the requirements for the degree of Doctor of Philosophy, University of Minnesota. Joint contribution, Experimental Farms and Science Service, Canada Department of Agriculture, and Department of Soils, University of Manitoba. Contribution No. 280, Chemistry Division, Science Service, Ottawa.

[2]Department of Soils, The University of Manitoba, Winnipeg, Man.

Reproduced with permission from *Canadian Journal of Agricultural Science,* Vol. 35, 1955, p. 407-421. Published by the Agricultural Institute of Canada, Ottawa, Canada.

the analytical data acquired in detailed studies of the soil profiles obtained from sites where the soil-forming factors other than parent material appear to be more or less uniform.

The object of this paper is to present the results of a series of analyses dealing with the effect of parent material on the formation of soils developed under similar and under different environmental conditions. The soils were selected from well-drained sites of similar relief.

MATERIALS AND METHODS

Physical and chemical analyses were conducted on the major horizons of ten profiles which included a Dark Brown-Black Transition or Intergrade; a Blackearth; a non-calcic Blackearth; a "Northern" Blackearth; a Degrading Blackearth; a Grey Wooded; a Rendzina; a Degrading Rendzina; a Brown Podzolic and a Podzol soil. (See Table 1 and accompanying illustration). All were virgin profiles developed on materials of Mankato age, but they differed from one another in some aspect of climate, parent material or vegetative cover.

The analyses included mechanical composition, lithology of coarse fractions, mineralogical composition of clay fractions, pH values, inorganic and organic carbon and analysis of the major chemical elements. The methods have been described in detail by Ehrlich (2) and are outlined below.

Mechanical Analysis

The pipette method as described by Kilmer and Alexander (5) was followed with minor variations. Hydrogen peroxide was used as the digesting agent for the removal of organic matter, and sodium carbonate was used as the dispersing agent for the mineral fractions. Sand was separated with a 300-mesh screen, and the silt and clay in suspension were sampled with a 25-ml. pipette.

Lithology of Coarse Fractions

Approximately 4 lb. of soil were weighed and crushed with a wooden rolling-pin. The rock particles (2 to 50 mm.) were removed by sieving and weighed. The results were calculated as percentage of the original mass.

Percentages of limestone, shale and other rocks in the parent material of each profile were obtained by determining the limestone by solution with hydrochloric acid and by separating the shale and other rocks remaining as residue after treatment with acid.

Composition of Clay Fractions

Segregation of the clays was made according to the method proposed by Jackson et al. (3). Three clay fractions—coarse (2.0-0.2 μ), medium (0.2-0.1 μ) and fine

Table 1—Nature and environment of soils

Type of soil	PARENT MATERIAL			ENVIRONMENT				
	Nature of boulder till	Texture	Carbonates as per cent $CaCO_3$	Vegetation	Climate[1]			Soil profile
					P.E[2]	T-E[2]		
Dark Brown-Black Transition	Moderately calcareous	Loam	20.2	Prairie grasses	23.6	38.0		Waskada
Blackearth	Moderately calcareous	Clay loam	17.5	Tall prairie grasses	24.5	40.5		Darlingford
"Northern" Blackearth	Moderately calcareous	Clay loam	18.1	Tall prairie grasses and recent woods	25.2	34.4		Newdale
Degrading Blackearth	Moderately calcareous	Clay loam	15.1	Tall prairie grasses and deciduous woods	25.2	34.4		Erickson
Grey Wooded	Moderately calcareous	Loam	24.6	Deciduous woods—some conifers	25.2	34.4		Waitville
Rendzina	Strongly calcareous	Loam	57.4	Tall prairie grasses	26.0	38.9		Isafold
Degrading Rendzina	Strongly calcareous	Loam	65.0	Deciduous and coniferous woods	27.8	34.8		Komarno
Brown Podzolic	Non-calcareous (ferruginous)	Coarse sand	0.4	Coniferous woods—some deciduous trees	25.2	31.4		Falcon
Podzol	Non-calcareous (siliceous)	Fine sandy loam	0.1	Coniferous woods—some deciduous trees	25.2	31.4		Telford
Non-calcic Blackearth	Non-calcareous (shaly)	Clay loam	0.2	Tall prairie grasses	24.6	40.5		Manitou

[1] Climatic data are approximate; they are based on recordings of the nearest climatological station to the site of sampling.
[2] Precipitation effectiveness and temperature efficiency values are calculated according to the method used by Thornthwaite (10).

FIGURE 1.

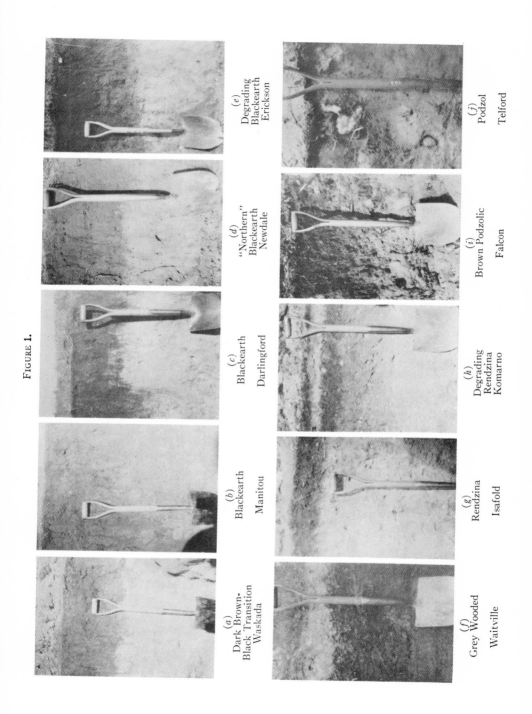

(a) Dark Brown-Black Transition Waskada

(b) Blackearth Manitou

(c) Blackearth Darlingford

(d) "Northern" Blackearth Newdale

(e) Degrading Blackearth Erickson

(f) Grey Wooded Waitville

(g) Rendzina Isafold

(h) Degrading Rendzina Komarno

(i) Brown Podzolic Falcon

(j) Podzol Telford

($< 0.1\mu$)—were obtained from major horizons of eight profiles and each was subjected to X-ray and differential thermal analyses.

pH Values

Air-dry samples were moistened with water to a paste consistency near the lower liquid limit and the pH determined with a Coleman glass electrode apparatus.

Inorganic Carbon

Inorganic carbon was determined by decomposition of the carbonates using hydrochloric acid and absorbing the resultant carbon dioxide evolved in ascarite.

Organic Carbon

Organic carbon was estimated by subtracting inorganic carbon from total carbon. The latter was obtained by a wet combustion method which is a modification of the ones given by Adams (1) and Waynick (11).

Chemical Analysis of the Major Constituents in Soils

Silicon, iron, calcium, phosphorus and the sesquioxides were determined with methods described by Wright et al. (12). The method used for titanium was the one proposed by Robinson (8). Alumina was calculated by subtracting the sum of the oxides of iron, titanium, and phosphorus from the total of the ignited oxides. Magnesium was determined gravimetrically as magnesium pyrophosphate. The method used for manganese was that outlined by Piper (6). For sodium and potassium determinations a Beckman DU flame photometer was used on dilute HCl extracts from which organic matter and silica had been removed. In all cases, the results were expressed as the oxide of the element.

RESULTS AND DISCUSSION
Mechanical Analysis

In comparing the mechanical analysis data of the various soils and respective horizons in Table 2, it is noted that the clay content is generally higher in the sola than in the parent materials. In some profiles the difference is negligible, yet the tendency is sufficiently apparent to imply the effect of pedogenic processes.

In the Northern Blackearth, Degrading Blackearth and Grey Wooded soils developed from calcareous sediments, the quantity of clay is higher in the "B" than in the "A" horizons. It is observed that the soils, in the order of Newdale, Erickson, Komarno and Waitville profiles, show progressively greater differences in clay content between the "A" and "B" horizons. In contrast to clay translocation in these de-

Table 2—Mechanical analysis, calcium carbonate[*], organic carbon and pH values

(In percent of oven-dry weight)

Soil profile (soil group)	Horizon	Depth (inches)	Sand 2.0-0.05 mm.	Silt 0.05-0.002 mm.	Clay <0.002 mm.	CaCO₃	Organic carbon	pH
Waskada	A	0- 6	43.0	36.6	20.4	0.2	4.9	7.1
(Dark Brown-Black)	B	6-13	50.7	29.0	20.4	0.6	2.0	7.3
(Transition)	Ca	13-27	42.4	37.1	20.6	24.2	0.5	7.9
	C	27-48	45.2	37.6	17.2	20.2	0.2	8.0
Darlingford	A	0-12	20.5	49.3	30.2	0.6	6.6	7.2
(Blackearth)	B	12-14	28.2	42.7	29.1	3.1	2.7	7.4
	Ca	14-25	24.8	50.1	25.1	24.4	1.0	7.9
	C	25-48	20.5	49.8	29.7	17.5	0.3	7.8
Newdale	A	0- 9	36.9	41.0	22.1	0.4	5.7	7.3
("Northern")	B	9-17	36.7	37.6	25.7	0.1	1.6	7.4
(Blackearth)	Ca	17-26	38.4	35.7	25.9	22.6	0.3	8.0
	C	26-48	43.1	36.2	20.7	18.1	0.1	8.1
Erickson	A	0- 6	29.1	43.2	27.7	0.1	7.1	7.2
(Degrading)	B₂	6-14	29.9	36.5	33.6	0.5	1.3	6.9
(Blackearth)	B₃	14-18	31.0	40.3	28.7	10.1	1.0	7.3
	Ca	18-24	34.7	38.5	26.8	18.6	0.6	7.5
	C	24-48	36.0	40.0	24.1	15.1	0.2	7.7
Waitville	A₄	0- 5	63.7	29.6	6.7	—	0.6	6.1
(Grey Wooded)	B₁	5- 9	41.3	29.3	29.3	0.1	0.6	6.0
	B₂	9-13	40.0	28.4	31.6	0.6	0.6	6.4
	B₃	13-19	45.7	29.6	24.8	10.8	0.5	7.3
	Ca	19-30	46.0	34.7	19.4	30.4	0.4	7.7
	C	30-48	44.6	36.0	19.4	24.6	0.4	7.7
Isafold	A	0- 6	42.5	44.8	12.7	4.1	7.1	7.6
(Rendzina)	C₁₁	6-14	29.5	54.0	16.5	49.8	0.8	8.0
	C₁₂	14-24	38.1	46.3	15.5	58.3	<0.1	8.4
	C₂	24-48	40.0	46.6	13.4	57.4	<0.1	8.4
Komarno	A₂	0- 2	50.6	38.1	11.3	0.3	0.9	6.8
(Degrading)	B₂	2- 5	32.6	43.3	24.2	1.3	0.7	6.6
(Rendzina)	B₃	5-14	37.7	44.4	18.0	40.1	0.4	7.6
	C₁	14-28	33.5	49.9	16.7	50.5	0.3	7.9
	C₂	28-48	62.9	28.1	9.1	65.0	0.1	8.3
Falcon	B₂	0- 6	72.5	23.6	4.0	0.6	1.3	4.5
(Brown Podzolic)	B₃	6-13	80.9	14.4	4.7	0.2	0.8	5.4
	C	13-40	87.8	8.8	3.4	0.4	0.2	5.9
Telford	A	0- 5	55.7	42.3	2.0	0.1	1.2	4.9
(Podzol)	B	5-13	57.2	40.9	1.9	0.1	0.6	5.3
	C	13-40	50.4	48.0	1.6	0.1	0.3	5.4
Manitou	A	0-17	26.6	49.8	23.6	—	4.8	6.1
(Non-calcic)	B	17-24	26.5	49.2	24.3	—	0.8	6.1
(Blackearth)	C₁	24-36	46.9	28.8	24.3	—	0.3	6.0
	C₂	36-48	46.0	32.0	22.0	0.2	0.3	6.1

[*] Inorganic carbon converted to calcium carbonate.

grading calcareous types, the Falcon (Brown Podzolic) and Telford (Podzol) profiles show no significant trend of clay movement. The latter are podzolized soils which appear to be developed from primary acidic sediments rather than from decalcified materials.

Lithology of Coarse Fractions

The percentages of rock particles in each horizon and the percentages of limestone, shale and other rocks in the rock particles of the parent materials as given in Table 3 lead to two assumptions: (a) Either rock decomposition or disintegration has occurred in the "A" and "B" horizons of each profile, since there are fewer rock particles in these horizons than in the underlying parent material; (b) Limestone has weathered more rapidly than the igneous rocks, and shales have disintegrated to finer particles at a more rapid rate than the other two groups of rocks. The latter assumption is strengthened by the results obtained by Ehrlich (2) on the petrographic analysis of fine sand in these profiles.

Further examination of the data reveals that the shaly Manitou soil shows the greatest rock fragment variation from the solum to the parent material, and the Podzolic soils the least. In the others, two features are worthy of interest: *First,* more intense weathering has occurred under the prolonged influence of forest vegetation; and *second,* rock particle decomposition has been retarded and development restricted in soils that are high in limestone fragments. The Isafold (Rendzina) soil is a good example of high-lime type in which decomposition of non-calcareous rocks has been inhibited and solum thickness restricted. This soil is well drained, yet its solum is only 6 inches thick. The Komarno (Degrading Rendzina) is another example, notwithstanding the fact that it has been under the influence of forest for a long period of time. This inverse relationship of high lime and thick solum has been frequently observed in soils by other workers.

Examination of the rock particles obtained from the site of the Brown Podzolic soil revealed that they were dominantly basaltic and schistose, high in ferromagnesian minerals. Approximately one-half of these rocks were partially weathered and in consequence were stained with limonite. From this observation it was evident that that the profile developed from this type of parent material would be strongly stained with iron.

The Podzol, on the other hand, had a parent material high in silicic sediments and low in iron-bearing minerals. Although the degree of decomposition of the silicic rock materials was similar to that of the iron-bearing minerals in the Brown Podzolic, the rotted forms of the former were light in colour.

Composition of Clay Fractions

Although five distinct types of parent materials occur among the various soils investigated, only three could be identified by the mineralogical analysis of the clay fractions. This analysis does not include inorganic carbonates present in calcareous soils because they are removed by acid pretreatment in the clay segregation procedure. Furthermore, it gives no information in respect of the coarser fractions which also are of importance in the differentiation of parent materials.

From the data on the mineralogical analysis of the clay fractions reported in Tables 4, 5 and 6, it is noted that all soils except the Brown Podzolic and Podzol, are, in many respects, quite similar, the predominant minerals being montmorillonoids and illite followed by lesser quantities of feldspars, micas and quartz. In the

Table 3—Rock particles (2-50 mm.) in the horizon and limestone,
shale and other rocks in the parent materials
(Grouped according to composition of parent material)

Profile[1]	Horizon	Rock particles[2]	Limestone[3]	Shale[3]	Other rocks[3]
Waskada	A	1.6			
	B	3.9			
	Ca	5.2			
	C	6.0	49.6	8.1	42.3
Darlingford	A	2.0			
	B	3.0			
	Ca	8.5			
	C	7.7	49.7	1.4	48.9
Newdale	A	3.2			
	B	3.1			
	Ca	10.9			
	C	13.7	57.1	9.0	33.9
Erickson	A	1.4			
	B_2	2.2			
	B_3	3.7			
	Ca	7.2			
	C	6.8	51.4	9.7	38.9
Waitville	A_2	2.2			
	B_1	6.9			
	B_2	8.8			
	B_3	12.3			
	Ca	17.4			
	C	15.3	57.5	6.7	35.8
Isafold	A	6.1			
	C_{11}	9.2			
	C_{12}	13.4			
	C_2	14.3	74.8	—	25.2
Komarno	A_2	3.6			
	B_2	3.4			
	B_3	11.6			
	C_1	15.5			
	C_2	24.6	77.4	—	22.6
Falcon	B_2	25.6			
	B_3	48.6			
	C	42.3	5.4	1.4	93.2
Telford	A	3.8			
	B	10.1			
	C	8.5	2.9	0.5	96.6
Manitou	A	1.0			
	B	1.5			
	C_1	23.0			
	C_2	25.6	11.1	87.7	1.2

[1] In this and subsequent tables, the series name only is used for the sake of brevity.
[2] As per cent of horizon.
[3] As per cent of rock particles in parent material.

Brown Podzolic soil, iron oxides in addition to montmorillonoid and illite minerals
are the prominent components. Hematite is high in the surface horizon and goethite
in the parent material. These iron compounds, common in the coarser sediments
as well as in the clays, are the cause of the reddish brown coloration normal to soils
in the Brown Podzolic Great Soil Group. On the basis of the iron content alone, it

Table 4—Mineralogical composition[1] of clay fractions in soils from sediments low in lime carbonate

Profile	Horizon	Clay fraction[2]	Montmorillonoids	Vermiculite	Chlorites	Micas	Illite	Mixed layers	Kaolinite group	Quartz	Feldspars	Al$_2$O$_3$ compounds	Hematite	Goethite	Apatite	Sepiolite	Talc	Gypsum	Palygorskite	Calcite	Others (some are not confirmed)
Manitou	A	C			2	4	2			4	3	1		1		<1					αCristobalite
		M	7		1	2	4	3	Tr		1		1								
		F	11		1	1	2	1			1	1		Tr	Tr	Tr					
	C₂	C				5	1			4	5							2			αCristobalite
		M	6				5	2			3		1								
		F	10		1	1	1	1			2	2			Tr						
Falcon	B₂	C			1		3	3	1	2	2		6								
		M	6		2		3	3	1				4	Tr							
		F	8	1		Tr	1	3				1	Tr		1				1		
	C	C			2		2	1	1	3	2										
		M	6			1	4	2	1		1		6								
		F	7			Tr		3			1	1	7		1				1		
Telford	A₂	C	2		1	1	3		1	3	4	1	1	6		1			2		Goethite Boehmite Bayerite
		M	4		1	2	1	2	1		2	1	1	5	1	2			1		
		F	1	1	2		1	2			3	2		2				2			
	B	C	1		1	2	2	2	1	3	3		1				<1		2		Boehmite Bayerite αCristobalite
		M	2	1	1	1		3	1	<1	2		<1						2		
		F	3	1	1	1	1	2	<1		3		1					<1	2	<1	
	C	C		1	2	1	3	1	1	2	2		1								Goethite Boehmite
		M	2	1	2	2	1	1	1	1	1										
		F	2	1	2	2	1	3			1	2	1							<1	

[1] The results are in the scale of 1-20, i.e.; 1 = 1-5 per cent, 2 = 6-10 per cent, etc.

[2] C = Coarse, M = Medium, F = Fine.

Table 5—Mineralogical composition[1] of clay fractions in soils from sediments high in lime carbonate

Profile	Horizon	Clay fraction[2]	Montmorillonoids	Vermiculite	Chlorites	Micas	Illite	Mixed layers	Kaolinite group	Quartz	Feldspars	Al_2O_3 compounds	Hematite	Goethite	Apatite	Sepiolite	Talc	Gypsum	Palygorskite	Calcite	Others (some are not confirmed)
Isafold	A	C	—	—	2	2	1	—	2	4	3	2	—	2	—	—	—	1	—	—	Ilmenite
		M	5	—	1	—	3	2	1	—	1	3	—	—	Tr	—	—	2	—	—	
		F	9	—	1	1	2	4	—	—	1	—	—	—	—	—	—	—	—	—	
Komarno	C_2	C	—	—	2	2	2	—	2	5	4	2	1	—	—	—	—	—	—	—	αCristobalite
		M	3	—	1	2	3	4	2	—	2	3	—	1	—	—	—	—	—	—	
		F	4	—	1	—	3	4	—	—	2	—	—	—	—	—	—	—	—	2	
	A_2	C	—	—	2	3	2	—	2	7	2	—	—	—	—	—	—	—	—	—	
		M	8	—	2	2	5	—	2	—	1	—	—	—	—	—	—	—	—	—	
		F	14	—	2	—	2	—	—	—	—	—	—	—	—	—	—	—	—	—	
	B_2	C	—	—	3	3	3	—	1	6	3	—	—	—	—	—	—	—	—	—	
		M	6	—	2	2	5	—	1	—	2	2	—	1	—	1	—	—	2	1	
		F	12	—	—	—	2	—	—	—	—	—	—	—	—	—	Tr	—	—	—	
	C	C	—	—	3	—	3	—	2	6	4	—	—	—	—	—	—	—	—	—	
		M	5	—	3	2	5	—	1	—	3	—	—	—	—	—	—	—	—	1	
		F	5	—	—	—	2	—	—	—	3	3	—	2	Tr	1	—	—	—	—	

[1] The results are in the scale of 1-20, i.e.; 1 = 1-5 per cent, 2 = 6-10 per cent, etc.

[2] C = Coarse, M = Medium, F = Fine.

Table 6—Mineralogical composition[1] of clay minerals in soils from sediments medium in lime carbonates

Profile	Horizon	Clay fraction[2]	Montmorillonoids	Vermiculite	Chlorites	Hydromica	Muscovite	Illite	Mixed layers	Kaolinite group	Quartz	Feldspars	Sepiolite	Talc	Gypsum	Calcite	Others (some are not confirmed)
Darlingford	A	C	2	1				4	not recorded	1	4	1					not recorded
		M	10+	<1		2		2		1	1	<1	1		1	1	
		F	10+	1		1		1		1	<1	1	1		1	1	
	C	C	4					5		2	5	2			<1		
		M	8			1	1	3		2	1	3	1				
		F	10+	2		1	1	1			<1	3	1			2	
Newdale	A	C	3	1		1		4	2	2	3	3		1				Hematite, Spinel Boehmite, Goethite, and Gibbsite
		M	3	<1		1		5	2	1	1	2	1				1	
		F	6			1		4	4	1	1	2	1	1	1	<1		
	B	C	2			1		4	2	2	4	3					1	Hematite, Boehmite Goethite and Lepidocrocite
		M	4	1		1		7	1	1	1	2					1	
		F	5	1		1		3	3	1	2	1				<1	1	
	C	C	2	1		1		5	2	1	2	2		1			1	Bayerite, Goethite, Spinel, and Hematite
		M	2	1		<1		2	4			1	1		1		1	
		F	3	1		3		1	4			2			1		1	
Waitville	A₂	C	1		1	1	2	3		1	6	1					1	Gibbsite, Diaspore and Bayerite Goethite, Hematite and Boehmite
		M	5	1	1	1	1	2	1		1	2		*				
		F	6	1		2	1	1	1		<1	2	1			<1		
	B₂	C	2		1	1	2	3		1	3	2					1	Bayerite, Boehmite Diaspore and Hematite
		M	8		1	1	<1	2	1		1	3		**		1		
		F	7			1		2	1		1	1	3					
	C	C	1	2	1	3	1	2		2	5	2				1		Goethite and Bayerite
		M	6			1	1	1	2	2	1	3					
		F	10				<1		1			1	1	2			1	

[1] The results are in the scale of 1-20, i.e.; 1 = 1·5 per cent, 2 = 6-10 per cent, etc.

[2] C = Coarse, M = Medium, F = Fine.

* Weak lines.

** Strong lines.

is obvious that this soil type contains a parent material different in composition from any of the others examined. The Podzol differs from the other soils primarily in its relatively higher content of feldspars and somewhat lower quantity of montmorillonitic and illitic clays. In this profile, as well as in the others, the prominence of feldspar and quartz in the clay fractions implies that the process of disintegration has been active.

Despite the evidence of physical disintegration, no marked decomposition or alteration of the more important minerals in the clay is indicated by the analysis. This viewpoint is supported by the equal distribution of the minerals throughout the profile. Here, kaolinization of sediments in post-glacial time has been slight, even in soils which appear to be intensely weathered. From examination in the field, both the Brown Podzolic and Podzol soils appear to be intensely weathered, but the mineral analyses of their sand and clay separates do not support any such conclusion. They are therefore, in the primary stage of weathering, and the relationship to their counterparts in more humid, warmer and older regions is morphological rather than chemical.

pH Values

The pH values of the sola in grassland soils developed from calcareous sediments indicate a high degree of base saturation. In Table 2, it is noted that the changes in reaction as affected by intensified leaching in the "A" horizon of the Degrading and Grey Wooded are not great and a high degree of base saturation is still evident. Although the carbonates are low in the surface horizons, periodic regeneration or regrading of the complex with calcium through the influence of vegetation and weathering apparently has been sufficient to maintain a high base-status.

The composition of sediments from which the soils have developed also has had a pronounced effect on the soil reaction. Soils tend to maintain a fairly constant pH as long as adequate reserves of limestone fragments are available. This is illustrated in the pH data, Table 2, in the case of soils developed from calcareous till. Changes in reaction will be gradual even under intense leaching until most of the lime has been dissolved and removed. Under grassland conditions, acidic properties may not be strongly pronounced for a long period of time after the free limestone has been dissolved in the upper portion of the soil profile, due to the replacement of calcium brought from lower levels by vegetation, and to the difficulty of removing calcium from the complex by other cations. This is demonstrated in the Manitou (non-calcic Blackearth) soil which is devoid of calcium carbonate in the solum at the present time. The Manitou soils originally were low in calcium but a sufficient quantity was available in the initial state of soil development to provide a high base status and in turn to maintain a fairly constant pH.

Inorganic Carbonates

Differentiation of parent materials on the basis of the presence or absence of lime carbonate is one of the criteria used in the classification of soils. The figures in Table 2, showing the carbonates in the soils investigated, indicate the several distinct types of parent materials. The quantities of carbonates in the "C" horizons vary from small amounts of less than 1 percent to large amounts of over 60 percent. With the exception of the shaly Manitou soil, it is possible to place the parent materials into three groups on the basis of their carbonate content (providing other characteristics such as texture are similar).

In the first group, a similarity in carbonate content of the parent material is noted in the Waskada, Darlingford, Newdale, Erickson and Waitville soils. Although these show some zonal characteristics that are different from each other, they have developed from material of similar composition. In the second group, both the Isafold and Komarno soils can be placed together because of their exceptionally high carbonate content. In the last group, the Falcon and Telford can be placed together because of their very low carbonate content. However, the grouping together of the Falcon and Telford soils, which are classified as Brown Podzolic and Podzol, respectively, may be open to criticism because they differ from each other in composition of sediments other than limestone content.

The role of calcium in profile development is exceedingly important. In addition to neutralizing acidic conditions and supplying a nutrient for organisms, it has a decided effect on the type of profile that is formed under grassland or forested conditions. In grassland regions, where exceptionally high quantities of carbonates are present, the sola will be thin due to the flocculating and neutralizing effect. With decreasing amounts of carbonates, the sola, in general will be thicker. A comparison of the Manitou, Darlingford and Isafold (Blackearth-like) profiles, shown in Figure 1, emphasizes that point very strongly. In forested regions, the thickness of sola also is proportionate to the amount of carbonates present. This is shown in the Komarno (Degrading Rendzina) and Waitville (Grey Wooded) profiles.

An additional feature characteristic of forest soils, developed from sediments with appreciable amounts of lime, is the formation of typical structured and illuviated "B" horizons with finer textures than those found in the "A" horizons. This type of "B" horizon is not considered representative of Brown Podzolic or Podzol soils—although the distinction is a question of some dispute among various workers.

Organic Carbon

Variations in organic carbon content of the soils investigated are primarily atributable to local climatic conditions, to the type of native vegetation, and to the nature of the parent materials. The effect of changes in environment on this constituent is well demonstrated if the profiles found under grass are compared with those found under forest (see Table 2). However, under a similar environment, differences in orgainc carbon content are apparent to a lesser degree in soils developed on different parent materials.

The Manitou and Darlingford soils are influenced by similar climatic conditions but the parent materials are dissimilar. The Manitou soil has developed from noncalareous shaly material and the Darlingford soil from somewhat finer textured sediments, high in calcareous materials. As a result of the nature of parent materials, the Manitou has a solum that is 24 inches thick and the Darlingford a solum only

14 inches thick. Notwithstanding this wide differential in solum thickness, the total carbon in the "A" and "B" of each soil is approximately equal. In the case of the Darlingford profile with a high organic carbon content, the accumulation of organic matter is restricted to a shallower depth. The same holds true in the case of the Isafold soil. Its parent material is extremely calcareous and the organic matter is largely concentrated in the surface 6 inches. This relationship of thin profiles and high organic matter in well-drained Blackearth soils has been noted in other soils in Manitoba.

In the forested zone, the composition of parent materials will influence the nature of vegetative cover and microbial activity. For example, on the Komarno and Waitville soils which have developed from calcareous materials, the prevailing tree cover is deciduous, whereas on the Falcon and Telford soils, formed from acidic sediments, the tree cover is dominantly coniferous. In addition, there is a relationship between the quantity of available nutrients in the soil and the ash content of the vegetation produced. Consequently the composition of parent material is an important factor in modifying vegetative residues, biological processes and soil formation. Well-drained soils with an abundant supply of calcium are favourable for bacterial activity and in consequence the "A_0" tends to be composed of "mild" humus in contrast to the raw humus characteristic of the "A_0" on acid soils low in calcium. Furthermore, the organic colloids that are rendered mobile in the upper part of the profile become precipitated by calcium in the "B" horizons as they move downwards.

Chemical Analysis

The data in Table 7 show the chemical composition, by horizon depths, of the profiles previously described, and indicate the degree of weathering that has taken place. It is obvious that weathering has occurred in all soils particularly in those developed from calcareous sediments.

In the grassland soils, the weathering appears to be confined principally to the release of calcium and magnesium. Very little movement of the other elements is indicated.

Where forest is the prevailing vegetation, some of the less soluble constituents, notably iron, have been either partially translocated or have passed out of the soil in solution. In the case of soils developed from calcareous material, various constituents have been translocated but not removed, whereas the soils developed from acidic sediments, on the other hand, indicate a small loss of materials from the soil profile. As a whole, however, the weathering of sediments, other than limestone, may be considered as in the primary or early stages. This is strongly supported by mineral examination as well as by the chemical analysis data, and is particularly evident in the Falcon (Brown Podzolic) and Telford (Podzol) soils, which are under the influence of moderately acid conditions and coniferous forest vegetation, but in which the weathering of non-calcareous rocks and minerals has not advanced beyond the initial phases.

Table 7—Chemical analysis

(Percent of sample after ignition)

Profile	Horizon	SiO$_2$	Al$_2$O$_3$	Fe$_2$O$_3$	TiO$_2$	CaO	MgO	K$_2$O	Na$_2$O	P$_2$O$_5$	MnO
Waskada	A	74.83	12.62	3.17	0.60	2.79	1.49	1.54	1.11	0.31	0.21
	B	75.56	12.56	3.25	0.56	2.09	1.62	1.66	1.36	0.23	0.17
	Ca	64.87	9.68	3.09	0.48	13.53	4.15	1.34	0.83	0.13	0.17
	C	65.81	11.42	3.34	0.32	11.49	4.60	1.32	0.94	0.18	0.16
Darlingford	A	74.30	12.82	3.58	0.35	2.90	1.75	1.69	0.82	0.25	0.32
	B	72.95	13.08	4.48	0.52	2.84	2.12'	1.71	0.81	0.15	0.19
	Ca	52.47	10.77	2.28	0.41	23.08	6.89	1.38	0.64	0.19	0.10
	C	62.45	15.67	4.16	0.60	10.83	2.74	1.78	0.52	0.21	0.19
Newdale	A	76.38	11.34	3.50	0.64	2.44	1.63	1.82	1.02	0.25	0.24
	B	74.80	12.61	3.75	0.58	1.85	1.64	1.71	1.18	0.13	0.27
	Ca	65.87	10.94	2.69	0.46	12.13	3.97	1.40	0.86	0.13	0.21
	C	68.33	11.09	3.25	0.47	9.52	4.15	1.40	0.86	0.15	0.17
Erickson	A	74.10	13.20	3.75	0.62	2.67	1.56	1.86	0.87	0.30	0.30
	B$_2$	73.72	14.34	3.99	0.54	1.98	1.83	1.93	0.89	0.11	0.27
	B$_3$	68.97	12.96	4.32	0.55	6.67	2.62	1.61	0.78	0.19	0.19
	Ca	66.40	10.98	3.58	0.56	10.85	3.29	1.45	0.74	0.16	0.19
	C	69.00	10.79	3.75	1.08	8.01	3.22	1.40	0.74	0.22	0.24
Waitville	A$_2$	82.51	8.65	1.87	0.42	1.57	0.70	1.47	1.36	0.11	0.30
	B$_1$	75.80	12.73	4.64	0.60	1.22	1.72	1.82	1.11	0.05	0.30
	B$_2$	73.87	12.62	5.62	0.50	2.03	1.61	1.72	1.09	0.08	0.19
	B$_3$	72.13	10.01	5.79	0.36	4.48	3.30	1.47	1.00	0.26	0.21
	Ca	61.36	8.53	2.85	0.42	18.99	3.57	1.15	1.11	0.07	0.17
	C	65.31	10.18	3.10	0.40	13.27	3.68	1.26	1.03	0.04	0.27
Isafold	A	67.88	14.02	4.32	0.51	4.82	3.39	1.86	1.37	0.07	0.21
	C$_{11}$	43.41	17.41	2.85	0.36	21.31	11.19	1.41	1.00	0.10	0.13
	C$_{12}$	39.88	11.52	1.96	0.31	27.53	15.17	1.19	1.23	0.09	0.10
	C$_2$	43.91	9.59	1.30	0.14	25.37	15.52	1.27	1.21	0.06	0.10
Komarno	A$_2$	76.16	11.47	2.93	0.25	3.19	1.34	1.59	1.53	0.11	0.21
	B$_2$	66.78	18.83	4.13	0.54	1.74	3.25	1.96	1.20	0.08	0.17
	B$_3$	49.69	13.05	3.83	0.42	16.61	12.74	1.55	0.89	0.17	0.17
	C$_1$	47.99	11.38	3.34	0.26	20.73	13.35	1.13	0.71	0.10	0.13
	C$_2$	43.92	6.13	1.38	0.21	27.75	16.89	0.72	0.71	0.07	0.10
Falcon	B$_2$	64.77	13.73	14.18	1.02	1.39	1.12	1.53	1.10	0.24	0.13
	B$_3$	61.95	11.93	18.82	1.13	1.27	1.38	1.40	1.00	0.18	0.07
	C	60.13	11.71	21.10	0.65	1.16	1.51	1.37	0.99	0.16	0.07
Telford	A	76.07	11.81	2.44	0.42	2.96	1.31	1.80	2.06	0.03	0.16
	B	74.03	13.21	3.50	0.43	2.32	1.60	1.82	2.18	0.02	0.16
	C	73.57	12.78	3.83	0.40	2.90	1.51	1.84	2.18	0.03	0.10
Manitou	A	78.24	10.89	3.17	0.55	1.96	1.56	1.34	0.74	0.21	0.32
	B	78.11	11.70	3.25	0.32	1.45	1.54	1.47	0.82	0.12	0.24
	C$_1$	81.14	9.97	2.69	0.49	1.33	1.55	1.00	0.53	0.04	0.13
	C$_2$	81.30	10.42	2.36	0.45	1.12	1.72	0.97	0.42	0.07	0.24

CONCLUSIONS

1. The composition of soil parent material has played an important role in determining or modifying certain types of soil profiles developed in Manitoba on sediments of Mankato age.

2. Disintegration of clastic materials has been more active in the soil profiles than in the underlying substrate, but mineral decomposition within the soil profiles has been relatively slight.

3. The rate of weathering of coarse clastic sediments, ranging in size from 2 to 50 millimeters, indicated the following sequence: shale > limestone > other rock fragments.

4. Montmorillonite and illite were the dominant clay minerals found in all the representative genetic soil types in both the grassland and forest regions except in the case of the Brown Podzolic and Podzol types. In the Brown Podzolic soil, iron oxides were found to be important clay components, and feldspars were in greater proportion in the clay of the Podzol soil than in other types.

5. Most of the montmorillonoid and illite minerals were assumed to be pre-Mankato weathering products because of their relatively uniform distribution throughout the profiles. Small amounts of kaolinite also were found commonly in all horizons of the various profiles, which indicated that this mineral was not formed in situ by recent soil-forming processes.

6. The percentage of inorganic carbonates in the soil parent material was one of the important factors that influenced the development of specific morphological charactistics peculiar to certain great soils groups—parent material can determine or cause differentiation in Grey Wooded and Podzol or Brown Podzolic soils; and it can differentiate between the formation of Blackearth and Rendzina types.

7. Abnormally shallow soil profiles resulted when they were developed on excessively high-lime parent materials.

8. In the forested zone, medium textured soils, developed from calcareous sediments, had an accumulation of clay in their "B" horizons, whereas those developed from highly silicic non-calcareous materials studied had little or no clay concentration in any part of the profiles.

9. The lime content of parent material can be a prime factor in determining the extent to which mobile organic colloids are precipitated and retained in the "B" horizon, or removed by downward passage through the profile.

10. The pH or soil reaction is usually considered to be a reflection of the degree of base saturation of the soil adsorption complex. However, it also may be a reflection of the composition of the materials from which the soil is derived.

11. Soils that have high-base status, as the result of the composition of the parent material, may be a more favourable media for organisms and organic decomposition than soils developed in parent materials low in bases.

12. The Brown Podzolic and Podzol soils examined were considered to be young soils in a primary stage of weathering. The relationship of these to their counter-

parts in more humid, warmer, and older regions appeared to be more morphological than chemical.

13. The data indicate that the only difference between the Grey Wooded, Brown Podzolic and Podzol soils is parent material and it is here inferred that the term "zonal soil" can be a misnomer.

REFERENCES

1. Adams, J. E. Determination of total carbon in soils by the wet combustion method. J. of Ind. and Eng. Chem., Anal Ed., 6:227. 1934.

2. Ehrlich, W. A. Pedological processes of some Manitoba soils. Thesis, Univ. of Minn. 1954.

3. Jackson, M. L., L. D. Whittey, and R. P. Pennington. Segregation procedure for the mineralogical analysis of soils. Soil Sci. Soc. Am. Proc. 14: 77-81. 1949.

4. Jenny, H. Factors of soil formation. 1st ed. McGraw-Hill Book Co., Inc., New York and London. 1941.

5. Kilmer, V. J., and L. T. Alexander. Methods of making mechanical analysis of soils. Soil Sci. 68: 15-24. 1949.

6. Piper, C. S. Soil and plant analysis. Interscience Publishers Inc., New York. 1950.

7. Polynov, B. B. Das Muttergestein als Faktor der Bodenbildung und als Kriterium fur die Boden-klassification. Soil Res. 2: 165-180. 1930.

8. Robinson, W. O. The fusion analysis of soils. Soil Sci. 59: 7-12. 1945.

9. Stobbe, P. C. The morphology and genesis of Gray-Brown Podzolic and related soils in Eastern Canada. Soil Sci. Soc. Amer. Proc. 16: 81-84. 1952.

10. Thornthwaite, C. W. The climates of North America. Geol. Rev. 21: 633-654. 1931.

11. Waynick, D. D. A simplified wet combustion method for the determination of carbon in soils. J. Ind. and Eng. Chem. 11: 634. 1919.

12. Wright, L. E., et al. Chemical method of soil analysis. Chem. Div., Science Service, Ottawa. 1949.

FRAGIPAN AND WATER-TABLE RELATIONSHIPS OF SOME BROWN PODZOLIC AND LOW HUMIC-GLEY SOILS [1]

Leland H. Gile, Jr. [2]

ABSTRACT

Ground-water levels in relation to the fragipan were studied in Paxton, Scituate, and Ridgebury soils at two field sites in southeastern New Hampshire in 1956 and 1957. The first two series are Brown Podzolic soils and the last a Low Humic-Gley soil. Horizons of Scituate and Ridgebury soils at one of the sites were sampled for laboratory determination of particle size distribution, cation-exchange data, free iron content, and organic matter. Bulk density measurements were made of selected horizons, and thin sections for microscopic studies were prepared for parts of the fragipans. All three soils have coarse textures, low cation-exchange capacity, and low base status. Free iron oxides in the upper solum are lower in the Ridgebury than in the Scituate but the former has an appreciable concentration in the upper part of the fragipan. A mechanism is proposed for this concentration of iron oxides.

Ground-water levels were measured in a number of access wells. These measurements indicate that the water table (1) remains in the upper solum of Ridgebury soils during the late fall, the winter, and most of the spring, (2) remains in the upper solum of the Scituate soils for short periods and in the lower solum for long periods, and (3) seldom rises above the fragipan in Paxton soils. Some of the factors affecting observed water tables are discussed.

Soils with fragipans are the most important upland soils in southeastern New Hampshire. They occur on drumlins and on moraines which are characterized by smooth, gentle slopes. The following catenas are concerned:

1. The Paxton-Woodbridge-Ridgebury-Whitman catena. These soils are developed from glacial till derived mainly from schist.
2. The Essex-Scituate-Ridgebury-Whitman catena, soils developed from glacial till derived mainly from granite.

All are Brown Podzolic soils except for the Ridgebury series (Low Humic-Gley) and the Whitman series (Humic-Gley), which serve as the poorly drained and very poorly drained members, respectively, of both catenas.

---

[1] Contribution from the Soil Conservation Service, USDA. Presented before Div. V, Soil Science Society of America, Nov. 20, 1957, at Atlanta, Ga. Received Jan. 27, 1958. Approved July 28, 1958.

[2] Soil Scientist, Soil Survey Investigations, SCS, USDA, State College, N. Mex., formerly Soil Scientist, Rochester, N. H. Grateful acknowledgment is made to Walter H. Lyford, Senior Soil Correlator, SCS, for counsel throughout the progress of this study.

Reproduced with permission from *Soil Science Society of America Proceedings,* Vol. 22, 1958. p. 560-565. Published by the Soil Science Society of America, Madison, Wisconsin, U.S.A.

The pan is considered to be a fragipan, as defined in the Soil Survey Manual (5), except that it is only slightly less firm when moistened.

Where soils and fragipans occur on gently sloping drumlins with broad, level or nearly level crests, drainage grades from poor on the lower slopes of the drumlin to moderately good on its upper slopes and crest. If the drumlin crest is sharper, a well-drained soil is present.

A site similar to the former was chosen for detailed study (site 1), in the summer of 1956. Work was begun later in the year on an area similar to the latter (site 2).

MATERIALS AND METHODS

Site 1

Site 1 (figure 1) is located on a broad, gently sloping drumlin approximately 1½ miles northeast of Rochester, in Strafford County.

Scituate Fine Sandy Loam [3]

The Scituate fine sandy loam occurs on the upper slopes and crest of the drumlin:

Horizon	Depth, inches	Morphology
A_p	0-9	Very dark grayish brown (10 YR 3/2, moist) fine sandy loam; weak medium crumb structure; friable; many roots; medium acid; clear wavy boundary.

---

[3] Terminology used in soil descriptions is in accordance with the Soil Survey Manual, USDA Handbook 18(5).

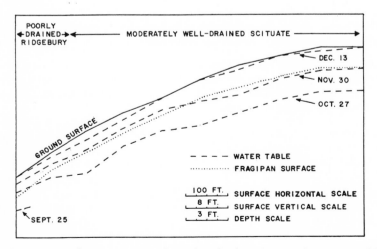

Figure 1—Cross section of site 1. Catenary relationship of soils is shown at the top. Rise of the water table and an increase in its slope on selected days during the fall of 1956 are shown by dashed lines.

B_{21g}	9-14	Brown (10YR 5/3, moist) sandy loam; mottles of yellowish brown are few, fine, and faint; massive to single grain; friable; many roots; medium acid; clear wavy boundary.
B_{22g}	14-18	Olive ((5Y 5/3, moist) fine sandy loam; mottles of yellowish brown are common, medium and distinct; weak medium platy structure; firm in place, friable when removed; few roots; medium acid; abrupt wavy boundary.
B_{23gm}	18-36	Dark brown and light brownish gray (10 YR 3/3, 2.5Y 5/2-6/2, moist) fine sandy loam; in many places, ¼- to 1-inch layers with the above colors, appearing as horizontal streaks in the profile; few of light brownish gray layers underlain by yellowish red layers, 1/8-inch in thickness; moderate medium platy structure, with clean grains of medium sand between plates; very firm in place, light-colored material usually friable when removed, firmness increasing with darkness to very or extremely firm; weakly to extremely brittle; few roots; medium acid; diffuse boundary.
C_g	36 +	Yellowish brown (10YR 5/4, moist) sandy loam to fine sandy loam; mottles of strong brown are few, fine, and faint; strong fine platy structure; firm in place, friable when removed; no roots; in places, layering effect as in fragipan occurs but colors are not as prominent; medium acid.

Ridgebury Stony Loamy Sand

The Ridgebury stony loamy sand occurs on the lower slopes of the drumlin (laboratory data for this soil are in tables 3 and 4):

Horizon	Depth, inches	Morphology
A_{00}	2-1½	Recently fallen leaves.
A_0	1½-0	Partly decomposed litter.
A_1	0-1	Grayish brown (10YR 5/2, moist) fine sandy loam; weak medium crumb structure; very friable; very strongly acid; clear wavy boundary.
A_{2g}	1-10	Light brownish gray (10YR 6/2, moist) loamy sand; mottles of yellowish brown are few, fine, and faint; massive to single grain; very friable; roots common; very strongly acid; clear wavy boundary.
B_{21g}	10-18	Grayish brown (2.5Y 5/2, moist) loamy sand; few, fine, and faint mottles of yellowish brown; massive to single grain; friable; roots common; strongly acid; clear wavy boundary.
B_{22g}	18-20	Olive (5Y 5/3, moist) sandy loam; many coarse prominent mottles of very dark brown, some peds being coated with that color, others very dark brown throughout; weak coarse platy structure; friable; ¼-inch to 1/32-inch layers of dark reddish brown organic

		matter and many fine roots between plates; strongly acid; abrupt wavy boundary.
B$_{23irgm}$	20-23	Light brownish gray (2.5Y 6/2, moist) to yellowish red (5YR 4/8, moist) loamy sand; massive to weak medium platy; very firm in place, firm when removed; weakly to very brittle; many coarse prominent mottles of dark reddish brown to yellowish red in places, red colors are dominant and continuous; few roots; strongly acid; clear wavy boundary.
B$_{24gm}$	23-31	Yellowish brown to light olive brown (10YR-2.5Y 5/4, moist) sandy loam to fine sandy loam; massive; extremely firm in place, firm when removed; few roots; few vertical grayish streaks 2 to 3 inches deep by ½-inch wide, with a yellowish red edge of approximately 1/32-inch; in places these grayish areas occur as rounded blotches; strongly acid; gradual boundary.
C$_{1g}$	31-43	Yellowish brown (10YR 5/8, moist) loamy sand, mottles of light olive brown are common, medium, and prominent; weak medium platy structure; firm in place, friable to firm when removed; no roots; strongly acid; gradual boundary.
C$_{2g}$	43-59	Olive (5Y 5/3, moist) loamy sand; many coarse, prominent mottles of yellowish brown and dusky red; weak medium platy structure; friable to firm; no roots; strongly acid.

Site 2

Site 2 is on a gently sloping drumlin, about 4 miles northwest of site 1. It differs from site 1 in that the crest of the drumlin is sharper, and there is a well-drained soil (Paxton series) on the crest and upper slopes.

The glacial till in which these soils have developed is extremely firm in place. It is difficult to determine whether a boundary exists between the fragipan and the till.

Light-colored streaks are characteristic of the fragipan in the soils at site 2. The streaks occur in soils of good, moderately good, and poor drainage, and are nearly vertical in the profile. The streaks present a roughly polygonal appearance when viewed in a horizontal plane and divide the fragipan into units which range from a few inches to several feet in diameter. Similar streaks in fragipans have been described in New York (2), Maryland (3), and Europe (4).

The color of the main part of the fragipan grades from olive in the well-drained Paxton to brown or yellowish brown in the poorly drained Ridgebury soils. Within the fragipan, grayish brown to light brownish gray streaks range from ½ to several inches in width, and are bounded vertically by yellowish red edges which are ¼-inch thick.

The structure of the main part of the fragipan is moderate fine to medium platy, while the material in the streaks ranges from massive to single grain. Texture of the main part of the fragipan is fine sandy loam. Texture of the material in the streaks ranges from sandy loam to loamy sand. Material in the streaks is friable or very friable in consistence; the main part of the fragipan is firm to extremely firm.

Ground-Water Wells

The study area at site 1 is 900 by 400 feet in size, with the short axis transverse to the slope. Seventy-six ground-water wells, in six lines, were installed during the summer of 1956. In 3 lines the wells rested on top of the fragipan. In 1 line the wells penetrated 6 inches into the fragipan. In 2 lines wells were installed at a depth of approximately 4 feet.

During the latter part of 1956 several wells were installed in the well-drained Paxton soil at site 2. In April, 1957, a line of wells was installed down the slope at at site 2, so that comparison of results could be made with studies at site 1. Depths to water table in soils of similar drainage were very comparable.

Occasionally water moved along the surface of the fragipan into a well. This happened when the water table was below the fragipan surface, and substantial precipitation occurred. At these times it was necessary to wait a few hours until the water dropped below the fragipan surface. The well was then pumped dry. The depth was measured after the water table rose to equilibrium.

RESULTS AND DISCUSSION

Water-Table Studies

Water appeared in the wells during the latter part of September. Water table measurements were begun at that time and were continued through the following fall, winter, and spring (table 1).

The water table is closely related to precipitation. Water did not come into the wells until several inches of rain had fallen. As the water table nears the ground surface, progressively smaller amounts of precipitation are necessary to effect further rises. The slope of the water table increases with precipitation until it approximates the surface of moderately well and poorly drained soils (figure 1). Within 1 or 2 days after precipitation has stopped, the water table starts to fall slowly in moderately well-drained soils. It falls much more slowly in poorly drained soils. The water table continues to lower until sufficient water enters the soil to affect it.

The water table dropped faster in soils on the upper portion of the slope than in soils on the lower portion. This indicates slow lateral movement of water downslope. When the water table was present in the solum, pits were dug in sloping soils at both sites. Water moved very slowly down-slope in the main part of the fragipan. Water moved more readily above the fragipan and in streaks.

The water table remained in the upper solum of the poorly drained Ridgebury soil at site 1 during the late fall, winter, and most of the spring. Lateral movement of water downslope maintains the water table at this high level. Poorly drained soils occur on that portion of the slope above which the water table remains high enough to maintain this lateral movement. The soil slope-water table relationship is an important factor in determining soil drainage at these sites.

In the upper solum of the moderately well-drained Scituate soil at site 1, the water table remained only for short periods. It remained for longer periods in the lower solum. Marked fluctuation is characteristic of the water table in this soil. On the

Table 1—Precipitation (in inches) and water-table levels (inches from ground surface) in well-drained, moderately well-drained, and poorly drained soils with fragipans, from Sept. 1956 to June 1957.

September 1956 – December 1956

	Sep 25	Sep 28	Oct 4	Oct 6	Oct 11	Oct 13	Oct 16	Oct 20	Oct 24	Oct 27	Oct 30	Nov 2	Nov 5	Nov 8	Nov 11	Nov 13	Nov 15	Nov 17	Nov 21	Nov 23	Nov 28	Nov 30	Dec 4	Dec 7	Dec 10	Dec 13	Dec 17	Dec 20	Dec 27
Water-table levels:																													
Poorly Drained Ridgebury—Site 1	29	32	38	37	26	25	27	28	8	12	14	16	17	17	18	11	14	15	12	6	4	5	7	5	4	0	2	3	2
Moderately well-drained Scituate—Site 1									38	36	39	41	44	45	47	44	44	46	45	29	16	18	25	22	11	0	0	6	5
Well-drained Paxton—Site 2																												28	25
Precipitation*			0.4		1.1					1.3			0.3						0.7	0.8	1.0		0.8	0.6		1.0			0.9

January 1957 – March 1957

	Jan 3	Jan 7	Jan 10	Jan 14	Jan 18	Jan 22	Jan 23	Jan 24	Jan 28	Jan 31	Feb 4	Feb 7	Feb 11	Feb 14	Feb 21	Feb 25	Feb 26	Feb 28	Mar 4	Mar 11	Mar 14	Mar 18	Mar 20	Mar 22	Mar 25	Mar 28
Water-table levels:																										
Poorly drained Ridgebury—Site 1	5	6	6	6	7	5	0	0	3	4	5	6	4	5	7	7	2	0	4	5	3	2	3	2	5	5
Moderately well-drained Scituate—Site 1	14	19	19	21	23	21	0	4	18	23	24	26	26	32	38	34	31	16	19	22	23	15	19	10	14	16
Well-drained Paxton—Site 2	38						21	31	39																	
Precipitation*	1.0	0.4	0.5				0.3		0.1	0.4		0.1		0.4		0.3		0.6		0.5				0.2		0.3

April 1957 – June 1957

	Apr 1	Apr 2	Apr 4	Apr 6	Apr 8	Apr 11	Apr 15	Apr 18	Apr 22	Apr 25	Apr 29	May 2	May 6	May 9	May 13	May 16	May 20	May 21	May 23	May 27	May 29	Jun 1	Jun 3	Jun 4	Jun 6	Jun 10	Jun 12	Jun 14	Jun 17	Jun 20	Jun 24
Water-table levels:																															
Poorly drained Ridgebury—Site 1	6	2	5	0	3	3	5	5	8	10	10	12	14	16	12	6	12		4	9	10	12	17	13	16	20	21	24	27	31	29	46
Moderately well-drained Scituate—Site 1	18	5	16	0	5	4	14	19	26	30	33	37	43	47	44	47	41	43													
Well-drained Paxton—Site 2		20		26	21	25	36																								
Precipitation*	0.1	0.5		0.7		0.6						0.5	0.6		0.8	0.3		0.2	0.3				0.4							0.2	0.5

*Means from several nearby weather stations. The figures are cumulative from the day following the date of preceding water table measurement.

nearly level crest of the drumlin, moderately well-drained soils occur because the water table here has a broad, flat surface. Lateral movement of water in these soils is parallel to the surface of the ground. The water table lowers slowly as water moves laterally downslope.

In the well-drained Paxton soil at site 2, the water table rose above the fragipan only when it was at the surface of the adjoining moderately well-drained soil and substantial precipitation occurred. Several days after precipitation stopped, lateral movement downslope caused the water table to lower below the fragipan surface. Well-drained soils occur at site 2 because the crest of the drumlin is sharper.

Depth to the water table may vary markedly from year to year. A dry period from April 10 to May 9, 1957, resulted in a substantial lowering of the water table (table 1). There was more precipitation during this period in 1956. On June 11, 1956, the water table was 18 inches from the surface of the moderately well-drained Scituate soil on the crest of the drumlin at site 1.

The water table is affected by seasonal variations in transpiration. Precipitation in the fall of 1956 contributed to rises in the water table. Precipitation in May and June 1957 did not markedly slow the lowering of the water table.

Although temperatures occasionally dropped below 0 F, no ice occurred in wells where the snow was a foot or more in depth. This suggests that lateral leaching is active during the winter in soils protected by deep snow.

When the water table is below the fragipan surface and substantial precipitation occurs, water may "perch" on the fragipan for short periods. Horizons overlying the fragipan are friable and moderately coarse textured. In most places soil slopes are gentle to strong. These factors limit "perching" to periods of several days.

During the late fall, winter, and early spring, a substantial portion of the water which enters the surface of poorly drained soils does not reach the fragipan. The water moves directly into the water table which is above the fragipan at this time, and then moves laterally downslope.

Depth to the water table could be estimated within several inches. This was done by obtaining one well reading and determining the drop from the previous reading. The water in all other wells dropped a proportionate amount determined by location on the slope. If sufficient correlation of rainfall, seasonal variations in transpiration, and depths to the water table could be obtained, it should be possible to predict depth to the water table in these soils without measurement.

Table 2—Bulk density of the fragipan.

Location and soil type	Depth, inches	Bulk Density	
		with > 2mm. fraction	without > 2mm. fraction
Site 1—Scituate fine sandy loam	19 (top of fragipan)	1.88	1.76
	19 (top of fragipan)	1.87	1.74
	27	1.85	1.68
	27	1.93	1.80
Site 2—Ridgebury fine sandy loam	18 (top of fragipan)	1.82	1.64
	21	1.80	1.69
Site 2—Paxton fine sandy loam	24 (top of fragipan)	1.91	1.82

Moderately good to poor drainage of soils at these sites is caused by the presence of the water table in the solum during late fall, winter, and early spring. The high level of the water table at this time appears to be mainly dependent upon the following factors: (1) precipitation; (2) marked lowering of transpiration rates in the fall, winter, and early spring; (3) slow movement of water in the fragipan and in the compact glacial till which lies beneath it; and (4) the soil slope-water table relationship.

Bulk Density

Bulk density determinations were made with Volumeasure CN 980 (table 2). Bulk density appears to be relatively uniform in the fragipan. Values are slightly lower than those of the Volusia fragipan in New York.[4] Removal of the > 2 mm. fraction resulted in lower values. This fraction was composed primarily of schistose and granitic material.

Laboratory Data

Soils on different slope positions at site 1 were analyzed (Tables 3,4).

Sand fractions show little variation throughout horizons of each soil. Textures in the Ridgebury are coarser than those usually occurring in this soil.

Organic carbon and nitrogen are highest in the surface of the two Scituate soils, and gradually decrease downward. This is typical of "modal" Brown Podzolic soils of the area. Organic carbon and nitrogen of the Ridgebury soil exhibit a second maximum in the B horizon. The cation-exchange capacity is low, but percent base saturation increases in the fragipan.

From the crest to the lower slopes of the drumlin, there is a progressive decrease in free iron in the horizons above the fragipan. There is an increase in free iron in the fragipan surface of the poorly drained soil on the lower slope.

Water-soluble products of plant decomposition, moving downward from the surface, cause solution and reduction of ferric oxide encountered during their passage (1). Water moves slowly in the downslope direction of the water table. When the water table is above the fragipan, the leaching action of the lateral movement moves some of the ferrous oxide downslope. A marked difference in firmness and structure of the fragipan, as compared to the horizons above, tends to slow water at the fragipan surface. This allows oxidation of ferrous iron. Newly acquired ferric oxide is capable of fixing further amounts of ferrous iron (1). Thus, free iron oxide coatings could accumulate on peds and sand grains in the fragipan surface. Such an accumulation is characteristic of the fragipan surface on lower slopes at both sites. Substantial accumulation of ferric oxide on the fragipan surface of upper slopes was not observed.

At site 1, horizontal streaks are characteristic of the fragipan in the soil on the nearly level drumlin crest. Thin sections from the fragipan were examined with the

---

[4] Carlisle, F. J. Characteristics of soils with fragipans in a Podzol region. Unpub. Ph.D. thesis, Cornell University, Ithaca, N. Y. 1954.

Table 3—Mechanical analysis of three soils at site 1.*

Depth, inches	Horizon	Particle size distribution, %										Textural class
		Very coarse sand 2-1 mm.	Coarse sand 1-0.5 mm.	Medium sand 0.5-0.25 mm.	Fine sand 0.25-0.10 mm.	Very fine sand 0.10-0.05 mm.	Silt 0.05-0.002 mm.	Clay <0.002	0.2-0.02 mm.	0.02-0.002 mm.	> 2 mm.	
		Scituate sandy loam (crest of drumlin)										
0-9	Ap	4.4	15.3	15.1	20.6	11.1	27.4	6.1	34.5	14.0	9	sl
9-13	B21	5.2	16.2	15.0	20.8	11.6	28.2	3.0	34.4	15.6	11	sl
13-16	B22g	5.2	18.2	16.9	21.8	11.6	23.9	2.4	33.8	12.4	8	ls/sl
16-24	B23gm	4.5	12.7	13.0	20.0	13.4	31.2	5.2	38.3	16.6	10	sl
24-36	B24gm	6.1	13.6	10.6	18.5	15.9	29.8	5.5	40.7	15.2	10	sl
36-48	C1g	5.2	16.0	11.6	20.6	16.4	25.0	5.2	42.1	10.8	9	sl
48-64	C2g	3.6	10.2	10.4	22.6	19.5	29.1	4.6	49.9	12.0	5	fsl
64-83	C3g	3.7	10.3	10.6	21.8	16.8	26.9	9.9	43.2	13.0	6	fsl
		Scituate fine sandy loam (middle slopes)										
0-7	Ap	4.2	12.7	11.7	21.5	15.8	28.0	6.1	41.4	14.0	11	fsl
7-13	B21	4.4	12.9	11.0	21.8	18.5	27.3	4.1	45.9	12.5	8	fsl
13-18	B22g	5.2	13.1	12.6	25.6	20.2	20.5	2.8	48.3	7.3	12	ls
18-24	B23gm	4.9	13.2	12.0	23.9	18.4	23.5	4.1	45.7	9.6	13	sl/ls
24-33	B24gm	5.3	14.2	12.0	23.0	18.8	23.1	3.6	45.3	9.9	10	fsl/ls
33-42	C1g	4.0	13.8	12.0	23.5	17.8	25.1	3.8	46.6	9.5	14	fsl/ls
42-55	C2g	5.1	13.4	12.0	23.7	18.0	23.9	3.9	45.4	10.4	10	sl/ls
55-62	C3g	6.2	14.7	12.4	24.2	18.3	20.8	3.4	45.0	7.9	18	ls
		Ridgebury stony loamy sand (lower slopes)										
0-1	A1	—(Not determined—highly organic)—										
1-10	A2g	6.4	14.1	14.5	26.8	17.0	19.9	1.3	43.8	7.8	13	ls
10-18	B21g	5.6	14.7	15.1	26.9	17.1	17.9	2.7	42.2	7.0	13	ls
18-20	B22g	5.5	15.8	15.3	25.9	17.0	18.5	2.0	41.7	7.5	10	ls
20-23	B231rgm	5.1	17.4	17.2	28.1	14.0	15.4	1.7	37.1	6.5	12	ls-sl
23-31	B24gm	5.8	12.3	11.7	23.6	17.8	26.1	2.7	46.1	11.1	9	fsl/ls
31-43	C1g	6.2	14.7	13.0	25.1	19.2	20.0	1.8	45.7	7.7	19	ls
43-59	C2g	4.5	14.1	12.2	22.7	18.5	25.4	2.6	45.1	11.7	15	sl/ls

*Analyses made by the Soil Survey Laboratory, Beltsville, Md.

Table 4—Laboratory data for three soils at site 1.*

Depth, inches	pH 1:1	Organic matter		Free Fe_2O_3	Cation-exchange capacity (sum)	Extractable cations me. per 100 g. soil					Base saturation %
		Organic carbon	Nitrogen			Ca	Mg	H	K	Na	
Scituate sandy loam (crest of drumlin)											
0-9	5.4	2.61	0.227	1.4	17.2	3.7	0.3	12.9	0.2	0.1	25
9-13	5.7	0.80	0.062	1.3	7.9	0.7	0.2	6.7	0.2	0.1	15
13-16	5.7	0.51	0.044	1.1	5.6	0.4	0.2	4.8	0.1	0.1	14
16-24	5.8	0.10	0.028	1.0	3.9	0.6	0.1	3.0	0.1	0.1	23
24-36	5.4	0.08	0.020	1.0	3.9	0.4	0.2	3.0	0.2	0.1	23
36-48	5.5	0.03	0.007	0.7	4.6	1.3	0.2	2.8	0.2	0.1	39
48-64	5.6	0.03	0.006	0.6	3.6	1.1	0.2	3.0	0.2	0.1	44
64-83	6.0	0.01	0.006	0.6	3.7	1.5	0.2	1.6	0.2	0.2	57
Scituate fine sandy loam (middle slopes)											
0-7	5.2	3.21	0.204	1.0	19.9	2.0	0.1	17.5	0.2	0.1	12
7-13	5.2	0.73	0.057	0.9	9.4	0.2	<0.1	9.0	0.1	0.1	4
13-18	5.5	0.25	0.028	0.6	4.6	0.4	0.2	3.8	0.1	0.1	17
18-24	5.6	0.07	0.010	0.6	3.7	0.2	0.2	3.2	0.1	<0.1	14
24-33	5.6	0.05	0.009	0.6	3.5	0.6	<0.1	2.8	0.1	<0.1	20
33-42	5.8	0.02	0.005	0.6	2.7	0.6	0.1	1.8	0.1	0.1	33
42-55	5.8	0.02	0.006	0.7	2.9	0.7	0.2	1.8	0.1	0.1	38
55-62	5.9	0.02	0.007	0.6	2.5	0.6	0.1	1.6	0.1	0.1	36
Ridgebury stony loamy sand (lower slopes)											
0-1	4.5	13.0	0.292	—	41.7	0.7	1.6	38.8	0.5	0.1	7
1-10	4.6	0.15	0.018	0.2	1.8	<0.1	0.1	1.6	0.1	<0.1	11
10-18	4.7	0.49	0.050	0.2	5.1	<0.1	0.2	4.8	0.1	<0.1	6
18-20	4.8	0.69	0.040	0.2	8.1	0.1	0.1	7.8	0.1	<0.1	4
20-23	5.1	0.38	0.014	0.6	4.4	0.0	0.1	4.0	0.1	<0.1	7
23-31	5.4	0.03	0.005	1.3	2.1	<0.1	0.1	1.8	0.1	0.1	14
31-43	5.6	0.03	0.004	0.6	1.7	<0.1	0.1	1.4	0.1	0.1	18
43-59	5.8	0.01	0.006	0.6	2.3	0.6	0.3	1.2	0.1	0.1	48

*Analyses made by the Soil Survey Laboratory, Beltsville, Md.

Table 5—Percentages of free Fe_2O_3, Al_2O_3 and MnO in streaks,
yellowish red edge, and main part of fragipan.*

Area of fragipan	% Fe_2O_3	% Al_2O_3	% MnO
Light-colored streak	0.08	0.08	nil
Yellowish red edge	2.01	0.52	nil
Main part of fragipan	0.62	0.26	nil

*Analyses performed by the Soil Survey Laboratory, Beltsville, Md.

petrographic microscope.[5] There appeared to be two conditions between the plates. In one, the sand and silt grains were very clean and appeared to be quite loose in the parting. In the other condition there were no clean grains but there was a thin, continuous, dark brown coating on one or both faces of the parting. In places the coating showed birefringence, indicating that it is at least partly fine clay.

In the soils on the nearly level crest of the drumlin, lateral movement of water is parallel to the surface of the ground and to the platy structural units in the fragipan. In the field as well as in the microscope, clean grains of sand were observed between plates. These grains were probably cleanly leached by laterally moving solutions. Dark brown coatings on peds are probably areas of deposition.

At site 2, light-colored vertical streaks with yellowish red edges are prominent in the fragipan. The main part of the fragipan from the Ridgebury soil at site 2, the adjoining streaks and yellowish red edges are analyzed (table 5). There is a marked depletion of free Fe_2O_3 and Al_2O_3 in the streak and a notable enrichment of these compounds in the yellowish red edge.

Examination of this sections showed that the main part of the fragipan is very compact and has little pore space. Interstices are densely packed with fine material. Most of the clay is uniformly distributed. Thin sections from the streaks showed that some of the fine interstitial material between the coarse grains has been removed. There has been translocation of iron oxide and clay from the streak to the edge. The edge is densely impregnated with iron oxide which has even penetrated cracks in sand grains. Fills and skins of clay are quite common in the edge.

In many places the streaks contain roots. The upper portions of most streaks probably have contained roots at some time since their formation. Organic matter could reduce any ferric oxide in the streaks. Also, ferrous oxide is probably leached into the streaks from the overlying horizons. When the water table is below the fragipan and substantial precipitation occurs, the first part of the fragipan which will receive water is the streaked portion. Water moves more readily in the streaks than in the main part of the fragipan. Thus, portions of the fragipan adjoining the streaks are recharged with water first. Slow movement of water from the streaks into the main part of the fragipan might cause ferrous oxide and clay to be leached from the streaks. The ferrous oxide could then be oxidized at the edges in a similar manner to that suggested for the fragipan surface.

---

[5] Thin sections examined by John G. Cady, Soil Survey Laboratory, Beltsville, Md.

LITERATURE CITED

1. Bloomfield, C. Experiments on the mechanism of gley formation: Jour. Soil Sci. 2: 196-211. 1951.
2. Carlisle, F. J., Knox, E. G., and Grossman, R. B. Fragipan horizons in New York soils: I. General characteristics and distribution. Soil Sci. Soc. Amer. Proc. 21: 320-321. 1957.
3. Nikiforoff, C. C., Humbert, R. P., and Cady, J. G., The hardpan in certain soils of the coastal plain. Soil Sci. 65: 135-153. 1948.
4. Plaisance, Georges. Observations sur les sous-sols marmoroides de certains sols de limons: Des de L'academie des Sciences, Tome 236, No. 25, 22 June. 1953.
5. Soil Survey Staff. Soil survey manual: USDA Handbook 18, 1951.

CHEMICAL, MORPHOLOGICAL AND MINERALOGICAL CHARACTERISTICS OF A CHRONOSEQUENCE OF SOILS ON ALLUVIAL DEPOSITS IN THE NORTHWEST TERRITORIES[1]

J. R. Wright, A. Leahey and H. M. Rice

Canada Department of Agriculture, Ottawa, Ontario

Received for publication October 6, 1958

ABSTRACT

Three distinct profile types of soil found on alluvial deposits appeared to represent a chronosequence in soil formation. The chemical. morphological and mineralogical characteristics of these soils, classified as Alluvial, Brown Wooded and Grey Wooded, are given and soil development is discussed.

INTRODUCTION

The Grey Wooded soil zone in Canada occupies the forested parts of the Great Plains region in Western Canada as far north as Fort Simpson, Northwest Territories. In the northwestern part of this soil zone three distinct profile types of soil are often found on alluvial deposits. These profile types have been classified as belonging to the Alluvial, the Brown Wooded and the Grey Wooded groups. Usually the Alluvial soil occupies the lowest terrace, the Brown Wooded the middle terraces, and the Grey Wooded the highest terraces above the river. Since the occurrence of these profile types is directly related to their height above the river it would appear that they represent a chronosequence in soil formation.

MATERIALS AND METHODS

The samples of the soils reported on in this paper were collected from sites on a terrace adjacent to and near the mouth of the Hay River in the Northwest Territories. This terrace slopes gently northward parallel to the river and at a somewhat greater gradient than the river. Hence the difference in elevation between the terrace and the

---

[1] Joint contribution from Chemistry Division, Science Service (Contribution No. 415), and Field Husbandry, Soils and Agricultural Engineering Division, Experimental Farms Service, Canada Department of Agriculture, Ottawa, Ont.

Reproduced with permission from *Canadian Journal of Soil Science,* Vol. 39, 1959, p. 32-43. Published by the Agricultural Institute of Canada, Ottawa, Canada.

stream decreases from south to north. Figure 1 shows the areal soil pattern and the location of the sampling sites. The field work was done during the course of a soil survey along the Mackenzie Highway in the Northwest Territories (3).

Parent Materials

The parent materials of the soils at the three sampling sites consisted of layers of fine textured calcareous alluvium with occasional thin layers of organic matter. While slight differences in texture and in the thickness of the alluvial layers occurred, the parent materials at the three sites appeared to be quite similar.

Vegetation

The soil areas sampled are covered with a heavy stand of mixed woods, dominantly spruce and aspen poplar. Spruce is dominant on the Alluvial soil while aspen is dominant on the Grey Wooded soil.

Climate

Meteorological records taken at Hay River, a few miles from the sampling sites, give the mean annual temperature as 24 F and the mean temperature for the 3-month period June, July and August as 55 F. Precipitation is low, averaging 11.8 inches, of which 4.6 inches comes in the form of snow.

Under these vegetative and climatic conditions, the soils are always cool and often dry. In the middle of July, when the soil samples were taken, the temperature at the 6-inch depth in the mineral soil was 42 F, and at 12 inches 40 F, and the soils were dry. These mineral soils do not have a permafrost layer but the subsoils may not completely thaw out until July.

Soils

Alluvial Soil:

This is a very young well-drained soil, usually found just above the present flood levels of the river. It shows little evidence of profile development, except that free lime has been leached from the upper few inches of the mineral soil. The following is a brief description of the profile sampled:

3—0 in. A_0	: Partly decomposed organic layer	pH 6.4
0—3 in. A_{11}	: Grey (10YR5/1 dry) silty clay loam	pH 6.5
3—5 in. A_{12}	: Greyish brown (10YR5/2 dry) silty clay loam	pH 6.8
5—8 in. C_1	: Dark greyish brown (10YR4/2 dry) silty clay loam, calcareous	pH 8.2
8—13 in. C_2	: Mixed organic and mineral matter, calcareous	pH 8.2

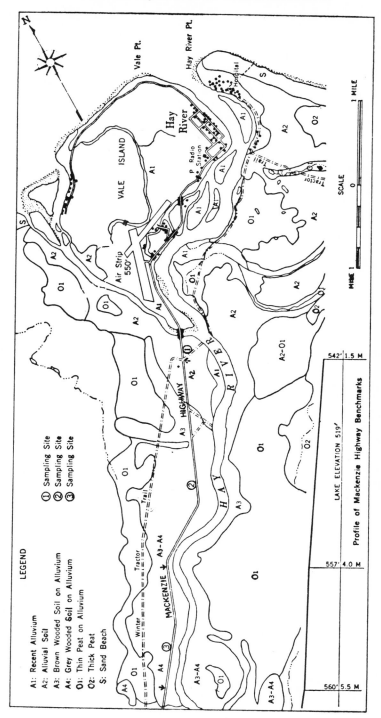

LEGEND

A1: Recent Alluvium
A2: Alluvial Soil
A3: Brown Wooded Soil on Alluvium
A4: Grey Wooded Soil on Alluvium
O1: Thin Peat on Alluvium
O2: Thick Peat
S: Sand Beach

① Sampling Site
② Sampling Site
③ Sampling Site

Fig. 1—Hay River area, showing soil pattern and sampling sites.

13—18 in. C_3 : Light grey (10YR7/2 dry) silt loam, calcareous   pH 8.4
Friable throughout with weak granular structure

Brown Wooded Soil:

This is a well-drained, relatively youthful soil. It shows more development than the Alluvial soil, in that the upper 9 inches are browner in colour, apparently as a result of the loss of organic matter. Carbonates have also disappeared from this layer. This upper mineral layer often is uniform in colour and structure but occasionally, as in the case of the profile sampled for this study, very weakly developed A_2 and B horizons appear to occur. The following gives a brief description of this profile:

3—0 in. A_0 : Partly decomposed organic layer   pH 6.2
0—3 in. A_2 : Greyish brown (10YR5/2 dry) silty clay loam. Weak
granular structure   pH 6.4
3—9 in. B : Brown (10YR4/3 dry) silty clay loam. Weak irregular
blocky structure   pH 6.5
9—14 in. C_1 : Dark greyish brown (10YR4/2 dry) silty clay loam with
granular structure   pH 8.0
14—21 in. C_2 : Pale brown (10YR6/3 dry) silt loam with soft granular
structure   pH 8.2
All horizons were friable

Grey Wooded Soil:

This well-drained soil is the zonal type for the region. It is characterized by an A_0 horizon, a well-developed light coloured A_2 underlain by a darker, finer textured B horizon. The profile sampled for this study is described as follows:

2—0 in. A_0 : Partly decomposed organic layer with some moss   pH 5.1
0—4 in. A_2 : Very pale brown (10YR7/3 dry) loam, somewhat platy   pH 5.8
4—5 in. A/B : Transitional layer—not sampled
5—10 in. B_{21} : Pale brown (10YR6/3 dry) clay loam, strong granular
structure   pH 5.7
10—14 in. B_{22} : Yellowish brown (10YR5/6 dry) clay loam, strong granular structure   pH 6.0
14—17 in. : Mixed partly burnt organic and mineral matter, calcareous, not sampled
17—20 in. C : Light yellowish brown (10YR6/4 dry) silt loam, soft
granular structure   pH 8.4
All horizons were friable

Investigational Techniques

Samples of the various horizons of each profile were taken by means of a brass cylinder of 275-cc. capacity in order to determine bulk density. The samples were air-dried, ground and passed through a 2-mm. sieve in preparation for physical and chemical analysis. The clay contents of the samples were determined by the hydrometer method of Bouyoucos (1) and the free iron oxide data were obtained by the method described by MacKenzie (4). Iron was determined by reduction with metallic silver and titration with ceric sulphate. Titanium was estimated colorimetrically by the hydrogen peroxide method in a perchloric acid solution. All other methods of analysis used were those given in "Chemical Methods of Soil Analysis" (5).

Samples of the C_2 and C_3 horizons of the Alluvial profile, the C_1 and C_2 horizons of the Brown Wooded profile and the B_{22} and C horizons of the Grey Wooded profile were examined mineralogically. The sand was separated into three specific gravity groups and representative samples were examined by means of a petrographic microscope, a minimum of 300 grains in each being identified. The silt and clay fractions (coarse, medium, and fine) were examined with a Norelco x-ray diffractometer using Ni-filtered Cu K_α radiation. The general procedure was similar to that used in most clay mineralogy laboratories.

RESULTS AND DISCUSSION

It seems pertinent at this point to restate the general equation of soil formation: Soil = f (climate, vegetation, soil drainage, parent material, time). In the development of these soils, the soil-forming factors—climate, vegetation, soil drainage and parent material—appeared to be relatively constant, while time was the variable.

Data obtained from selected physical and chemical analyses are shown in Table 1. The disappearance of carbonates and accompanying fall in pH as a function of depth indicate the chronological order of these profiles to be Alluvial, Brown Wooded, and Grey Wooded, and thus support the order of maturity of these profiles as indicated by field observations.

The Allvuial and Brown Wooded profiles are well supplied with organic matter while the Grey Wooded is low in this constituent. The loss of organic matter in the profiles is associated with the removal of carbonates. Both the organic matter content and the C/N ratio decrease in the sola with increasing age of the soils.

There is no evidence of translocation of clay in the Alluvial and Brown Wooded profiles. In the Grey Wooded profile, however, the clay content is highest in the B horizon, indicating significant eluviation of clay from the A and its accumulation in the B horizon. Values for bulk density also attain a maximum in the B, possibly because of clay moving into voids in this horizon resulting in an increase in weight without concomitant increase in volume.

The effects of the podzolization process(es) become quite evident in the Grey Wooded profile. In the younger profiles the values for "free" iron, expressed as percent of the total iron, are higher in the upper parts of the profiles, indicating mainly *in situ* deposition rather than translocation of this element. In the Grey Wooded profile, however, values of 52.1, 65.7 and 56.6 for the A_2, B_{22} and C horizons, respectively, show significant translocation of iron. Similarly, the data for total Fe_2O_3 and Al_2O_3, given in Table 2, show a pronounced sesquioxide bulge in the B horizon of the Grey Wooded profile, even when the data for the C horizon are recalculated on a carbonate-free basis.

Total chemical analyses of the various mineral horizons of the profiles are recorded in Table 2. Such detailed and complete analyses on the chemical composi-

Table 1—Selected physical and chemical analyses of three soil profiles

Horizon	Depth	pH	$CaCO_3$ [1]	Organic [1] matter	N [1]	C/N ratio	Clay [1]	Bulk density	"Free"[1,2] Fe_2O_3	"Free"/Total iron
	in.		%	%	%		%		%	%
ALLUVIAL										
A_0	3-0	6.4	—	85.8	1.63	30.5	—	0.11	—	
A_{11}	0-3	6.5	0.0	9.2	0.30	17.8	40	0.74	2.62	55.8
A_{12}	3-5	6.8	0.0	5.7	0.21	15.8	40	0.81	2.84	55.6
C_1	5-8	8.2	14.8	7.7	0.34	13.2	33	0.86	1.79	44.8
C_2	8-13	8.2	18.4	6.1	0.27	13.1	—	0.98	1.98	47.9
C_3	13-18	8.4	17.5	3.0	0.13	13.4	—	1.22	1.98	45.6
BROWN WOODED										
A_0	3-0	6.2	—	81.4	1.84	25.7	—	0.10	—	
A_2	0-3	6.4	0.0	4.1	0.18	13.2	39	0.97	2.92	57.6
B	3-9	6.5	0.0	3.2	0.12	15.4	37	1.16	2.90	56.0
C_1	9-14	8.0	6.7	7.2	0.32	13.1	—	1.10	2.40	55.1
C_2	14-21	8.2	14.4	1.8	0.09	11.7	27	1.33	2.05	51.3
GREY WOODED										
A_0	2-0	5.1	—	73.3	1.53	27.8	—	0.09	—	
A_2	0-4	5.8	0.0	1.4	0.07	11.6	18	1.14	1.86	52.1
B_{21}	5-10	5.7	0.0	1.0	0.09	6.5	35	1.43	2.57	55.2
B_{22}	10-14	6.0	0.0	0.8	0.06	7.7	35	1.47	3.16	65.7
C	17-20	8.4	15.4	1.4	0.07	11.6	24	1.36	1.93	56.6

[1] Data expressed on a moisture-free basis
[2] "Free" iron oxide removed from the soil by MacKenzie's sodium hydrosulphite method

Table 2– Total chemical analyses of three soil profiles
(Data expressed on a moisture-free basis)

Horizon	Depth	Loss on ignition	SiO$_2$	Al$_2$O$_3$	Fe$_2$O$_3$	TiO$_2$	CaO	MgO	K$_2$O	Na$_2$O	P$_2$O$_5$	Total
	in.	%	%	%	%	%	%	%	%	%	%	%
ALLUVIAL												
A$_{11}$	0–3	14.32	61.34	13.81	4.70	0.70	1.47	1.57	2.02	0.53	0.14	100.60
A$_{12}$	3–5	10.73	63.78	14.52	5.11	0.72	1.26	1.64	2.24	0.51	0.11	100.62
C$_1$	5–8	17.94	54.24	9.82	4.00	0.50	8.82	1.81	1.90	0.50	0.18	99.71
C$_2$	8–13	17.93	52.09	9.78	4.14	0.52	10.66	2.04	1.92	0.47	0.14	99.69
C$_3$	13–18	14.05	55.05	10.90	4.35	0.59	9.33	2.34	2.23	0.47	0.16	99.47
BROWN WOODED												
A$_2$	0–3	8.28	67.85	13.57	5.07	0.74	0.98	1.43	2.34	0.60	0.13	100.99
B	3–9	7.21	68.61	13.21	5.18	0.71	0.98	1.53	2.25	0.57	0.10	100.35
C$_1$	9–14	13.60	60.93	11.18	4.36	0.52	4.56	1.72	2.18	0.52	0.16	99.73
C$_2$	14–21	10.73	62.63	9.32	4.00	0.57	7.55	2.20	1.86	0.60	0.16	99.62
GREY WOODED												
A$_2$	0–4	3.78	79.34	8.93	3.57	0.61	0.54	0.85	1.77	0.69	0.14	100.22
B$_{21}$	5–10	4.41	73.54	12.54	4.66	0.62	0.59	1.27	2.20	0.66	0.10	100.59
B$_{22}$	10–14	4.43	72.74	12.17	4.81	0.58	0.78	1.25	2.08	0.63	0.12	99.59
C	17–20	9.96	65.72	8.44	3.41	0.48	7.58	1.92	1.52	0.63	0.16	99.82

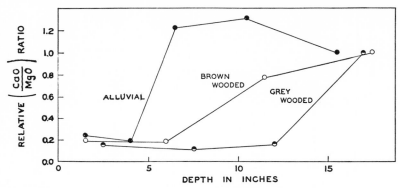

Fig. 2—The relative ratio of calcium oxide to magnesium oxide plotted as a function of depth for three profiles.

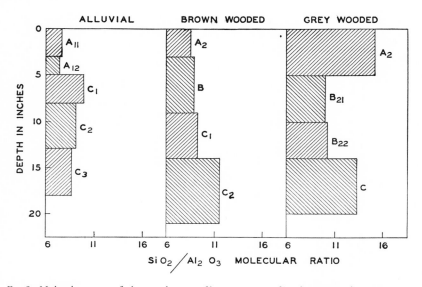

Fig. 3—Molecular ratios of silica to alumina of horizons in profiles forming a chronosequence.

tion of soils of this region were not previously available. Further interpretation of these data was done by utilizing molecular values which give a clearer picture of stoichiometric relationships than do weight data. Furthermore, ratios of these values eliminate the effects of additions of organic matter, losses of carbonates, etc., and thus afford a method of detecting relative translocations of elements.

Figure 2 shows the relative molecular ratios of CaO to MgO plotted as a function of depth with the ratio of the lowest horizon of each profile set at unity. The curves show that calcium is more readily leached from these materials than is magnesium. From the CaO/Al_2O_3 and MgO/Al_2O_3 data of molecular ratios presented in Table 3, it is apparent that approximately 90 percent of the calcium compared with 50 percent of the magnesium has been removed from the parent materials during the development of the sola of these profiles.

Table 3—Molecular ratios calculated from total chemical analyses data[1]

Horizon	$\dfrac{SiO_2}{Al_2O_3 + Fe_2O_3}$		$\dfrac{CaO}{Al_2O_3}$		$\dfrac{MgO}{Al_2O_3}$		$\dfrac{Na_2O}{Al_2O_3}$		$\dfrac{K_2O}{Al_2O_3}$		$\dfrac{K_2O}{Na_2O}$	
	Abs.[1]	Rel.[2]	Abs.	Rel.	Abs.	Rel.	Abs.	Rel.	Abs.	Rel.	Abs.	Rel.
ALLUVIAL												
A_{11}	6.20	0.91	0.19	0.12	0.29	0.53	0.06	0.89	0.16	0.72	2.51	0.80
A_{12}	6.10	0.89	0.16	0.10	0.29	0.53	0.06	0.82	0.17	0.75	2.90	0.93
C_1	7.45	1.09	1.64	1.05	0.47	0.86	0.08	1.18	0.21	0.95	2.51	0.80
C_2	7.13	1.04	1.99	1.27	0.53	0.97	0.08	1.12	0.21	0.96	2.70	0.86
C_3	6.84	1.00	1.56	1.00	0.55	1.00	0.07	1.00	0.22	1.00	3.13	1.00
BROWN WOODED												
A_2	6.86	0.77	0.13	0.09	0.27	0.45	0.07	0.69	0.19	0.86	2.57	1.26
B	7.06	0.79	0.14	0.09	0.30	0.49	0.07	0.67	0.18	0.85	2.61	1.27
C_1	7.42	0.83	0.74	0.50	0.39	0.65	0.08	0.72	0.21	0.98	2.76	1.35
C_2	8.97	1.00	1.48	1.00	0.60	1.00	0.11	1.00	0.22	1.00	2.04	1.00
GREY WOODED												
A_2	12.04	1.14	0.11	0.07	0.24	0.42	0.13	1.02	0.21	1.10	1.72	1.08
B_{21}	8.06	0.77	0.09	0.05	0.26	0.45	0.09	0.71	0.19	0.97	2.20	1.38
B_{22}	8.12	0.77	0.12	0.07	0.26	0.45	0.09	0.69	0.19	0.95	2.18	1.37
C	10.53	1.00	1.64	1.00	0.58	1.00	0.12	1.00	0.20	1.00	1.59	1.00

[1] Absolute ratios
[2] Relative ratios based on the lowest horizon as unity

Silica-alumina ratios for the three profiles are shown in Figure 3. Comparing the youngest (Alluvial) with the oldest (Grey Wooded) profile, there is a marked decrease in alumina with respect to silica in the A horizons with time. However, these ratios and the $SiO_2/Al_2O_3 + Fe_2O_3$ relative ratios given in Table 3 indicate that in the earlier stages of development (Alluvial and Brown Wooded) there have been greater losses of silica relative to sesquioxides in the sola. In the next stage in the development of these soils, exemplified by the Grey Wooded profile, the significantly higher silica-sesquioxide ratios for the A horizon reflect greater leaching of the sesquioxides with respect to silica. Apparently, after depletion of carbonates, a further modification of the soil material occurred before significant translocation of sesquioxides took place. Thus, with continued loss of bases, particularly calcium, and accompanying decrease in pH from 6.4 in the A horizon of the Brown Wooded to 5.8 in the A horizon of the Grey Wooded soil, marked losses of sesquioxides relative to silica have occurred.

Jenny (2) has pointed out that potassium and sodium are particularly sensitive criteria of leaching intensities as a result of weathering and soil formation. Although the Na_2O/Al_2O_3 and K_2O/Al_2O_3 ratios given in Table 3 show some leaching of sodium and potassium, it is apparent that chemical alterations within the profiles as regards these elements are not very profound. The trends of the K_2O/Na_2O molecular ratios, given in Table 3, do indicate greater loss of sodium than potassium with age, reflecting a greater degree of weathering.

The results of mineralogical analyses are presented in Tables 4, 5 and 6 for the sands, silts and clays respectively. In the sands, the quartz content was lowest in the Alluvial soil and highest in the Grey Wooded C sample. The quartz grains in the latter were clear, oval and highly polished with no sharp edges, probably the result of considerable resorting in water. The most prevalent mineral group was the feldspars. Weathered feldspars were present in greatest amount in the Grey Wooded C horizon. Garnets were most numerous in the Alluvial C_3 sample. Many of the garnets in the Grey Wooded horizons showed considerable strain and incipient weathering to epidote, indicating that they had probably passed through several weathering cycles. Four titanium minerals were identified. The grains of brookite in the C horizon of the Grey Wooded profile were the first of this type to be identified in these laboratories.

In the silts, the distribution of all minerals identified was relatively uniform among all samples. Quartz was predominant and was slightly lower in amount in the fine than in the medium and coarse fractions. The clay mineral components of the medium and fine clay fractions were largely illite and a mixed-layer complex of illite and montmorillonite. The coarse clays had an appreciable amount of quartz and less mixed-layer material.

The mineralogical composition of the silts and clays is very similar among the C horizons of the three profiles. As far as the sand fractions are concerned, differences demonstrate the variablility that can be expected in alluvial deposits. The sands have probably been transported relatively short distances and hence might be considered as derived from local sources. The silts and clays are more likely to have been carried over greater distances and thoroughly mixed in the process.

Table 4—Minerals of the sand fractions (as percent of sand)

Sample		Total sand[1]	Quartz	Feldspars		Micas	Garnets	Titanium minerals					Topaz	Tour-maline	Zircon	Others
				Total	Weathered			Ilmenite	Brookite	Rutile	Titanite	Total				
Alluvial	C₂	1.6	2.9	73.2	7.7	4.8	—	0.28	—	0.01	—	0.29	0.03	0.03	—	18.8
	C₃	0.7	1.8	69.3	6.5	8.4	0.8	0.29	—	0.02	0.03	0.34	0.01	0.03	0.01	19.3
Brown Wooded	C₁	7.1	10.7	63.2	10.4	7.4	0.1	0.31	—	0.11	0.03	0.45	0.05	0.02	—	18.1
	C₂	20.0	6.7	61.5	14.9	2.9	0.2	0.15	—	0.01	—	0.16	0.02	0.07	0.01	28.4
Grey Wooded	B₂₂	22.9	9.3	67.8	11.6	2.1	0.2	0.08	—	0.04	0.04	0.16	0.01	0.04	—	20.4
	C	23.3	25.7	50.3	18.5	3.2	0.3	0.03	0.05	0.03	—	0.11	—	0.05	—	20.3

[1] As per cent of moisture-free, salt-free and organic matter-free sample

Table 5—Minerals of the silt fractions

Sample		Quartz	Feldspars	Micas and Illite	Chlorite	Kaolinite
Alluvial						
C_2	Coarse[1]	+++	+	−	−	−
	Medium[2]	+++	+	+	+	+
	Fine[3]	++	+	+	+	+
C_3	Coarse	+++	+	−	−	−
	Medium	+++	+	+	+	+
	Fine	++	+	+	+	+
Brown Wooded						
C_1	Coarse	+++	+	tr.	+	−
	Medium	+++	+	++	+	+
	Fine	++	+	+	+	+
C_2	Coarse	+++	+	tr.	+	−
	Medium	+++	+	+	+	+
	Fine	++	+	+	+	+
Grey Wooded						
B_{22}	Coarse	+++	+	+	tr.	−
	Medium	+++	+	+	+	+
	Fine	++	−	+	+	+
C	Coarse	+++	+	+	tr.	tr.
	Medium	+++	+	+	+	+
	Fine	++	−	+	+	+

[1] Coarse silt...............50–20μ
[2] Medium silt...............20– 5μ
[3] Fine silt...................5– 2μ

+++　strong pattern
++　moderate pattern
+　weak pattern
tr.　pattern barely perceptable

Table 6—Minerals of the clay fractions

Sample		Quartz	Illite	Mont-morillonite	Chlorite	Kaolinite	Mixed layer
Alluvial							
C_2	Coarse[1]	++	++	tr.	+	+	+
	Medium[2]	−	+++	tr.	tr.	+	++
	Fine[3]	−	++	−	−	tr.	+++
C_3	Coarse	++	++	tr.	+	+	+
	Medium	−	++	−	−	tr.	++
	Fine	−	++	+	−	tr.	++
Brown Wooded							
C_1	Coarse	++	++	tr.	tr.	+	+
	Medium	tr.	++	tr.	−	tr.	++
	Fine	−	++	+	−	+	++
C_2	Coarse	++	++	tr.	+	+	+
	Medium	−	++	tr.	−	+	++
	Fine	−	+	+	−	tr.	+++
Grey Wooded							
B_{22}	Coarse	++	++	tr.	tr.	+	+
	Medium	−	++	+	−	+	+++
	Fine	−	++	+	−	tr.	+++
C	Coarse	++	++	+	tr.	+	+
	Medium	−	++	tr.	−	+	++
	Fine	−	++	+	−	−	++

[1] Coarse clay...............2.0–0.2μ
[2] Medium clay...............0.2–0.1μ
[3] Fine clay...................<0.1μ

+++　strong pattern
++　moderate pattern
+　weak pattern
tr.　pattern barely perceptable

CONCLUSIONS

The present studies indicate that the pattern of development in the formation of these soils on calcareous alluvial materials in Northwestern Canada is as follows:

1. Accumulation of organic matter in the upper part of the calcareous soil-forming materials. Occurrence of high organic layers in the sub-soils is attributed to burial by alluvium during the build-up of the parent materials.
2. Decomposition of carbonates, with calcium being removed about twice as rapidly as magnesium, followed by the depletion of organic matter.
3. Greater loss of silica than sesquioxides in the earlier stages of development probably during depletion of carbonates.
4. Continued loss of bases, particularly calcium, subsequent to depletion of carbonates accompanied by a further decrease in pH and further loss of organic matter.
5. Marked eluviation of clay and accelerated leaching of iron and aluminium with respect to silica resulting in a distinct siliceous eluviated layer (A_2) underlain by a clay-and sesquioxide-enriched layer (B).

ACKNOWLEDGEMENT

The authors wish to thank R. Levick for making the total chemical analysis, and L. M. Patry for the petrographic analysis.

REFERENCES

1. Bouyoucos, G. J. A recalibration of the hydrometer method for making mechanical analysis of soils. J. Amer. Soc. Agron. 43:434-438. 1951.
2. Jenny, H. Factors of soil formation. McGraw-Hill Book Co., New York, N. Y. 1941.
3. Leahey, A. Preliminary soil survey of lands adjacent to the MacKenzie Highway in the Northwest Territories. Mimeo. Rept., Can. Dept. Agr., Ottawa. 1953.
4. MacKenzie, R. C. Free iron-oxide removal from soils. J. Soil Sci. 5: 167-172. 1954.
5. Wright, L. E., et al. Chemical methods of soil analysis. Chem. Div., Sci. Service, Can. Dept. Agr., Ottawa. 1949.

GEOMORPHIC SURFACES AND THE NATURE OF SOILS

Robert V. Ruhe

U. S. Department of Agriculture[1]

Received for publication May 28, 1956

In the Greenfield Quadrangle, Adair County, Iowa, a landscape occurs that is characteristic of most of the southern half of Iowa. Regional field studies (10, 11) showed that at least five major geomorphic surfaces are delineable, and that specific soils or soil associations are related to each geomorphic surface. Detailed field studies in a part of the Greenfield Quadrangle (secs. 7, 8, 17, 18, T.76N., R.31W., and secs. 12, 13, T.76N., R.32W.) now permit a more exact definition of the relationships of soils to geomorphic surfaces.

LANDSCAPE

The modern surface in the Greenfield Quadrangle does not slope continuously from the divides to the major drainages. Slopes along the axes of interfluves are broken at two or three places by distinct changes in gradient. Each interfluve has a sequence of stepped levels that rise from the valley shoulders to the upland divide. For example, along the profile from A to B (fig. 1) a low level is separable from an intermediate level which, in turn, is separable from the high level of the upland. This sequence of areally juxtaposed levels is the result of multicyclic erosion of a glacial-till landscape. It is further complicated by the mantling of the glacial-till landscape by loess.

The high level, mantled by Farmdale-Iowan-Tazewell loess, is controlled by the Yarmouth-Sangamon surface (fig.2). This surface is essentially a weathered relict of the Kansas drift plain that has not been changed by erosion since Kansan time (11). The surface is characterized by deep, intensively weathered paleosols that in most places remain buried.[2]

---

[1] Joint contributions of Soil Survey Investigations, Soil Conservation Service, U. S. Dept. Agr., and Iowa Agr. Expt. Sta.; Journal Paper J-2942 of the Station; Project No. 1250. Author is Research Geologist, Soil Survey Investigations, Soil Conservation Service, U. S. Dept. Agr.

[2] A paleosol is a "fossil" soil that was formed on a landscape during the geologic past. Since sedimentation subsequent to pedogenesis buried and preserved ("fossilized") the soil profile, this kind of paleosol *is a buried soil.* Erosive stripping of the protective mantle of sediment in many places, however, resulted in the resurrection of the paleosolic profile *in toto,* so that now the paleosol occurs within the continuum of soils on the modern surface. Since it is foreign to its present environment, the soil must continue to be designated a paleosol, but it *is no longer a buried soil.*

Reproduced with permission from *Soil Science,* Vol. 82, 1956, p. 441-455. Copyright © 1956, The Williams and Wilkins Company, Baltimore, Maryland 21202, USA.

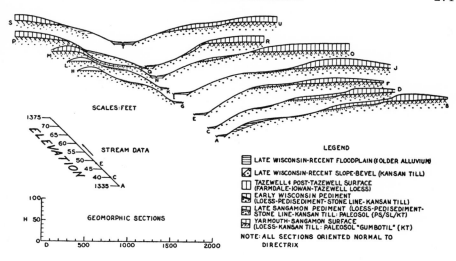

Fig. 1—Geomorphic profile-sections of interfluves peripheral to drainage tributary to South Turkey Creek, Adair County, Iowa *(Sections A-B . . . S-T-U located on figure 2)*

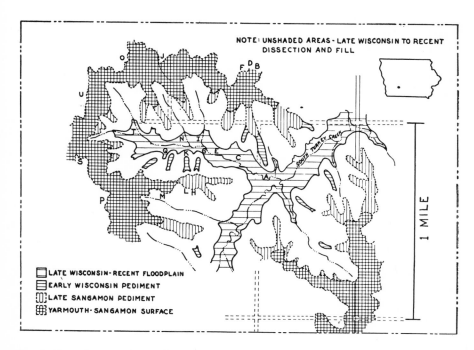

Fig. 2—Map of geomorphic surfaces along South Turkey Creek in part of Greenfield Quadrangle, Adair County, Iowa *(Farmdale-Iowan-Tazewell loess deleted)*

The intermediate level, in most places mantled by Farmdale-Iowan-Tazewell loess, in the Late Sangamon erosion surface, which is (11) a pediment[3] that was cut into Kansan till below the level of the Yarmouth-Sangamon surface. The Late Sangamon surface (fig. 2), in directions toward the upland divide, rises gradually up the pediment-footslope and then more sharply up a concave pediment-backslope[4] to the level of the Yarmouth-Sangamon surface (fig. 1) and is characterized by a lag-gravel erosion pavement (stone line) on the Kansan till. The stone line is overlain by finer-textured sediment (pedi-sediment) derived from the till. A paleosol, somewhat lesser developed than the Yarmouth-Sangamon paleosol, occurs in the pedi-sediment, stone line, and upper most part of the Kansan till (fig. 1).

The low level of the landscape is the Early Wisconsin pediment that is cut into Kansan till below the Late Sangamon surface (figs. 1, 2). At some places the Early Wisconsin surface is mantled by Iowan-Tazewell loess, but no paleosol separates the till from the loess. The lack of a paleosol at this stratigraphic position indicates that loess deposition must have followed closely the cutting of the erosion surface, and that sufficient time was not available for soil development in the uppermost part of the till prior to the mantling of the surface by Iowan-Tazewell loess. These lithologic and stratigraphic relationships identify the age of the surface as Early Wisconsin.

The complex of surfaces of varying ages has been subjected to erosion and sedimentation in Late Wisconsin-Recent time. All the surfaces, Yarmouth-Sangamon, Late Sangamon, and Early Wisconsin, are disected (figs. 1,2) and now occur on upland divides or on interfluves. The uppermost increment of the mantling Wisconsin loess, the Tazewell (11), also is bevelled by the slopes, indicating that the slopes are post-Tazewell or Late Wisconsin in age. Alluvial fills in valleys at the bases of the slopes are believed to be contemporary with the Post-Tazewell loess gully-fill cycle in south western Iowa (10). The basal fill of this alluvial cycle has been dated at 6800± 300 years by radiocarbon analysis (9, W-235). Hence the slopes also must post-date the Late Wisconsin and are of Recent age. As a generalization, however, the slopes are classified in the complex of Late Wisconsin-Recent.

The latest erosion cycle exhumed the Yarmouth-Sangamon and Late Sangamon paleosols, so that these relict soils now occur within the continuum of soils on the modern surface (fig. 3). In some places on narrow interfluves, the loess has been stripped from the footslopes of the Early Wisconsin pediment so that the Kansan till was exposed to soil development in Late Wisconsin-Recent time.

As a result of such geomorphic history of the landscape, the sequence of levels that rise from the valley shoulders to the upland divide along the interfluves is characterized by a suite of soils developed in Kansan glacial till. A soil that developed in Late Wisconsin time occurs on the level to slightly rounded footslopes of the Early Wisconsin pediment, the low level of the stepped sequence (figs. 1,2). A soil that developed in Late Sangamon time occurs on the level to slightly rounded foot-slopes of the Late Sangamon pediment, the intermediate level of the stepped sequence.

---

[3]A pediment is an erosion surface that lies at the foot of a receded slope, is underlain by rocks or sediments of the upland, is barren or mantled by a layer of alluvium (pedi-sediment), and displays a longitudinal profile normally concave upward [definition modified after Howard (6)].

[4]The pediment footslope is the surface of low gradient that extends from the foot of and away from the receded slope. The pediment backslope (the receded slope) is generally concave upward and rises from the pediment footslope to the upland.

Fig. 3—(A) Outcrop *(light-colored area)* of Yarmouth-Sangamon Paleosol, "gumbotil" on Late Wisconsin-Recent slope The paleosol, within the continuum of soils on the modern surface, is classified
as the Clarinda silty clay loam. The paleosol is developed in Kansan till and overlain by Wisconsin loess. Note poor stand of alfalfa in outcrop area of paleosol.

(B) Dissected Late Sangamon Pediment Late Sangamon paleosol crops out on shoulders of slopes
(light-colored area). Footslope of pediment rises gradually in a distance of 1600 feet to west *(away
from viewer)*, and then rises sharply up pediment backslope to level of Yarmouth-Sangamon surface in distance. Both paleosolic surfaces are mantled by Wisconsin loess. Note poor stand of
vegetation in outcrop area of Late Sangamon paleosol.

Soils that developed in Yarmouth-Sangamon time occur on the undulating, relict
Kansan drift surface, the high level of the stepped sequence.

SOILS OF THE GEOMORPHIC SURFACES

Yarmouth-Sangamon Paleosols

The undulating, swell, and swale Yarmouth-Sangamon surface has a relief of 5-10 feet. Distances between crests of swells and centers of swales approximate 1/8 mile. Thus, on the Yarmouth-Sangamon surface variable moisture conditions existed. Aeration and soil drainage were better on the swells than in the swales. A buried Yarmouth-Sangamon paleosol on the crest of a swell has the following morphology:

Profile H (figs. 4,5) [5]

Horizon and Depth	
0-153 in.	Iowan-Tazewell loess with modern soil in upper part.
IA$_{ib}$ 153-167 in.	Dark grayish brown (10YR4/2)[6] silt loam with yellowish red (5YR4/5-5/6) iron oxide concretions and "pipestems"; weak fine to medium platy; friable; leached Farmdale loess.
IIA$_{gb}$ 167-177 in.	Gray (10YR5/1) silty clay loam with yellowish red (5YR5/6) iron oxide stain on aggregate faces; fine subangular blocky; clay skins lacking; friable; gritty but no weatherable mineral fragments visible; leached upper horizon of Yarmouth-Sangamon paleosolum in Kansan till.
IIB$_{1gb}$ 177-182 in.	Gray (10YR5/1) heavier silty clay loam; yellowish red (5YR4/6) and red (2.5YR4/6) iron oxide stain on aggregate faces; moderate medium subangular blocky; clay skins moderately abundant; moderately plastic; gritty but only resistant minerals visible; leached.
IIB$_{21gb}$ 182-192 in.	Gray (10YR4/1) clay; yellowish red and red iron oxide stain on aggregate faces; strong medium subangular blocky; clay skins cover aggregate faces; plastic; gritty with only resistant minerals visible; leached.
IIB$_{22gb}$ 192-203 in.	Dark gray (10YR4/1) clay; brown (7.5YR4/4) and reddish brown (5YR4/4 iron oxide stain on aggregate faces; strong medium subangular blocky; clay skins cover aggregate faces; plastic; gritty with resistant minerals visible; leached.
IIB$_{3gb}$ 203-221 in.	Gray (5Y6/1) heavy clay loam; mottled with strong brown (7.5YR5/8); moderate medium subangular blocky; clay skins on aggregate faces in upper part of horizon, channelized vertically in tubules in lower part; increasingly gritty in lower part with weatherable minerals visible; leached lower horizon of Yarmouth-Sangamon paleosolum in Kansan till.

---

[5] Roman numerals preceding A, B, or C indicate differences in parent material. All other horizon symbols follow the Soil Survey Manual (14).

[6] Munsel colors, moist soil.

IIC_b
221- in.

Strong brown (7.5YR5/8) clay loam; mottled with gray (5Y6/1); coarse angular blocky; prominent clay skins channelized along vertical tubules; very gritty with weatherable minerals visible; leached Kansan till.

This paleosol is comparable morphologically to modern planosols. A leached light-textured A_2 horizon with a clay ($< 2_\mu$) content of 32 percent overlies a thin B_1 horizon (5 inches thick) that is sharply delineated from an underlying B_2 horizon with a clay content of 58 percent (fig. 4). The Yarmouth-Sangamon profile developed in Kansan till is similar texturally to a modern planosol, the Rolfe silt loam that is developed in Mankato till (fig.4). The paleosol may be classified as a paleo-planosol.

The part of the solum B_{1gb} -B_{3gb} conforms to the "gumbotil" of Pleistocene geology terminology (7). Simonson (12) pointed out the high degree of similarity between the Yarmouth (-Sangamon) buried soils and the modern planosols.

A problem involved in studies of paleosols, whether buried or exposed, is the application of proper laboratory analytical methods so that characteristics of the soils may be compared. Standard soil-chemistry methods cannot be applied. Originally developed in calcareous Kansan till, leaching removed bases to great depths below the solum. The soil was subsequently buried, however, by calcareous Wisconsin loess, which was later leached. Solutions percolating downward undoubtedly enriched the buried paleosolum. Field and laboratory analyses show such secondary enrichment.

Carbonate concretions commonly occur in the upper part of the paleosolum, even though the matrix of the soil is leached. Pipestems (vertically elongate, cylindrical iron-oxide concretions) in the paleosolum can be traced upward into the lower parts of the overlying Wisconsin loess. These are evidences that the paleosolum has been enriched in calcium, magnesium, and iron.

Hydrogen-ion concentrations are misleading. The A_2 horizon of the paleosol has a pH of 6.4 and the B_2 6.6 Simonson (12) reported similar pH values for comparable paleo-planosols. Yet Ulrich (14) reported that less intensely weathered modern planosols in Iowa have pH values in the A_2 horizon of 5.0 and in the B_2 horizon of 5.6.

A method that can be applied to paleosols is a detailed mineralogical study of the very fine sand fractions (0.62-0.125 mm.) of the horizons of the sola.

Among the heavy minerals Dryden and Dryden (3) showed the following stability indexes: zircon, 100; tourmaline, 80; the amphibole, hornblende, 5; and the pyroxene, hypresthene, 1. Thus, a weathering ratio for heavy minerals (W_{rh}, fig. 5) may be established from the percentage by count of the resistant minerals zircon and tourmaline to the percentage by count of the less-resistant mineral groups, amphiboles and pyroxenes.

Analysis of the mineralogy of the heavy-mineral fractions of the A_2, B_2, and C horizons of the Yarmouth-Sangamon paleosol (H) shows an orderly decrease of the weathering ratios (W_{rh}, fig. 5). In the A_2 horizon the ratio is 1.55:1.00 (56 percent resistants, 36 percent weatherables, table 1). In the B_2 horizon the ratio is 1.38:1.00 (54 percent resistants, 39 percent weatherables). In the C horizon the ratio is 1.24: 1.00 (49 percent resistants, 40 percent weatherables). These data show that the A_2

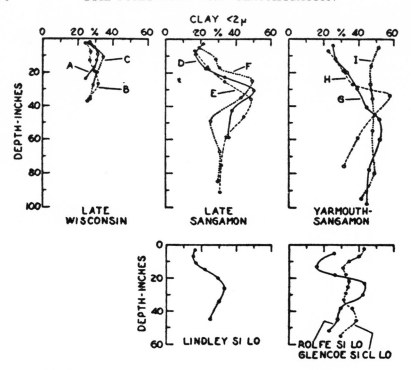

Fig. 4—Texture profiles of soils of gemorphic surfaces. Late Wisconsin-Recent soils are developed on Early Wisconsin pediment *(figs. 1, 2)* from which Iowan-Tazewell loess has been stripped. (Lindley, data from R. C. Prill, and Rolfe and Glencoe, data from E. M. Richlen, profiles for comparison)

horizon is more intensely weathered than the B_2 horizon, which in turn is more intensely weathered than the C horizon.

Goldich (4) showed the increasing resistance to weathering among the light minerals of the series plagioclase, microcline-orthoclase, and quartz. Thus, a weathering ratio for light minerals (W_{rl}, fig. 5) may be established from the percentage by count of the resistant quartz to the percentage by count of more weatherable feldspars.

Analysis of the mineralogy of the light-mineral fraction of the A_2, B_2, and C hroizons of the Yarmouth-Sangamon paleo-planosol (h) show an orderly decrease of the weathering ratios (W_{rl}, fig. 5). In the A_2 horizon the ratio is 4.00:1.00 (80 percent resistants, 20 percent weatherables). In the B_2 horizon the ratio is 3.16: 1.00 (76 percent resistants, 24 percent weatherables). In the C horizon the ratio is 2.70:1.00 (73 percent resistants, 27 percent weatherables). These data also show that the relative intensity of weathering decreases from the A_2 horizon to the B_2 to the C horizon.

In the coarser sand fractions (0.5-2.0 mm.) only fragments of resistant quartz, quartzite, chert, and sandstone occur in the A_2 and B_2 horizons. In the C horizon, fragments of weatherable granite, diorite, and basalt occur.

In the swales, or more poorly drained positions, on the Yarmouth-Sangamon surface, a different kind of paleosol occurs. It has the following morphology:

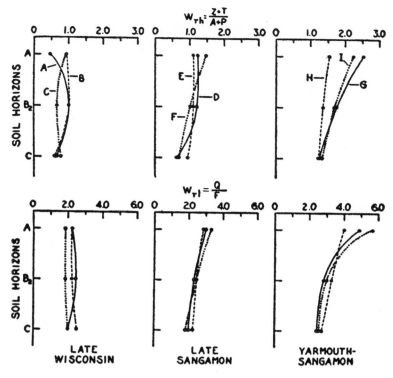

Fig. 5—Curves of weathering ratios of heavy-mineral and light-mineral fractions of soils of geomorphic surfaces *(see table 1)*

Profile I (figs. 4,5)

Horizon and Depth	
0-48 in.	Iowan-Tazewell loess with modern soil in upper part.
IA$_{1b}$ 48-57 in.	Very dark gray (2.5Y3/0) heavy silty clay; coarse angular blocky; plastic; clay skins on aggregate faces; iron oxide concretions; very little grit; leached "wash" on Kansan till.
IA$_{3gb}$ 57-71 in.	Gray (10YR5/1) silty clay; coarse angular blocky; plastic; clay skins on aggregate faces; iron oxide concretions; very little grit but only resistant minerals visible; leached "wash" on Kansan till.
IB$_{1gb}$ 71-79 in.	Gray (10YR5/1) silty clay; strong coarse angular blocky; very plastic and compact; clay skins on aggregate faces; very little grit but only resistant minerals visible; leached "wash" on Kansan till.
IB$_{21gb}$ 79-88 in.	Dark gray (10YR4/1) silty clay; strong coarse angular blocky; very plastic and compact; clay skins on aggregate faces; mod-

	erately gritty but only resistant minerals visible; leached "wash" on Kansan till.
IIB$_{22gb}$ 88-113 in.	Light gray (10YR6/1) silty clay; coarse angular blocky; plastic; clay skins on aggregate faces; gritty but with weatherable minerals visible in lower part; leached Kansan till.
IIB$_{3gb}$ 113-133 in.	Gray (10YR6/1) silty clay; coarse angular blocky; clay skins on aggregate faces in upper part, channelized vertically in lower part gritty with weatherable minerals; leached Kansan till.
IIC$_{1b}$ 133- in.	Yellowish brown (10YR5/8)clay loam; mottled with gray (10YR 6/1); coarse angular blocky; firm; gritty with weatherable minerals; leached Kansan till.

This Yarmouth-Sangamon paleosol is comparable morphologically to the modern humic-gley soils. Its textural profile (fig. 4) is somewhat similar to the modern humic-gley, the Glencoe silty clay loam which is developed in Mankato till. Simonson (12) has discussed comparable paleo-humic-gley soils in Iowa. The horizons IA$_{1b}$ - IIB$_{3gb}$ are the "gumbotil" of Pleistocene geology terminology (7).

Total sand contents in the horizons IA$_{1b}$-IIB$_{2gb}$ are less than 6 percent, which is abnormal for Kansan till. Sand gradually increases to 15 percent in the IIB$_{3gb}$ horizon, and increases slightly with further depth. The material in the upper part of the solum is probably finer-textured sediment washed from the adjacent slopes around and above the swale on the Yarmouth-Sangamon surface. By weathering contemporaneous with accretion or subsequent to sedimentation, the sediment has become incroporated into a "giant" solum 85 inches thick.

The paleo-humic gley apparently is more intensely weathered in the upper part of the solum than is the paleo-planosol. Weathering ratios of the heavy-mineral fractions (W$_{rh}$; I, fig. 5; table 1) are greater. Weathering ratios of the light-mineral fractions (W$_{rl}$, fig. 5; table 1) also show more intensive weathering in the upper parts of the solum.

In the coarser sand fractions (0.5-2.0 mm.) only resistant quartz, quartzite, chert, and sandstone occur in the A$_3$ and B$_2$ horizons. In the C horizon fragments of weatherable granite, diorite, and basalt, as well as the more resistant mineral types, are common.

A third Yarmouth-Sangamon paleosol, profile G (fig 4), has a textural profile which suggests that the soil may be an intergrade between the paleo-planosol (H) and the paleo-humic gley (I).

The curves of the weathering ratios (W$_{rh}$ and W$_{rl}$, fig. 5) of profile G are similar to those of profile I. The curves of both profiles are displaced to the right relative to the curve of profile H, the paleo-planosol. More intensive weathering in the upper parts of the sola of G and I is indicated. The greater weathering in the paleo-humic gley soils may be explained by: (a) pedogenetic processes operative in a more moist environment,[7] (b) partial weathering of primary minerals on the slopes above the swales prior to wash into the swales and slow accretion with final breakdown, or (c) a combination of both factors.

The paleo-planosols and paleo-humic gley soils of the Yarmouth-Sangamon sur-

---

[7]Bray (1, 2) pointed out that the more advanced chemical weathering in the wetter modern soils developed in loess in Illinois.

Table 1—Abundance of major resistant and weatherable minerals in very fine sand fraction

Soil		Heavy Minerals		W_{rh}‡	Light Minerals		W_{rl}**
		Resistant*	Weatherable†		Resistant§	Weatherable¶	
		%	%		%	%	
A	A₃	32††	66	0.48:1.00	68	32	2.12:1.00
	B₂	50	48	1.04:1.00	69	31	2.22:1.00
	C	38	59	0.64:1.00	67	33	2.03:1.00
B	A₃	48	51	0.95:1.00	69	31	2.22:1.00
	B₂	50	47	1.06:1.00	69	31	2.22:1.00
	C	37	61	0.61:1.00	72	28	2.57:1.00
C	A₃	47	49	0.95:1.00	66	34	1.94:1.00
	B₂	40	59	0.67:1.00	66	34	1.94:1.00
	C	43	54	0.78:1.00	67	33	2.03:1.00
D	A₂	53	43	1.22:1.00	75	25	3.00:1.00
	B₂	52	42	1.21:1.00	72	28	2.57:1.00
	C	38	58	0.66:1.00	67	33	2.03:1.00
E	A₂	51	46	1.11:1.00	74	26	2.85:1.00
	B₂	51	46	1.11:1.00	71	29	2.45:1.00
	C	43	44	0.97:1.00	69	31	2.22:1.00
F	A₂	56	37	1.49:1.00	77	33	3.34:1.00
	B₂	49	48	1.03:1.00	71	29	2.45:1.00
	C	38	55	0.69:1.00	65	35	1.86:1.00
G	A₃	53	21	2.52:1.00	83	17	4.88:1.00
	B₂	50	29	1.75:1.00	74	26	2.85:1.00
	C	49	39	1.27:1.00	71	29	2.45:1.00
H	A₂	56	36	1.55:1.00	80	20	4.00:1.00
	B₂	54	39	1.38:1.00	76	24	3.16:1.00
	C	49	40	1.24:1.00	73	27	2.70:1.00
I	A₃	63	28	2.25:1.00	85	15	5.66:1.00
	B₂	56	32	1.73:1.00	75	25	3.00:1.00
	C	55	34	1.34:1.00	72	28	2.57:1.00

* Zircon and tourmaline.

† Amphiboles and pyroxenes: hornblende, hypersthene, augite, enstatite.

‡ $W_{rh} = \dfrac{\text{zircon + tourmaline}}{\text{amphiboles + pyroxenes}}$.

§ Quartz.

¶ Orthoclase, microcline, plagioclase.

** $W_{rl} = \dfrac{\text{quartz}}{\text{feldspars}}$.

†† Percentages by count.

face occur within the continuum of soils on the modern surface where Late Wisconsin-Recent slopes angularly truncate the old surface (A, fig. 3), or on narrow interfluves where Wisconsin loess has been stripped. The paleosols are classified as the Clarinda soils in the scheme of classification. They may be identified by their neutral gray colors, excessive thickness of sola, heavy-textured B horizons (clay or heavy silty clay), strong subangular blocky structure in the B horizons, and by the absence of weatherable mineral material in the coarse particle-size fractions throughout the sola.

Late Sangamon Paleosols

Late Sangamon paleosols are buried beneath the Wisconsin loess, or have been exhumed by loess stripping, on the intermediate level of the landscape. These paleosols are characterized by a complex nature of parent materials. During pediment-ation that formed the erosion surface, a veneer of lag gravel was developed on the cut surface in the Kansan till. Contemporaneously with development of the lag gravel, a finer-textured transported sediment derived from till was deposited on the lag gravel. With stabilization of the surface, soil-forming processes operated in the entire complex so that the resultant solum is developed in the finer-textured pedi-sediment, the stone line, and the uppermost part of the Kansan till.

The Late Sangamon pediment was a surface of low relief with transverse, level, and slightly rounded interfluves that stood 5 to 10 feet above adjacent drainages. Thus, on the surface there were positions of good and poor aeration and drainage, as well as intermediate types. On the well-drained landscape the soils are very similar morphologically. A profile in a well-drained position is:

Profile F (figs. 4,5)

Horizon
and
Depth

0-40 in.	Iowan-Tazewell loess with modern soil in upper part.
IA_{1b} 40-52 in.	Dark brown (10YR4/3) silt loam; weak medium granular; friable; leached Farmdale loess.
IIA_{2b} 52-62 in.	Yellowish brown (10YR5/4) silt loam; weak coarse platy; friable; gritty with weatherable minerals visible; leached Late Sangamon pedi-sediment.
IIB_{1b} 62-67 in.	Yellowish brown (10YR5/4) silty clay loam; weak medium sub-angular blocky; sparse clay skins on aggregate faces; friable; gritty with weatherable minerals visible; leached Late Sangamon pedi-sediment. At base of this horizon is dark brown (7.5YR4/4) gravelly loam with abundant cobbles of granite, basalt, quartz-zite, quartz; Late Sangamon stone line.
$IIIB_{2b}$ 67-80 in.	Dark brown (7.5YR4/4) clay; mottled with reddish brown (5YR 4/4) and red (2.5YR3/4); strong medium subangular blocky; abundant clay skins on aggregate faces; plastic; very gritty, pebbly with weatherable minerals; leached Kansan till.
$IIIB_{3b}$ 80-87 in.	Strong brown (7.5YR5/8) clay loam; moderate medium sub-angular blocky; moderately plastic; clay skins moderately abundant on aggregate faces; very gritty and pebbly with weatherable minerals visible; leached Kansan till.
$IIIC_{1b}$ 87-107 in.	Strong brown (7.5YR5/6) light clay loam; coarse angular firm; clay skins channelized along vertical tubules; gritty and pebbly with weatherable minerals visible; leached Kansan till.
$IIIC_{2b}$ 107-122 in.	Yellowish brown (10YR5/6) clay loam; mottled with light gray (5Y7/1); coarse angular blocky; firm; sparse clay skins chan-nelized along vertical tubules; gritty with weatherable minerals; leached Kansan till.
$IIIC_{cab}$ 122- in.	Yellowish brown (10YR5/6) clay loam; coarse angular blocky; firm; carbonate concretions up to 3 inches in diameter; gritty and pebbly with weatherable minerals; calcareous Kansan till.

This paleosol is somewhat similar morphologically to modern gray-brown pod-zolic soils. The color differs in that stronger chromas and redder hues prevail. The textural distribution in the profile is similar to the modern gray-brown podzolic Lindley silt loam (fig. 4), although the paleosol is heavier in the B and C horizons. Two other Late Sangamon paleosols (D and E, fig. 4) have similar morphologies and texture profiles. The horizons B_{2b}-B_{3b} conform to the "ferretto" till of Pleistocene-geology terminology. Simonson (12) considered comparable buried soils in Iowa to be gray-brown podzolic soils.

The paleo-gray brown podzolic soils of the Late Sangamon erosion surface are buried beneath Farmdale-Iowan-Tazewell loess that was originally calcareous. The loess has been leached, so that the underlying paleosol has been enriched by mater-ial carried in downward percolating solutions. Prill[8] showed that buried gray-brown podzolic soils (Late Sangamon paleosols) have pH values that vary only from 6.4 to 6.8 and base saturations of approximately 90 percent throughout the pale-osola. But in modern gray brown podzolic soils (Late Wisconsin-Recent age) Prill recorded pH values of 4.8 to 5.8 in the sola and base saturations of 60 to 70 percent.

Because of secondary enrichment, standard soil-chemistry methods cannot be used to analyze the Late Sangamon soils, but the mineralogical technique can be employed. Weathering ratios in the paleosols show an orderly, progressive decrease both in the heavy and light mineral fractions from the A_2 horizon to the B_2 and to the C horizons (fig. 5, table 1).

In addition to the morphological continuity of the paleo-gray brown podzolic soil profiles, even though interrupted by a stone line, the weathering ratios are further evidence of genetically related horizons of the soils.

In the coarser sand fractions (0.5-2 mm.) weatherable mineral material such as granite, diorite, and basalt is abundant in all horizons of the sola. Resistant mater-ials occur also.

The Late Sangamon paleosols are exposed and occur within the continuum of soils on the modern surface where the older erosion surface is angularly truncated by slopes of Late Wisconsin-Recent age, or on summits of narrow interfluves where the Wisconsin loess has been stripped (B, fig. 3). Where a paleo-gray brown pod-zolic soil is exposed *in toto,* the soil is classified as a variant of Lindley silt loam[8]. Where secondary-cycle Brunizemic characteristics are evident in the profile, the Late Sangamon paleosol has been considered as a part of the Shelby soils. The class-ification problem currently is undergoing re-examination.

Late Wisconsin-Recent Soil

On the level to slightly rounded summits of the low level of the stepped sequence of surfaces of the landscape, Late Wisconsin-Recent erosion has resulted in the strip-ping of Iowan-Tazewell loess from the Early Wisconsin pediment. Thus, soils of the younger age are developed in Kansan till. A profile of this character is:

[8]R. C. Prill. Variations in forest-derived soils formed from Kansan till. Unpublished Ph.d. thesis, Iowa State College, 1955.

Profile C (figs. 4,5).

Horizon and Depth	
A$_p$ 0-7 in.	Very dark gray (10YR3/2) heavy loam; weak medium granular; friable; gritty and pebbly with weatherable minerals visible; leached Kansan till.
A$_3$-B$_1$ 7-15 in.	Dark brown (10YR4/3) light clay loam; weak medium subangular blocky; friable; sparse clay skins on aggregate faces; gritty and pebbly with weatherable minerals; leached Kansan till.
B$_2$ 15-25 in.	Dark brown (10YR4/3) clay loam; moderate medium subangular blocky; clay skins common on aggregate faces; weak plastic; gritty and pebbly with weatherable minerals; leached Kansan till.
B$_3$ 25-29 in.	Dark yellowish brown (10YR4/4) light clay loam; coarse angular blocky; firm; sparse clay skins; gritty and pebbly with weatherable minerals; leached Kansan till.
C$_1$ 29-34 in.	Yellowish brown (10YR5/8) light clay loam; coarse angular blocky; firm; gritty and pebbly with weatherable minerals; leached Kansan till.
C$_{ca}$ 34- in.	Light yellowish brown (10YR6/3) loam; coarse angular blocky; firm; carbonate concretions; gritty and pebbly with weatherable minerals; calcareous Kansan till.

Two other profiles (A and B, fig. 4) of similar soils on the low-level surface have similar morphologies but differ slightly in that the carbonate horizon occurs at a slightly greater depth in one and a slightly shallower depth in the other. The textural profiles (fig.4) of these soils are somewhat similar in distribution, but differ slightly in degree of differentiation. These soils occur on the modern landscape, and as such are more in harmony with their environment than the Late Sangamon and Yarmouth-Sangamon paleosols.

For comparison, the mineralogical-analytical technique was applied to the Late Wisconsin-Recent soils. A random distribution of weathering ratios of both the heavy and light mineral fractions is evident (fig. 5, table 1). These weathering ratios indicate that the soils have not been subjected to intensive weathering. Soil development has not resulted in destruction of weatherable minerals with the resultant orderly arrangement of weathering ratios, as in the Late Sangamon and Yarmouth-Sangamon palesols.

In the coarser sand fractions (0.5-2 mm.) weatherable mineral materials, such as granite, diorite, and basalt, are abundant in all horizons of the sola. Resistant minerals occur also.

The Late Wisconsin-Recent soils on the low level of landscape are designated, within the current concepts of classification, as Shelby Loam.

Table 2—Comparison of some characteristics of soils of the geomorphic surfaces

Soil		Thickness of Solum	Thickness of B Horizon	Texture of B Horizon
		in.	*in.*	*% < 2μ clay*
Late Wisconsin-Recent				
	A	15	11	31.2
	B	32	23	32.2
	C	29	22	34.6
Average		*25*	*19*	*32.3*
Late Sangamon				
	D	46	32	50.7
	E	70	56	49.1
	F	39	29	49.5
Average		*52*	*39*	*49.7*
Yarmouth-Sangamon				
	G	87	70	51.4
	H	68	44	57.7
	I	85	62	50.7
Average		*80*	*59*	*53.2*

Comparison of Soils of the Geomorphic Surfaces

Inspection of the texture profiles (fig. 4) of the soils of the Late Wisconsin-Recent, Late Sangamon, and Yarmouth-Sangamon surfaces shows distinct contrasts of characteristics. Thickness of the sola increases from profiles on the youngest surface to profiles on the oldest surface (table 2). Average thickness of the sola on the Late Wisconsin-Recent surface is 25 inches, on the Late Sangamon surface 52 inches, and on the Yarmouth-Sangamon surface 80 inches.

The thickness of the B horizon increases from soils on the youngest surface to soils on the oldest surface (table 2). On the Late Wisconsin-Recent surface the average thickness is 19 inches, on the Late Sangamon surface 39 inches, and on the Yarmouth-Sangamon surface 59 inches.

The clay content of the B horizon increases from soils on the youngest surface to soils on the oldest surface (table 2). In the Late Wisconsin-Recent soils the average clay content is 32.3 percent, in the Late Sangamon soils 49.7 percent and in the Yarmouth-Sangamon soils 53.2 percent.

A comparison of the average weathering ratios of soils of the geomorphic surfaces also shows progressive differences. Curves of average values (fig. 6) are displaced toward the right from soils of the youngest surface to those of the oldest surface. Intensity of mineralogical weathering increases to the right, that is, greater ratios indicate greater amounts of resistant minerals relative to weatherable minerals. The relationship holds true for weathering ratios of both the heavy-mineral and light-mineral fractions.

Curves of average values (fig. 6) show several interesting relationships of mineralogy and weathering. In the Late Wisconsin-Recent soils very little mineralogic destruction has occurred in weathering, and as a result, an orderly arrangement has not been established among the weathering ratios (W_{rh} and W_{rl}) of the horizons of the soil profiles. In both instances values of the A horizons lie to the left of

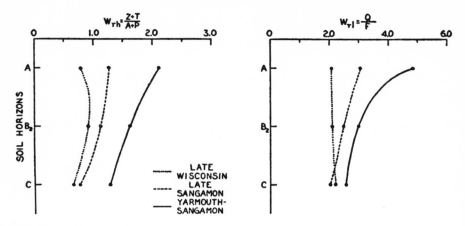

Fig. 6—Curves of averages of weathering ratios of horizons of heavy-mineral and light-mineral fractions of soils of geomorphic surfaces *(see table 3)*

values of the B horizons. In the Late Sangamon paleosols mineralogic weathering has progressed to the point where an orderly arrangement of ratios has been established among the values of the profile horizons. Significantly, in the horizon of theoretically greatest weathering, the A_2 of the paleo-gray brown podzolic soils, there is a relatively greater displacement of values to the right in contrast to the subjacent, less-weathered B horizons. The values of the C horizons of the Late Sangamon paleosols group closely with those of the relatively unweathered Wisconsin-Recent soils.

In the most intensely weathered Yarmouth-Sangamon paleosols (fig. 6) there is a greater displacement of values to the right. Again values of the ratios of the A_3 horizons of the paleo-humic gley soils and the A_2 horizons of the paleo-planosol are displaced farther to the right than the subjacent less but still intensely weathered B horizons. Values of the C horizons also are displaced to the right in comparison to values of the C horizons of the Late Wisconsin-Recent and Late Sangamon soils. Apparently, even though the lowest horizons of the Yarmouth-Sangamon paleosols have the morphological characteristics of C horizons, they are within the zone of mineralogic weathering. Texture profiles (fig. 4) substantiate such a conclusion. Two of the profiles have clay contents greater than 40 percent in the lowest horizons. The sola may extend to depths greater than indicated by the morphologies of the profiles.

Undoubtedly the major cause of the differences in the three groups of soils is age. The youngest group developed on a stabilized till surface following the stripping of the Tazewell loess. The surface stabilization may be related to the alluviation cycle that began 6800 years ago. Thus, a maximum time of exposure to weathering would approximate that time. The Late Sangamon soils were buried under Farmdale loess approximately 25,000 years ago (11). A radiocarbon date of Late Sangamon time is greater than 38,000 years (11). The minimum exposure of the Late Sangamon soils would be 13,000 years, but in all probability the exposure time is much greater. The duration of Yarmouth-Sangamon time only can be estimated at the present time. Estimates (5,8) of exposure of the uneroded Kansan till surface prior to Wisconsin-loess sedimentation are of the order of several hundred thousand years.

REFERENCES

1. Bray, R. H. 1934 A chemical study of soil development in the Peorian loess region of Illinois. Am. Soil Survey Assoc. Bull. 15, p. 58-65.

2. .... 1935 The origin of horizons in claypan soils. Am. Soil Survey Assoc. Bull. 16, p. 70-75.

3. Dryden, L., and Dryden, C. 1946 Comparative rates of weathering of some common heavy minerals. J. Sediment Petrol. 16: 91-96.

4. Goldich, S. S. 1938 A study in rock weathering. J. Geol. 46: 17-58.

5. Hough, J. L. 1953 Pleistocene climatic record in a Pacific Ocean core sample. J. Geol. 61: 252-262.

6. Howard, A. D. 1942 Pediment passes and the pediment problem. J. Geomorphology 5; 3-31.

7. Kay, G. F., and Apfel, E. T. 1929 The pre-Illinoian Pleistocene geology of Iowa. Iowa Geol. Survey 34: 1-304.

8. .... 1931 Classification and duration of the Pleistocene period. Bull. Geol. Soc. Amer. 42: 425-466.

9. Rubin, M., and Suess, H. E. 1956 U. S. Geological Survey rodiocarbon dates: III. Science 123: 442-448.

10. Ruhe, R. V. 1954 Pleistocene soils along the Rock Island relocation in southwestern Iowa. Am. R. Eng. Assoc. Bull. 514, p. 639-645.

11. ...., and Scholtes, W. H. 1956 Ages and development of soil landscapes with relation to climatic and vegetational changes in Iowa. Soil Sci. Soc. Amer. Proc. 20: 264-273.

12. Simonson, R. W. 1954 Identification and interpretation of buried soils. Am. J. Sci. 252: 705-732.

13. Soil Survey staff 1951 Soil Survey Manual. U. S. Dept. Agr. Handbook 18, Washington, D. C.

14. Ulrich, R. 1951 Some chemical changes accompanying profile formation of the nearly level soils developed from Peorian loess in southwestern Iowa. Soil Sci. Soc. Amer. Proc. 15: 324-329.

A TWO-CYCLE THEORY OF TROPICAL PEDOLOGY

C. D. Ollier

(Soil Survey of Uganda)

SUMMARY

Evidence from geomorphology and mineralogy is presented which indicates that many tropical soils in Uganda are formed on pre-weathered rock. The first cycle of weathering took place before the formation of the African surface, probably in Mid-Tertiary times or earlier. Further weathering and pedological change is taking place in the present cycle.

A variety of profiles are explained on this basis and some catenary relationships are also described. A number of previous ideas are discussed to indicate how the present theory differs from earlier ones.

INTRODUCTION

For the past three years the author has been concerned with a soil and geomorphology survey of Northern and Eastern Uganda, and a wide range of soils has been encountered. It has been found that the connexion between soils and geomorphology is most important in tropical soils, more so perhaps than in soils of temperate regions, where parent rock and parent material are often more nearly synonymous. From the literature it seems very probable that the relationships discovered in Uganda are also found in many other areas, and the ideas derived from a study of Uganda soils may have a wider application.

Many authors have described tropical soils and accounted for their features in various ways. Some of these ideas are incorporated in the following account, but it is impossible in a short paper to refer to all previous writers. Instead the position in Uganda will be described, and the ideas of some recent authors will be considered later.

THE PRESENT THEORY

The fundamental idea in the theory propounded here is pre-weathering: present day soils are formed on pre-weathered rock. This is supported by evidence from geomorphology and mineralogy as well as pedology. A brief account of the geomorphology of Busoga District in Eastern Province, Uganda, is given below as an example of the evidence from that subject.

Reproduced with permission from *Journal of Soil Science,* Vol. 10, 1959, p. 137-148.
Published by the British Society of Soil Science, England.

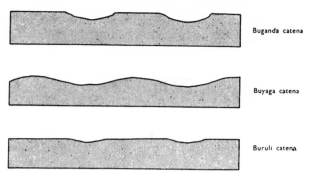

Fig. 1.

The highest summits of Busoga occur in the south and are remnants of an old peneplain (or other type of erosion surface) known as the Gondwana surface. This has been eroded by a later cycle period which formed the African surface. There is a gradation between the surfaces as shown in Fig. 1, giving rise to three catenas, the Buganda, Buyaga, and Buruli. The African surface was cut across deeply weathered rock, and fresh rock outcrops in relatively small areas. The remnants of the Gondwana surface are almost entirely on quartzite which is highly resistant to weathering, and other rocks generally only outcrop as inselbergs or tors.

The postulated geomorphic histroy is shown in Fig. 2.

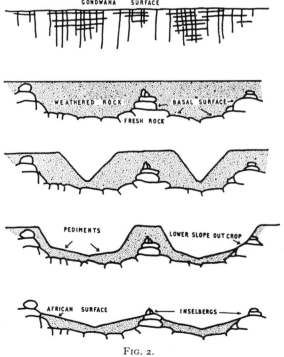

Fig. 2.

Very deep weathering took place below the Gondwana surface to form a thick layer of rotted rock. The junction between the weathered rock and fresh rock is irregular but remarkably sharp, and is known as the basal surface of weathering, or simply the basal surface. The African cycle of erosion removed much of the rotted rock, but the base level of erosion was reached before it was all removed, and consequently the African surface is largely cut across rotted rock. Where the basal surface was reached by erosion, fresh rock emerges, usually as inselbergs or tors. This is the only satisfactory way to account for the observed fact that inselbergs of fresh rock are separated from each other by wide plains of rotted rock. The African surface is generally regarded as of End-Tertiary age, and as the weathering must have happened before this, it is Mid-Tertiary at least, and possibly very much earlier. The geomorphic history has been described in detail elsewhere (Ollier, *in lit.*).

From the pedological point of view the most significant feature of the geomorphic history is that erosion has exposed pre-weathered rock as the parent material on which soils could develop. A variety of such soils are described below.

Soil Profiles of Two-Cycle Origin

1. *Weathered rock to surface.* There are many sites, particularly on upper slopes, where rotted rock reaches the surface with very little modification. Quartz bands or other indications of rock structure reach the surface, and the only soil factors are slight eluviation of clay from the topsoil, and accumulation of a little organic matter.

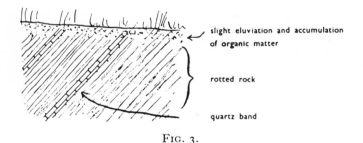

slight eluviation and accumulation
of organic matter

rotted rock

quartz band

FIG. 3.

2. *Weathered rock, resorted at the surface.* These profiles are derived from those described above by sorting of the upper layers. Eluviation has been more intense and biotic activity has resulted in the breakdown of any rock structures in the top few feet of the profile.

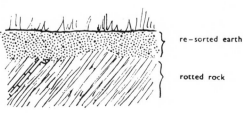

re–sorted earth

rotted rock

FIG. 4.

3. *Stone line profiles.* Profiles of this type are a special case of type 2 above, but are extremely common. It is necessary for quartz bands to be fairly frequent in the rotted rock, and for termites to be present. The termites build mounds above the surface, but cannot carry particles much above a millimetre in diameter, so coarse fragments and stones are left below. Eventually the mounds break down but new ones are made and the process continues until perfect layering is achieved. The upper layers of fine soil have been worked and reworked by termites and the stones accumulate as a stone line at the base of the zone of termite activity. Below the stone line there is, of course, weathered rock *in situ.* Other soil-forming processes are also active and there is some eluviation of topsoils, accumulation of organic matter, and sometimes lateritization as described below.

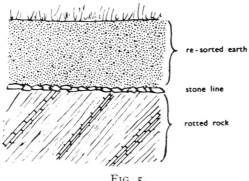

re-sorted earth

stone line

rotted rock

FIG. 5.

A variety of this profile is found where the rotted rock is a nearly amorphous regolith, and there are very few quartz bands. This happens especially on amphibolites or very micaceous schists. A thin stone line can occasionally be formed, but the soil above it looks just the same as the weathered rock below. There can be no doubt that it is weathered rock, for profiles go down for many tens of feet on sites which preclude drift.

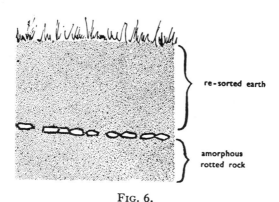

re-sorted earth

amorphous
rotted rock

FIG. 6.

4. *Weathered rock with stone line at surface.* As in profile 3 above, the starting-point is rotted rock traversed by quartz bands. Sheet erosion removes the finer

material, and coarse material accumulates on the surface, often as a layer of quartz stones. Such profiles are common in Karamoja, and elsewhere where there is poor vegetation cover and much erosion. Other soil-forming processes have little chance to act, and the profile is simply a stone line over rotted rock.

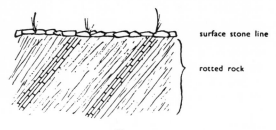

FIG. 7.

5. *Lateritized profiles.* Laterite (or ironstone concretions called 'murram' in Uganda) is formed by iron enrichment of certain layers in the soil profile and it occurs in regions with well-marked wet and dry seasons. Iron is leached out of upper layers of the soil in the wet season, carried both downslope and down the profile, and redeposited at depth when the soil dries out. The maximum concentration takes place where the drainage changes, and this most often coincides approximately with the stone line. If laterite forms in weathered rock *in situ* it is massive and vesicular, full of irregular hollow channels which are lined with layers of limonite. If laterite forms in the upper, sorted layers of the profile it tends to form murram pisoliths which may be cemented to form sheet laterite. The pisoliths do not show concentric banding. Murram and laterite often form a continuous sheet below the ground surface and parallel to it.

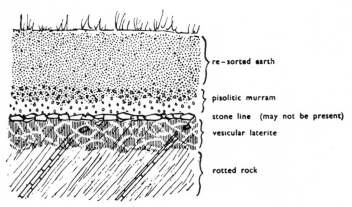

FIG. 8.

The process of lateritization is enhanced on flat sites, where thicker and more massive laterite is usually found. Well-preserved remnants of old erosion surfaces often have a thick cover. Erosion in a later part of the cycle may cause the laterite sheet to outcrop on valley sides. When it is exposed to the air it develops a skin of iron hydroxide and becomes much harder than it is in the ground.

Lateritization is a special phenomenon which can operate on many rocks and sediments. It complicates the present account, but is not relevant to the main point, for lateritization does not depend on pre-weathering of rocks.

6. *Drift soils.* Another factor which can complicate the soil profiles so far described is the occasional presence of hill-creep or other colluvial deposits. Most catenas provide no evidence of colluvial deposits and even on the slopes profiles usually appear to be sedentary. The slopes were graded before soils were developed from the underlying rotted rock and they are still in equilibrium. Any slope must be suffering slight erosion, but on many slopes in Uganda there is little evidence for it. Some lower slopes appear to have a rather large thickness of soil, which may be due to colluviation from the upper slopes, but there is rarely any definite evidence. Stone lines and derived laterite sometimes indicate drift movements.

The only well-marked drift soils occur round some large fresh rock outcrops, where debris derived from the fresh rock is spread out as an apron around the rocks. Here there is a profile with a topsoil rich in weatherable minerals overlying a subsoil of rotted rock from which virtually all weatherable minerals have gone.

7. *Other soil types.* It is not intended to discuss alluvial soils, soils formed on fresh rock in the present cycle, or other such types. These are obvious in the field, and do not affect the contention that a great many tropical soils are formed on pre-weathered rock.

Modification Due to Rock Type

The processes outlined above are mostly applicable to areas of granite and granitic gneisses. Quartzites are highly resistant to weathering and form ridges which modify the topography and thus the arrangement of soil types. Schists and schistose gneisses have bands of different weatherability and their associated soils vary to some extent in accordance. Rock outcrops are rare or absent on highly weatherable rocks such as amphibolite. Rocks of Tertiary age or younger do not show deep pre-weathering, but give rise to straightforward one-cycle profiles of weathering.

The Effect of Zones of Weathering

The pre-weathering of almost all rocks gave rise to a regolith consisting largely of quartz, clay (mostly kaolinite), and iron oxides. However, there is some evidence for zones of different degrees of weathering within the regolith, especially just above the basal surface. There one finds relatively weatherable minerals such as feldspar, micas, and epidote are still present. This lower zone of weathering outcrops around fresh rock inselbergs, and soils here have a parent material which is slightly different from most pre-weathered rock.

Mineralogical Evidence

Besides geomorphic evidence, there is mineralogical evidence to support the two-cycle theory of soil formation, and also demonstrate the sedentary nature of the soils.

On a wide scale it is seen that kyanite is only found in soils developed from kyanite schists, garnet in soils developed from an originally garnetiferous rock, and so on. There is no evidence of widespread and much travelled drift or 'mantle' soils as described by Charter (1958).

To show the detailed use of mineralogy a brief account of one catena may be given. The whole catena has been described elsewhere (Radwanski and Ollier, 1959) and only the main features of the mineralogy will be summarized here. The data are shown in Table 1.

TABLE I

		% feldspar in light fraction	% magnetite in heavy fraction	Main nonopaque heavy minerals
Shallow	0–3 in.	56	50	Z, T, E
	–10	45	50	Z, T, E, M
	–18	75	20	Z, T, E, M
	–36	72	50	Z, T, E, M, B
	–60	70	40	Z, T, E, M, B
	–72	75	60	Z, T, E, M, B
Red	0–3	0	5	Z, T
	–8	0	5	Z, T
	–18	1	10	Z, T
	–40	1	10	Z, T
	–60	1	20	Z, T
	–72	0	10	Z, T
Brown	0–3	0	5	Z, T
	–8	0	5	Z, T
	–20	6	5	Z, T
	–36	10	5	Z, T
	–60	6	5	Z, T
	–72	1	5	Z, T

Z, Zircon; T, Tourmaline; E, Epidote; M, Muscovite; B, Biotite.

Buwekula Shallow soils are found on upper slopes, usually around granite tors. Buwekula Red occurs on upper mid-slopes and Buwekula Brown on lower mid-slopes. It is seen that Buwekula Red and Brown are very poor in mineral species, while Buwekula Shallow, which has presumably suffered approximately the same amount of weathering in the present cycle, has a comparative abundance. According to the present hypothesis this can be accounted for by supposing that the parent materials of the Buwekula soils suffered pre-weathering, but Buwekula Shallow is formed on the lowest zone of the regolith, while Buwekula Red and Brown were formed on the more intensely pre-weathered upper zones. Any one-cycle hypothesis of weathering must suppose that weathering has been much more intense on the mid slopes than on the upper ones, which seems very unlikely. The change in mineral proportions through the Buwekula Shallow profile gives some indication of the amount of weathering that has taken place in the present cycle.

The possibility of hill-creep modifying the profiles can be disproved. Drift from the rock outcrops on to Buwekula Shallow would enrich the top of the profile in weatherable minerals, but in fact it is found that the topsoil is depleted in weatherable minerals indicating weathering *in situ*. Drift from Buwekula Shallow on to Buwekula Red or Brown would contain considerable feldspar. In fact there is no feldspar in the topsoils of Buwekula Red or Brown.

Supposed two-cycle soils in other parts of Uganda often have a heavy mineral assemblage of opaques and a few zircon grains only. Supposed one-cycle soils on either fresh Basement Complex rocks of the Acholi surface, Tertiary volcanics or Plio-Pleistocene lacustrine sediments, all have much richer mineral assemblage than two-cycle soils

Catenas and Other Combinations of Soil Types

The kinds of soil profile described above occur in various combinations which constitute the soil-mapping units of the Uganda Soil Survey. Some of these are described below:

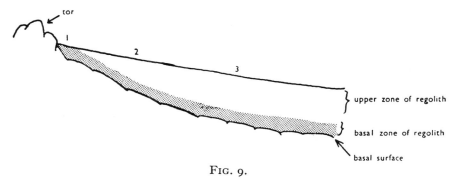

FIG. 9.

I. *Catena with rock outcrops.* There are rock outcrops on the hill top. At 1 there are soils formed on the lowest zone of weathering which contains some weatherable minerals. There may be a drift of debris derived from the fresh rock of the outcrop in some instances. At 2 there is highly weathered rock as the parent material. There may be resorting of the upper part of the solum and a stone line or murram may be present. Profiles at 3 are very much the same as 2 but there may be some colluvium. Alluvial associates usually occur farther downslope. Complications in the

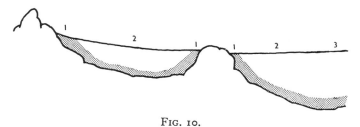

FIG. 10.

catena may occur if there are lower slope outcrops, which lead to a repetition of upper-slope profiles on the lower slopes.

II. *Catenas without rock outcrops.* These occur mainly in watershed areas.

At 1 there is weathered rock almost to the surface and usually only a little sorting of the upper solum. At sites 2 and 3 the profiles are exactly as in the first catena described. A variation of this catena occurs where a remnant of a former erosion

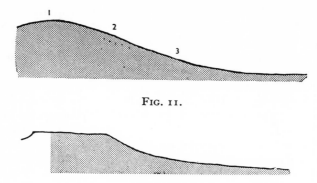

FIG. 11.

FIG. 12.

surface is preserved as a hill top. This will usually have a laterite cap, and the remains of the soil above the laterite are often truncated. The lower part of the catena is unaffected.

III. *Soils developed on plains of advanced erosion.* Many parts of the African surface in Northern Uganda are well-developed plains, and very flat, but on these are sedentary red soils similar to those on lower slopes in areas of more marked relief. It sometimes happens, however, as in the southern part of West Nile district, that a new cycle of erosion cuts across the rocks at such a low level that almost all the weathered rock is removed and a new surface (the Acholi surface in this case) is cut across mostly fresh rock. On the fresh rock surface sedentary, juvenile soils have formed. There is almost always some pre-weathered rock, following bands of certain petrology, generally micaceous; on this are found the two-cycle soil types. This arrangement is not a catena, for the soil pattern depends on geology and there is no repetitive pattern of distribution. Diagrammatically the soil variation looks like this:

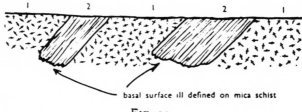

basal surface ill defined on mica schist

FIG. 13.

At 1 is skeletal soil over hard fresh rock.
At 2 is somewhat resorted soil over pre-weathered rock.

DISCUSSION

A few previous accounts of tropical soils will now be discussed to show how they differ from the present thesis.

Greene (1945) described red-loam catenas on pre-weathered rock formed in Miocene times, thus anticipating the theory presented in the present paper. His pre-weathering catenas are characterized by remnants of erosion surfaces with ironstone, as in Fig. 12 above. He also describes a red-loam catena similar to catena II, Fig. 11 above, which is believed to be formed directly on acid crystalline rock. From the description of this catena it could be fitted into the present theory, but it is possible that a one-cycle soil might reach this high degree of weathering under suitable conditions. It is said that the red loams of the two catenas are apparently identical.

Charter (1958) described some soils of southern Tanganyika. His diagrams show soil profiles of the same types described here, but he believed that the soils were drift soils. He says, '. . . the upland soils . . . are *not*, as previously assumed, developed directly by the weathering in place of the underlying bedrock. They are, instead, derived from a mantle of red earth of varying thickness which overlies, and had its origin from, the rocks of the basement complex. This relationship between mantle and bedrock is analogous to that which exists in the northern parts of the temperate zone. There one has mantle rock derived, by glacial attrition and transport, from the underlying bedrock and it is on the surface of this mantle that the soils are developed.'

He described the weathered rock as 'mantle' and it might seem, from his Fig. 1 and some of the text, that this is the layer of pre-weathered rock of the present account. However, he later makes it clear that he is referring to the soil above the stone line, and in his diagrams marks the layer below the stone lines as 'Weathered surface of bedrock' and 'more or less unweathered bedrock'. Charter also believed that stone lines were formed at the ground surface and were later buried by the mantle.

The main difference between Charter's account of profile development and the present one is that he thinks the upper soil is transported. He has some evidence for this, but in Uganda most soils have proved to be sedentary when investigated by mineralogical methods. Charter did not try to account for the distribution of rock outcrops and weathered rock; nor did he consider pre-weathering very important, although he supposed there had been a change of climate since his 'mantle' accumulated.

Anderson (1957) described many soils derived from very weathered rock, and follows Milne (1947) in believing that the depth of weathering could not be produced by present rainfall, and that soils over about 2 metres are 'fossil relics' of a wetter period in the past. No suggestion is made of how much past, but in the present paper the period of great weathering is pushed back at least to a time before the African surface was developed, probably Mid-Tertiary. Anderson believes stone lines are due to termite activity but suggests that soils with over 2 metres of earth above the stone line are probably 'mantle soils'. He seems to consider the movement of the mantle much less than Charter supposed, and the present writer has no objection to such small movements.

Nye (1954) described a catena very like catena number I in the present account. He does not attempt to account for weathered rock being the parent material of the soils, or for the occasional presence of rock outcrops. He attributes the upper soil to the activity of soil fauna, but believes that soil creep is nevertheless important, even on slopes of only 5 percent.

Spurr (1954) described an area of composite topography in Tanganyika. He gives no detailed profile descriptions, but the profiles seem to be like those described by the other authors referred to, and generally underlain by deep pre-weathered rock—now usually kaolinitic red earths or ferralites.

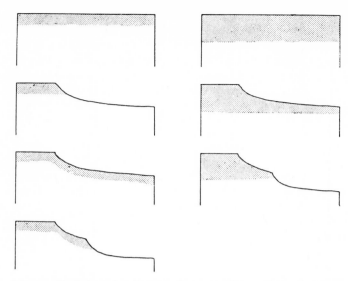

FIG. 14. Evolution of multiple surfaces according to Spurr (left) and
the present account (right).

Spurr believes that the deep weathering is a continuous process, and as each new erosion level is produced it undergoes deep weathering. This gives rise to a flight of erosion levels, all having soils of similar type but of different age. According to the present account the deep weathering took place at the time of the oldest erosion level, and successive erosion cycles bevelled new surfaces across the pre-weathered rock. The result is the same in either case.

Although Spurr believes in a continuous process of weathering he does say that ' . . . where topsoils do exist, although they have admittedly been formed under present vegetal and climatic conditions, the material from which they have developed is often soil material which had its origin in past erosion cycles as part of a former catena. Sub-soils over thirty feet in thickness are common where weathering has been deep and continuous, or where a soil has developed from transported material which itself lies deep on bedrock. The development of these sub-soils has been very little affected by their present-day environment.' He believes that this is only a local complicating factor, but it is the very essence of the thesis of the present paper.

Spurr describes Pleistocene and recent levels which, like their Acholi surface eqivalent in Uganda, have skeletal and freely drained soil fromed in the present cycle. He presumably attributes this to lack of time to form a soil such as occurs on the older surfaces. In the present account it is believed that erosion has reached a level below the basal surface of the pre-weathered rock. The evolution of the lowest surface of Fig. 14 above shows this diagrammatically.

ACKNOWLEDGEMENTS

This paper is published by permission of the Director of Agriculture, Uganda. Thanks are also due to Dr. E. M. Chenery and Mr. S. A. Radwanski for helpful criticism and discussion.

REFERENCES

1. Anderson, B. 1957. A Survey of Soils in the Kongwa and Nachingwea Districts of Tanganyika. University of Reading.
2. Charter, C. F. 1958. Report on the environmental conditions prevailing in Block 'A', Southern Province, Tanganyika Territory. Ghana Dept. Agric. Occ. Pap. No. 1.
3. Greene, H. 1945. Classification and use of tropical soils. Proc. Soil Sci. Soc. Amer. 10, 392-6.
4. Milne, G. 1947. A soil reconnaissance journey through parts of Tanganyika. J. Ecol. 35, 192-265.
5. Nye, P. H. 1954. Some soil-forming processes in the humid tropics. I. A field study of a catena in the Western African forest. J. Soil Sci. 5, 7-21.
6. Ollier, C. D. Etchplains and inselbergs in Uganda. (In the Press.)
7. Radwanski, S. A., and Ollier, C. D. 1959. A study of an East African catena. J. Soil Sci. 10, 149-68.
8. Spurr, A. M. M. 1954. A basis of classification of the soils of areas of composite topography in central Africa, with special reference to the soils of the southern highlands of Tanganyika. Second Inter-Afr. Soils Conf. 1, 175-90.

(Received 1 December 1958)

Part IV

OUTLINE OF A GENERALIZED THEORY OF SOIL GENESIS[1]

Roy W. Simonson[2]

ABSTRACT

Processes of soil formation have been related to prominent great soil groups by means of names such as podzolization, laterization, and solonization. A change from this point of view seems necessary when soils of the world are considered as a continuum with a number of properties in common. It is therefore proposed that soil genesis be considered as two overlapping steps; viz, the accumulation of parent materials and the differentiation of horizons in the profile. Of these two steps, the second is of more immediate concern to soil scientists.

Horizon differentiation is ascribed to additions, removals, transfers, and transformations within the soil system. Examples of important changes that contribute to development of horizons are additions of organic matter, removals of soluble salts and carbonates, transfers of humus and sesquioxides, and transformations of primary minerals into secondary minerals. It is postulated that these kinds of changes, as well as others, proceed simultaneously in all soils. It is further suggested that the balance within the combination of changes governs the ultimate nature of the soil profile. If this point of view is valid, the same kinds of changes occur in horizon differentiation in soils as unlike as Chernozems and Latosols, but the balance among the processes is not the same.

Theories of soil genesis reflect the state of knowledge in the soil science of their day. This state of knowledge includes the extent to which soil properties are known and understood. It includes the relative prominence given to various soils in the classification system in use. It includes the very concept of soil itself. As knowledge of soils has grown over the years, there have been a number of changes in concept of soil. These have been followed in turn by changes in theories of genesis. Review of a few theories widely held in the past will bear out these observations. Furthermore, changes in theories of genesis are part of a continuing process which will not stop in our time. Concepts in soil genesis need continuing scrutiny and modification. This paper is an effort to sketch the outlines of a theory of soil genesis consistent with a concept of soil widely held at the present time.

[1] Contribution from the Soil Survey, Soil Conservation Service, U. S. Department of Agriculture. Presented before Div. V, Soil Science Society of America, Atlanta, Ga., Nov. 18, 1957. Received Feb. 17, 1958. Approved May 27, 1958.

[2] Director, Soil Classification and Correlation.

Reproduced with permission from *Soil Science Society of America Proceedings*, Vol. 23, 1959, p. 152-156. Published by the Soil Science Society of America, Madison, Wisconsin, U.S.A.

PAST CONCEPTS OF SOIL

Most scientists concerned with soil a century ago, and even a half century ago, thought of it as disintegrated rock mixed with some decaying organic matter. This is evident from published reports (4, 10). If soil is considered to be disintegrated rock, weathering alone provides an adequate explanation for its formation. Nothing further is necessary to provide a satisfactory theory of soil genesis.

This early concept was replaced first in Russia (5) and later in other countries by the idea that soils were more than weathered rock and that they had profiles consisting of genetically related horizons. After this concept was developed, weathering alone was no longer an adequate theory of soil formation. A modified theory was required to explain the evolution of the profile with its related horizons. As a consequence, soil genesis was considered to be a combination of weathering and certain additional changes due to interactions between living organisms and weathered rock. In the early Russian studies (5, 11), much stress was placed on climate and vegetation as factors of soil formation though parent materials, relief, and time were also considered. Functional relationships between soils and their environment were recognized in these studies.

The studies of Dokuchaeiv and his colleagues were centered on soils with marked horizonation, such as the Chernozems and Podzols (11). These and parallel groups have continued to receive much attention in soil science. In this country, processes of soil formation have been related directly to prominent great soil groups by names such as podzolization, laterization, and solonization (7). These processes have been thought to differ from one another in a number of essentials. In fact, some pairs of processes such as podzolization and laterization have been considered to be opposites in large measure.

A number of shifts in theories of soil genesis have occurred since attention was first focused on the profile and on multiple factors of soil formation in Russia some 75 years ago. One point of view developed in that country holds soil evolution to be a continuous process (11, 12). According to this view, all kinds of soils existing on the earth at any given time are temporary stages. Each kind represents one stage which may disappear, recur, disappear, and recur again. Each stage is succeeded by some other stage in the process of continuing evolution. Thus, the patterns of distribution of soils can change over the face of the earth even though, collectively, the kinds of soils remain the same.

PRESENT CONCEPT OF SOIL

A concept of soil widely held in this country at the present time is a further modification of earlier ones. According to this concept, soils are natural bodies formed on the land surface, occupying space, and having unique morphology. The character of the soil profile remains important though it must share place with other features of the soil. Looking upon soils as geographic bodies entails certain consequences which do not follow as long as attention is focused exclusively on the profile.

First of all, each body of soil occupies volume or space. It is an entity with three dimensions; namely, length, breadth, and depth. Each soil body has a distinct upper

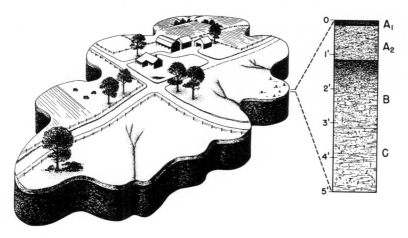

Figure 1—Sketch to illustrate a single body of soil as it occurs together with a diagrammatic soil profile. This body would be shown as one delineation on a detailed soil map.

boundary where it meets the atmosphere. Each has a less distinct perimeter where it meets other soils. Each has an indefinite lower boundary where it grades into weathered rock. This idea is illustrated diagramatically in figure 1, which also shows the relationship of the soil profile to the soil body (17).

Individual bodies of soils are seldom set apart from their neighbors by sharp boundaries. Adjacent bodies commonly grade into one another. The normal gradation between adjacent soil bodies is well known to every man who has helped make a soil survey. Thus, the soils of the world form a continuum or a continuous mantle over most of the land surface.

Every soil type comprises a number of separate geographic bodies or segments of the soil continuum. For the most part, the individual bodies are small so that several occur within a limited area, such as 10 acres. For example, bodies of Fullerton, Dewey, and Emory soils occur in a single small field in east Tennessee. Comparable illustrations can be drawn from any other section of the country. The pattern of small individual soil bodies thus introduces local differences into the soil continuum.

Every soil type has a characteristic region of occurrence. It occurs as a number of separate bodies or segments of the continuum within a certain geographic region or regions. Most soil types commonly occupy characteristic positions in a given landscape. The occurrence of specific soil types in definite geographic regions is reflected in regional differences in the soil mantle of the earth. Thus, there are differences of importance between soils of central Maine and soils of central Arizona, normally greater than local differences in either place.

Although the soil continuum varies both locally and regionally, all soils are alike in some ways. All are three-phase systems; i.e., solid, liquid, and gas. All or nearly all consist of the same major components; i.e., mineral matter, organic matter, water, and air. The proportions of these major components vary widely. All soils have profiles of some kind, and all occupy space. In other words, all form small segments of the surface mantle of the earth. Common to all soils, these features are of consequence to theories of genesis.

To be adequate, a theory of soil genesis must be consistent with the similarities and differences known to exist among the soils of the world. This seems almost too obvious to be worthy of mention but it does deserve emphasis. A theory of soil genesis should be consistent with the existence of soils of the world as a continuum, of features common to all soils, of the normal gradations from one soil to its neighbors, and of differences expressed to various degrees among soils.

STEPS AND PROCESSES IN SOIL GENESIS

Soil genesis can be viewed as consisting of two steps; viz, (a) the accumulation of parent materials, and (b) the differentiation of horizons in the profile. It is not suggested that these steps are clear-cut and distinct or that they lead only in one direction. The two merge and overlap so that it is impossible to tell where one begins and the other ends. For purposes of discussion, however, it is convenient to subdivide the broad and complex topic of soil genesis, as has been done in many earlier discussions. Examples are (a) the reference to combined effects of weathering and of living organisms by Dokuchaeiv (11); (b) the outlining of distructional activities of weathering and of constructional biological activities by Kellogg (7); (c) the distinctions between weathering and soil evolution made by Nikiforoff (13); and (d) the subdivision of soil formation into soil wasting, the organic cycle, and the inorganic cycle by Taylor and Cox (19).

Subsequent discussions in this paper are focused on horizon differentiation. This is not intended to imply that the accumulation of parent material is unimportant. The nature of the regolith in which horizon differentiation proceeds does affect the rate and direction of changes immensely. Lack of space, however, precludes full discussion of either of the two steps. Furthermore, the theory of soil genesis outlined in this paper is more directly concerned with the second step.

Horizon differentiation in soils is considered due to four basic kinds of changes. These are additions, removals, transfers, and transformations in the soil system. These four kinds of changes cover a wide range of processess. In his lectures 30 years ago, Marbut (9) observed that processes of soil development did a "good many things" in making soils from parent materials. His examples included decomposition of minerals, accumulation and assimilation of organic matter, removal of substances, translocations of substances, and development of structure.

Each of the four kinds of changes affects many substances comprising soil. For example, there may be additions, removals, transfers, or transformations of organic matter, soluble salts, carbonates, sesquioxides, or silicate clay minerals. Organic matter is added to the soil in the form of fresh residues. It is transformed and lost through decay. It may be transferred from one horizon to another. Rapid and continuing changes thus affect the organic matter in soils, accompanied by much slower alterations of the mineral fraction. Soluble salts may be lost from the profile or moved from one part to another. Silicate clay minerals may be formed by the transformation of primary minerals, or they may be lost by weathering. They may also be moved from the upper to the lower horizons. Transfers of substances from one horizon to another operate in many soils. Transformations of substances from one form to another proceed in all horizons. Considering the soil as a whole, all of these changes, and others, may contribute to differentiation of horizons.

The additions, removals, transfers, and transformations in soils do not necessarily promote horizon differentiation. Some tend to offset or retard it. For example, the materials transferred from one horizon to another by animal activity (20) or by the cracking and churning of certain clays (16) may retard or offset the differentiation of horizons. Similarly, the mixing of soil by windthrow in the northeastern United States (3) also retards the evolution of horizons in a profile. The uptake of nutrient elements from the deeper profile by growing plants is another example of transfer which does not necessarily contribute to horizon differentiation. Thus, the additions, removals, transfers, and transformations may act to promote or retard the development of horizons. Some changes operate in one direction and some in the other. The various processes operating at the same time in the same profile may be in conflict to some degree.

ROLE OF ORGANIC MATTER

Additions, removals, transfers, and transformations in organic matter during horizon differentiation are discussed briefly in this section of the paper. The purpose is to illustrate the kinds of changes that do occur. Organic matter has been chosen for the discussion as one example of a major constituent, not necessarily the most important. Parallel discussions would be possible for silicate clays, sesquioxides, silica, or soluble salts and carbonates. It should, therefore, be stressed that the discussion of organic matter is simply meant to illustrate what can happen through gains, losses, transfers, and transformations. Lack of space precludes discussion of other substances rather than any lack of importance in soil genesis. The discussion in this section is focused mainly on mineral soils. Organic matter regimes in soils have been considered at length by Jenny (6) in his discussion of the functions of living organisms in soil formation.

Additions of organic matter are an early step in horizon differentiation in most soils. The additions of organic matter to the upper part of the regolith commonly exceed the rate of decay for a time after soil development begins. For example, a borrow pit used in the construction of a railroad in North Dakota about 50 years ago is now marked by a darkened A_1 horizon approximately 6 inches thick. Crocker and Dickson (2) found appreciable accumulation of organic matter in soils being formed from fresh glacial drift in Alaska within a matter of decades. After a period estimated to be 150 years, soils on this glacial drift were as high in organic matter as are most of those in the eastern part of the United States. Thus, gains in organic matter seem to be greater than losses for a time after horizon differentiation begins.

For most soils, the balance between gains and losses in organic matter seems to shift as horizon differentiation moves out of the earliest stages. The rates of loss through decay and transfer increase until they equal those of gain from plant and animal residues. Under a given set of conditions, the gains and losses tend to become equal after a time. Thus, the quantity of organic matter in a soil stabilizes and remains fairly constant even though additions continue.

The nature and amount of organic matter in each horizon of a soil depends upon the additions, transformations, and transfers in the past and present. These are in turn governed by climate, the nature of flora and fauna, the age of the soil, and the like. For example, the additions of organic matter are small in Desert soils. So are losses. The rates of additions and decay are both higher in Chernozems. They are still higher in many Latosols. The points of balance between additions and losses differ among these three groups of soils. Quantities of organic matter are low in Desert soils and relatively high in Chernozems and many Latosols.

Gains in organic matter have been of special importance in the differentiation of horizons in the soils of grasslands in temperate zones. The prominent A_1 horizons of Chernozems, Brunizems, Chestnut soils, and Humic-Gley soils[3] are due largely to additions of organic matter in the past. Other changes have also occurred but the additions of organic matter have been of special importance in setting apart the prominent A_1 horizons.

Relatively rapid turnover in organic matter is the rule in most soils. The soil is simply a way-station for organic matter moving in a larger cycle. Additions of fresh residues are made periodically. Transformations of organic matter through decay proceed all the while. Losses through decay and transfers also continue. The bulk of the organic matter added as fresh residues during a single growing season decays and disappears before the next arrives. Some indication of the rate of change is given by radiocarbon data for A horizons of certain soils formed under grass in the Midwest. Samples were obtained from the deeper part of the A horizon in uncultivated areas, except in the one instance. The data (1) for these samples are as follows:

Barnes	350 years ± 120
Clarion	440 years ± 120
Cresco-Kenyon intergrade	210 years ± 120
Cresco-Kenyon intergrade (plowed)	<100 years
Webster	270 years ± 120

The above data indicate that a small part of the organic matter added to the soils in grasslands persists for a long while. At the same time, the implications of the data are consistent with other observations, which indicate that the bulk of the organic matter added to soils decomposes and disappears rapidly.

Transfers of organic matter within the profile contribute to horizon differentiation in many soils. Such transfers may be due to downward moving water, as in Podzols and solodized-Solonetz, or they may be due to the activities of animals.

Evidence of downward transfer of organic matter by water seems clear in Podzols. Narrow moving fronts which appear to be humus can sometimes be observed as water moves downward through the A_2 horizons of Podzol profiles. The marked accumulation of humus in the B_2 horizons of many Podzols is almost certainly due to downward transfer. This is indicated by position of the humus B horizon in relation to the water table in Ground-Water Podzols in Florida and Holland. The depth at which the humus B horizon occurs may vary widely, depending upon the

---

[3] Concepts of these great soil groups and others referred to later are those given by Thorp and Smith (21), except for Brunizems, defined by Simonson et al. (18), and Latosols, defined by Kellogg (8).

position of the water table. Downward movement is also indicated by the nature of organic matter in certain Podzol profiles in Michigan. According to data of Norman and Bartholomew (14), approximately twice as much of the organic carbon is in the form of uronides in the B horizon as in the A horizon. Downward transfer of organic matter high in uronides seems essential to explain this difference in composition.

Downward movement of humus by water is also indicated in the profiles of solo-dized-Solonetz and Planosols. The faces of prisms or columns in B_2 horizons of many solodized-Solonetz profiles have dark coatings. These have been found to be higher in organic matter than the interiors or caps of the prisms or columns (15). The distribution of the coatings on the vertical faces of the peds and their associa-tion with clay films indicate that the humus was transferred downward into the B horizon.

The transfer of organic matter from the A to the B horizon also seems to have occurred in a number of Planosols. For example, the distribution curve for organic matter against depth has two maxima in a profile of Edina silt loam from Lucas County, Iowa. The first and most important is in the A_1 horizon (4.41 percent) and the second smaller one is in the B_2 horizon (1.47 percent). The A_2 horizon has the first minimum of 0.90 percent and the C horizon the second minimum of 0.32 percent. These differences in amounts of organic matter are not large, but they suggest transfers of organic matter.

Losses of organic matter are apparent in the deeper A horizons of Brunizems which have been occupied by forest and are gradually being changed to Gray-Brown Podzolic soils. The appearance and gradual expansion of light-colored A_2 horizons in the profile are accompanied by parallel decreases in organic matter (22). Dark coatings on the peds in the underlying B horizons also suggest that organic matter is being transferred downward from the A horizons.

Organic matter is transferred by animals from one horizon to another in many soils. Burrowing animals move soil materials low in organic matter from the deeper horizons to the surface and vice versa in many places (20). For example, the author has observed as many as four crotovinas per square foot of horizontal cross-section in the upper C horizon of Webster profiles in north central Iowa. That number is unusual but 1 per square foot is common. Earthworms mix organic matter with the mineral fraction and move it in many soils. In soils such as Oak Lake silt loam in Brookings County, South Dakota, earthworms have completely mixed upper horizons to a depth of 2 feet or more, transferring organic matter down in the pro-cess. Earthworms transfer organic matter downward and mix it with the mineral fraction in profiles of Brown Forest soils in New York. These are a few examples which indicate transfers of organic matter by animals from one horizon to another. Collectively, for all soils, the magnitude of such transfer is substantial.

For the most part, the evidence of transfer of organic matter is not clear cut. It seems probable, nevertheless, that there is some transfer of organic matter from upper horizons to deeper ones in most soils, if not in all of them. The relative impor-tance in horizon differentiation of such transfers may be either large or small.

The preceding discussion of organic matter is meant to illustrate the kinds of changes which affect one major soil constituent as horizons are developed. As em-phasized in the first part of this section, parallel discussions could be prepared for other substances. Other illustrations could also be drawn of additions, removals, transfers, and transformations. Though not complete, the discussion still suggests the variety and complexity of changes that affect a single major constituent. The discussion also suggests differences in relative importance among the several basic kinds of processes from one soil to another.

COMBINATIONS OF PROCESSES

It is postulated that additions, removals, transfers, and transformations of the same constituents proceed in horizon differentiation in most if not all soils. Thus, the processes in horizon differentiation in Podzols would be the same as those in Latosols, Chernozems, or Desert soils. Following this line of thought, there would be some solution and transfer of sesquioxides in all of these soils, though not necessarily the same amounts. There would also be additions of organic matter, transfers of humus within the profile, and losses through decay in all of the soils. There would be one or more of additions, removals, transfers, or transformations of silicate clay minerals. The same combinations of processes would be operating in horizon differentiation in all of these soils.

It is further postulated that the relative importance of each process operating in horizon differentiation is not uniform for all soils. The relative importance of the several processes differs from one soil to another. The relative importance may also change with time in a single profile. For example, the solution and transfer of sesquioxides is far more important in the differentiation of horizons in Podzols than in Chernozems. Additions of organic matter are important in the development of A horizons in Humic-Gley soils and much less important in Red-Yellow Podzolic soils. Differences in relative importance of any process in the full combination are small when two similar soils are compared. The differences are much larger between soils that are themselves unlike in many ways.

The combination of processes operating in horizon differentiation and the balance among them may be illustrated by a diagram consisting of arrows of different lengths, as in figure 2. The length of each arrow indicates the importance of a single process. The balance among the several processes is suggested by the relative lengths of the arrows. This balance can be altered by changes in the length of any one arrow or by changing the lengths of several simultaneously. Similarly, the relative importance among the processes may be altered by changes in one or more of those processes. It should further be recognized that in certain combinations some processes may be of little importance. By and large, however, the full variety of processes seems to leave its imprint on soil character.

Further examples as applied to a few specimen groups of soils may be helpful. In Desert soils, there are small losses of soluble salts and carbonates from the profile, downward transfers of salts and carbonates into deeper horizons, small additions of organic matter, limited transfers and transformations of clay minerals, and limited transfers of sesquioxides. In Podzols, there is much greater removal of salts and carbonates, appreciable gains in organic matter, marked transfers of sesquioxides and organic matter, limited losses of sesquioxides and clay minerals, and some loss of silica. In Latosols, there are marked removals of salts and carbonates, appreciable additions of organic matter, some losses of sesquioxides, marked losses of silica, and transformations and losses of clay minerals.

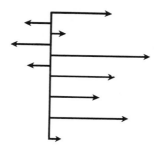

Figure 2—Diagram illustrating a combination of processes of differing importance in horizon differentiation.

The balance among individual processes in a given combination thus becomes the key to the nature of a soil. The relative importance of each process in the combination is reflected in the ultimate character of the soil itself. Additions of organic matter are of little importance in the combination of processes that differentiate horizons in Desert soils. Removals and transfers of sesquioxides are also of little importance. On the other hand, these same processes are of great importance in horizon differentiation in Latosols. This further illustrates the importance of the balance among processes in any given combination.

The variety of changes proceeding during the differentiation of horizons in a profile depend themselves upon a host of simpler processes such as hydration, oxidation, solution, leaching, precipitation, and mixing. These simpler and more basic reactions proceed in all soils. They are controlled in their turn by factors such as climate, living organisms, parent materials, and topography.

Thus, the theory of soil genesis outlined in the preceding discussions requires a shift in emphasis from theories of soil formation held in the past. The theory does not so much discard ideas held earlier as modify them and place them in a different setting. Primary emphasis is placed upon the operation of processes in combinations, with some processes promoting and others offsetting or retarding horizon differentiation. Major emphasis is also placed upon the balance among processes in any combination. It is further suggested that shifts in balance among combinations of processes are responsible for soil differences rather than the operation of markedly different genetic processes. The emphasis on widespread operation of the same kinds of changes in horizon differentiation seems consistent with the existence of the soils of the world as a continuum over the land surface. It is also consistent with the common lack of sharp boundaries between one soil and the next. It can accommodate the existence of both local and regional differences among soils. Finally, it is consistent with the sharing of some properties by all soils.

LITERATURE CITED

1. Broecker, W. S., Kulp, J. L., and Tucek, C. S. Lamont natural radiocarbon measurements: III. Science 124:162. 1956.

2. Crocker, R. L., and Dickson, B. A. Soil development on the recessional moraines of the Herbert and Mendenhall glaciers, southeastern Alaska. J. Ecol. 43:427-448. 1955.

3. Denny, C. S. Surficial geology and geomorphology of Potter County, Pennsylvania. U. S. Geological Survey Prof. Paper 288. p. 55-66. 1956.

4. Fallou, Fr. Alb. Pedologie oder allgemeine und besondere Bodenkunde. Dresden. p. 180-182. 1862.

5. Glinka, K. D. Dokuchaeiv's ideas in the development of pedology and cognate sciences. Russian Pedological Invest.; Acad. Sci. U.S.S.R. 32 p. 1927.

6. Jenny, Hans. Factors of Soil Formation. McGraw-Hill, New York. p. 197-260. 1941.

7. Kellogg, C. E. Development and significance of the great soil groups of the United States. USDA Misc. Publ. 229. 40 p. 1936.

8. .... Tropical soils. Trans. Inter. Congr. Soil Sci. 4th Congr. Amsterdam. 1:266-276. 1950.

9. Marbut, C. F. Soils: Their Genesis and Classification. Soil Sci. Soc. Am., Madison. p. 25. 1951.

10. Merrill, G. P. A Treatise of Rocks, Rock Weathering, and Soils. The MacMillan Co., New York. 1906.

11. Neustruev, S. S. Genesis of soils. Russian Pedological Invest.; Acad. Sci. U.S.S.R. 98 p. 1927.

12. Nikiforoff, C. C. Fundamental formula of soil formation. Am. J. Sci. 240:847-866. 1942.

13. ...., Weathering and soil evolution. Soil Sci. 67:219-230. 1949.

14. Norman, A. G., and Bartholomew, W. V. The chemistry of soil organic matter: I. Distribution of uronic carbon in some soil profiles. Soil Sci. 56:143-150. 1943.

15. Retzer, J. L., and Simonson, R. W. Distribution of carbon in morphological units from the B horizons of Solonetz-like soils. J. Am. Soc. Agron. 33:1009-1013. 1941.

16. Simonson, R. W. Morphology and classification of the Regur soils of India. J. Soil Sci. 5:275-288. 1954.

17. ...., What soils are. In USDA Yearbook of Agr. Soil. U. S. Government Printing Office, Washington, D. C. p. 17-31. 1957.

18. ...., Riecken, F. F., and Smith, G. D. Understanding Iowa soils. Wm. C. Brown Co., Dubuque. p. 23. 1952.

19. Taylor, N. H., and Cox, J. E. The soil pattern of New Zealand. New Zealand Soil Bureau Publ. 113. 1956.

20. Thorp, J. Effects of certain animals that live in soils. Sci. Monthly 48:180-191. 1949.

21. ...., and Smith, G. D. Higher categories of soil classification: Order, suborder, and great soil group. Soil Sci. 67:117-126. 1949.

22. White, E. M., and Riecken, F. F. Brunizem—Gray-Brown Podzolic soil biosequences. Soil Sci. Soc. Am. Proc. 19:504-508. 1955.

A STUDY OF ROCK WEATHERING WITH REFERENCE TO THE SOILS OF THE MALVERN HILLS
PART I. WEATHERING OF BIOTITITE AND GRANITE

I. Stephen

(Pedology Department, Rothamsted Experimental Station)

INTRODUCTION

From the view point of petrology soil may be regarded as the residuum resulting from the disintegration and decomposition of rocks under the influence of climate and vegetation. Many of the primary rock minerals result from processes occurring at depth and at high temperatures and pressures, but their alteration in the soil occurs at the surface of the earth at low energy levels. While minerals in rocks are mainly broken down initially under the influence of reactive aqueous solutions penetrating intercrystalline cracks, their further decomposition occurs under the more immediate influence of the chemical and physical conditions resulting from the additional interplay of climate and vegetation with which they are in metastable equilibrium. The minerals in a soil may therefore be described in terms of the common rock-forming minerals and their secondary products of weathering.

The soils chosen for this study are from the Malvern Hills in Worcestershire, England. The hills are formed of a narrow ridge of hard crystalline rocks, presumably of Pre-Cambrian age, rising abruptly from the flat Triassic plain on the east Plate I, A), and passing into the hill-and-dale country of the Silurian and Old Red Sandstone formations on the west. The range lies in a north to south direction, is about 9 miles long, and nowhere exceeds 1 mile in width. The elevation ranges from about 700 ft. to 1,395 ft. at Worcestershire Beacon. The district studied lies between the Wyche Cutting in the south and Worcestershire Beacon in the north. The area is a suitable one for weathering studies, as it was not traversed by any large ice-sheet, so there is no glacial drift to introduce ambiguities into the relationship of soil, subsoil, and bedrock. In addition the suite of rocks is comprehensive, varying from granite to ultra-basic rocks rich in hornblende and biotite.

On a broad scheme of classification, all the soils would be included in the Major Soil Group of Brown Earths. They are, in general, shallow, very stony, and carry a dense turf covering. A tendency to excessive drainage is shown by their dry fluffy nature, and appears to be conditioned by two main factors: their coarse mineral texture, and the ready percolation of rain-water through the faults and fractures characteristic of the underlying rocks.

The mineralogical changes which occur during the formation of soil from two contrasted rock-types, granite and biotitite, found in proximity in the field, are described in this paper. A similar study of representatives of the hornblendic rocks will be presented in a later communication.

Reproduced with permission from *Journal of Soil Science*, Volume 3, 1952, p. 20-33.
Published by the British Society of Soil Science, England.

EXPERIMENTAL

Preparation of samples. In preparing the soils for mineralogical analysis the following procedure was adopted. The clay($< 2\mu$) was first separated from the soil by an adaptation of the beaker method of mechanical analysis as described by Piper (1944). The silt (20-2μ) was also separated from the same sample by sedimentation after the removal of the clay. The residue of sand was divided into two sizegrades by sieving, corresponding approximately to 2.0-0.2 mm. (coarse sand) and 0.2-0.02 mm. (fine sand).

Petrographic examinations. Thin sections prepared from fresh and weathered rock samples were used to characterize optically the composition of the parent rocks and the initial stages of mineral breakdown. Heavy liquid separations of the sand fractions of the soils were made, the liquid consisting of a mixture of acetylene tetrabromide and nitrobenzene standardized at s.g. 2.90 ± 0.01: this effects a separation of the hydrous micas, chlorites, feldspars, and quartz from the heavier minerals. The soils were not treated with hydrogen peroxide to remove organic matter as they contain vermiculitic minerals readily exfoliated by peroxide; this pre-treatment would have yielded very false estimates of their relative abundance in microscopic counts.

X-ray analysis. The two methods used were the 'oriented-aggregate' (Nagel-schmidt, 1941) and powder techniques, using filtered copper radiation and a 90-mm. powder camera of the type described by MacEwan (1949). In order to facilitate the examination of the clays by the aggregate technique it is desirable to remove both organic matter and free oxides and hydroxides of iron and aluminium, since their presence not only obscures the diffraction pattern, but also adversely affects the orientation of the flaky minerals. The organic matter was destroyed by treatment with hot hydrogen peroxide. The 'free' iron compounds were removed by the method proposed by Galabutskaya and Govorova (1934) which employs sodium hydrosulphite ($Na_2S_2O_4$). This method compares favourably with others suggested and appears to have little (if any) effect on the clay minerals.

FIELD DATA

In the Malvern crystalline-complex veins of coarsely crystalline to pegmatitic biotitite occur,[*] which in places consist of 80 percent or more of coarse biotite in flakes up to an inch or more in diameter. Such veins are well exposed in the main Tolgate (N) Quarry, north of Wyche Cutting. An exposure in a slip at the top of the quarry yields a very satisfactory profile of the residual soil, only slightly contaminated with granitic material. The biotitite occurs as a vein-like mass (at this locality sheared), about 4 ft. wide, flanked by granitic country rock (Plate I, B). Even at the lowest level exposed (about 4 ft. 6 in.) the rock is highly weathered and can easily be dug with a spade. At 12-15 in. from the surface there is a fairly sharp boundary between the rock and the overlying soil.

---

[*] A brief note on the field occurrence has been given by R. W. Pocock, A. Brammall, and W. N. Croft (1940).

A. Malvern Hills from the east.

B. Residual biotitite profile.

I. STEPHEN—PLATE I

The residual soil over the granite is very shallow and stony in comparison with the deeper soil on the more readily weathered biotitite, and rubbly granite fragments are abundant even in the surface soil. Both soils are freely drained, their porous nature allowing water to percolate readily. They are acid in reaction, the pH range being 3.6-3.8 in the granite soil and 4.6-4.9 in the biotitite soil.

PETROGRAPHY OF THE PARENT ROCKS

Biotitite

In the fresh rock the biotite occurs in large brown glistening flakes and is normally free from any alteration products. Optical examination of thin sections from a block of weathering biotitite shows clearly the alteration of the biotite to a green optically negative chlorite. The alteration begins around the margin and along the cleavage traces of the biotite and gradually proceeds inwards, resulting in the formation of a chloritic pseudomorph. X-ray diagrams of the chlorite flakes, photographed with the (001) plane parallel to the beam, show a pattern similar to that given by artificially oriented aggregates of clays (Nagelschmidt, 1941). It appears therefore that on weathering the biotite breaks down into a polycrystalline aggregate of a chloritic material, with a marked preferential orientation corresponding to that of the original mica.

The chloritization of the biotite is accompanied by the segregation of the liberated titania in association with lime and silica into abundant crystallites of secondary sphene (Plate II, A), normally occurring in feathery groupings and needle-shaped aggregates. Iron oxides, finely granular yellow pleochroic epidote, and calcite occur sparingly as weathering products.

A micrometric analysis of five micro-sections of the weathered rock underlying the profile sampled gives the following modal composition (volume percent): biotite (cholritized) 57.0, amphibole 24.5, epidote, zoisite, and clinozoisite 6.7, iron ore (magnetite and ilmenite) 4.6, clinochlore 3.0, sphene 2.5, apatite, quartz, a sodic plagioclase, rutile, and calcite 1.7.

The chloritized biotite occurs in greenish, moderately pleochroic flakes, up to 5 mm. in size, rather bent, often fractured, and showing a marked excretion of iron oxides (Plate II, B). The optical properties, determined on flakes separated from the weathered rock at a depth of 30-36 in., are slightly variable, but all the flakes are sensibly uniaxial and optically negative. Average values for the refractive indices are n_β (= n_γ) = 1.590±0.003; birefringence 0.003-0.004. A relationship to penninite is suggested by the low birefringence and the 'ultra-blue' abnormal interference colours, which according to Winchell (1933) are characteristic of this variety of chlorite.

On X-ray analysis the flakes give a typical chlorite-type diagram with four orders of the 14.2 Å basal reflection of about equal intensity and the fifth weak (Fig. 1, A). Vermiculites also give a strong 14 Å basal reflection but with weak second and third orders. This enables a distinction to be drawn between chlorite and vermiculite, and indicates the dominantly chloritic nature of the flakes. After heating at 540 C for several hours, the first-order reflection develops a 'tail', becoming asymmetrical towards higher angles, and all the spacings become diffuse except the third order

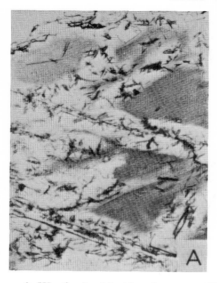 

A. Weathering biotitite phenocryst. Dark areas are original biotite, surrounded by secondary chlorite enclosing abundant crystallites of sphene. Ordinary light, × 50.

B. Biotitite. The bent and fractured nature of the flakes is well seen. The other constituents are a tremolitic amphibole, iron oxide, and sphene. Ordinary light, × 50.

 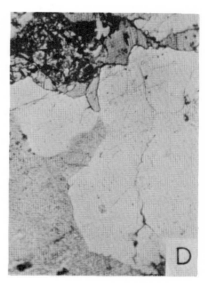

C. Microcline, in granite, showing polysynthetic twinning. Crossed nicols, × 50.

D. Granite, showing aggregate structure of the dark minerals (top of field). The minerals of these basic 'clots' are epidote, chlorite, magnetite, sphene, and apatite. The other constituents are highly sericitized plagioclase (bottom left), and quartz with characteristic inclusions. Ordinary light, × 50.

Photomicrographs by V. Stansfield, F.R.P.S.

I. STEPHEN—PLATE II

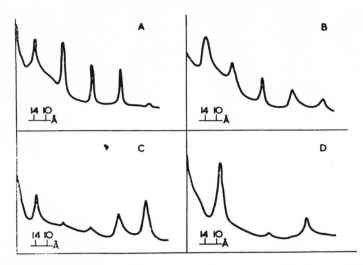

Fig. 1—Microphotometer tracings of X-ray diagrams of (A) coarse flakes from weathered biotitite, and (B) the same after heating at 540 C for several hours; (C) brownish micaceous flakes from sand fractions of overlying soil, and (D) the same after heating at 750 C for several hours.

(Fig. 1, B). This behaviour suggests that (1) a random mixture is present, a *small* amount of material occurring with layers of smaller spacing than the chlorite, and (2) the spacing of the third order, i.e. 4.72 Å, is almost exactly a submultiple of the smaller spacing. Thus the smaller spacing must be close to $4.72 \times 2 = 9.44$ Å. This figure corresponds closely to the spacing obtained on heating vermiculite to the same temperature, indicating the presence of some vermiculite-like units interleaved in the chlorite structure. The later suggestion is confirmed by the ready exfoliation of the flakes in cold hydrogen peroxide (cf. Groves, 1939).

The exchange capacity, determined on material lightly ground to pass the 120 I.M.M. sieve, is 28 m.e./100g. Values for vermiculites (Barshad, 1948) are about 140 m.e./100 g.; therefore assuming no exchange capacity for chlorites, the amount of interleaved vermiculite layers is of the order of 20 percent.

The other constituent present in the rock in appreciable amount is a tremolitic amphibole occuring in long-bladed, often interlocking crystals which in section are either colourless or show slight pleochroic variation from pale green to colourless. It is highly resistant to weathering and is concentrated in the sand fractions of the soil.

Granite

Under the microscope the texture is typically granitic, all the constituents being allotriomorphic. A mineral analysis of the unweathered rock underlying the profile sampled gives the modal composition (average of 7 micro-sections): quartz 23.0, feldspar (microcline-perthite, oligoclase, orthoclase) 64.0, penninite 6.0, epidote-clinozoisite 3.2, iron ore 1.3, amphibole, sphene, apatite, &c., 2.5.

The most abundant feldspar is microcline, in part perthitic, occurring in plates

up to about 5 mm. in size, showing the typical polysynthetic twinning in two directions (Plate II, C), and also occasionally a major twinning of the Carlsbad type.
Even in sections of the weathered rock the microline is always fresh when the other
feldspars are considerably altered. The orthoclase is always turbid and clouded with
secondary products. The plagioclase is a usually twinned oligoclase or oligoclase-
andesine. Since it has been altered in part to an irregular network of white mica
(Plate II, D), present in the unweathered facies, it has apparently been subjected to
hydrothermal processes.

The quartz crystals occur in mosaic intergrowths, the individual crystals being of
smaller grain size than the surrounding feldspar. The crystals normally show un-
dulatory extinction, and frequently contain liquid and dust-like inclusions (Plate II,
D).

At this locality the granite is slightly contaminated by the incorporation of xeno-
lithic basic material, now represented hydrothermally by aggregates of mafic minerals (Plate II, D). The minerals comprising these basic 'clots' are chlorite (penninite), yellow pleochroic epidote and clinozoisite, magnetite, brownish sphene, and
apatite. The chlorite occurs as well-developed plates up to 2 mm. in size with the
following optical characteristics: pleochroic with $X = Y =$ green $> Z =$ very pale yellow-
ish-green, birefringence very low, anomalous chocolate-brown interference colours,
negative elongation, and positive optic sign. Alteration of the chlorite, as seen in
sections of the weathered rock, result in the formation of optically negative yellowish-
brown to brown pseudomorphs of a vermiculitic character.

Minerals present in small amounts include biotite, usually as irregular-shaped
chloritized flakes, a pale green to colourless amphibole, allanite (?), garnet, and
zircon. Primary muscovite is rare in the granite at the locality sampled, although
elsewhere it is locally abundant, very large pockets of coarse muscovite-pegmatite
occurring at several points in the Tolgate-Wyche area.

TREND OF ALTERATION IN THE SAND FRACTIONS

Minerals occurring in the 'light separates' (s.g. < 2.90) of the sands of the soils
are quartz, feldspar, chlorite-vermiculite, white mica (sericite), and chalcedony, but
their relative amounts differ markedly in the two profiles dependent on the character
of the underlying rock. This is illustrated in Fig. 2 for the fine sands,[*] where chlorite-vermiculite are the dominant minerals in the biotitite soil, while quartz and
feldspar approximate to 85 percent in the granite soil. The proportions are similar
in the coarse sands, but this fraction is unsuitable for detailed mineral analysis
owing to the occurrence of large amounts of composite mineral aggregates. Minerals
present in small amounts in both profiles are sericite and chalcedony (very rare).
In the granite soil, sericite occurs as colourless micaceous flakes, about equal in
amount to the chlorite-vermiculite, but of smaller grain size. It is rare in the biotitite
soil.

As quartz and feldspar occur only in accessory amounts in the biotitite, their
presence in the overlying soil is due largely to contamination from the neighbouring

---

[*] Percentages are based on microscopic counts of approximately 500 particles in about 25 random
fields for each sample.

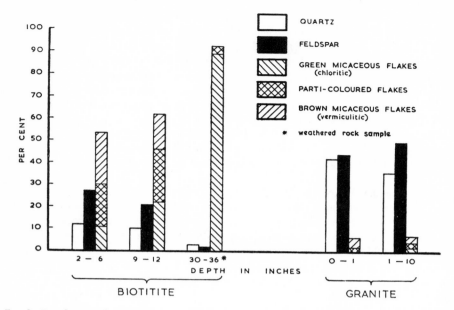

Fig. 2—Distribution of quartz, feldspar, and chlorite-vermiculite in the fine sands of soils overlying biotitite and granite.

granite. It seems very probable, however, that the data imply more contamination than exists, due to the stability of these grains compared with that of the micaceous minerals.

A characteristic feature of this soil is the presence of yellowish-brown to brown micaceous flakes with a golden or bronzy lustre. Their X-ray diagrams are distinct from those of the chloritic flakes characteristic of the underlying rock in that they have strong first, fourth, and fifth orders of the basal reflection, and weak second and third orders (Fig. 1, C). On heat treatment at 750 C, the first-order basal reflection at 14.32 Å is condensed to 9.45 Å (Fig. 1, D), consistent with data given by Gruner (1934) and Barshad (1948) for vermiculites.

Optically the flakes are fairly strongly pleochroic with $X =$ very pale yellowish-brown $< Y=Z=$brown. The acute bisectrix is nearly normal to (001) as in biotite, and $(-)$ $2V$ attains a maximum of 8 degrees. Refraction indices are n_α 1.563, n_β ($= n_\gamma$) 1.582±0.003; birefringence 0.019. These values correspond closely with data given by Shannon (1928) for a sample of vermiculite (jefferisite) from West Chester. Pa., but are considerably lower than those given by Walker (1949) for vermiculite occurring in the soils of north-east Scotland.

The transition from the dominantly chloritic weathering product of biotite to the vermiculite in the sands is shown by a progressive colour change from green to yellowish-brown. The trend of alteration is shown in Fig. 2, in which these minerals have been subdivided on a colour basis. Such a division is approximate, but the colour is a fairly reliable guide, while X-ray and optical examinations suggest that there is a continuous gradation. Essentially only the green chloritic type occurs in the weathered rock, but the vermiculite becomes increasingly frequent in passing into the soils.

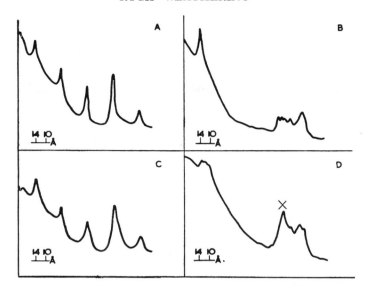

Fig. 3—Microphotometer tracings of X-ray diagrams of clay from the weathered biotitite, (A) before and (B) after heating at 540 C; and from the surface soil, (C) before and (D) after similar heat treatment.

The 'heavy separate' (s.g. < 2.90) of the fine sands of the biotitite soil is more than 55 percent by weight in both layers of the profile, and is characterized by a 'flood' of amphibole (over 80 percent). The principal subordinate minerals are members of the epidote-clinozoisite group, iron oxides and sphene. A few grains of zircon, rutile, and apatite are also present.

By contrast, the amount of heavy residue in the corresponding fractions of the granite soil is small, being 8 percent in the 0-1 in. layer and 5 percent in the basal soil, the low percentage being due to the small amounts of ferromagnesian minerals in the parent rock. In order of relative abundance, epidote-clinozoisite. amphibole, and iron oxides make up the bulk of the separate. Garnet, zircon. and sphene are the commonest of the remaining minerals. Tourmaline, kyanite. and apatite are rare. Apatite forms from 3-4 percent of the heavy residue from samples of the powdered rock, but was not observed in the surface soil. Its elimination is doubtless due to the acid conditions under which weathering is taking place.

CLAY MINERALOGY

Biotitite

The X-ray reflections given by oriented aggregates of the clays from the weathered rock and from the surface soil are shown in Fig. 3.

The diagrams of the unheated clays show an integral series of (00*l*) reflections with spacings of approximately 14 Å and submultiples. The basal spacing and the intensity of the first five lines of the (00*l*) series are given in Table 1.

Table 1—Basal Spacing and Intensity of Basal Reflections

	Soil clay 2–6 in.	Soil clay 9–12 in.	Clay from rock 30–36 in.
Basal spacing (Å)	14·08	14·07	14·06
Order		*Intensity*	
I	s	s	ms
2	m	m	m
3	m	m	m
4	ms	ms	ms
5	w	w	w

Note: X-ray intensities, estimated visually, are given on the following scale: very strong (vs), strong (s), medium-strong (ms), medium (m), medium-weak (mw), weak (w), very weak (vw).

The spacings are not affected by treatment with glycerol, which excludes the possibility that montmorillonite (MacEwan, 1944) or 'swelling chlorite' (Stephen and MacEwan, 1950) contributes to the 14 Å line. Of the known clay minerals, the remaining possibilities are chlorite and vermiculite.

The recordings (A) and (C) in Fig. 3 are very similar and in both cases, heat treatment increases the intensity of the fifth-order basal reflection and eliminates the second and third orders. The first-order basal reflection develops a composite structure, a feature which is particularly marked in (D).

The structures developed on the outer (low-spacing) side of the 14 Å line were analysed in the following way (Fig. 4). The curve was re-plotted on a horizontal base line to eliminate the background. The peak near 14 Å was then completed assuming that it is symmetrical and that the inner (high-spacing) edge represents its true shape. The peak thus obtained was subtracted from the curve and the residue re-plotted. The process was repeated on this curve and continued until the residue itself was symmetrical.

This analysis reveals that four peaks are present in the clays from both the weathered rock and the soils. The clays from the soils give peaks at identical spacings, namely, 9.7, 10.2, 11.8, and 13.9 Å, and it is probable that these same peaks are also present in the clay from the weathered rock, the small differences in spacings observed being due to experimental error.

These results may be most readily interpreted on the basis that there are *three* main crystalline phases present, namely:

(a) a chloritic phase giving a 13.9 Å reflection on heating;

(b) a vermiculitic phase giving an approximately 10 Å reflection on heating;

(c) a random mixture of (a) and (b) in roughly equal proportions. Little significance is attached to the lower spacing at 9.5-9.7 Å, as it is very broad and its magnitude is of the order of the experimental error.

The structure of the heated chlorite (a) is analogous to that observed in penninite and other magnesian chlorites heated at a higher temperature (Brindley and Ali, 1950). When penninite was heated at 600 C, marked changes occurred in the intensities of the basal reflections, the (001) reflection becoming much more intense, while (002), (003), and (004) were considerably weakened. The position of the lines, how-

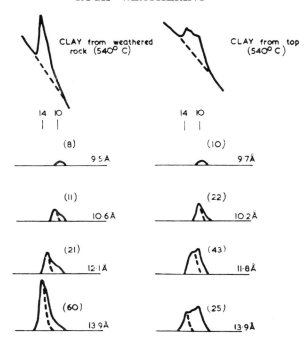

Fig. 4—Analysis of the peaks in the 10-14 A region of heat-treated clays from the weathered biotitite and top soil. Figures in brackets give the areas of individual peaks as a percentage of the total area of the curve.

ever, remained essentially the same, and the structure was still that of a chlorite. Brindley and Ali have explained the change in intensities by migration of the inter-lamellar magnesium ions, resulting in a MgO-like structure between the main sheets.

The vermiculitic phase (b) is probably a 'potassium vermiculite', which gives a mica structure on heat treatment. The evidence for its presence is the strong basal reflection at approximately 10 Å with the development of the strong third-order basal reflection at 3.33 Å (X, Fig. 3, D) in the band which develops at 3.47-2.80 Å, the limits of this band corresponding approximately to the fourth and fifth orders of the original structure. The material cannot be a *fully* saturated potassium-vermiculite, as Barshad (1948) has shown that this, unheated, gives a diagram similar to that of biotite-phlogopite and shows no 'expanded state'. It is probable, however, that sufficient potassium ions are associated with the main sheets to stabilize the structure at a mica-spacing after heat treatment. The 9.5-9.7 Å reflection may then be explained as due to a small proportion of true vermiculite, i.e. without potassium ions.

A photograph of the clay from the surface soil, after saturation with potassium ions, but without heating, shows two components, unchanged chlorite and a mixture of chloritic and mica-like layers, which is in full accord with the proposed composition.

The proportions of the 14 Å (chloritic) and 10 Å (vermiculitic) components can be determined by measuring the area under each peak (Fig. 4), the 12 Å peak being taken to represent a random mixture of approximately equal parts of the

Table 2—Calculated Proportions of Chloritic and Vermiculitic Layers as determined by Heating at
540 C, and applying Theory of Diffraction by Randomly Mixed Layers

	% Chlorite (*14 Å*)	% Vermiculite (*10 Å*)	% 'Residue' (*9·5–9·7 Å*)
Clay from soil (2–6 in.)	45	45	10
Clay from soil (9–12 in.)	40	50	10
Clay from weathered rock (30–36 in.)	70	20	10

components. The results are shown in Table 2, the proportions being given to the nearest 5 percent.

It has been assumed in these calculations that the 10 and 14 Å peaks have the same absolute intensity, so that the peak area is proportional to the amount present. Any correction, however, for actual intrinsic intensity will not affect the conclusions regarding the changes in *relative* amounts of the components in the different layers of the profile. It will be noted that the proportion of vermiculitic layers is higher in the soil clays than in the clay from the weathered rock, but does not alter appreciably between the lower and upper soil layers.

Powder photographs of the clays show a marked similarity to that of penninite, but with fewer lines: this is probably due to randomness in the structure, which is accounted for by the presence of vermiculitic layers.

Granite

X-ray diagrams of oriented aggregates of the soil clays show a prominent series of basal reflections of 10 Å and submultiples, indicating a mineral of the mica group (illite),[*] and weaker reflections at 7.1 and 3.5 Å which can mainly be referred to a kaolin mineral (Fig. 5, A). By heating at 540 C the kaolin lines are eliminated, and a pattern is left with strong basal reflections at 10, 5, and 3.33 Å referable to mica, and very weak lines at 13.8 and 11.8 Å attributable to a chlorite-vermiculite crystallization (Fig. 5, B). The latter appears to be identical with the type of clay material composing the soil clays over the biotitite. Quartz is present in accessory amount, the strong reflection at 3.35 Å being superimposed on the third-order basal mica reflection, and a weak reflection at 4.26 Å can be seen on the tracings (Fig. 5, A and B).

The illite is dominantly (or exclusively) of the dioctahedral (muscovite-like) variety, as is shown by the strong second-order basal reflection at 5 Å (Nagelschmidt, 1937) and the strong (060) line at 1.49 Å (MacEwan, 1949). It will be noted on the aggregate photograph (Fig. 5, A) that the illite basal reflection at 10 Å is somewhat asymmetrical, being sharp on the outer edge but forming a 'tail' towards lower angles. This 'tail' is eliminated after heating at 540 C (Fig. 5, B), from which it can be assumed that it is due to hydration of the illite caused by the interpolation of layers of water molecules between the structural sheets, suggesting that the illite

---

[*] Grim, Bray, and Bradley (1937) proposed the term *illite* as a general one for the mica-like clay mineral of argillaceous sediments.

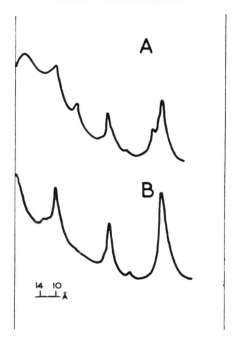

Fig. 5—Microphotometer tracings of X-ray diagrams of the clay from the basal layer of the granite soil, (A) before and (B) after heating at 540 C.

is tending to break down to a montmorillonitic product. The absence of a reflection at 17.7 Å in glycerol-saturated samples shows, however, that true montmorillonite is not present.

It has not been possible to ascertain the type of kaolin mineral present, as the amount is too small to discriminate between kaolinite proper and the 'fireclay mineral' described by Brindley and Robinson (1947). The presence of halloysite is improbable owing to the sharpness of the reflections. By comparing photographs of mixtures of hydro-muscovite and kaolinite in definite proportions with those of the unheated aggregates, the amount of kaolin in the clays is estimated to be 15±5 percent.

The clays show only slight variation in the amounts of the different minerals present, kaolin and quartz, however, being slightly more abundant relative to the other minerals in the surface soil than in the basal layer. X-ray diagrams of coarse (2-0.5μ) and fine (< 0.5μ) clay, however, show a marked differentiation, the quartz and chlorite being concentrated in the coarser clay, and being essentially absent in the finer clay, which consists almost exclusively of illite and kaolin.

DISCUSSION

The observations show that as weathering proceeds in the biotitite soil, the dominantly chloritic material of the weathered rock is being converted into a vermiculitic material, this being so for both the coarse flakes of weathered biotite and the clays.

These results and those of previous workers show the common occurrence of the process of *vermiculitization* in the weathering of primary biotite. The vermiculitic product may apparently be reached either through mixed-layer mica-vermiculite intermediate stages (Kerr, 1930; Wager, 1944; Walker, 1949), or mixed-layer biotite-chlorite and chlorite-vermiculite stages as shown here. The relationship between chlorite and vermiculite and the probable mechanism of the transition will be discussed in Part II of this communication.

The dominant mineral in the clay of the granite soil is a member of the dioctahedral illite (clay-muscovite) group, whose presence can be attributed to the alteration of the feldspar of the bedrock. The alteration appears to be in part hydrothermal and in part due to weathering. It is difficult, if not impossible, to draw a definite boundary between these processes. In the apparently unweathered granite, shred-like white mica is widespread as a secondary mineral derived mainly from the acid plagioclase, and the orthoclase is turbid and clouded with secondary products. It appears very probable that this pre-weathering alteration initiates or facilitates the subsequent alteration by dilute solutions at normal temperatures and pressures (Bosazza, 1948).

Dioctahedral illites contain the same major elements as potash feldspars, and it is probable that in the early stages of weathering much of the potassium liberated by the breakdown of the latter is 'fixed' by a reaction involving the accompanying alumina and silica, the resulting product being an aluminiferous member of the illite group. The alteration of plagioclase to illite probably requires the introduction of potassium from external sources, although in acid plagioclases potassium is commonly present in some quantity.

Crystalline constituents of the clays occurring in minor amounts are minerals of the chlorite-vermiculite crystallization, whose presence can be related to the weathering of the basic contaminants. The small amount of quartz is attributable to the physical breakdown of crystals present in the parent bedrock.

SUMMARY

The importance of the parent bedrock in determining the mineralogical composition of the derived soils is shown by the present study. This is true both for the coarser 'inherited' mineral particles and also for the clays which may be assumed to represent the 'weathering complex', the latter in the biotitite soil being a chlorite-vermiculite crystallization, while in the granite soil it is dominantly an illite-kaolin association.

ACKNOWLEDGEMENTS

The writer wishes to express his indebtedness to Dr. A. Brammall for advice which greatly facilitated the choice of the most suitable sites for sampling, and for his continued interest during the progress of the work. The helpful criticism and encouragement given by Dr. A. Muir must be acknowledged. Thanks are also due to Dr. D. M. C. MacEwan for useful discussion on the interpretation of X-ray data. This paper is based on part of a thesis approved by the University of London for the Ph.D. Degree.

REFERENCES

1. Barshad, I. 1948. Vermiculite and its relation to biotite as revealed by base exchange reactions, X-ray analyses, differential thermal curves, and water content. Amer. Miner. 33, 655-78.

2. Bosazza, V. L. 1948. The Petrography and Petrology of South African Clays. Lund Humphries & Co. London and Bradford.

3. Brindley, G. W., and Ali, S. Z. 1950. X-ray study of thermal transformations in some magnesian chlorite minerals. Acta Cryst. 3, 25-30.

4. ...., and Robinson, K. 1947. An X-ray study of some kaloinitic fire-clays. Trans. Brit. Cer. Soc. 46, 49-62.

5. Galabutskaya, E., and Govorova, R. 1934. Bleaching of kaolin. Mineral. Suir'e, 9, 27-32.

6. Grim, R. E., Bray, R. H., and Bradley, W. F. 1937. The mica in argillaceous sediments. Amer. Miner. 22, 813-29.

7. Groves, R. 1939. Exfoliation of vermiculite by chemical means. Nature, 144, 554.

8. Gruner, J. W. 1934. The structure of vermiculites and their collapse by dehydration. Amer. Miner. 19, 557-75.

9. Kerr, P. F. 1930. Kaolinite from a Brooklyn subway tunnel. Amer. Miner. 15, 144-58.

10. MacEwan, D. M. C. 1944. Identification of the montmorillonite group of minerals by X-rays. Nature, 154, 577-8.

11. .... 1949. Some notes on the recording and interpretation of X-ray diagrams of soil clays. J. Soil Sci. 1, 90-103.

12. Nagelschmidt, G. 1937. X-ray investigations on clay. Pt. III. The differentiation of micas by X-ray powder photographs. Z. Krist. 97, 514-21.

13. .... 1941. The identification of clay minerals by means of aggregate X-ray diffraction diagrams. J. Sci. Instr. 18, 100-1.

14. Piper, C. S. 1944. Soil and Plant Analysis. Monograph, The Waite Agricultural Reasearch Institute, Adelaide.

15. Pocock, R. W., Brammall, A., and Croft, W. N. 1940. Easter field meeting, Hereford. Proc. Geol. Assoc. 51, 52-62.

16. Shannon, E. V. 1928. Vermiculite from the Bare Hills near Baltimore, Maryland. Amer. J. Sci. 15, 20-24.

17. Stephen, I., and MacEwan, D. M. C. 1950. 'Swelling chlorite.' Geotechnique, 2, 82-3.

18. Wager, L. R. 1944. A stage in the decomposition of biotite from the Shap granite. Proc. Yorks. Geol. Soc. 25, 366-72.

19. Walker, G. F. 1949. The decomposition of biotite in the soil. Miner. Mag. 28, 693-703.

20. Winchell, A. N. 1933. Elements of Optical Mineralogy. Pt. II. Description of minerals. 3rd edition. New York and London.

(Received 24 July 1951)

CHELATION AND THE VERTICAL MOVEMENT OF SOIL CONSTITUENTS

H. J. Atkinson and J. R. Wright

Canada Department of Agriculture [1]

Received for publication February 1, 1957

In the process of soil formation, the vertical movement of soil constituents results in the development of horizons usually distinguished by differences in color or texture or both. This differentiation is very pronounced in the podzolization process which occurs over large areas of the North American continent. One of the fundamental characteristics of podzol profile development is the movement of iron and aluminum from the A horizon and their precipitation in the B horizon. Many mechanisms have been proposed to account for this mobilization and subsequent reprecipitation. Bloomfield (3) observed that "Broadly speaking, the various suggested mechanisms fall into two classes; according to the first and probably more widely held theory. the free oxides are transported as humus- or silica-protected sols while, according to the second hypothesis. the iron and aluminium move in the form of soluble metal-organic compounds."

Studies on the process of podzolization have been linked with organic acids and soil organic matter. The development of ideas concerning this process has been well covered by Joffe (8). In recent years, the term "chelation" has been used to a considerable extent to describe the process whereby metallic constituents are translocated in soil formation (1, 13, 17).

CHELATION AND COMPLEX FORMATION

Martel and Calvin (11), in discussing the chemistry of metal chelates. pointed out the difference between chelates and complexes. Schwarzenbach (16) gave the following classification of complexing agents: (a) Simple unidentate ligands: complexes are mononuclear and charged; complex salts are soluble. (b) Lattice-building ligands: multidentate; complexes are infinite lattices; complexes are insoluble precipitates. (c) Chelate ligands. multidentate: complexes are mononuclear and when uncharged are often insoluble in water but soluble in organic solvents, and when charged are highly soluble in water but insoluble in organic solvents (examples of the latter are tartrates, citrates, and complexonates); the complexones include nitrilotriacetic acid and ethylenediaminetetraacetic acid.

[1] Contribution No. 344, Chemistry Division, Science Service, Department of Agriculture. Ottawa, Canada.

Reproduced with permission from *Soil Science,* Vol. 84, 1957, p. 1-11. Copyright © 157. The Williams and Wilkins Company, Baltimore, Maryland 21202, USA.

COMPLEX FORMATION IN SOILS

In 1946 Bremner et al. (5) advanced the theory that "in soil, part of the polyvalent metals is combined as coordination complexes with part of the organic matter and that the presence of the metals renders the organic matter in the complexes insoluble in water, and in neutral solvents that do not themselves form complexes with the metals." Jackson and Sherman (7) stated that "certain types of organic matter, particularly organic acids, form complexes with the sesquioxide ions and move them from the upper horizon to the subsoil, and to some extent out into the ground water." Beckwith (2) found evidence for the existence of complexes between the divalent ions of the metals of the first transition group (for example, Cu. Mn) and soil organic matter and suggested that the trivalent metals iron and aluminium may form much stronger complexes than the divalent ions. In the case of one soil, he obtained evidence that strongly suggested that calcium was complexed with the soil organic matter. Thus evidence for the presence of complexes of metals in soils is becoming recognized.

CHELATION IN SOILS

In discussing soil development Barshad (1) stated that "the production or liberation from organic matter of substances with highly chelating properties for iron and aluminum is, in part, responsible for the movement of uncombined iron from the surface to the subsoil horizon. On the other hand, the destruction by microorganisms of the chelating properties of these organic substances in the subsoil horizon could possibly explain the deposition and accumulation of iron and aluminum oxides in this horizon.

Schatz et al. (13, 14) referred to the importance of chelation reactions in pedogenesis and pointed out that "humus. lignin. and certain complex compounds of bacteria, fungi, lichens. and higher plants chelate metals, persist in appreciable quantities, are more resistant to microbial attack, and can react with soil minerals." They concluded that " the abundance of microbial and higher plant products with chelating properties. the marked stability of organic metal co-ordination covalent complexes, and the wide range of pH over which chelation occurs. emphasize the importance of this kind of reaction in pedogenesis."

Swindale and Jackson (17) introduced the term "cheluviation" and described it as a "process in which minerals are decomposed by chelation in solution. and eluviation." It depends on the presence of moving water as well as on organic substances derived from the biosphere. The process would remove "aluminum, iron and other strongly chelated elements faster than it would silicon and other weakly chelated elements . . . the accumulation of iron and aluminum oxides at a lower depth in the profile of a monogenetic soil may be evidence that the profile above the zone of accumulation has undergone cheluviation."

RECENT STUDIES ON MOBILIZATION OF FE AND AL

In recent years, Bloomfield working at the Rothamsted Experimental Station and DeLong in the Department of Chemistry at Macdonald College have investigated the effect of leachates or extracts from materials deposited by tree cover, on the mobilization of iron and aluminum. In Bloomfield's first paper dealing with a study of podzolization (3), he reported that "an aqueous extract of pine needles is capable of causing the non-biological solution of ferric and aluminium oxides; during the solution, the ferric ion is reduced to the ferrous state. . . . The ferrous iron formed by the extract, and possibly the dissolved aluminium, are present in the form of organic complexes." In the fifth paper of this series (4), he further stated that "Aqueous extracts of aspen and ash leaves have been found to react with ferric and aluminium oxides to form soluble metal-organic complexes. . . . In contrast to the conifers, the aspen extract retains its activity almost unimpaired at high pH values, which provides an explanation for the development of a strong A_2 horizon in certain neutral or only slightly acid soils."

DeLong and Schnitzer (6), in studying the capacities of leaf extracts and leachates to react with iron, concluded from their data that "poplar extract is capable of leaching both iron and aluminum from each of the soil horizons studied (A_2 and B_2) and that in general a greater amount of aluminum than of iron was removed under the experimental conditions used." In a further study (15), the same authors concluded that "Both the forest canopy and the forest floor contribute solutions capable of the mobilization and transport of iron under favorable conditions. They may transport aluminum and calcium also." They could not find, however, "any clear-cut evidence of the formation of chelation complexes" and concluded that "the primary function of the organic material(s) in the solutions under investigation . . . is to act as a peptizing agent and as a protective colloid."

From the foregoing, it appears probable that complex formation or chelation or both play an important role in soil profile development. Specific information on the problem is still rather meager, however, and about three years ago, work was begun in our laboratories in an attempt to increase this information (19). If chelation is involved, then it seemed that the addition of a chelating agent should, under suitable conditions, bring about changes analogous to those obtained in the field, that is, the mobilization, transportation, and redeposition of mineral constituents. Recent widespread uses of ethylenediaminetetraacetic acid (EDTA) as a chelating agent suggested its use for such a study. The selection of a soil parent material with little or no organic matter content seemed advisable. Leaching with solutions of EDTA and, for comparison, with distilled water was adopted as the general procedure.

EXPERIMENTAL

The soil material used was a calcareous sand of particle size less than 100-mesh. It had a clay ($< 2\mu$) content of approximately 1.5 percent and was practically devoid of organic matter (N < 0.01 percent).

Experiment A

Equal amounts of this soil material were carefully introduced into two pyrex glass chromatographic tubes of 2.6×40 cm. inside dimensions. Each column was slowly wetted from the bottom to allow air to escape. The tubes were then wrapped with black paper. The leaching liquid was introduced from a separatory funnel mounted to the top of each glass tube with an airtight connection. The level of liquid in the tubes was maintained above the top of the soil throughout the experiment. One column was leached with distilled water and the other with a 5×10^{-4} M solution of the disodium salt of EDTA (pH 4.9). Percolation was adjusted to the same rate for both columns and proceeded 9 hours per day for approximately 17 months.

Experiment B

Two pyrex glass tubes of 5.0×60 cm. inside dimensions were filled as in Experiment A with the same soil and wetted. One was leached with distilled water and the other with an EDTA solution of the same strength as in Experiment A, although the leaching in this instance was carried out intermittently to allow alternate wetting and drying of the soil columns to a depth of about 6 inches. Approximately 1 liter per day was added twice a week from December 1953 to July 1955 when staining near the top of the column indicated that some iron was being deposited. In an attempt to speed up the process, the strength of the EDTA solution was increased to 1×10^{-2} M. Leaching in the same manner was then continued for a further 16 months.

When each experiment was terminated, the columns were allowed to drain and were quick-frozen. After the glass tubes were removed, the soil cores were bisected veritcally under refrigerated conditions and samples representing selected depths were taken for laboratory examination.

RESULTS

In Experiment A, a "profile" formed in the column leached with EDTA (fig. 1) which resembled that of a podzolic soil with the A_0 or A_1 horizons or both removed. Distinct bands, resembling A_2 and B horizons, were formed. On the other hand, in the column leached with distilled water the only visible change was a slight browning of the top half-inch of soil.

A comparison of certain characteristics of the H_2O and EDTA columns is given in table 1. As would be expected, depth to carbonates in the EDTA column was greater than that in the H_2O column. The brown bands formed would seem to indicate staining of particles with iron compounds. The brown color of the noncalcareous layer in the H_2O column could be due to the removal of light-colored carbonate coatings, but it is probably due to solution and redeposition *in situ* of hydrated oxides of iron. In the EDTA column, mobilization, transport, and redeposition of iron was indicated by the formation of a bleached A_2 and dark brown B horizons.

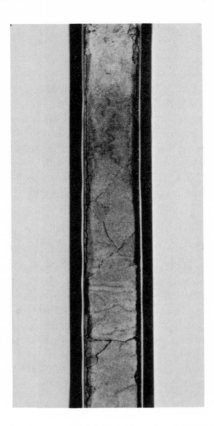

Fig. 1—The "profile" formed in a column of calcareous sand leached with EDTA.

The distribution patterns for "easily soluble" iron and aluminum, expressed as molar concentrations of the oxides, are shown in figure 2. The data represent the iron and aluminum extracted by treating the soil with small increments of 0.2 N HCl and warming (to remove carbonates) until a pH of 3 could be maintained for several hours. The prevalance of iron-stained particles after treatment indicated that there was no more than a partial removal of coatings. Greater amounts of aluminum than of iron were extracted.

Another measure of "soluble" iron was obtained by extraction with $Na_2S_2O_4$ according to the method of Mackenzie (10). These results are shown in figure 2. The distribution in the profile was quite similar to that obtained by using 0.2 N HCl.

Weathering in the top half-inch of the H_2O column apparently resulted in the formation and accumulation *in situ* of hydrated oxides of iron and aluminum. In contrast, the iron and aluminum in the EDTA column apparently were mobilized, transported, and deposited, in part, lower in the column, resulting in the formation of a B horizon. Occasional analysis of the leachates established the fact that not all the sesquioxides moving down the column were redeposited. Average losses from the H_2O column were 1×10^{-6} and 6×10^{-6} moles per liter for iron and aluminum respectively, compared with 13×10^{-6} and 5×10^{-6} moles per litter from the EDTA

Table 1—Characteristics of soil columns leached with water and with EDTA (Experiment A)

Depth in Soil Column	Characteristics of Leached Soil Columns	
	Color*	pH
in.		
	H₂O column	
0–¼	Brown (10 yr. 5/3)	7.3
¼–½	Pale brown (10 yr. 6/3)	8.2†
½–1	Gray-brown (10 yr. 5/2)	8.4†
1–1½	Gray-brown (10 yr. 5/2)	8.4†
2–2½	Gray-brown (10 yr. 5/2)	8.4†
2½	Gray-brown (10 yr. 5/2)	8.3†
	EDTA column	
0–1¼ (A₂)	Light gray (10 yr. 7/1)	6.9
1¼–1½ (B₁)	Brown (10 yr. 5/3)	7.3
1½–2 (B₂₁)	Dark brown (10 yr. 4/3)	7.5
2–2¾ (B₂₂)	Dark brown (10 yr. 4/3)	8.3†
2¾–3¼ (B₃)	Dark gray-brown (10 yr. 4/2)	8.4†
3¼–3¾ (C₁)	Gray-brown (10 yr. 5/2)	8.4†
3¾ (C)	Gray-brown (10 yr. 5/2)	8.4†

* Munsell color notation—moist.
† Calcareous.

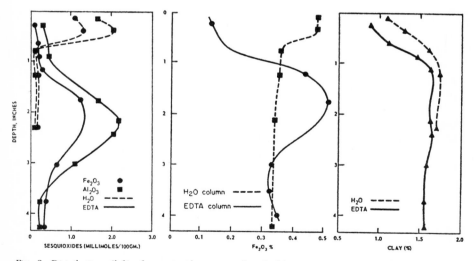

Fig. 2—Distribution *(left)* of sesquioxides extracted with dilute acid; *(center)* of iron extracted with Na₂S₂O₄; and *(Right)* of clay, in soil columns leached with H₂O and with EDTA *(results on a carbonate-free basis).*

column. Similar average losses for calcium and magnesium were 130×10^{-6} and 3×10^{-6} moles per liter from the H₂O column and 850×10^{-6} and 200×10^{-6} moles per litter from the EDTA column. Losses of silicon in solution from both columns were of the order of 20×10^{-6} moles per liter.

Table 2—Material extracted from leached-soil column samples by 1 + 3 HCl (Experiment A)

Depth in Soil Column	Material Extracted from Leached Soil by 1 + 3 HCl				
	Total* extracted	CaO*	MgO*	Fe₂O₃*	Fe₂O₃†
in.	%	%	%	%	%
H₂O column					
0–¼	2.94	0.33	0.20	0.70	0.71
¼–½	5.98	1.67	0.61	0.73	0.76
½–1	14.03	5.50	1.44	0.64	0.73
1–1½	17.24	6.82	1.48	0.67	0.78
1½–1¾	16.64	6.45	1.57	0.65	0.76
1¾–2	17.10	6.74	1.56	0.65	0.75
2–2¼	16.90	6.66	1.52	0.65	0.75
2¼–2½	16.90	6.56	1.68	0.66	0.76
EDTA column					
0–¾ (A₂₁)	0.92	0.07	0.12	0.22	0.22
¾–1¼ (A₂₂)	1.40	—	0.14	0.48	0.48
1¼–1½ (B₁)	1.50	0.16	0.19	0.40	0.40
1½–2 (B₂₁)	2.84	0.12	0.34	0.68	0.69
2–2¾ (B₂₂)	4.67	0.72	0.49	0.82	0.85
2¾–3 (B₃₁)	5.20	1.01	—	0.72	0.75
3–3¼ (B₃₂)	9.34	2.83	0.92	0.71	0.77
3¼–3¾ (C₁)	16.50	6.33	1.51	0.65	0.76
3¾ (C)	16.75	6.57	1.44	0.65	0.76

* On moisture-free basis.
† On moisture- and carbonate-free basis.

The vertical distribution of $< 2\mu$ clay for both columns is also shown in figure 2. After treatment of the soil to remove carbonates and soluble salts, the soil suspension was adjusted to pH 8.5-9.0 with NaOH and dispersed. The clay was separated by repeated decantation.

Although the clay content of the original soil material was low, a loss of clay from the upper part of both columns is shown to have occurred. The clay distribution patterns for both columns were similar and, even when the results were calculated on a carbonate-free basis, incipient development of a zone of clay accumulation is indicated particularly when the $< 0.05\mu$ clay is considered. In the H_2O column, the distribution of clay compared with that of "easily soluble" iron and aluminum would seem to be incongruous with the hypothesis of the transport of these elements as oxide coatings on clay particles. It must be admitted, however, that a zone of clay accumulation has not been definitely established.

Samples of both columns were extracted with boiling HCl (1 + 3) for 5 minutes. This extractant is used in the examination of certain substances, for example, limestone, to obtain a measure of acid-soluble materials present. It was thought that this procedure might reveal the extent to which the EDTA had reacted with the soil constituents. The results are presented in table 2. The low values for total amounts extracted from the top inch and a half of the EDTA column indicate that the EDTA solution used over a period of 17 months removed almost as much from the soil material as did boiling 1 + 3 HCl. Acid-soluble constituents were markedly reduced in this column to a depth of 3¼ inches whereas, in the H_2O column, the marked reduction was apparent only in the surface half-inch. The results for calcium and

Table 3—Material extracted from leached-soil column samples by 1 + 3 HCl (Experiment B)

Soil Column Samples		Material Extracted from Soil Column Samples by 1 + 3 HCl*			
Depth	pH	Total	CaO	MgO	Fe$_2$O$_3$
in.		%	%	%	%
0–1	7.5	0.92	0.09	0.06	0.27
2–3	7.5	0.87	0.08	0.08	0.25
4–5	7.4	1.30	0.10	0.09	0.43
7–8	7.5	1.19	0.09	0.11	0.41
9–10	7.5	1.14	0.05	0.12	0.49
12–13	7.5	1.44	0.05	0.12	0.51
15–16	7.3	1.80	0.06	0.14	0.65
18–19	7.5	1.60	0.04	0.14	0.63

* Results are on moisture-free basis.

magnesium followed the same trend. In the case of iron, however, there appeared to be an accumulation between 2 and 2¾ inches in what has been termed the B$_{22}$ horizon.

In Experiment B, when the leaching was discontinued the horizon differentiation in the EDTA column was not the marked differentiation so noticable in Experiment A. This experiment differed from the previous one in that (a) leaching was intermittent, and alternate wetting and drying occurred in the surface 6 inches, (b) the time of leaching extended over a much longer period, and (c) the strength of the leaching solution was greatly increased during the last 16 months. As a result, the free lime was removed from the whole column and it was practically uniform in color throughout its entire length. However, at a depth of 6 to 8 inches, there was a detectable area, irregular in shape, which was slightly browner in color. From observations made during the period of leaching, there was evidence of some accumulation of iron nearer the top of the column as already indicated. Perhaps with the increased strength of the EDTA solution this iron was moved and redeposited at the bottom of the zone of intermittent drying and, with continued leaching, was again mobilized. At the bottom of the column, there was a distinct area which was yellowish-brown in color, indicating a slight coating of particles with iron. In contrast, the color of the H$_2$O column was unchanged except in the surface inch and was the same as the water-leached column of Experiment A.

The pH values and the amounts of certain constituents soluble in boiling 1 + 3 HCl are presented in table 3 for samples representing selected depths in the EDTA column. None of the samples was calcareous and the pH values ranged between 7.3 and 7.5. On the other hand, in the H$_2$O column, carbonates had been removed from only the surface half-inch.

The amounts of material extracted by the HCl were relatively low throughout the whole column and were approximately the same order as those found in the surface inch and one-half of the EDTA column in Experiment A (table 2). The same applies to the values for calcium, magnesium, and iron. Apparently the solution of EDTA used was sufficiently strong to decompose the carbonates and to move the greater part of the acid-soluble constituents almost completely out of the column. The iron values, as well as the appearance of the soil, indicate that there may have been some accumulation of iron near the base.

DISCUSSION

In the leaching experiments, the first action of the EDTA appears to have been the decomposition of the carbonates. As a result, calcium and magnesium were mobilized and moved downward probably in both the chelate and ionic forms. There is some evidence that the ratio of calcium to magnesium being transported narrowed with time. As the pH and the concentration of the alkaline earth metals in solution decreased at the top of the column, increased amounts of iron and aluminum were sequestered and carried downward. It is probable that, with depth, increasing competition from the hydroxyl ions with rising pH, and greater concentrations of the alkaline earths, have caused displacement of some iron and aluminum and their precipitation as hydrated oxides. FeEDTA has been shown (9) to be unstable at pH values between 7 and 8. Barshad's (1) suggestion that destruction of the chelating properties of organic substances by soil microorganisms causes deposition of iron and aluminum oxides does not hold in this case. Wallace (18) pointed out that polyamino-polyacetate chelates are not decomposed by soil microorganisms.

The action of EDTA solutions in dissolving a considerable amount of soil material would seem to be of no little importance when used over a long period of time or in sufficiently high concentration. Where large amounts of EDTA and related compounds are used as soil applications to add certain plant nutrients which are deficient in the growing crop, there could be a danger of serious changes in soil composition as they become leached through the solum.

The results obtained in these experiments probably raise more questions than they answer. One might, for example, speculate on what would happen in the leaching of acidic parent material. If the precipitation of the sesquioxides is due to increased hydroxyl ion concentration in the case of calcareous material, the same result might not be obtained with acidic material. Lunt et al. (9) did observe the disappearance of chelated iron from soil solutions under acid conditions, though the reasons for this disappearance remained obscure.

Another question is the effect of EDTA on the mineralogical composition of the profile. Some reaction of EDTA with minerals can be expected. For example, Perkins and Purvis (12) found that aluminum was chelated and potassium released from orthoclase by EDTA treatment which resulted in degradation of the mineral.

The trace elements, for example Zn, Mn, Cu, are known to form chelates with EDTA and they can be expected to translocate in the experiments described. That such action does take place is indicated by preliminary studies and further work is under way.

To clarify some of these points, a more intensive study of the materials already leached has been undertaken, and leaching experiments similar to those described herein are being continued in these laboratories, using both calcareous and noncalcareous soil parent material and employing other known chelating and complexing agents such as tannic acid, acetic acid, and citric acid, as well as EDTA.

CONCLUSIONS

It has been shown that leaching a calcareous soil material with a chelating agent (EDTA) in a solution of a certain strength can result in the mobilization, transport, and redeposition of iron and aluminum and in the development of a profile with well-defined horizons. It has also been shown that, when the strength of the solution of the same chelating agent is increased sufficiently, serious changes in soil material can result.

REFERENCES

1. Barshad, I. 1955 Soil development. (In Chemistry of the Soil, A.c.s. Monograph series No. 126, Reinhold Publishing Corp., New York.)
2. Beckwith, R. S. 1955 Metal complexes in soils. Australian J. Agr. Research 6:685-698.
3. Bloomfield, C. 1953 A study of podzolization :I. J. Soil Sci. 4: 5-16.
4. .... 1954 A study of podzolization: V. J. Soil Sci. 5: 50-56.
5. Bremner, J. M., et al. 1946 Metallo-organic complexes in soil. Nature 158: 790-791.
6. DeLong, W. A., and Schnitzer, M. 1956 Investigations on the mobilization and transport of iron in forested soils: I. Soil Sci. Soc. Amer. Proc. 19: 360-363.
7. Jackson, M. L., and Sherman, G. D. 1953 Chemical weathering of minerals in soils. Advances in Agron. 5: 219-318.
8. Joffe, J. S. 1949 Pedology. Pedology Publications, New Brunswick, N. J.
9. Lunt, O. R., Hemaidan, N., and Wallace, A. 1956 Reactions of some polyamine polyacetate iron chelates in various soils. Soil Sci. Soc. Amer. Proc. 20: 172-175.
10. Mackenzie, R. C. 1954 Free iron-oxide removal from soils. J. Soil Sci. 5: 167-172.
11. Martell, A. E., and Calvin, M. 1952 Chemistry of the Metal Chelate Compounds. Prentice-Hall Inc., New York.
12. Perkins, H. F., and Purvis, E. R. 1954 Soil and plant studies with chelates of ethylenediamine-tetraacetic acid. Soil Sci. 78:325-330.
13. Schatz, A., et al. 1954 Chelation (sequestration) as a biological weathering factor in pedogenesis. Proc. Penn. Acad. Sci. 28: 44-51.
14. Schatz, V. 1956 Significance of lichens as pedogenic (soil-forming) agents. Proc. Penn. Acad. Sci. 30: 62-69.
15. Schnitzer, M., and DeLong, W. A. 1956 Investigations on the mobilization and transport of iron in forested soils: II. Soil Sci. Soc. Amer. Proc. 19: 363-368.
16. Schwarzenbach, G. 1955 The complexones and their analytical application. Analyst 80:713-729.
17. Swindale, L. D., and Jackson, M. L. 1956 Genetic processes in some residual podozilized soils of New Zealand. Trans. Intern. Congr. Soil Sci. 6th Congr. Paris E: 233-239.
18. Wallace, A. 1956 Symposium on the Use of Metal Chelates in Plant Nutrition, p. 4-23, The National Press, Palo Alto, Calif.
19. Wright, J. R., and Levick, R. 1956 Development of a profile in a soil column leached with a chelating agent. Trans. Intern. Congr. Soil Sci., 6th Congr. Paris E: 257-262.

MINERAL OCCURRENCE IN RELATION TO SOIL PROFILE DIFFERENTIATION

by

John G. Cady*

The minerals in a soil or in any horizon of a soil profile are inherited from the parent material, formed in place by weathering or moved into the position they occupy by soil-forming processes. Some soil materials have a simple mineralogical composition and profiles develop little variation in composition among horizons, though many soils in such material have definite morphological horizons. Other soil materials have a complex mineralogical composition and in these materials soils develop with contrasting mineralogy between horizons, even when field evidence of horizon expression is weak.

Mineralogical differences among horizons are often due to stratification in the parent material. Such lithologic discontinuities can be recognized by application of standard methods and will not be discussed. Obviously a great variety of combinations of parent material and factors of soil development exist. This paper considers some examples of relationships between some types of parent materials and the distribution of minerals, particularly the clay minerals, in soil profiles.

The origin and composition of soil parent material is directly related to the mineralogical composition of the soil. One class of parent material most widely distributed in tropical and warm temperate regions is produced by weathering of hard igneous or metamorphic rocks along a sharp front leaving saprolite consisting of secondary minerals and resistant primary minerals in which the soil develops.

The other large class of parent materials contains weatherable minerals throughout the soil column and different reactions can take place at different depths according to the ambient conditions. This material includes loose sediments and rocks which weather by disintegration.

Weathering along a sharp front and some soils derived from parent material produced in this way have been studied in hypersthene norite, epidote greenstone and other rocks in the Piedmont region of the Southeastern United States, in basalt in Hawaii, and in a variety of rocks in other places. In basalts and other basic rocks there is fresh rock on one side of a boundary and an assortment of secondary minerals on the other; often the complete transition extends over a distance of less than two millimeters. Thin sections across such boundaries in samples from several localities have shown lath-shaped plagioclase phenocrysts which were intact at one

* Soil Conservation Service, USDA, Plant Industry Station, Beltsville, Maryland.

Reproduced with permission from *Transactions of the 7th International Congress of Soil Science,* Vol 4, 1960, p. 418-424. Published by the International Society of Soil Science, c/o Royal Tropical Institute, Amsterdam, Netherlands.

end and completely altered to gibbsite and allophane at the other. Other examples have been observed where the product was halloysite. Similar close proximity of fresh and weathered material is observed in pyroxenes and amphiboles.

In coarse-textured rocks, especially those with quartz, such as granite and gneiss, the transition zone between fresh rock and saprolite is somewhat wider than it is in basalt, and may be measured in centimeters rather than millimeters. Kaolinite in vermicular or book-like aggregates is usually the dominant clay mineral formed in weathering of granitic rocks.

The sharp front type of weathering is accompanied by, or preceded by, loss of most of the divalent and monovalent cations, such as potassium, calcium and magnesium, and loss of varying amounts of the non-quartz silica. In the weathering of basalt to form the parent material of some of the high-sesquioxide soils of Hawaii the silica drops from about 40 percent to about 3 percent across a distance measured in millimeters. When kaolin minerals form, less silica is lost. The main addition is water of hydration and possibly oxygen. Density decreases greatly and total porosity increases.

This type of weathering usually takes place with little volume change and the form of the rock is maintained. The alteration to gibbsite or halloysite results in a replica structure with one or the other of these minerals occupying the position of the feldspars, mixtures of these minerals and iron oxides in place of some of the ferromagnesian minerals and well-crystallized iron oxide minerals in place of others. When coarse kaolinite aggregates are the product the structure is not maintained completely but quartz grains spaced about the same as in the original rock indicate that the volume change is slight. Elements of this replica structure often persist and can be identified in the upper horizons of the soil.

Weathering which proceeds along a sharp front leaves a product consisting of resistant primary minerals and various combinations of kaolin clays, gibbsite, geothite, hematite and incompletely characterized substances, many of which are amorphous. As a soil parent material this product is relatively simple and inert. Weathering in the solum can occur but is slow. Colloidal sized components can move, clay minerals can weather and the oxides can dissolve and be precipitated at greater depth or removed.

The Red-Yellow Podzolic soils and some related soils, such as the Davidson series, are derived from well-weathered parent material. These soils and some soils in the tropics have horizons of clay accumulation as indicated by clay coatings on ped faces, in pores and in other openings. However, they show little difference in mineralogical composition between horizons. The clay that moves is finer but is mineralogically the same as the clay still in place in the matrix. Clay mineral movement may be accompanied by movement of iron oxide attached to the clay particles or in suspension or solution; the moved clay is often dark red and is apparently coated with iron oxide. In some cases the fine clay may be accompanied by organic matter as it is in the African Dark Horizon Latosols.

Several important tropical soils which cover large areas such as the Low-Humic Latosols of Hawaii and some of the Latosols of Puerto Rico have rather featureless profiles with only structural horizon differences. Chemical and mineralogical compositions are quite uniform throughout the solum. Information obtained from thin sections and from other observations shows no evidence of clay movement to form clay skins or other clay accumulations separate from the matrix. The structure which distinguishes the horizons in these soils is due to clay orientation to form pressure-faces or micro-slickensides. Most of these soils are high in clay and sesqui-oxides and low in quartz.

Reasons for development of soils with textural horizons in some strongly weathered parent materials, and soils with very weak illuvial horizons in others, are still only hypothetical. The Red-Yellow Podzolic soils, which have textural horizons, derived from weathered rock are distributed over the Southeastern United States. Most of them are from coarse-textured rocks and are high in kaolinite; many are high in quartz. Free drainage in such material may promote the formation of textural profiles. In the mild temperate climate some clay-forming minerals may have escaped the initial rock weathering to be available for weathering in the solum.

The Low-Humic Latosols of Hawaii do not have textural profiles and are in drier regions than Hawaiian soils with similar composition that show evidence of clay movement. Both groups of soils appear to be developed in strongly-weathered material, so amount and distribution of rainfall may influence the type of profile developed.

In several tropical regions geomorphological evidence and certain characteristics of the soils themselves, especially their microstructure observed in thin sections, has suggested that most of the soils with clay skins are in material that is in place and that the soils without clay movement are derived from transported material, such as local alluvium or pedisediment. The thin sections show relic rock structure in the soils with clay skins and random structure with pressure-oriented clay in the others. Transportation by water might tend to remove dispersible clay and leave only that which is cemented together by iron oxides.

In summary, it can be said that weathering along a sharp boundary produces a parent material with a simple composition consisting of secondary minerals and unweatherable minerals. The secondary minerals present in various combinations are kaolinite, halloysite, gibbsite, iron oxide minerals and sometimes amorphous mixed oxides and allophane. The 2—1 lattice minerals are absent, transitory or minor. This weathered product may remain in place or be transported locally. Whether transported or not, the soils which develop in such material have little mineralogical horizon differentiation and may have only structural horizon differentiation. They do not have weathering sequences from the lower horizons to the upper ones and are usually dominated by one clay mineral. Such parent materials and soils are located in the warm temperate and tropical regions. The degree of textural horizon development generally appears to be greater in the cooler parts of these regions.

The distribution of soils derived from saprolite is limited to areas not covered by glacial drift. Their possible past distribution in cooler regions is unknown so the relative importance of time and climate is difficult to determine. Soils with mixed mineralogy, weatherable minerals in the solum, an abundance of 2—1 layer silicate clays and differences in mineralogy among horizons are found in the tropics and warm termperate regions in alluvium and over rock which weathers to a mixed residuum. This suggests that either youth or conditions existing in a loose material with heterogeneous mineralogy favors the development of profiles with mineralogical differentiation.

Glacial till, loess, volcanic ash, some kinds of alluvium and disintegrated, partly-weathered rock are examples of parent materials containing weatherable minerals at all depths. The relation between pedogenesis and mineral distribution in such materials is more complex than it is in saprolite. A variety of reactions affecting minerals can take place at different depths. Weathering, secondary mineral formation, movement and complete removal of constituents can take place in waves or sequences or can be simultaneous at one depth. Effects of small differences in climate, drainage, vegetation or other factors are often sharply expressed by differences in soil morphology and composition.

Resistance of minerals to various weathering agencies may differ; a mineral species which survives the action of one process at a certain depth may be altered by another process at a shallower depth. Mineralogical heterogeneity within the profile may be great between horizons or even within one horizon.

Sequences of weathering from the C horizon upward may be observed especially in the micas and clay minerals. Movement of clay often results in fractionation of the mineral species when several are present, with relatively large amounts of one clay mineral accumulating in a particular horizon.

The mineralogical composition of the clay fraction of the soils is strongly influenced by the minerals in the clay in the original deposit. Till and loess in the Northern Mississippi Basin are high in montmorillonite. Glacial deposits in the Northeastern States are high in mica and montmorillonite is rare or absent.

In Gray-Brown Podzolic soils and their relatives developed in calcareous glacial till in Indiana and neighboring states in the Middle West, weathering and soil profile development are believed to take place in a sequence. The first step is leaching out of the lime which proceeds along a rather sharp but irregular boundary. This causes an increase in clay. partly real due to release of clay formerly cemented into aggregates by lime and partly apparent due to removal of sand and silt size carbonate mineral grains. Weathering of the other minerals occurs and shows its effects first on the smallest sized particles and most easily weathered minerals.

Clay mineral distribution and clay content in the various horizons of the profile are affected by weathering and clay movement. The dominant clay mineral in the C horizon is mica; small amounts of montmorillonite and vermiculite are present. Mica decreases progressively from the C horizon upward. Montmorillonite is dominant in the B horizon and vermiculite dominant in the A. The clay content in the B horizons is higher than in horizons above or below. This sections show that most of this clay increase is due to clay movement from above. Optically oriented clay coatings are visible on ped faces and in all pores and openings. This clay differs from the clay in the matrix in having finer size, greater homogeneity and probably different composition.

Mica weathers to vermiculite and possibly some of the vermiculite weathers to montmorillonite. The montmorillonite, whether present in the original material or formed by weathering, having a small particle size, moves out of the A horizon and the top of the B horizon and accumulates farther down in the B. often near the top of the calcareous till.

Thin section observations and petrographic study of the sand and the silt fractions show a slight decrease in amphibole. pyroxene and feldspar in the upper part of the profile. However, the mineralogical changes in the formation of these soils consist mostly of removal of lime, weathering in the clay fraction, clay movement and a little weathering of primary silicates in the sand and silt.

In the Northeast the Gray-Brown Podzolic soils contain no montmorillonite. The clay in the C horizons is dominantly mica, with some chlorite present in some local-ities. The mica weathers to vermiculite, and the profiles show mica decreasing pro-gressively upward and vermiculite increasing. Often there is a rather sharp break at the top of the B horizon with mica almost absent in the A.

These soils have textural B horizons but no differential accumulation of a par-ticular mineral. Perhaps because the climate is somewhat cooler and moister in the Northeast than in the Middle West conditions approach those required for Podzol formation and clay destruction accounts for some of the difference in clay content between horizons. Another explanation is lack of weathering in the B horizon with the apparent decrease in mica being due to movement and accumulation of fine vermiculite.

The absence of montmorillonite may have several explanations. Weathering may be so mild that it does not carry the sequence beyond the vermiculite stage. The presence of montmorillonite in the A_2 horizons of some Podzols appears to support this explanation and to contradict the possibility that montmorillonite is destroyed or leached out completely as fast as it is formed. Presence of montmorillonite in the parent material may be required in order to have this mineral in these weakly weathered soils.

If Gray-Brown Podzolic soils contain montmorillonite it appears to be the mineral which moves most readily. If montmorillonite was absent in the source material or weathering conditions do not favor its formation, clay movement can occur, but the textural B horizons formed are not as pronounced as they are where montmori.-lonite is present.

The formation of true Podzols causes the destruction of weatherable minerals in the A_2 horizon and the movement of the products out of the solum or into the B horizon. In Podzols in glacial material containing an assortment of weatherable minerals, particularly hornblende, aguite and hyperstene, from the C horizon up-ward to the top of the B horizon these minerals are fresh-appearing and their per-centages are almost the same in both horizons. On the other hand, in the A horizon the percentage of such minerals drops by 60 to 75 percent and the remaining grains show etching and pitting, some to such an extent that they appear skeletal. The re-sult is a profile with a strong contrast in mineralogy between horizons with a de-crease in the iron-containing silicates in the A horizon and an addition of free iron and possibly amorphous forms of free aluminum to the B horizon but with essen-tially no weathering taking place in the B. The translocated free oxides coating the sand and silt grains may actually protect them.

Soils with a large variety of minerals in all horizons are not restricted to the young glacial deposits. In some regions in certain types of hard rocks, especially diabase and gabbro, some minerals weather enough to cause the rock to disintegrate into a material consisting of a mixture of clay and primary minerals from the rock. The Iredell and some associated soils of the Piedmont in Virginia and North Caro-lina are formed in this kind of material. The first stage of weathering converts the feldspar of the diabase parent material into halloysite but leaves the augite or horn-blende virtually unaltered. At a later stage, in the upper C horizon and the B hori-zon the ferromagnesian minerals weather slowly and montmorillonite is synthesized. Unweathered pyroxenes are abundant even in the A horizon, and there is a con-tinuous supply of magnesium, silica and alumina as these weather. The montmoril-lonite content of the B horizons increases relative to the A and C horizons by a combination of clay movement from the A and synthesis in place from products of the weathering ferromagnesian minerals.

SUMMARY

Some examples have been given of the relationship between the physical and mineralogical composition of soil parent material and the mineral distribution which develops in soil profiles as a result of the soil forming environment. Soils without mineralogical differentiation are present in strongly weathered, relatively inert parent materials and in young, unweathered materials. Different mineralogy in different horizons is brought about by weathering as in the case of the Podzols and by movement of clay in the soils with textural B horizons. Soils with mineralogical profiles are generally found in parent material that has a variety of weatherable minerals throughout the depth in which the solum develops. Soils with textural profiles but without segregation of particular mineral species by depth are found in both well-weathered material and slightly weathered material.

CLAY ORIENTATION IN SOILS

by

I. Stephen

B. Sc., Ph. D., Rothamsted Experimental Station, Harpenden.

The lower limit for the study of the shape and optical properties of mineral particles with the petrological microscope is of the order of 5μ , but the clay material of soils and other sediments may show optical properties such as birefringence and extinction phenomena similar to those of larger crystalline individuals. This was recognised by the early workers in soil microscopy, and Fry (11) stated that "between crossed nicols, the aggregates of soil colloids may or may not be doubly refracting. Those showing some degree of double refraction are perhaps more common than those showing none. Absence of double refraction, isotropy, seems usually associated with high iron content." Attention was drawn to differences in the optical properties of the aggregates: degree of completeness of the extinction directions, character of the interference figure and refractive indices.

The clay fraction of the majority of soils consists mainly of the so-called clay minerals (hydrous alumino-silicates) with subsidiary amounts of finely divided oxides and organic matter. Clay particles differ in shape, but many of the common clay minerals are micaceous in habit and form thin hexagonal flakes or shreds with well defined basal cleavage. Advantage has been taken of their anisodimensional shape to prepare aggregates for X-ray analyses by allowing clay suspensions to sediment with the consequent orientation of the (001) planes parallel to the surface of deposition. The optics of such aggregates have been studies by Williamson (34) using a ·clay consisting of 60 percent kaolinite, 30 percent illite and 10 percent quartz. Sections normal to the (001) planes showed a high degree of extinction parallel to these faces, the extinction direction being one of positive elongation. The same orientational relationships would hold for most clays, as the majority of the clay minerals such as micas (illites), kaolinite, vermiculites and montmorillonites have similar properties to muscovite in that they are optically negative with X about normal to (001); their extinction is essentially parallel to the cleavage traces and sections normal to the cleavage will therefore show sensibly straight extinction and positive elongation (Fig. 1). It can therefore be assumed that the optical anisotropy of clay aggregates in sediments results from the orientation of the individual platelets and, further, that the degree of extinction gives information about the perfection of the orientation, while the character of the elongation reveals the spatial relationships of the aggregates.

Reproduced with permission from *Science Progress,* Vo. 48. 1960, p. 323-331.
Published by Blackwell Scientific Publications, Oxford, England.

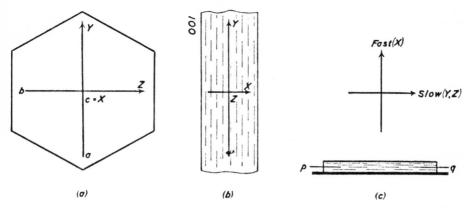

Fig. 1—Orientation of muscovite. Sections (*a*) parallel to (001); (*b*) parallel to (010); (*c*) fast and slow vibration directions in sedimented clay; *p-q* is trace of (001) planes.

The degree and nature of the orientation of the clay which could be expected in soils has been investigated by several workers. Peterson (27) mixed montmorillonite and kaolinite with varying proportions of acid-washed fine sand, and the preparations were alternately wetted and dried. Thin sections showed areas of birefringent clay, but the patterns were different according to the type of clay. Montmorillonite formed a "sponge-like" structure with connecting wedges or bands of oriented clay between the sand grains, whereas with kaolinite vertical sections showed a laminated structure consisting dominantly of "islands" of oriented clay with threads of birefringent material penetrating an apparently unoriented matrix. These and other experiments together with field observations suggested that kaolinite is associated with the formation of platy structures in soils, but this has been questioned by McMillan and Mitchell (21) who described the occurrence of well developed platy A_2-horizons in podzolised and solonised soils in Saskatchewan, which contain very little kaolinite. Clearly insufficient is known at present to generalise about the effects of specific minerals in structure formation.

Brewer and Haldane (5) introduced clay-sized material, consisting of 60 percent illite, 30 percent kaolinite and 5 percent quartz, saturated with different cations, into quartz sand by percolation or capillarity. The clay formed strongly oriented coatings around the sand grains, and the orientation was unaffected by the method of introduction or the nature of the saturating cation. Another set of experiments concerned the drying of the clay after mixing with different amounts of coarser material of various size distributions. When highly flocculated clay was dried in a mass, little or no orientation occurred, but bands and coatings of strongly oriented clay were produced in clay-sand mixtures when the amount of clay was insufficient to fill the spaces between the sand grains. A gradual decrease in the degree of orientation was observed with either increasing proportions of clay or the introduction of silt into the mixtures. The authors considered that, when soluble salts are not present in excessive amounts in a soil profile, clay migration would result in strongly oriented clay bands and coatings developing in the illuvial horizons, and evidence from natural profiles supported this conclusion. If, however, owing to a high percentage of soluble salts, eluviated clay is rapidly flocculated and deposited in large pore spaces in illuvial horizons it will be only weakly oriented; this type of orientation was observed in illuviated clay in some solodised solonetz soils of Southern Australia. The heavy-textured grey and brown soils of the Riverine plain containing appreciable amounts of silt show no textural differentiation and have a degree of clay orientation comparable with that produced in experiments with mixtures of similar mechanical composition, and the orientation appears to be due primarily to the conditions of deposition of the soil parent material.

In a comprehensive treatise on soil formation Kubiena (14) included detailed descriptions of thin section analyses of a variety of soil groups. One of the most widespread microfabrics described is that occurring in the terra fusca (limestone braunlehm) associated with limestone and dolomite in Central Europe, and in the braunlehm formed by the weathering of silicate and other rocks under sub-tropical and tropical conditions. These soils have ochre-yellow, ochre-brown to reddish coloured (B) or B-horizons, which are compact and plastic with a pronounced waxy appearance. In section, the uniform fabric is dense, with the very finely divided iron (probably mainly in the form of goethite) diffusely dispersed, giving the clay a light yellowish brown colour. The clay is capable of becoming mobile and may be strongly oriented when deposited in situations where it can dry, such as in cracks, around grains or on walls of cavities. The general groundmass is anisotropic and mainly weakly oriented; small areas, however, are moderately well or strongly oriented, but are randomly arranged in relation to surrounding units. This distribution somewhat resembles the decussate fabric of crystalline rocks and probably results mainly from small scale plastic deformations caused by the alternate wetting and drying of the clay *in situ* effecting the orientation of the particles with respect to one another and to the coarser-grained minerals in the soil. Kaolinite and halloysite (and occasionally mica and montmorillonite) appear to be the common clay mineral constituents of the braunlehms (1, 14, 29), and kaolinite is dominant in the rotlehms, the corresponding red-coloured tropical soil formations (14, 15). The physical behaviour of the soils is explained by Kubiena (14) on the basis of the presence of colloidal silica as a protective colloid, which acts as an efficient peptising agent and "confers on the kaolinitic and halloysitic clays their high swelling capacity and plasticity as well as their extraordinary hardness when dry."

Two distinct processes of transformation of braunlehm material have been described: rubefaction (formation of rotlehm) and laterisation (16). Laterisation is regarded as a kind of regional diagenesis, generally under stable moisture conditions, leading to a slow separation of iron and its precipitation in fissures and other pore spaces producing a wide variety of structural forms. In contrast the process of rubefaction results in a comparatively uniform morphology and takes place in a strongly contrasting wet-dry climate, especially in well drained sites. Under these conditions the iron separates more quickly (probably as microcrystals of haematite) and becomes distributed in the groundmass of the fabric as localised deposits and flecks with diffuse edges (Iwatoka-precipitates). The fabrics of the rotlehms, therefore are considered to consist of two phases: (1) the yellowish brown, anisotropic, mobile, silica-rich clay characteristic of the braunlehm and (2) the secondary, immobile, iron-enriched Iwatoka-precipitates which are brilliant red in reflected light and show little double refraction between crossed nicols. The rubefaction first results in the formation of single flecks and then extends progressively, so that it is possible to recognise a complete sequence from the non-rubefied braunlehms to rotlehms of the Iwatoka variety (earthy rotlehm), as described (13) from the Sudan, in which the fabric consists mainly of very fine deep red thrombus-like deposits, the yellowish brown mobile clay occurring only in small amounts, mainly in cavities protected from leaching. With progressive rubefaction the physical properties of the clay are greatly altered so that the Iwatoka rotlehm is not dense and waxy, but loose and crumbly with a uniform spongy fabric. The importance of micro-morphological studies in investigating the products of laterisation and rubefaction is stressed, as chemical methods do not enable a distinction to be made between the products of these two different processes.

One of the most important uses of thin section analyses is in deciding whether clay migration has been an operative process in the development of textural profiles, as it is becoming abundantly clear that clay content increasing with depth is not proof of illuviation, as seems often to have been assumed in earlier pedological investigations. Several different reasons have been suggested for the presence of finer-textured subsoil horizons; these include deflocculation and downward movement of clay-sized material; the net difference between the amount of clay formed *in situ* and that destroyed being greater in the B-horizon than in the surface layers; and non-uniformity of parent material. Uniformity (or otherwise) of the parent material within the solum can usually be ascertained by standard petrological techniques, such as a comparison of the resistant heavy mineral suites of successive layers, but conclusive evidence about clay migration is less easy to obtain, although in some soils the surfaces of the peds have a visible coating of clay ("clay skins"), often with small ripple-like markings suggestive of its movement under the influences of percolating waters. In thin section, however, the microfabrics of many subsoil horizons show distinctive features which are difficult to reconcile with any process other than the deposition in them of illuviated clay. Such features are the presence of more or less homogeneous clay deposits, non-uniformly distributed and concentrated on ped surfaces, lining channels and cracks and partially or completely filling pore spaces (Fig. 2, A). This type of distribution was noted by Frei and Cline (9) in grey-brown podzolic soils developed from calcareous till in New York State, and it was argued that "if the clays were the weathering products of primary minerals originally in this part of the profile or were residual from clays originally present in the till, one would expect to find them more uniformly distributed throughout the horizon. . . . In addition, the layering and optical continuity of the clayey bodies would be unlikely if the clays were residual from either clays or other minerals originally present in this part of the profile. The mode of occurrence and optical continuity both suggest that the clays have been deposited on the walls of channels through which percolating waters pass."

Recent Russian investigations (25, 35) show that, in a wide variety of soils with illuvial horizons (podzolic soils, grey forest soils, degraded chernozems), there is a strong development of clay films that show orientation (colloform clay). Chemical, X-ray and d.t.a. examinations of the fine clay films led to the conclusion that the clay was in part a new formation, which was named polynite (a 2:1 layer lattice silicate), but another Russian worker (22) believes that the clay has been illuviated, the view that is generally accepted.

These illuviated deposits may show a fairly wide range in properties, but a discussion of their characteristics from a brick-pit at Prestwood, Bucks., where clay

Fig. 2—(A) Strongly oriented clay coating channel walls in lenticles of fine sandy clay-overlying "Clay-with-flints," near Chesham Bois, Bucks. (Grid Ref.: SU/972996.) Magnification: x 35.

(B) Laminated clay-layers in "brickearth," Prestwood brick-pit, Bucks. (SP/859014). Magnification: x 35.

(Drawings by Mr. D. V. Jones, Soil Survey of England and Wales.)

skins are well developed, will illustrate some of their micromorphological features (30). At this locality a superficial deposit of flinty clay overlies weakly laminated "brickearth." The latter is seamed with narrow, roughly vertical, fissures several feet long but often less than 1/10 in. thick practically filled with red-brown clay that contrasts strongly with the yellow-brown "brickearth." With increasing depth several fissures unite to form clay-joints up to ¾ in. thick. The deposits are often layered, the layering being parallel to the walls of the fissures (Fig. 2, B). The structure probably arises through clay, from the overlying drift, being carried in thin films of water and deposited on the mineral skeleton of the "brickearth"; once any crevices and irregularities have been filled deposition becomes regular, and the layered nature of the clay suggests a process of repeated (cyclic) sedimentation. Examination of thin sections cut normal to the layering reveals a very high degree of optical continuity, a field showing positive elongation changing to one showing negative elongation on rotation through 90 degrees, the slow vibration direction of the clay aggregates being parallel to the channel walls; this is consistent with the drying out and consequent orientation of the (001) planes parallel to the surface of deposition as demonstrated in laboratory experiments (see Fig. 1). In circular cavities the clay exhibits convex layering, and shows multiple dark interference bands between crossed nicols. The clay shows pronounced pleochroism from deep chocolate brown (Y, Z) to pale yellowish brown (X). The reason for the pleochroism is not clear as the iron, which is responsible for the colour, is probably not an integral part of the clay mineral structure, but is in the form of free iron oxide coating the particles; epitaxic growth of crystalline iron oxides in a definite orientation on the clay particles, as occurs in the system kaolinite-goethite (10), is probably responsible.

The favourable physical conditions at Prestwood, with the existence of well fissured strata, appear to have provided suitable conditions for the maximal development of

clay skins showing a very high degree of preferred orientation and associated properties, but comparable phenomena, including layering and pleochroism, have been
noted by several workers in the B-horizons of the soils of a number of great soil
groups. Brewer (4) has pointed out that, although the term clay skins may be adequate for a macromorphological description, micromorphologically they may show
considerable variation and " may be oriented to any degree from perfectly to practically unoriented. They may be composed of innumerable thin lamellae or a few
thick layers. The layers may be uniform in colour or vary from one edge to the
other, and so on. Each of these different characteristics is due to some difference in
genesis or conditions of formation." Further observations along these lines would be
expected to yield additional information about the mechanisms of clay illuviation in
soil horizons.

Microfabrics indicative of clay migration in colloidal suspension and its accumulation to form textural B-horizons have been described in a number of grey-brown
podzolic soils developed from calcareous parent materials of glacial, fluvioglacial
and loessial origin of the Great Plains and north-eastern United States (9, 12, 19,
26, 33), and in the red-yellow podzolic and related reddish brown lateritic soils in
the Piedmont area of the south-eastern United States (6, 20, 24). The red-yellow
podzolic soils are intensely weathered with reddish, reddish yellow and yellow subsoil horizons; the yellow colours are associated with siliceous and feldspathic parent
materials, whereas the redder members of the group occur on parent materials
which contain larger amounts of ferromagnesian minerals and intergrade to the
reddish brown lateritic soils on basic rocks. Whereas in the C_1 and B_3-horizons
the clay accumulations a r e mainly *in situ* alterations of primary minerals, the
B_2-horizons have prominent continuous and usually thick clay skins with illuviated clay in channels, pores and on ped surfaces. McCaleb (20) considers that
"the genesis of red-yellow and grey-brown podzolic soils seems to be alike in kind,
but differs considerably in the degree and intensity of expression of similar horizon
sequences formed under quite diffent environments. The red-yellow soils of the United
States are older genetically than the grey-brown podzolic soils. This maturity is
expressed in terms of degree of primary mineral alteration, dominant clay mineral
suites present, amount of clay and its distribution, profile development, and the extreme acid conditions resulting from base depletion."

Descriptions of fabrics apparently closely akin to those of the grey-brown podzolic
soils have been given by Altemuller (2) and Kubiena (17) for soils developed in loess
in Western Europe. On the weathering of the loess a sequence of soils is formed from
AC-soils (black earths, pararendzinas) to soils with an ABC-horizonation. In the
early stages of development of the latter soils field evidence of clay migration is
lacking, but thin sections of the subsoil horizons show the presence of yellowish
brown oriented clay mainly on the walls of channels and in pore spaces. Further
evolution leads to the formation of distinct A and A_e-horizons depleted of clay,
and the whole fabric of the illuvial B-horizon is permeated by oriented clay deposits,
which also fill numerous and well developed conducting channels. Muckenhausen
(23) introduced the term parabraunerde for such soils, and they have been equated
by Kubiëna (17) with the *sols lessives* of the French pedologists and with a segment
of the grey-brown podzolic soils of the United States.

From the few micromorphological studies that have been made on British soils some soils on limestone, *e.g.* on Devonian limestone in Devon (7), and on Oolitic limestone in the Cotswolds (31), have patterns of clay orientation comparable with that of the terra fuscas, and soils developed in loessial deposits and in parent materials containing loessial additions have features in common with the parabraunerde and the grey-brown podzolic soils of the United States, involving differential accumulation of clay by translocation within the profile. These include soils developed from the valley brickearths in Kent (8), deep silty deposits overlying the Carboniferous limestone in the Mendips (31), and calcareous drifts (Coombe deposits) which incorporate substantial amounts of material of loessial origin in the Chilterns (3). Most of these soils may be correlated with the grey-brown podzolic soils as defined by Tavernier and Smith (32), but the soils of the Chiltern plateau developed on "Clay-with-flints" and allied deposits have thick intensely weathered subsoils that are generally low in bases throughout and conform in most respects to the red-yellow podzolic soils (3). The soils have a superficial mantle of loessial material incorporated with the underlying "Clay-with-flints" which itself consists largely of the weathered remains of Chalk and Eocene sediments and has a locally rubefied braunlehm fabric probably formed under the hotter, wetter tropical or sub-tropical conditions of the early Pleistocene or Tertiary. Thin sections provide evidence of clay migration in these soils, which have developed by the superimposition of pedogenic processes on composite parent materials further accentuating the original textural differences.

From this brief review it is evident that several distinctive patterns of clay morphology exist in undisturbed soils, and detailed investigation of the micromorphology yields valuable information on the conditions of deposition of the parent material and on the genesis of the soils, and assists in their classification. The processes by which soils are formed are probably relatively few, but the resulting fabrics are influenced by their interaction on a diversity of parent materials under different climatic conditions. Features indicative of clay migration may be found in a variety of great soil groups, *e.g.* in the grey-brown podzolic soils of temperate regions, the red-yellow podzolic soils of the subtropics and the latosolic soils of the tropics (18, 28), but other fabrics such as those of the rubefied soils appear to be characteristic of particular climatic regimes. Should this relationship between specific fabrics and climate be firmly established, micromorphological studies should also throw much light on the problem of the conditions of formation of buried and relic soils.

REFERENCES

1. Albareda, J. M., Aleixandre, V., and Sanchez Calvo, M. del C. (1955), An. Edafol. Fisiol. veg., 14, 543-63.
2. Altemüller, H. J. (1956), Z. PflErnähr. Düng., 72, 152-67.
3. Avery, B. W., Stephen, I., Brown, G., and Yaalon, D. H. (1959), J. Soil Sci., 10, 177-95.
4. Brewer, R. (1957), Report of overseas visit. C.S.I.R.O. (Australia).
5. .... and Haldane, A. D. (1957), Soil Sci., 84, 301-9.
6. Cady, J. G. (1950), Proc. Soil Sci. Soc. Amer., 15, 337-42.
7. Dalrymple, J. B. (1957), J. Soil Sci., 8, 161-5.
8. .... (1958), ibid., 9, 199-209.
9. Frei, E., and Cline, M. G. (1949), Soil Scil, 68, 333-44.
10. Fripiat, J. J., and Gastuche, M. C. (1952), Publ. Inst. Nat. agron. Congo belge, Ser. Sci. No. 54.
11. Fry, W. H. (1933), USDA Tech. Bull., 344.

12. Johnston, J. R., and Peterson, J. B. (1941), Proc. Soil Sci. Soc. Amer., 6, 360-7.
13. Kubiēna, W. L. (1943), Beitr. z. Kolonialforschung, 3, 48-58.
14. .... (1948), Entwicklungslehre des Bodens. Springer-Verlag, Wien.
15. .... (1953), The Soils of Europe. Murby & Co., London.
16. .... (1956), Rep. 6th int. Congr. Soil Sci., E, 247-9.
17. .... (1956), Eiszeitalter und Gegenwart, 7, 102-12.
18. Laruelle, J. (1956), Pedologie, 6, 38-58.
19. McCaleb, S. B. (1954), Soil Sci., 77, 319-33.
20. .... (1959), Proc. Soil Sci. Soc. Amer., 23, 164-8.
21. McMillan, N. J., and Mitchell, J. (1953), Canad. J. agric. Sci., 33, 178-83.
22. Minashina, N. G. (1958), Pochvovedenie No. 4, 90-6.
23. Muckenhausen, E. (1955), Entwurf einer Systematik der Boden Deutschlands.
24. Nyun, M. A., and McCaleb, S. B. (1955), Soil Sci., 80, 27-41.
25. Parfenova, E. I., and Yarilova, E. A. (1958), Pochvovedenie No. 12, 28-35.
26. Peterson, J. B. (1937), Proc. Soil Sci. Soc. Amer., 2, 9-13.
27. .... (1944), ibid., 9, 37-48.
28. Ruhe, R. V., and Cady, J. G. (1954), Trans 5th int. Congr. Soil Sci., 4, 401-7.
29. Sanchez Calvo, M. del C. (1956), Rep. 6th int. Congr. Soil Sci., E, 433-7.
30. Stephen, I., and Osmond, D. A. (1957), Rep. Rothamst. exp. Sta. for 1956, 65.
31. .... (1959), ibid., for 1958, 62.
32. Tavernier, R., and Smith, G. D. (1957) Advanc. Agron., 9, 217-89.
33. Thorp, J., Cady, J. G., and Gamble, E. E. (1959), Proc. Soil Sci. Soc. Amer., 23, 156-61.
34. Williamson, W. O. (1947), Amer. J. Sci., 245, 645-62.
35. Yarilova, E. A., and Parfenova, E. I. (1957), Pochvovedenie No. 9, 37-48.

MORPHOLOGY AND GENESIS OF A CHERNOZEMIC TO PODZOLIC SEQUENCE OF SOIL PROFILES IN SASKATCHEWAN[1]

R. J. St. Arnaud and E. P. Whiteside

*Department of Soil Science, University of Saskatchewan,.Saskatoon, Saskatchewan,
and Department of Soil Science, Michigan State University,
East Lansing, Michigan, respectively*

Received April 16, 1963

ABSTRACT

Chemical, physical, and micropedological studies were made of Orthic Black, Orthic Dark Grey, Dark Grey Wooded, and Orthic Grey Wooded profiles developed from relatively uniform glacial till material. The general gradation of morphological properties observed for the Black to the Grey Wooded soils is reflected in the thickness of the Ah horizons and of the sola, the development of Ae and textural B horizons, and in the structure and microfabrics of the soil horizons.

All four soils are highly base-saturated, calcium being the dominant cation on the exchange complex. Particle size distribution has been affected by both translocation of clay as well as by physical breakdown of coarse fractions particularly within surface horizons. Iron translocation within all four profiles appears to be closely associated with clay movement. The uniform iron content of the fine clay fraction indicates that iron may occur as an integral part of the clay structures and that the clays have undergone little alteration as a result of weathering.

INTRODUCTION

Soils which grade between Chernozemic Black and Podzolic Grey Wooded possess both chernozemic and podzolic features and were originally designated as degraded chernozems by both Canadian and American pedologists (10, 11, 14, 21). Most of these soils are regarded as former grassland profiles which have been changed by the influence of invasion of trees (11) although some workers are undecided on this point (14). According to the present Canadian system of classification (13) such soils would be classified as Dark Grey Chernozemic or Dark Grey Wooded soils depending upon the degree of degradation expressed.

---

[1]Authorized for publication by the Director as Journal Article No. 3194 of the Michigan Agricultural Experiment Station, East Lansing, Michigan.

Reproduced with permission from *Canadian Journal of Soil Science,* Vol. 44, 1964, p. 88-99. Published by the Agricultural Institute of Canada, Ottawa, Canada.

The purpose of this investigation was to study the chemical, physical, and morphological properties of a sequence of soils ranging from Black to Grey Wooded in Saskatchewan in order to provide a better assessment of the changes which occur during the development of such soils.

MATERIALS AND METHODS

Four soil profiles representative of Orthic Black, Orthic Dark Grey, Dark Grey Wooded, and Orthic Gray Wooded types were selected for this study. All were developed on calcareous medium-textured glacial till probably of Condiean age (2) and occurred within a relatively small area located in the Touchwood Hills of Saskatchewan. The Touchwood Hills form an island within the main boundaries of the Black soil zone and rise approximately 400 ft above the surrounding plain, reaching a maximum elevation of just over 2200 ft above sea level. The changes in vegetation and in associated soil types resulting from the increase in elevation facilitated the selection of profiles on much more uniform parent material than would have otherwise been possible.

All four profiles were selected from sites of undulating topography on well-drained 3 to 4 percent slopes. The Orthic Black profile occurred on a southwest slope under grass vegetation, whereas the other three soils were located on northwest slopes on which trees, mainly aspen, formed the dominant vegetative species. The maturity and density of tree stands increased in going from the Dark Grey to the Grey Wooded sites.

Previous studies on these same soils have indicated that montmorillonite and illite are the dominant clay minerals in both the fine ($< 0.2\,\mu$) and coarse ($2.0-0.2\,\mu$) clay fractions (16). However, more illite is present in both the fine and coarse clays of the A and B horizons than in the underlying C horizons. A process of illitization is believed to have taken place, particularly within the surface horizons of the grassland soils. Minor amounts of kaolinite and chlorite also occur within the clay fractions.

Description of the four profiles selected are given in Table 1. Horizon designations and terminology for structure and consistence are those recommended by the Canadian National Soil Survey Committee (13). Dry soil colors are reported according to the Munsell notations (17).

Investigational Techniques

Mechanical analyses were made by the pipette method(5) following the destruction of lime and organic matter prior to dispersion with sodium metaphosphate. The $< 0.2\,\mu$ clay was determined using a No. 2 International centrifuge.

Soil pH, electrical conductivity, total nitrogen, inorganic and organic carbon, exchangeable cations, cation exchange capacity, and total iron were determined by standard methods. Mackenzie's method (8) of extracting free iron was used, iron being determined colorimetrically by the ferron method (4).

Thin sections were prepared from natural soil clods impregnated with castolite and examined under a petrographic microscope.

Table 1—Morphological characteristics of the soil studied

Profile	Horizon, in.	Color	Texture	Structure	Consistence	
					Moist	Dry
Orthic Black (Oxbow Association)	Ah (0–7)	10YR 3/1–2/1	Loam	Medium to coarse blocky breaking to fine granular	Very friable	Soft
	AB (7–9)	2.5Y 4/2	Sandy loam	Medium prismatic breaking to fine granular	Friable	Slightly hard
	Bt1 (9–16)	10YR 4/2–2/2	Sandy clay loam	Medium prismatic breaking to medium blocky to fragmental	Firm	Hard
	Bt2 (16–19)	10YR 4/2–5/4	Sandy clay loam	Faintly prismatic breaking to fine granular	Firm	Hard
	CB (19–31)	2.5Y 6/2	Loam	Massive to faintly prismatic breaking to fine granular	Friable	Slightly hard
	C (31–54)	2.5Y 6/2–5/2	Loam	Massive, faintly laminated crushing to fine granular	Friable	Slightly hard to soft
Orthic Dark Grey (Oxbow Association)	L–H (3/4–0)	—	—	—	—	—
	Ah (0–7)	10YR 3/1–2/1	Loam	Coarse blocky breaking to fine granular	Very friable	Soft
	Ahe (7–11)	10YR 4/1	Loam	Medium to coarse blocky, faintly platy, crushing to fine powder	—	—
	AB (11–13)	10YR 4/1	Loam	Medium prismatic breaking to fine granular	Firm	Slightly hard
	Bt1 (13–21)	10YR 5/2–4/2	Sandy clay loam	Medium prismatic breaking to fragmental	Firm	Slightly hard
	Bt2 (21–23)	10YR 5/2	Sandy clay loam	Medium prismatic breaking to fine blocky	Firm	Hard
	CB (23–31)	2.5Y 7/2–6/2	Sandy clay loam	Medium to coarse prismatic, faintly laminated, crushing to fine granular	Friable	Slightly hard
	C (31–50)	2.5Y 6/2–5/2	Loam	Massive, faintly laminated, crushing to fine granular	Friable	Slightly hard to soft
Dark Grey Wooded (Whitewood Association)	L–H (3/4–0)	—	—	—	—	—
	Ah (0–4)	10YR 3/1–2/1	Loam	Medium blocky, faintly platy, breaking to fine granular	Friable	Soft
	Ae (4–8)	10YR 4/1	Loam	Medium to thick platy, crushing to fine powder	Friable	Soft
	AB (8–10)	10YR 5/2	Loam	Coarse prismatic, faintly platy, crushing to fine granular	Firm	Hard
	Bt1 (10–16)	10YR 4/2	Clay loam	Irregular prismatic, breaking to fine angular blocky; dark coatings on peds	Firm	Very hard
	Bt2 (16–20)	10YR 4/2	Sandy clay loam	Medium prismatic breaking to fine blocky	Firm	Hard
	Bt3 (20–23)	10YR 5/2	Sandy clay loam	Massive, crushing to fine granular	Friable	Slightly hard
	CB (23–31)	2.5Y 6/2	Loam	Massive, faintly laminated, crushing to fine granular	Friable	Soft
	C (31–59)	2.5Y 6/2	Loam	Massive, crushing to fine granular	Friable	Soft
Orthic Grey Wooded (Waitville Association)	L–H (1–0)	—	—	—	—	—
	Ahe (0–1)	10YR 2/2–2/1	Silt loam	Fine granular to thin platy	Very friable	Soft
	Ae (1–5)	10YR 4/1	Loam	Thin platy crushing to fine powder	Very friable	Soft
	AB (5–7)	10YR 7/2 / 10YR 5/2–4/2	Clay loam	Massive to coarse platy breaking to fine angular blocky; silica coatings on surfaces of ped	Firm	Slightly hard
	Bt1 (7–18)	10YR 4/2	Clay loam	Fine subangular blocky; dark coatings on peds	Very firm	Very hard
	Bt2 (18–23)	2.5Y 5/2	Clay loam	Massive, breaking to medium blocky	Firm	Very hard
	CB (23–29)	2.5Y 6/2	Loam	Massive, crushing to fine granular	Very friable	Hard
	C (29–50)	2.5Y 6/2	Loam	Massive, moderately laminated, crushing to fine granular	Friable	Slightly hard

Table 2—Bulk density and mechanical composition of the four profiles

Horizon	Bulk density	Gravel > 2 mm,%	Sand 2–.05 mm,%	Silt .05–.002 mm,%	Clay < 2 μ,%	% fine clay < 0.2 μ,%
			Orthic Black			
Ah	1.04	2.4	51.7	27.8	20.5	10.9
AB	1.43	2.1	55.3	25.0	19.7	11.2
Bt1	1.44	3.0	46.5	25.2	28.3	18.2
Bt2	1.43	2.2	46.7	27.5	25.8	15.4
CB	1.49	3.6	49.6	29.0	21.4	11.8
Cl–1	1.65	5.1	53.2	28.7	18.1	7.5
Cl–2	1.71	5.6	51.1	29.8	19.1	10.8
Cl–3	—	—	50.2	29.9	19.9	11.1
			Orthic Dark Grey			
Ah	1.01	1.2	36.4	40.5	23.1	14.7
Ahe	1.10	0.4	39.8	39.9	20.3	8.6
AB	1.18	0.2	37.4	36.2	26.4	17.8
Bt1	1.56	1.3	46.8	26.7	26.5	13.7
Bt2	1.46	4.8	54.6	22.8	22.6	15.2
CB	1.58	12.5	55.5	24.2	20.3	12.3
Cl–1	1.66	5.4	47.8	30.1	22.1	10.5
Cl–2	1.66	—	46.7	30.9	22.4	12.1
Cl–3	—	—	45.7	31.9	22.4	11.9
			Dark Grey Wooded			
Ah	1.18	3.2	45.0	40.1	14.9	7.6
Ae	1.54	2.8	49.7	36.4	13.9	6.9
AB	1.56	3.3	43.7	31.1	25.2	16.4
Bt1	1.55	4.6	42.2	23.0	34.8	17.7
Bt2	1.62	7.5	53.2	23.4	23.4	16.1
Bt3	1.58	8.5	49.0	27.0	24.0	15.6
CB	1.65	7.8	49.8	38.0	22.2	11.1
Cl–1	1.63	7.1	50.4	28.0	21.6	12.7
Cl–2	1.76	—	48.0	30.5	21.5	11.3
Cl–3	—	—	47.5	30.6	21.9	11.2
			Orthic Grey Wooded			
Ahe	0.60	0.0	33.3	54.3	12.4	4.2
Ae	1.56	1.5	42.6	48.1	9.3	2.8
AB	1.41	2.1	36.2	34.5	29.3	17.7
Bt1	1.61	2.4	41.2	25.6	33.2	24.1
Bt2	1.56	5.7	44.7	28.3	27.0	16.5
CB	1.65	7.8	47.8	29.3	22.9	13.3
Cl–1	1.67	4.8	47.1	28.8	24.1	12.4
Cl–2	1.72	—	47.1	29.9	23.0	12.7
Cl–3	—	—	44.5	31.9	23.6	13.1

RESULTS AND DISCUSSIONS

The relatively uniform nature of the glacial till from which the four soils have developed is evidenced from the similarity in particle size distribution of the four parent materials as well as the uniformity in mechanical composition of each parent material with depth (Table 2). The accumulation of clay occurring in the B horizons of all four profiles is associated with a decrease in clay in the A horizons. Although the Ah and C horizons of the Black soil contain similar amounts of clay, the weathering of carbonates in the coarse fractions of the Ah horizon, as indicated by inorganic carbon values (Table 3) has likely increased the proportion of clay present. This may be masking any losses due to translocation.

The mechanical analysis and bulk density data (Table 2) confirm field observations that the B horizons become more dense from Orthic Black to Grey Wooded soils. Orthic Chernozemic soils developed from glacial till are characterized by good

Table 3—Chemical properties of the four profiles

Horizon	pH	Total nitrogen, %	Organic carbon, %	Inorganic carbon, %	"Free" iron (Fe_2O_3), %	Total Fe_2O_3, %
			Orthic Black			
Ah	7.2	0.39	4.58	0.10	0.68	3.12
AB	7.4	0.12	1.33	0.03	1.06	3.89
Bt1	7.4	0.08	0.96	0.01	1.28	4.26
Bt2	7.6	0.07	0.77	0.22	1.38	2.83
CB	7.9	0.05	0.59	2.66	0.71	2.57
Cl–1	8.3	0.03	0.31	2.35	0.47	2.78
Cl–2	8.3	0.02	0.39	2.57	—	—
Cl–3	8.3	0.01	0.12	2.34	—	—
			Orthic Dark Grey			
L–H	6.5	1.15	15.23	0.07	—	....
Ah	6.3	0.31	3.94	0.01	0.90	—
Ahe	6.5	0.22	2.60	0.02	0.94	—
AB	6.3	0.11	1.13	0.02	1.50	—
Bt1	6.5	0.05	0.45	0.03	1.24	—
Bt2	7.1	0.06	0.55	0.28	1.20	—
CB	7.7	0.04	0.34	2.34	0.84	—
Cl–1	7.7	0.02	0.29	2.54	0.59	—
Cl–2	8.0	0.02	0.25	2.60	—	—
Cl–3	8.0	0.02	0.25	2.54	—	—
			Dark Grey Wooded			
L–H	6.5	1.15	16.80	0.13	—	...
Ah	6.8	0.25	3.37	0.05	0.68	—
Ae	6.9	0.05	0.58	0.03	0.75	—
AB	6.8	0.04	0.44	0.01	1.52	—
Bt1	6.9	0.04	0.39	0.01	1.36	—
Bt2	7.3	0.05	0.45	0.98	1.03	—
Bt3	7.5	0.04	0.53	1.69	—	—
CB	7.6	0.02	0.30	2.80	0.90	—
Cl–1	7.8	0.01	0.17	2.78	0.53	—
C.–2	7.9	0.01	0.17	2.28	—	—
C.–3	7.8	0.01	0.12	2.34	—	—
			Orthic Grey Wooded			
L–H	5.8	1.11	19.67	0.10	—	—
Ahe	5.8	0.65	7.49	0.06	0.81	2.53
Ae	6.3	0.03	0.47	0.04	0.81	2.19
AB	6.1	0.04	0.49	0.05	1.63	3.67
Bt1	5.9	0.04	0.53	0.01	1.31	4.76
Bt2	7.2	0.05	0.43	0.71	1.24	3.28
CB	7.5	0.03	0.26	2.06	0.80	2.55
Cl–1	7.7	0.02	0.23	2.65	0.57	2.88
Cl–2	8.0	0.02	0.19	2.60	—	—
Cl–3	8.0	0.02	0.26	2.53	—	—

internal drainage throughout the solum. Translocation of colloidal materials from the A to the B horizons of the podzolic profiles has led to the development of denser, less pervious subsoils which restrict the internal drainage of these soils. Although textural B horizons often occur in Chernozemic soils (13, 18), they are generally weakly expressed and are not the main characterizing feature of the Chernozemic soils.

Chemical Properties

A general decrease in pH values from above pH 7.0 in the Black to below pH 6.0 in the Grey Wooded soil (Table 3) are evidence that the degree of leaching increases from the chernozemic to the podzolic soils. The pH of the Bt1 horizon in the Grey Wooded profile is 5.9, which is slightly lower than that of either the Ae or AB horizons, but above that of the thin Ahe layer. Earlier work (12) has shown

Table 4—Cation exchange capacity and exchangeable cation data, meq/100 g, for non-calcareous horizons of the four profiles

Horizon	C.E.C.	Ca^{++}	Mg^{++}	Na$^+$	K$^+$
		Orthic Black			
Ah	25.3	24.0	3.7	0.1	0.5
AB	14.5	13.6	3.4	0.1	0.3
Bt1	15.8	16.1	4.9	0.1	0.5
Bt2	17.0	17.8	4.4	0.1	0.4
		Orthic Dark Grey			
Ah	26.0	18.6	4.6	0.1	0.9
Ahe	22.7	15.9	4.5	0.1	0.5
AB	21.2	15.1	5.8	0.1	0.5
Bt1	17.6	13.5	5.6	0.1	0.5
Bt2	15.1	13.2	5.2	0.1	0.4
		Dark Grey Wooded			
Ah	19.0	14.9	3.7	0.1	0.7
Ae	8.8	7.2	1.8	Trace	0.4
AB	18.1	14.3	4.2	Trace	0.8
Bt1	22.0	16.1	6.0	Trace	0.9
Bt2	14.5	14.4	4.0	Trace	0.5
		Orthic Grey Wooded			
Ahe	43.8	34.8	4.0	Trace	1.1
Ae	6.2	5.0	1.2	Trace	0.4
AB	16.9	12.0	4.6	Trace	0.8
Bt1	21.5	14.4	6.5	Trace	0.3
Bt2	16.5	15.4	5.1	Trace	0.5

that the B horizon in Grey Wooded soils is often the most acidic of the mineral horizons.

Conductivity values for the four profiles are low (< 0.42 mmhos/cm) and reflect the absence of any appreciable salt concentrations. Inorganic carbon values are low in the A and upper B horizons, with maximum values appearing in the CB or C horizons indicating the removal of lime carbonates from the upper horizons.

The nitrogen and organic carbon values decrease sharply downward in the profiles. Only very slight increases are noted in the B horizons, these occurring in all but the Orthic Black profile. In the two podzolic profiles, the Bt2 horizons tend to have more organic matter than the overlying Bt1 horizons. The slight increase in nitrogen and organic carbon noted in the B horizon as compared with the Ae confirms trends previously reported (12).

The values for total exchange capacity (Table 4) are closely related to the amounts of colloidal and organic materials present, being highest in Ah and Bt1 horizons and lowest in Ae horizons. Calcium is the dominant cation on the exchange complex in all four soils. Although exchangeable hydrogen was not determined, the amounts would be small in terms of total exchange capacities, since the sum of the bases for each horizon closely approximates the total exchange capacity. Even though eluviation has been most pronounced in the Orthic Grey Wooded soil, the process has not reached the stage of high unsaturation typical of Podzol soils (19) since calcium is still the dominant cation on the exchange system.

Total and "Free" Iron

The horizon of maximum accumulation of free iron does not always coincide with the horizon of maximum clay accumulation in the four profiles studied (Fig. 1).

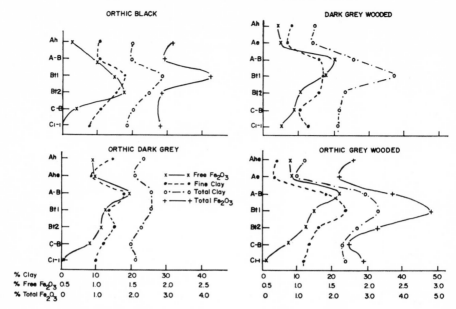

Fig. 1—Distribution of clay and iron within the four profiles.

As degradation increases, the extractability of iron changes; the layer of maximum iron solubility moves upwards from the lower B horizon in the Orthic Black profile to the AB transition zone in the Grey Wooded soil. A close association between clay and free iron has been reported by other workers (7,20); it appears that for the soils under study a closer relationship may exist between total iron and clay content than between free iron and clay content. The relationship between iron and clay becomes more evident from the total iron values of clay fractions themselves. Total iron values for the coarse $(2\text{-}0.2\mu)$ and fine $(<0.2\mu)$ clay fractions from the major horizons of the four profiles studied (Table 5) indicate a higher and a more uniform iron content for the fine fraction than for the coarse clays. This suggests that the fine clay fraction is dominated by iron-bearing clays which have been little affected by weathering.

The variations in iron content of the coarse clays within the solum of all but the Orthic Black profile may be due to weathering resulting in the accumulation of minerals containing little or no iron. This is substantiated by data presented in a previous paper (15) which indicate an increase in the quartz content of the coarse clay fractions of the sola as compared to those of the parent materials.

It is difficult to determine whether the soil organic fraction has played any part in affecting the mobility of iron within the profiles studied since no significant increases in organic carbon or nitrogen occur in the horizons of maximum iron accumulation. Also, calculations indicate that 60 to 85 percent of the total iron in these soils occurs in the clay fraction. If the bulk of this is present as an integral part of the clay mineral structures and has not been affected by weathering (and indications are that this is so), only a small portion of the total iron occurring in the soil may be present in forms readily affected by organic compounds which could effect its translocation.

Table 5—Total iron content of the coarse $(2-0.2\,\mu)$ and fine $(< 0.2\,\mu)$ clay fractions from the major horizons of the four profiles

Soil	Horizon	Coarse clay, % Fe_2O_3	Fine clay, % Fe_2O_3
Orthic Black	Ah	7.52	12.24
	Bt1	7.85	12.61
	C	7.22	12.23
Orthic Dark Grey	Ah	5.83	13.12
	Ahe	5.38	13.26
	Bt1	6.30	12.32
	C	7.45	12.42
Dark Grey Wooded	Ae	6.00	12.85
	Bt1	5.88	12.90
	C	7.36	12.32
Orthic Grey Wooded	Ae	5.70	11.74
	Bt1	7.16	12.51
	C	7.55	12.50

Microscopic Studies

In thin section, the most striking feature of the parent material is its uniform fabric. Skeletal grains are embedded in a homogeneous light brownish-grey to buff-colored matrix of finer materials (Fig. 2). The only accumulations which occur consist of small amounts of organic matter, in various stages of decomposition, along root channels, and concentrations of lime carbonates which line some of the voids. The unweathered appearance of the skeletal mineral grains which consist mainly of quartz, feldspars, calcite, and dolomite, with smaller amounts of hornblendes and other heavy minerals as well as ferruginous concretions, attest to their relatively unweathered condition.

The A Horizons

Although the organic matter accounts for only a small portion of the total weight of the Ah horizon of the Orthic Black soil, it appears to dominate the entire fabric (Fig. 3). The inorganic materials have become closely surrounded and bound together by the organic fraction of the soil into small, irregular-shaped, dark-colored aggregates, generally less than 0.2 mm in diameter. The mineral grains are not embedded in a continuous matrix as they are in the parent material, but rather are surrounded by inter-connected, irregularly-shaped aggregates of matrix material and numerous irregular-shaped voids. In most respects, the fabric of the Ah horizons of the Orthic Black and Dark Grey soils closely resembles that described by Kubiena (6) as intertextic, or more specifically as chernozemic fabric.

The fabric of the Ah horizon of the Dark Grey Wooded profile somewhat resembles a chernozemic type of fabric in that a well-aggregated appearance persists, but the organic-rich aggregates do not appear to dominate the fabric as they do in the Ah of the Orthic Black and Orthic Dark Grey soils. More of the silty clay matrix is evident, with local accumulations of organic matter interspersed throughout (Fig. 4). Consequently, larger structural units, consisting mainly of inorganic plasmic material and skeletal grains, appear to be bordered with clusters of organic colloids or aggregates rich in organic matter These dark-colored accumulations of organic

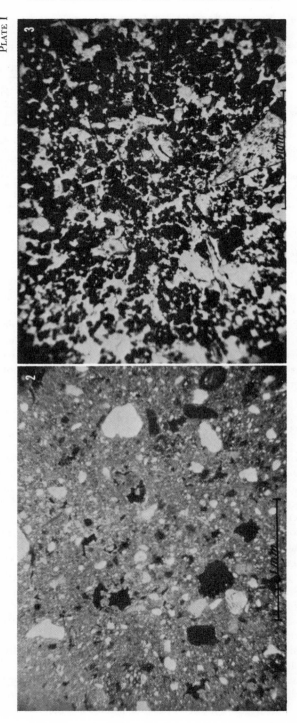

PLATE I

Fig. 3—Microfabric of the Ah horizon of the Orthic Black soil (plain light).

Fig. 2—Microfabric of the parent material of the Orthic Black soil (X-nicols).

PLATE II

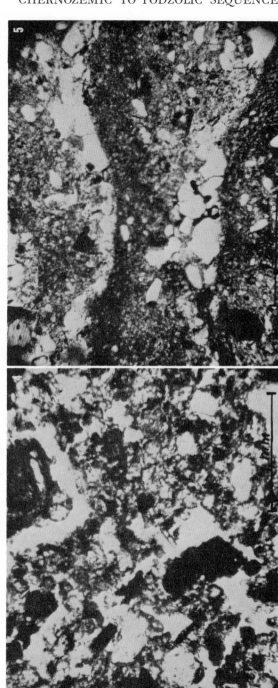

Fig. 5—Microfabric of the Ae horizon of the Orthic Grey Wooded soil (X-nicols).

Fig. 4—Microfabric of the Ah horizon of the Dark Grey Wooded soil (plain light).

PLATE III

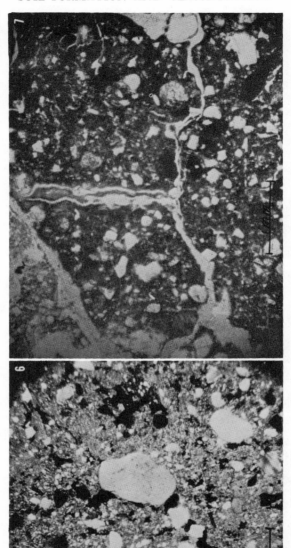

Fig. 6—Microfabric of the Bt1 horizon of the orthic Black soil (X-nicols).   Fig. 7—Microfabric of the Bt1 horizon of the Orthic Grey Wooded soil (plain light).

matter and organic-rich aggregates impart a dark brownish to greyish-black color to the horizon as a whole.

Of the four soils under study, all but the Orthic Black are characterized by the presence of an eluviated Ahe or Ae horizon. In thin section, the Ahe horizon of the Orthic Dark Grey soil appears similar to the Ah horizon of the same profile except that the fabric shows some evidence of faint platiness. The faint horizontal cleavages are usually 1.5 to 2.0 mm apart and are discontinuous.

The striking feature of the Ae horizon in the Dark Grey Wooded soil is the presence of platy or banded fabric. This horizon is much lower in organic matter content than the overlying Ah. The matrix is light brown in color and in many respects is similar to that of the parent material except that it contains a lower proportion of clay. The plates within the Ae vary in thickness between 0.65 and 1.5 mm. There is no marked difference in concentration of plasmic material within the bands. Occasional accumulations of organic matter and iron concretions are interspersed within the matrix.

The banded fabric is much more pronounced in the Ae horizon of the Grey Wooded soil (Fig. 5). The plates, which generally vary between 0.3 and 0.5 mm in thickness, tend to have a rolling form which imparts a wavy appearance to the bands within the microfabric. As can be seen in the photograph, each band shows a gradation in plasma content, with the highest content of fine material occurring near the top of the plate. This type of banded fabric is similar to that described by Kubiena (6) and McMillan and Mitchell (9). The loss of clay-size material from this horizon, which is indicated by mechanical analysis data (Table 2), is reflected in the overall appearance of the soil material.

The Ahe and Ae horizons of all three profiles have undergone leaching, but it has been most pronounced in the Grey Wooded soil. The platy structure associated with these eluviated horizons becomes more pronounced, the plates become thinner and gradations in particle size distribution within the bands more striking in passing from the Orthic Dark Grey to the Grey Wooded soil. In the Orthic Dark soil, it appears that leaching of a humic horizon has occurred, whereas in the other two profiles there is no evidence to indicate that the Ae horizons have ever been humified to any appreciable degree.

The B Horizons

In thin section, the Bt1 horizon of the Orthic Black soil (Fig. 6) is characterized by a dense, uniform, medium brown to yellowish-brown matrix surrounding skeletal grains of varying sizes. Numerous pore spaces are evident throughout the interior of the peds. Examination of the sections under crossed nicols reveals the presence of very fine flecks, orange-red in color, dispersed throughout the matrix. These minute accumulations appear to consist of oriented clays and exhibit uneven extinction upon rotation of the microscope stage. Acton (1) has reported the presence of similar accumulations in the B horizons of soils within a catena of the Dark Brown soil zone of Saskatchewan. He attributed their presence to reorientation of clay minerals *in situ* due to wetting and drying processes. He also suggested the possibility that such accumulations may, in some soils, be illuvial in nature. Their presence throughout the matrix of a soil would indicate that they were transported before the soil had a well-developed system of cleavages and channels through which water could percolate downwards. Under such conditions, water would move as a continuous front, carrying dispersed colloids into all portions of the soil material.

There is very little evidence to indicate that much of the clay in the B horizon of the Orthic Black profile is illuvial in nature. The accumulations of colloidal material along cleavages and pore walls are discontinuous and rare in this horizon. The higher clay content of the B horizon in comparison to the A and C horizons cannot definitely be attributed to illuviation since distinct cutans are lacking. There is insufficient evidence to determine whether the material from which the B horizon was formed was higher in clay at the time of deposition, whether clay has in fact moved into the B horizon from above without leaving any observable evidence of such movement, or whether clay has been formed *in situ*.

The Bt1 horizon of the Orthic Dark Grey soil is similar to that of the Orthic Black. The dense nature of the matrix, the abundance of skeletal grains embedded in it, and the high proportion of voids all attest to this similarity. However, in addition, diffuse accumulations of brownish materials appear along the surface of peds and bordering cleavages and root channels. Although no orientation is evident, these diffuse bands, less than 0.1 mm in thickness and often discontinuous, give the horizon a more dense appearance than the Btl of the Orthic Black profile. Flecks of oriented clays within the matrix still persist in this horizon.

The Bt1 horizons of the Dark Grey Wooded and Grey Wooded soils display high clay contents and more pronounced coatings which cover individual peds and channel walls. All of the ped surfaces are covered with plasmic material, the concentration of which decreases towards the center of the peds. The coatings are much more pronounced in the Grey Wooded soil (Fig. 7), although they are strongly expressed in both soils. Under crossed nicols, these coatings are dark orange-brown in color and appear streaky, indicating orientation parallel to the ped surfaces. The cutanic material shows uneven extinction when the clay skin is oriented parallel to the direction of vibration of the upper polarizer. Oriented colloids within the matrix of these horizons are also present, as they were in the two grassland profiles.

The accumulation of colloidal materials along the faces of peds and along root channels and other voids strongly suggests that illuviation of clays has occurred within the Bt horizons. The very marked concentrations of cutanic material and streakiness of these coatings becomes much more apparent at high power. The translocated clays display orientation parallel to the direction of the flow. Such flow structures, occurring in fabric referred to as channel fabric by Kubiena (6), are ample evidence that illuviation has occurred.

The physical nature of the A and B horizons of the soils studied appears to have been strongly influenced by the organic matter present in the surface horizons. The extent of stabilization of mineral colloids by the organic fraction, in large measure determines the extent to which clays undergo translocation during soil formation. This is evidenced in the lower clay content of the B horizons in the Black soil as compared to that of the Grey Wooded profile. This in turn affects physical breakdown which appears to be most pronounced in surface horizons underlain by heavy, textural B horizons (15). The periodic conditions of saturation which occur in the upper horizons due to restricted drainage of the subsoil are thought to favor conditions for disintegration of minerals by frost action. The greatest amount of breakdown occurred in the Ae of the Grey Wooded profile which possesses the most impervious B horizon of all four soils. This may account in part for the high silt content of Ae horizons since it appears that such breakdown is largely to silt or very fine sand size.

The development of platy structure also appears to be associated with the degree of drainage within the profile. Conditions which would favor the process of physical breakdown of mineral fractions would also favor the development of platy structure within surface horizons. The effect of ice lenses within a saturated soil could lead to the formation of platy structure (3). As was the case for physical breakdown, the highest degree of platiness occurred in the Ae of the Grey Wooded profile.

The results of this investigation, when complemented by results of concurrent studies on the same four soil profiles (15, 16), provide a better understanding of the changes due to soil-forming processes in these soils and, in particular, they point out the significant changes resulting from progressive podzolic degradation. The gradation in morphological properties observed in going from the Black to the Grey Wooded profile can be summarized as follows:

(1) a change from the absence to the presence of L–H layers;

(2) a decrease in the thickness of the Ah horizons and in the expression of blocky structure within the Ah horizons;

(3) an increase in the degree of leaching as exhibited by variations in fine clay, pH, color, and platiness of the Ahe and Ae horizons;

(4) a change from strong, well-developed to weaker and more irregular, and finally to the virtual absence of prismatic structure in the B horizons;

(5) an increase in the development and thickness of textural B horizons; and

(6) a change from the presence to the absence of a marked lime accumulation layer.

REFERENCES

1. Acton, D. F. 1961. Micropedology of the major profile types of the Weyburn catena. M.Sc. Thesis, University of Saskatchewan.
2. Christiansen, E. A. 1961. Geology and ground-water resources of the Regina Area, Saskatchewan. Geol. Div., Sask. Research Council, Rept. No. 2.
3. Czeratzki, W. 1956. Zur wirkung des frostes auf die structur des bodens. Zeit. Pflanz. Dung. Boden. 72, 15-32.
4. Davenport, W. H., Jr. 1949. Determination of aluminum in the presence of iron. Anal. Chem. 21, 710—711.
5. Kilmer, V. J., and L. T. Alexander. 1949. Methods of making mechanical analysis of soils. Soil Sci. 68, 15—24.
6. Kubiena, W. L. 1938. Micropedology. Collegiate Press Inc., Ames, Iowa.
7. Lutwick, L. E. 1960. The nature and distribution of free iron in the Grey Wooded (Podzolic) Soils of Saskatchewan. Ph.D. Thesis, University of Saskatchewan. Unpublished.
8. MacKenzie, R. C. 1954. Na S O method for extracting free iron oxides from soils. J. Soil Sci. 5, 167.
9. McMillan, N. J., and J. Mitchell. 1953. A microscopic study of platy and concretionary structures in certain Saskatchewan soils. J. Agr. Sci. 33, 178—183.
10. Mitchell, J., H. C. Moss, and J. S. Clayton. 1944. Soil Survey Report No. 12. University of Saskatchewan.
11. ...., ..., ... 1950. Soil Survey Report No. 13. University of Saskatchewan.

12. Moss, H. C., and R. J. St. Arnaud. 1955. Grey Wooded (Podzolic) soils of Saskatchewan, Canada. J. Soil Sci. 6, 293—311.

13. National Soil Survey Committee (Canada) 1960. A report of the 4th national meeting, held at Guelph, Canada.

14. Nygard, I. J., P. R. McMiller, and F. D. Hole. 1952. Characteristics of some Podzolic, Brown Forest and Chernozem soils of the northern portion of the Lake States. Soil Sci. Soc. Am. Proc. 16, 123—129.

15. St. Arnaud, R. J., and E. P. Whiteside. 1963. Physical breakdown in relation to soil development. J. Soil Sci. 14, 267—282.

16. ...., and M. M. Mortland. 1963. Characteristics of the clay fractions in a Chernozemic to Podzolic sequence of soil profiles in Saskatchewan. Can. J. Soil Sci. 43, 336—349.

17. Soil Survey Staff, USDA. 1951. Soil Survey manual. USDA Agriculture Handbook No. 18.

18. .... 1960. Soil Classification. A comprehensive system. 7th Approximation.

19. Stobbe, P. C., and J. R. Wright. 1959. Modern concepts of the genesis of Podzols. Soil Sci. Soc. Am. Proc. 23, 161—164.

20. Tavernier, R., and G. D. Smith. 1957. The concept of Braunerde (Brown Forest soil) in Europe and the United States. Adv. Agron. 9, 217—289.

21. Williams, B. H., and W. E. Bowser. 1952. Grey Wooded soils in parts of Alberta and Montana. Soil Sci. Soc. Am. Proc. 16, 130—133.

MECHANISMS OF FORMATION OF
SODIUM CARBONATE IN SOILS

I. MANIFESTATIONS OF BIOLOGICAL CONVERSIONS

L. D. Whittig and P. Janitzky

(Department of Soils and Plant Nutrition, University of California, Davis, California)

SUMMARY

Mechanisms of formation and accumulation of Na_2CO_3 have been studied in a graded sequence of salt-affected soils of the Sacramento Valley, California. The soils are confined within a drainageway which is inundated during winter with flood waters containing relatively low concentrations of neutral sodium, calcium, and magnesium salts. Heavy inundations and high water tables within the basin lead to microbiological reduction of sulfate and ferric iron. The resulting sulfide is held within the soil as FeS whereas the CO_2 released by biological oxidation of abundant organic matter forms bicarbonate. Lateral and upward migration of bicarbonate-charged water from the drainageway basin to soils nearer the basin rim results in yearly increases in concentration of soluble salts within these soils. $Ca(HCO_3)_2$ and $Mg(HCO_3)_2$ migrate from the zones of maximum CO_2 production and precipitate as carbonates. $NaHCO_3$ continues to move, along with the capillary water, and accumulates in the rim soils. As water evaporates or is used by growing plants, loss of CO_2 from the $NaHCO_3$ occurs, resulting in the formation of Na_2CO_3. The high Na_2CO_3 concentration at these rim positions has resulted in removal of divalent bases from the exchange complex, an equivalent increase in exchangeable sodium, and high pH.

INTRODUCTION

Since the beginning of systematic investigations of salt-affected soils, much attention has been directed toward the formation and subsequent influences of Na_2CO_3. The deleterious effects of this salt on soils are generally understood, yet the specific conditions favouring its formation or occurrence have not been clearly defined in many cases. Na_2CO_3 may form in soils in five different ways, Kelley (1951):

1. Interaction between hydrolysing silicates and CO_2, whereby Ca, Mg, Na, and K are released and HCO_3 is formed. Upon evaporation of the resulting solution, calcium and magnesium carbonates are precipitated, while $NaHCO_3$ gradually increases in concentration, loses CO_2, and is converted to Na_2CO_3.

2. Reaction between neutral Na salts and $CaCO_3$.

3. Replacement of exchangeable Na by H or Ca from their respective carbonates.

Reproduced with permission from *Journal of Soil Science,* Vol. 14, 1963, p. 322-333. Published by the British Society of Soil Science, England.

4. Decay of Na-containing plant tissue.

5. Biological reduction of Na_2SO_4 to Na_2S and subsequent reaction between the Na_2S and carbonated water.

Gedroiz (1912) proposed that Na_2CO_3 is formed in soil by reaction between Na-clay and H_2CO_3 or $CaCO_3$, conclusions subsequently supported by Cummins and Kelley (1923) and Cummins (1926). Hilgard and de Sigmond (see Kelley, 1951) considered reactions between soluble Na salts and $CaCO_3$ as the principal way in which Na_2CO_3 is formed in soils.

Recent research has re-emphasized the importance of biological formation of Na_2CO_3. Antipov-Karataev (1953) has kept open the question of Na_2CO_3 formation by mechanisms other than those proposed above. In several instances, significant relationships between sulfate-bearing groundwaters and Na_2CO_3 enrichment in soils had been observed. Accordingly, Antipov-Karataev pointed out that soils often become alkaline under the combined influences of anaerobic environment, an abundance of readily oxidizable organic matter, and moderate concentrations of soluble Na_2SO_4.

A series of possible reactions under such conditions was suggested by Frank-Kamenetskiy (see Antipov-Karataev, 1953) from his studies of Na_2CO_3 formation in lakes. The reactions include (a) biological reduction of SO_4^{--} to S^{--}, (b) hydrolysis of S^{--} to form OH^- and H_2S, and (c) subsequent reaction between OH^- and CO_2, released from organic matter by biological oxidation, to form HCO_3^-.

Van der Spek (1950) gives in detail reactions involved in formation of sulfides in polders under anaerobic conditions. Anaerobic bacteria such as *Desulfovibrio desulfuricans,* using organic matter as a source of energy, appear to be responsible for sulfate reduction. Verner and Orlovskiy (Antipov-Karataev, 1953) demonstrated reduction of up to 50 percent of the sulfate in groundwaters, collected under a Wiesenboden sequence, when the water was kept anaerobic for 39 days and with Na-K-tartrate provided as an additional source of energy for the micro-organisms. Production of HCO_3 and reduction of SO_4 to H_2S was directly related to the organic matter content of the systems. Antipov-Karataev and Kader (1953) treated samples of chernozem and chernozemic solonetz with varying amounts of Na_2SO_4 and Ca-lactate and kept the systems in an anaerobic environment. After 95 days, 75 percent of the added SO_4 was reduced. Alkalinity (i.e. HCO_3^+ CO_3 concentrations) increased from less than 1 to 20 me per 100 g soil during the same period. Gracie et al. (1934) concluded that SO_4 reduction has been critical in the formation of Na_2CO_3 in certain soils of the Nile Delta.

A number of soils of the Sacramento Valley, California, in situations offering favorable conditions for biological generation of Na_2CO_3, do contain relatively high concentrations of Na_2CO_3. The present field and laboratory studies of these soils have revealed positive relationships between SO_4 bearing waters and strongly alkaline, Na-saturated soils having substantial Na_2CO_3 accumulations.

Salt-affected soils of the Sacramento Valley. The western portion of the Sacramento Valley of California, bounded on the east by the Sacramento River and on the west by the Coast Range Mountains, is a valley complex of dissected terraces, alluvial fans, and flood plain deposits. Ground-water levels are often very close to the surface along the lower margin of many of the fans, along drainageways dissecting the terraces, and in flood plain basins near the river.

Salt accumulation is favoured by the climate. Rain falls only in the winter and the annual total is less than 20 in. Hot and very dry summers favour evaporation and upward capillary movement of salt-bearing waters. The ground waters vary in concentration and composition of soluble salts. The salt-affected soils have markedly different chemical and morphological properties by reason of the kinds of associated salts as well as topographic positions.

Saline soils, influenced by highly saline groundwaters, occur along outer margins of alluvial fans which extend from the Coast Range to near the tidal marshes of the lower Sacramento River. These soils have strong solonetzic morphological features in some cases, but high alkalinity has not been observed in this area. A second group of soils, characterized by relatively high concentrations of Na_2CO_3 and corresponding high alkalinity, occupy basin positions along the lower Sacramento River flood plain and within drainageways dissecting alluvial fans and terraces adjacent to the basin. The most severe alkalinity, as expressed by high pH and Na_2CO_3 accumulation, develops in soils along the rims of drainageways that are subject to periodic inundation by drainage waters. The waters generally have low soluble salt contents and the drainageways support abundant vegetation. Na_2CO_3 may accumulate on the surface of some of these soils during the dry summer months. In others, Na_2CO_3 accumulates below the surface.

THE SOILS AND THEIR ENVIRONMENT

The soils chosen for this investigation occur along a drainageway dissecting a terrace between the Coast Range and the Sacramento River in Solano County. A general plan view of the area is shown in Fig. 1.

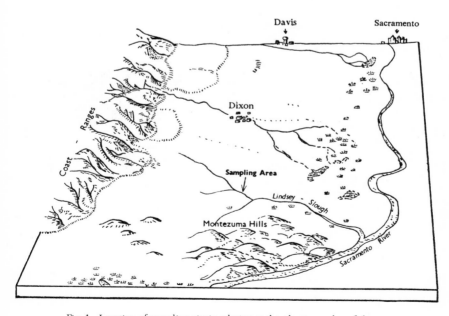

Fig. 1—Location of sampling site in relation to the physiography of the area.

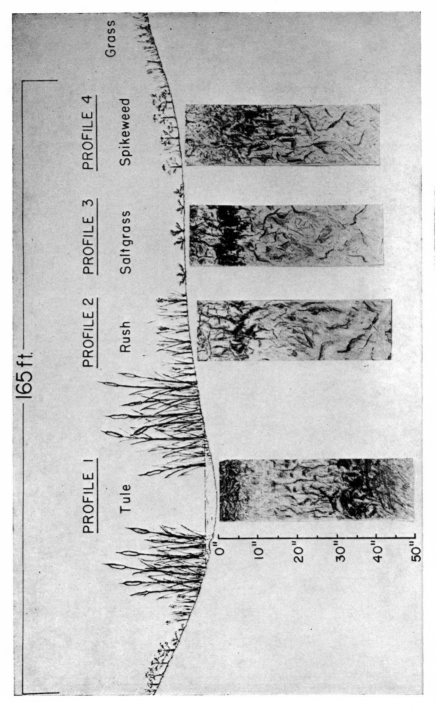

Fig. 2. Diagrammatic representation of the profile sequence in relation to the local topography.

L. D. WHITTIG AND P. JANITZKY—PLATE I

Terrace soils in this area show no evidence of salt accumulation to a depth of at least 6 ft. However, saline and sodic soils occur within and along the drainageways which carry surface and subsurface run off water during the rainy winter months. Most of the water is carried to the river but there are always pools of water remaining after the runoff. Although the surface water disappears during the dry summer months, the water table remains near the surface throughout the year. The abundance of subsoil water allows dense growth of tules, *Typha angustifolia,* in the basins of most of the drainageways. Remains of this plant are abundant in the basins to a depth of 6 ft below the soil surface. The water table is normally within 2 to 3 ft of the surface at the bottom of the basins during the summer, thus maintaining a permanent anaerobic environment.

The soils studied, shown in Plate I in their relative positions in the sequence, vary considerably in appearance and properties, presumably as a function of their position. Characteristics of the profiles are given in the following descriptions.

Profile I

Vegetation. Barren of vegetation at time of sampling. Numerous tule crowns remain at surface indicating that the soil has supported tules in the past.

Horizons

0—5 in.	Very dark grey (10 YR 3/1)[1] silt loam; very high organic matter content consisting of undecomposed and partially decomposed tules.
5—9 in.	Very dark grey-brown (2.5 Y 3/2) silt loam; massive with a few large pores; abundant organic matter; common, medium, distinct yellowish-brown mottles.
9—14 in.	Dark grey-brown (2.5 Y 4/2) silt loam; massive; less organic matter than above; many, fine, distinct yellowish-brown mottles.
14—18 in.	Very dark grey (5 Y 3/1) silty clay loam; weakly prismatic; many old roots and root channels but no undecomposed organic matter; common, fine, yellowish-brown mottles.
18—24 in.	Very dark grey-brown (2.5 Y 3/2) silty clay loam; weakly prismatic; many root channels but no undecomposed organic matter; common, fine, faint, yellowish-brown mottles.
24—27 in.	Dark olive-grey (5 Y 3/2) clay loam; weakly prismatic; numerous root channels; no undecomposed organic matter; common, medium, distinct yellowish-brown and few, medium, prominent dark reddish-brown mottles.
27—30 in.	Dark olive-grey (5 Y 3/2) clay loam; massive; contains few partly decomposed tule stems and roots; few bluish-black zones; very wet at time of sampling; few, medium, distinct yellowish-brown and dark reddish brown mottles and many, coarse, faint grey mottles.
30—40 in.	Black (10 YR 2/1) clay loam; massive; partially decomposed tule remains common; common, medium, distinct yellowish-

---

[1] All Munsell colour determinations were made on moist samples.

brown and few, medium, prominent bluish-grey mottles; upper boundary marks level of water table; H_2S smell strong upon exposure of the layer.

40+ in.   Very dark grey (5 Y 3/1) loamy sand; massive; few partially decomposed tule remains; strongly reduced but with few, fine, distinct yellowish-brown mottles.

Profile 2

Vegetation. Dense cover of rush *(Juncus* spp.)
Horizons

0—2 in.   Olive-grey (5 Y 5/2) clay loam; medium prismatic; abundant roots and pores.

2—8 in.   Dark grey (5 Y 4/1) loam; weak, medium prismatic; abundant roots of the rush vegetation; some organic staining.

8—13 in.   Dark grey (5 Y 4/1) clay loam; very weak, medium prismatic; roots abundant; very prominent dark grey organic staining covering over 80 percent of the surface.

13—15 in.   Olive-grey (5 Y 4/2) loam; massive; fine roots common; organic staining less common than above.

15—31 in.   Olive-grey (5 Y 5/2) sandy clay loam; massive; numerous roots.

31—56 in.   Same as horizon above but with high concentration of carbonates in a reticulate pattern throughout.

56+ in.   Same as horizon above but with carbonates more disseminated.

Profile 3

Vegetation. Dense cover of salt grass *(Distichlis spicata)* with scattered alkali heath *(Frankenia grandifolia).*
Horizons

0—2 in.   Dark greyish-brown (2.5 Y 4/2) clay loam; weakly platy; high organic matter content, roots abundant; few, weak, localized, dark grey, organic stains.

2—4 in.   Olive-grey (5 Y 5/2) loam; strong medium prismatic; higher in organic matter than below; few fine roots; few, weak localized, organic stains.

4—7 in.   Dark grey (5 Y 4/1) loam; strong, medium prismatic; organic staining same as above; few fine roots.

7—11 in.   Dark grey (5 Y 4/1) loam; strong medium prismatic; black organic staining over nearly entire surface, few fine roots, becoming less abundant near bottom of horizon; some salt crystallized on ped surfaces after exposure for a few hours.

11—16 in.   Olive-grey (5 Y 5/2) loam; weak coarse prismatic; few fine roots; zone of maximum salt accumulation as evidenced by salts crystallizing on surface after exposure for a few hours.

16—23 in.   Olive-grey (5 Y 5/2) sandy clay loam; massive; less salts and

| | less organic staining than above; few zones of Mn accumulation; few fine roots. |
| 23 + in. | Same as above except no organic staining and less evidence of soluble salts. |

Profile 4

Vegetation. Spikeweed *(Centromadia pungens)* predominant with a few aster.

Horizons

0—2 in.	Very dark grey-brown (2.5 Y 3/2) clay loam; weak granular; abundant medium and fine roots; few, fine, distinct yellowish-brown mottles.
2—7.5 in.	Very dark grey-brown (2.5 Y 3/2) loam; strong granular; abundant medium and fine roots; common, fine, distinct yellowish-brown mottles.
7.5—10.5 in.	Very dark grey-brown (2.5 Y 3/2) loam; massive; few fine roots, less than above; few patches stained with organic matter; common, coarse, distinct yellowish-brown and dark yellowish-brown mottles.
10.5—15 in.	Very dark grey-brown (2.5 Y 3/2) loam; weak medium prismatic; few fine roots; dark grey organic stains in localized zones throughout.
15—22 in.	Dark grey-brown (2.5 Y 4/2) loam; strong medium prismatic; very few roots; few localized patches of organic staining.
22—31 in.	Same as above.
31—41 in.	Olive-grey (5 Y 4/2) sandy clay loam; weak medium prismatic; few fine, distinct yellowish-brown mottles; few Mn concentrations.
41—56 in.	Same as above except for appearance of some carbonates in a reticulate pattern.

During the rainy season, all the profiles are inundated. Profiles 2, 3, and 4 emerge relatively soon after each rain and subsequent runoff. The water table drops during the summer season below 6 ft in all but profile 1 where it remains at about 30 in. The second profile remains moist below 15 in. during the summer, but water is below saturation for at least 6 ft of the surface.

METHODS OF ANALYSIS

Measurements of pH were made on saturated pastes. Soluble ions, obtained from saturation extracts, were analysed as prescribed by the U.S. Salinity Laboratory (1954); Na with a flame photometer, Ca as the oxalate, Mg by difference after versenate titration of Ca+Mg, CO_3 and HCO_3 by acid neutralization, SO_4 gravimetrically as $BaSO_4$, and Cl by titration with $AgNO_3$. Soluble ion concentrations were converted to me per 100 g soil. Electrical conductivities of the saturation extracts were determined.

Exchangeable cations, together with soluble cations, were extracted with 0.2 N $BaCl_2$, buffered to pH 8.2 with triethanolamine as outlined by Mehlich (1945).

and determined by methods used for soluble cations. Subtraction of soluble from total $BaCl_2$-extractable cations yielded exchangeable cation concentrations.

Cation exchange capacities were determined on samples after the $BaCl_2$ extraction. The barium was displaced with Na by washing the soil with N NaOAc in Buchner funnels. After excess NaOAc was removed with 95 percent ethanol exchangeable Na was displaced with N NH_4OAc and determined with the flame photometer. The ratios of soil to washing and extracting solutions were adjusted to conform to those used by Bower et al. (1952).

A measure of precipitated water-insoluble Ca+Mg was made by digesting samples in N NaOAc (adjusted to pH 5.0 with HOAc), a procedure described by Jackson (1956) for removal of carbonates. Water-soluble and exchangeable Ca+Mg, as determined separately, were subtracted from the total NaOAc-extractable Ca+Mg as determined by versenate titration.

The total sulfide content of one sample was determined. The sulfides were converted to H_2S by treatment of the sample with 3 N HCl. The H_2S was swept from the reaction vessel with N_2 and collected in saturated $Zn(OAc)_2$ solution. Sulfide was then determined iodometrically (Kolthoff and Sandell, 1947).

Table 1—Chemical Properties of the Soils Studied

Profile No.	Depth (in.)	E.C.* (mmhos/cm)	Soluble ions (me/100 g)						
			Na	Mg	Ca	CO_3	HCO_3	SO_4	Cl
1	0–5	3·30	0·7	1·5	1·3	..	0·5	2·0	1·0
	5–9	1·61	0·2	0·4	0·3	..	0·3	0·3	0·5
	9–14	1·14	0·2	0·3	0·2	..	0·2	0·2	0·6
	14–18	1·07	0·2	0·4	0·1	..	0·2	0·2	1·0
	18–24	1·25	0·2	0·4	0·1	..	0·2	0·2	0·9
	24–27	1·76	0·3	0·5	0·2	..	0·2	0·4	0·7
	27–30	1·84	0·3	0·7	0·2	..	0·2	0·8	0·6
	30–40	3·24	0·6	1·5	0·6	..	0·2	2·4	0·5
	40+	3·79	0·5	1·1	0·4	..	0·1	2·0	0·4
	Autumn ground water (me/l)		10·8	20·0	6·9	..	14·4	22·3	3·5
	Spring drainage water (me/l)		1·0	1·3		..	1·8	< 0·5	0·5
2	0–2	4·97	3·4	0·3	Tr	0·6	2·3	0·6	0·1
	2–8	5·66	4·1	0·1	..	1·0	2·1	0·6	0·1
	8–13	6·13	6·0	0·1	..	2·0	2·9	0·8	0·1
	13–15	5·44	5·0	0·1	..	2·7	1·6	0·7	0·2
	15–31	5·44	5·5	Tr	..	3·2	1·6	0·9	0·2
	31–56	2·65	2·9	0·1	..	0·7	1·1	0·9	0·3
	56+	1·20	0·9	0·1	..	0·2	0·5	0·2	0·3
3	0–2	6·49	2·3	0·8	0·4	..	0·4	0·2	0·2
	2–4	3·66	1·4	0·2	..	0·1	0·5	0·4	0·1
	4–7	5·63	2·7	0·1	..	0·4	1·0	1·5	0·1
	7–11	10·06	10·2	0·2	..	0·5	1·1	5·1	0·2
	11–16	9·49	8·4	0·1	..	0·5	0·7	4·5	0·2
	16–23	8·71	8·2	0·1	..	0·5	0·6	4·7	0·4
	23+	5·83	5·4	0·1	..	0·5	0·8	2·5	0·5
4	0–2	1·49	0·3	0·5	0·2	..	0·5	0·1	0·6
	2–7·5	0·54	0·1	0·2	..	..	0·2	Tr	0·1
	7·5–10·5	0·41	0·1	0·1	..	..	0·2	0·1	Tr
	10·5–15	0·86	0·2	0·3	..	Tr	0·4	0·1	Tr
	15–22	0·56	0·2	0·2	..	Tr	0·3	Tr	Tr
	22–31	1·30	0·6	0·2	..	0·1	0·4	0·2	0·4
	31–41	3·94	3·3	0·3	..	0·1	0·5	1·5	1·9
	41–56	2·54	2·3	0·2	..	0·1	0·4	1·4	1·1

* Electrical conductivity of saturation extract.

Total chloride content of plants associated with soils of the sequence was determined by the method of Johnson et al. (1958).

RESULTS

Results obtained during this investigation are presented in Tables 1 and 2.

Profile 1. The profile at the lowest position in the sequence has the lowest content of soluble salts (Table 1), varying between about 1 and 3.5 me/100 g. Soluble Mg is higher in concentration than either Na or Ca throughout the profile. Sulfate is the predominant anion in the surface 5 in. (2.0 me/100 g) and in the 31 to 40 in. depth (2.4 me/100 g). Soluble carbonate is absent and bicarbonate is relatively low in concentration (between 0.1 and 0.5 me/100 g) throughout. The electrical conductivity of extracts of all horizons was found to be less than 4 mmhos/cm. The only significant distributional difference in soluble salt content is a slight accumulation near the surface and again below about 30 in.

Distribution of exchangeable cations within the profile (Table 2) follows what one might predict from soluble cation concentrations. Exchangeable Mg and Ca predominate throughout, with Mg higher in most horizons than Ca. Exchangeable Na percentage (ESP) is relatively low in all horizons.

Table 2—pH, Precipitated Ca+Mg, and Exchangeable Cation Data

Profile No.	Depth (in.)	pH	Prec. Ca+Mg. (me/100 g)	Exchang. Cations (me/100 g) Na	Mg	Ca	Cation exch. capacity (me/100 g)	Exchangeable Na percentage
	0–5	5·2	23·2	0·9	9·6	11·8	36·9	2·4
	5–9	6·5	5·8	0·5	6·8	7·3	18·3	2·7
	9–14	7·8	28·8	0·4	6·9	7·9	16·5	2·4
	14–18	7·9	31·2	0·5	10·5	7·8	21·7	2·3
1	18–24	7·8	19·1	0·6	13·2	7·6	24·8	2·4
	24–27	7·7	13·7	0·5	12·1	6·1	21·3	2·4
	27–30	7·5	17·4	0·7	12·3	7·5	25·7	2·7
	30–40	6·9	13·9	0·7	11·9	7·1	27·4	2·6
	40+	6·2	6·0	0·5	6·2	2·8	13·9	3·6
	0–2	8·4	43·1	5·3	5·9	2·4	19·6	27·0
	2–8	9·7	25·0	10·2	1·3	0·1	14·8	68·9
	8–13	10·0	28·9	20·5	1·1	..	23·9	85·8
2	13–15	10·1	62·6	14·6	0·7	..	16·5	88·5
	15–31	10·0	102·9	15·4	6·8	..	17·0	90·6
	31–56	9·6	231·9	8·0	7·5	..	17·0	47·1
	56+	9·0	192·1	3·9	11·2	..	17·0	22·9
	0–2	5·9	11·3	2·2	7·0	7·0	27·0	8·1
	2–4	7·9	11·6	1·3	5·8	3·7	14·3	9·1
	4–7	8·9	15·3	5·6	4·6	1·3	12·2	45·9
3	7–11	9·4	43·3	18·5	4·9	..	25·6	72·3
	11–16	9·8	89·9	11·2	2·2	..	13·9	80·6
	16–23	9·7	69·0	11·4	2·2	..	14·3	79·7
	23+	9·7	83·8	13·3	1·5	..	15·6	85·3
	0–2	6·0	8·5	0·4	7·6	6·1	19·6	2·0
	2–7.5	6·6	12·9	0·4	9·1	5·6	18·7	2·1
	7.5–10·5	6·8	7·8	0·3	8·1	3·8	13·5	2·2
	10·5–15	8·0	25·3	0·4	10·0	3·8	14·8	2·8
4	15–22	8·6	47·2	0·5	10·2	0·8	11·3	4·4
	22–31	8·9	46·7	1·4	10·0	..	11·3	12·4
	31–41	8·9	77·2	5·4	11·1	..	16·5	32·7
	41–56	8·7	110·1	7·3	10·5	1·1	19·6	37·2

The pH fluctuates somewhat within the profile, with a minimum of 5.2 at the surface and a maximum of 7.8—7.9 between 9 and 24 in. in depth. The relatively low pH throughout the profile reflects the presence of neutral chloride and sulfate salts and the absence of appreciable exchangeable Na.

Active reduction of sulfates within the 30 to 40 in. zone is demonstrated by evolution of H_2S when the soil is exposed. The total sulfide content of this zone was found to be 235 mg per kg of soil.

Profile 2. The second profile in the sequence, which is inundated only during periods of heavy runoff in the winter months, is distinguished by relatively high concentrations of soluble Na, CO_3, and HCO_3 (Table 1), high ESP and high pH (Table 2).

Soluble Na, relatively concentrated throughout the profile, reaches a maximum of between 5 and 6 me/100 g in the 8 to 31 in. depth. Concomitant with high soluble Na, CO_3 and HCO_3 also show a pronounced accumulation. Sulfates are rather uniformly distributed throughout the profile whereas chlorides decrease in concentration nearer to the surface. Soluble salt concentration is reflected in the conductivity values which reach a maximum of 6.13 mmhos/cm in the 8 to 13 in. depth.

Excessive accumulation of carbonate and bicarbonate in the profile relative to SO_4 and Cl accounts for the high pH (up to 10.1) of the soil. The high concentrations of CO_3 and the resultant high alkalinity depress the concentration of soluble Ca and Mg. Consequently, the ESP is very high (up to 90.6 percent between 15 and 31 in. in depth) and exchangeable Ca and Mg percentages are correspondingly low.

Profile 3. Profile 3 has the highest concentration of soluble Na of any profile (Table 1) with a maximum of 10.2 me/100g between 7 and 11 in. in depth. In comparison with profile 2, however, soluble CO_3 and HCO_3 concentrations are lower and the soluble SO_4 concentration is considerably higher. Soluble Cl is low throughout and shows the same distribution pattern as in profile 2.

The ESP in profile 3 is lower than in the preceding profile (Table 2), although the soluble Na concentration is higher. The solubilities of Ca and Mg are not depressed as effectively since they exist largely as sulfates rather than as carbonates. This fact is substantiated by the increased concentration of soluble Mg in this profile. A greater competition is offered by Ca and Mg for the exchange sites.

Profile 4. The total soluble salt content of the highest profile in the sequence is low although there is an accumulation of Na_2SO_4 below 36 in. (Table 1). ESP, near 2 percent in the upper 15 in., increases markedly below 22 in. and attains a maximum of 37.2 percent below 41 in. (Table 2). Exchangeable Ca and Mg are more abundant in this profile than in profiles 2 and 3. In addition, exchangeable H is present in the upper 10.5 in. as shown by the pH (below 7.0) and the difference between the cation exchange capacity and the sum of the exchangeable bases.

DISCUSSION

The results demonstrate that $NaHCO_3$ and Na_2CO_3 may be formed in appreciable quantities in soils as a direct result of biological activity. Accumulation of these salts in specific zones is favoured by the topographic position of soils in the sequence studied.

The relatively low soluble salt content of profile 1 is a result of this profile being the lowest in the sequence. During the rainy season, profile 1 is completely and continuously inundated by surface and subsurface drainage waters of low soluble salt content. Under the influence of the drainage waters salts move downward in the profile.

The depression of soluble salts may be seen in the analytical values for the groundwater sampled in the autumn as well as those for the surface drainage water over the site the following spring (Table 1). The spring drainage water contained only 2.3 me/1 of soluble salts. The groundwater at this site, on the other hand, contained 40 me/1 of soluble salts in the preceding autumn. If the soluble salt content of the soil above the groundwater is converted into me/1 of soil solution, the salt concentration reaches a maximum of only about 20 me/1.

The slight accumulation of salts near the surface of profile 1 is probably due to deposition during evaporation of soil water rising by capillary movement during the hot, dry, summer months. Any marked accumulation of soluble salts in this soil is prevented, however, by the yearly inundation with relatively fresh drainage waters. Capillary conductivity in the upper 24 in. of the soil appears to be limited also as shown by a rather sharp boundary between moist and dry soil at this level in the autumn.

Accumulation of soluble salts in profiles 2 and 3 results from lateral and upward migration of these salts through the soil from the bottom of the drainageway to the slightly higher elevations along the adjacent slope. There are at least three factors which contribute to accumulation of salts in these profiles rather than in profile 1.

1. The effective depression of salts at the higher elevations is not so great as near the bottom of the drainageway because the amount of drainage water received and duration of inundation at the higher elevations are less.

2. Rate of evaporation from the soil surface at the bottom of the drainageway is restricted by the highly organic surface which acts as an effective mulch.

3. Vegetation is much more abundant at the higher elevations than in the bottom of the drainageway. The vegetation is effective in drawing water from the water table at the lower position throughout the summer months.

The relatively high concentrations of Na_2CO_3 and $NaHCO_3$ within profile 2 are related to biological transformations in profiles 1 and 2. Soil micro-organisms reduce sulfate to sulfide and ferric iron to the ferrous form under the combined influence of anaerobic environment and high organic matter content in the lower portions of profile 1 and in the upper 31 in. of profile 2. The micro-organisms in turn utilize organic matter present as a source of energy and release CO_2. Sulfides of calcium, magnesium, and sodium, upon hydrolysis, yield the corresponding hydroxides and H_2S. In the presence of ferrous iron and H_2S, insoluble FeS is formed, giving the soil its characteristic blue-black colour. The hydroxides of sodium and the alkaline earths react with the H_2CO_3 present to form the corresponding bicarbonates. The series of reactions which occur are represented as follows:

$$Na_2SO_4 + 8e^- \rightarrow Na_2S + 2O_2; \quad [CaSO_4 + 8e^- \rightarrow CaS + 2O_2];$$
$$Fe^{+++} + e^- \rightarrow Fe^{++}.$$

$$Na_2S + 2HOH \rightarrow H_2S + 2NaOH; \quad [CaS + 2HOH \rightarrow H_2S + Ca(OH)_2];$$
$$H_2S + Fe^{++} \rightarrow FeS + 2H^+.$$

$$NaOH + H_2CO_3 \rightarrow NaHCO_3 + HOH;$$
$$[Ca(OH)_2 + 2H_2CO_3 \rightarrow Ca(HCO_3)_2 + 2HOH].$$

Where the CO_2 pressure is relatively high (such as below 31 in. in profile 1), the alkaline earth bicarbonates are relatively stable, but they revert to insoluble carbonates as they migrate away from the zone of high CO_2 concentration. The Na HCO_3, on the other hand, remains soluble; it moves with the capillary water, and accumulates in profile 2 as the water evaporates from the soil surface or is used by the growing plants. Some loss of CO_2 from the $NaHCO_3$ occurs during evaporation of the solutions resulting in the formation of Na_2CO_3. The high alkalinity which develops causes organic matter to disperse and results in the characteristic staining of the soil.

The differential movement of $NaHCO_3$ and the alkaline earth bicarbonates is illustrated by data obtained, Na_2CO_3 and $NaHCO_3$ concentrations being at a maximum in profile 2 between 8 and 31 in. whereas precipitated Ca and Mg are at a maximum in the lower portion of the profile (Table 2). Calcium and magnesium bicarbonates, moving from the highly organic region of the drainageway bottom, precipitate as carbonates when they enter the lower portions of the profiles 2, 3, and 4, where the organic matter content is low and where, consequently, the CO_2 concentration is at a minimum. The build-up of precipitated Ca and Mg in these regions has, in all probability, been enhanced by displacement of these ions from the exchange complex by soluble Na entering the systems.

The possibility that the Na_2CO_3 has formed in these soils by reaction between NaCl or Na_2SO_4 and alkaline earth carbonates, a mechanism suggested by Hilgard, is not valid in this particular situation. If this mechanism were operative, the soluble Ca and Mg in profile 2 would be higher than recorded.

The relatively uniform distribution of sulfate in profile 2 suggests that sulfates are being reduced in this profile as well as in profile 1, thereby allowing little accumulation.

Profile 3 occupies a higher position in the sequence and the groundwater level is beneath the solum for a longer period during the year. In addition, the organic matter necessary for biological activity is low beneath the upper 4 in. of the profile. Conditions necessary for reduction of sulfates, therefore, are limited. Sulfates moving laterally into the soil are not so effectively reduced and carbonate and bicarbonate are not formed to any great extent. Hence, Na_2SO_4 rather than Na_2CO_3 and $NaHCO_3$, accumulates in this soil.

The chloride content of profiles 2 and 3 is less than in profile 1 and it is present in decreasing concentrations with proximity to the surface in each case. NaCl is more soluble than Na_2CO_3, $NaHCO_3$, or Na_2SO_4. The lack of accumulation of chloride in these profiles may be accounted for by its uptake and removal by the vegetation. Analysis of the vegetation over each of the profiles indicates that extraction of chloride by the plants is appreciable. The rush growing over profile 2 and the salt grass over profile 3 contain 1.72 percent and 1.58 percent chloride, respectively. The spikeweed over profile 4, on the other hand, contains only 0.46 percent chloride. Chlorides returned to the surface by this means could be washed from the system each year during the periods of flooding, thereby preventing accumulation in the soil.

Profile 4, situated at the highest position in the sequence, is sufficiently far removed from the basin of the drainageway so that soluble salts do not reach it in any quantity. In addition, leaching by drainage waters from the surrounding terrace during the late winter and spring keeps the salts that do reach the soil effectively

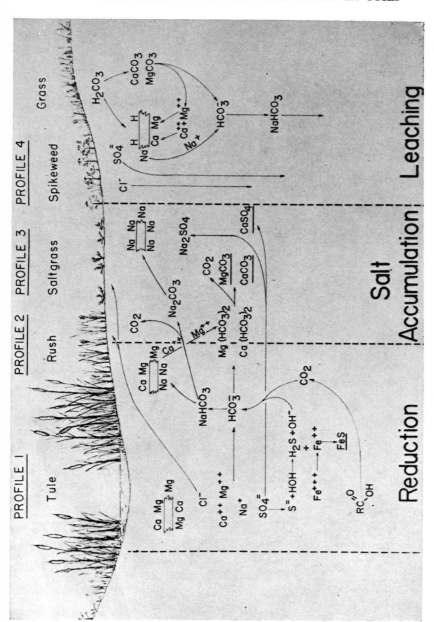

Fig. 3. Schematic representation of chemical transformations operative in the sequence.

L. D. WHITTIG AND P. JANITZKY—PLATE II

depressed to a lower position in the profile. Leaching has been sufficient to lower the pH below 7.0 in the upper 10½ in. of this profile. The lower pH of the soil increases the solubility of Ca and Mg, thereby enabling them to compete more actively for exchange sites.

Traces of organic staining in the 10 to 22 in. depth in profile 4 indicate that this soil has probably been subject to high pH and Na_2CO_3 accumulation some time in its past. It would appear that the organic staining is being obliterated in the present environment.

The chemical transformations and physical translocations responsible for Na_2CO_3 formation and accumulation in the sequence studied are summarized in Plate II. These are widespread in some areas of the Sacramento Valley, and are likely to be more widespread in the world than has yet been appreciated.

REFERENCES

1. Antipov-Karataev, I. N. 1953. Reclamation of solonetz soils in U.S.S.R. Acad. Sci., U.S.S.R.
2. Bower, C. A., Reitemeier, R. F., and Fireman, M. 1952. Exchangeable cation analysis of saline and alkali soils. Soil Sci. 73, 251—61.
3. Cummins, A. B. 1926. The solubility relationships of calcium carbonate with special reference to formation of sodium carbonate in soils. Ph.D. thesis, Univ. California.
4. .... and Kelley, W. P. 1923. The formation of sodium carbonate in soils. Calif. agric. expt. Sta. tech. paper No. 3.
5. Gedroiz, K. K. 1912. Colloidal chemistry as related to soil science. Zhur. Opyt. Agron. 13, 363—412.
6. Gracie, D. S., Rizk, M., Moukhtar, A., and Moustafa, A. H. I. 1934. The nature of soil deterioration in Egypt. Min. Agric. Egypt, Tech. and Sci. Ser. Bull. 148.
7. Jackson, M. L. 1956. Soil chemical analysis—advanced course. Publ. by author, Dept. Soils, Univ. Wisconsin.
8. Johnson, C. M., Huston, R. P., and Ozanne, P. G. 1958. Measurements of microgram amounts of chlorine in plant materials. J. Agric. Fd Chem. 6, 114—19.
9. Kelley, W. P. 1951. Alkali soils, their formation, properties, and reclamation. Reinhold Publ. Corp., N.Y.
10. Kolthoff, I. M., and Sandell, E. B. 1947. Textbook of quantitative inorganic analysis. The Macmillan Co., N.Y.
11. Mehlich, A. 1945. Effect of type of soil colloid on cation-adsorption capacity and on exchangeable hydrogen and calcium as measured by different methods. Soil Sci. 60, 289—304.
12. U.S. Salinity Laboratory Staff. 1954. Diagnosis and improvement of saline and alkali soils. USDA Handbook 60.
13. Van der Spek, J. 1950. Katteklei. Land. Boden. Inst. T.N.O., Groningen, Netherlands.

(Received 30 November 1962)

Part V

SOME CONCEPTS
IN SOIL CLASSIFICATION

BASIC PRINCIPLES OF SOIL CLASSIFICATION

Marlin G. Cline [1]

The purpose of any classification is so to organize our knowledge that the properties of objects may be remembered and their relationships may be understood most easily *for a specific objective.* The process involves formation of classes by grouping the objects on the basis of their common properties. In any system of classification, groups about which the greatest number, most precise, and most important statements can be made *for the objective* serve the purpose best. As the things important for one objective are seldom important for another, a single system will rarely serve two objectives equally well.

CLASSES

The smallest natural body that can be defined as a thing complete in itself is an *individual.* All the individuals of a natural phenomenon, collectively, are a *population.* Plants, animals, or soils, for example, are populations, each consisting of many individuals. The individuals of a population have many common properties, but the variation within a population is so great that man is unable to see similarities and understand relationships among individuals in the disorderly arrangement in which he finds them. He attempts to make the variation that he finds in nature orderly for his convenience by framing classes—by grouping individuals that are alike in selected characteristics. A *class* is a group of individuals, or of other classes, similar in selected properties and distinguished from all other classes of the same population by differences in these properties.

Classes as Segments of a Population

There is diversity in the degree of difference among classes. Among living things, for example, plants as a class are so unlike animals as a class that one thinks of them as separated by an insurmountable barrier of differences. Amoebae as a class and algae as a class are not so different; yet one is an animal and the other a plant. Similar situations may be found within every population. If one could place all the individuals in a row ranked from highest to lowest value of one property, the series formed would pass by almost imperceptible stages from one extreme of the property to the other. Any two adjacent individuals would be much alike; the two end mem-

---

[1] Marlin G. Cline is Professor of Soil Science, New York State College of Agriculture, Cornell University, Ithaca.

Reproduced with permission from *Soil Science,* Vol. 67, 1949, p. 81-91. Copyright © 1949, The Williams and Wilkins Company, Baltimore, Maryland 21202, USA.

bers would be vastly different. Classes based on that property would be segments of a continuous series. The end individual of one class would be more like the adjacent end member of the next class than like an individual at the other extreme of the same class. Classes of natural objects are not separated by insurmountable barriers; they grade by small steps into other classes.

The Modal Individual

Within every class is a central core or nucleus to which the individual members are related in varying degrees. The mean, the median, and the mode as used in statistics, for example, are estimates of the central nucleus of a class. A class of natural objects may be considered in terms of a frequency distribution according to value of a selected property. Commonly, within some small increment of value of that property, the frequency of occurrence of individuals is a maximum. This is the modal value of the property which defines the central nucleus of the class—the modal individual. The definition of the modal individual may be based on observed properties of a real individual, or it may be estimated by a statistic representing a hypothetical individual and derived from the observed properties of a sample of the class.

One may visualize a class as a group of individuals tied by bonds of varying strength to a central nucleus. At the center is the modal individual in which the modal properties of the class are typified. In the immediate vicinity are many individuals held by bonds of similarity so strong that no doubt can exist as to their relationship. At the margins of the group, however, are many individuals less strongly held by resemblance but more strongly held by similarity to this modal individual than to that of any other class. A class is a group of individuals bound from within, not circumscribed from without. The test of proper placement of any marginal individual is its relative degree of similarity to the modal individuals of different classes.

Characteristics of Classes

So far, variation in only a single property has been considered, but the same concepts and principles apply when two or more characteristics vary at the same time. Their application, however, depends upon an understanding of the different kinds of characteristics of classes.

Some property must be chosen as the basis of grouping. Individuals that are alike in that characteristic are placed in the same group; those that are unlike are placed in different groups. The property chosen as the basis of grouping is called the *differentiating characteristic.*[2] It serves to differentiate among classes; its mean value within each class defines the modal individual of that group. The test of any grouping is the number, precision, and importance of statements that can be made about each class for the objective. If the classes are well formed, a precise statement about the differentiating characteristic for each class should always be possible.

---

[2] The term is used here in a less restricted sense than that defined by Mill (5). As Mill used the term, it applied only to distinctions used to differentiate between greatly contrasting populations, such as plants and animals.

If the basis of grouping is good, the differentiating characteristic should be associated with a number of covarying properties. Texture, for example, is the differentiating characteristic of soil types within a soil series. A number of other properties, such as cation-exchange capacity of the inorganic fraction and water held at various tensions, change as texture changes. A precise statement can be made about these *accessory characteristics* as well as about texture in the soil type. Through accessory characteristics one multiplies the number of statements about each class and increases the significance of the classes formed. A well-conceived grouping is based upon that differentiating characteristic that (a) is itself important for the objective and (b) carries the greatest possible number of covarying accessory characteristics that are also important for the objective.

Those properties of the individuals of a class that vary independently of the basis of grouping are called *accidental characteristics*. They are not related to the differentiating characteristic, and no statement can be made about them for the class as a whole. Slope, for example, may vary independently of soil texture and is an accidental characteristic in classes based on texture.

Now consider the concept of a class as a group the members of which are ranged about a modal individual when many properties are variables. The modal individual may be defined precisely not only in terms of a value of the differentiating characteristic but also in terms of values of all its accessory characteristics. The class as a whole can be defined precisely in terms of (a) values both of the differentiating and of the accessory characteristics of the modal individual and (b) the respective deviations from those values within the range of the class. These should be the components of precise definition of classes. The mean values for both differentiating and accessory characteristics derived from a sample of the class define the modal individual. Their standard deviations define the variability of the class. The tests of statistical significance are measures of whether the differences between classes are real or only apparent.

Accessory characteristics grade into properties that are purely accidental. Some attributes are almost always accessory but in a few individuals bear no relationship to the differentiating characteristic. The dark color of the A_1 horizon of soils, for example, is usually associated with high organic matter, but in the "Regur" soils of the tropics it is not. Such properties cannot properly be specified in the definition of a class, but they can and should be described.

MULTIPLE CATEGORY SYSTEMS

When a population is so diverse that any single grouping fails to show the relationships desired, the classes formed may be subdivided to show more relationships. This is illustrated in table 1. A *category* in such a system is a series of classes, collectively, formed by differentiation within a population on the basis of a single set of criteria. A category must include all individuals of the population; groups within a category are classes at a defined *level of abstraction.* Classes of category 2 in table 1 consist of groups of classes of category 1. Both include all individuals of the population. The technical meaning of the term *category* in classification is not to be confused with its common use as synonymous with *class.*

Table 1—A simple two-category system of classification of surface soils

CATEGORY	DIFFERENTIATING CHARACTERISTIC	CLASSES			
2	Color value	Light		Dark	
1	Reaction	Acid	Alkaline	Acid	Alkaline

Categorical Rank and Homogeneity of Classes

The number of statements about classes in a multiple-category system increases in going from higher to lower categories. In table 1, the classes of category 2 are differentiated on the basis of color values. Statements about either of the two classes are limited to color and associated accessory characteristics. Reaction is purely an accidental characteristic in this category, and no statement can be made about it. This category by itself is a simple single-category classification. In category 1. however, each class of category 2 is subdivided on the basis of reaction. Each of these four classes may be defined in terms of (a) the differentiating *and* accessory characteristics of category 2, *plus* (b) the differentiating property of category 1, *and* all of its accessory characteristics. In any multiple-category system, regardless of the number of categories, the properties that are homogeneous in a given class consist of the accumulated differentiating and accessory characteristics of that category and all categories above it. The greatest number of statements can be made about classes of the lowest category; the least number of statements, about units of the highest category. Categories in which few differentiating and accessory characteristics have accumulated are at a high *level of abstraction* and have high *categorical rank;* those in which many have accumulated are at a low level of abstraction and have low categorical rank. Homogeneity of classes increases with decrease of abstraction and categorical rank.

Dependence of Classification Systems on State of Knowledge

When viewed in the opposite perspective. each successively higher category is a grouping of classes of the preceding lower category. Classes of a lower category are treated as individuals and grouped into classes of a higher category to show relationships among them.

The units of a lower category are not groups formed by applying a single differentiating characteristic to the entire population. They are homogeneous with respect not only to the differentiating property of that category but also to all characteristics used to differentiate in all higher categories. Formation of classes at a low categorical level in their final form, therefore, presupposes knowledge of the population adequate to complete all categories above it. *As the body of knowledge about any phenomenon increases, therefore, attempts to effect a complete natural system of classification must pass through a series of approximations.* The degree of improvement of each over its predecessor is in proportion to the increment of accumulated knowledge and its effects in basic concepts.

NATURAL AND TECHNICAL SYSTEMS

Although there are as many "best" systems of classification as there are objectives for grouping, not all are equally significant in organizing man's knowledge. The lowest category of the natural classification is a prerequisite of all other groupings.

In a natural classification, one classifies in such a way that the name of each class will bring to mind many characteristics and will fix each group mentally in relation to all others. The objective is to show relationships in the greatest number and most important properties. In the process, however, one gathers into classes of the lowest category the multitude of individual objects which are impossible of separate investigation by reason of sheer numbers. It has been shown that these classes are homogeneous with respect to the accumulated and differentiating and accessory characteristics of all categories of the system. They are homogeneous within the limits of existing knowledge about the properties of the population and about the significance of differences within it. The natural classification, therefore, performs the extremely important function of organizing, naming, and defining the classes that are the basic units used (a) to identify the sample individuals that are the objects of research, (b) to organize the date of research for discovering relationships within the population, (c) to formulate generalizations about the population from these relationships, and (d) to apply these generalizations to specific cases that have not been studied directly. No other grouping provides such units; it is this fact that sets the natural classification apart from all other groupings.

Given the classes of the lowest category of the natural classification, one can group them for a great variety of technical purposes, as illustrated by Orvedal and Edwards (6). One may group soil classes of the lowest category, for example, to select a sample representative of specified soil conditions for research on phosphorus fixation, to discover genetic relationships, or to apply engineering principles in highway construction. These are *techincal groupings,* each for a limited objective, each with a special bias dictated by the objective. Each must be based on those few properties that are most significant for the objective. Although only a few properties need be homogeneous in the classes that are grouped for any one objective, only the classes of the lowest category of the natural classification provide units that are homogeneous with respect to the variety of properties important for the large number of objectives for which technical groupings are made.

PRINCIPLES OF DIFFERENTIATION

As They Affect Classes

1. *A differentiating characteristic must be important for the objective.*

The statements about each class are confined to (a) the differentiating characteristics, (b) their accessory characteristics, or (c) interpretations of both. A grouping based on a property that is not important for the objective leads to classes about which the statements possible are not the most numerous or the most important for the purpose of grouping. In spite of this fact, attempts to interpret a grouping made for one purpose in terms of another objective are common. The category of soil series, for example, is a grouping purely to show similarities in properties of the soil profile, but one sees repeated attempts to define suitability of an entire soil series for land use. The bases of grouping soils into series do not provide units homogenous in all properties important for land use; the classes may range rather widely in such features as slope, degree of erosion, stoniness, and texture. A technical grouping of soil types and phases on the basis of an interpretation of all factors important in land use is required for this objective.

2. A differentiating characteristic must be a property of the things classified or a direct interpretation for the objective.

If the grouping is a natural classification, the bases must be properties of the things classified. The objective is to see similarities and understand relationships among those properties; to classify on the basis of any other factor is to conceal those similarities and relationships. If soils were to be classified on the basis of factors of soil formation, for example, similarities and relationships among properties would be brought out only to the extent that the cause and effect relationships between factors of soil genesis and soil properties are known. The system formed would conceal relationships as yet unknown. A technical grouping of areas to show known relationships of soil genesis or to discover new ones, however, may well be based on those factors for correlation with properties of natural soil groups. In many technical groupings, various interpretations of characteristics may serve the objective best. A grouping of soils according to lime requirement might be based on an interpretation of the aggregate of known soil characteristics, including such measurable properties as pH and cation-exchange capacity of the various horizons. The grouping might be based on direct experimental evidence if that were available.

3. The differentiating characteristic should carry as many accessory properties as possible for the objective.

In the grouping in table 1, color was purposely chosen to differentiate in category 2 as a property that carries few accessory attributes. What can one say about dark-colored surface soils beyond the fact that they are dark, if he considers that such a group would include Chernozem, Solenetz, "Regur," Half-Bog, and varieties in which color was inherited from the parent material? Choice of a differentiating characteristic that carries many covarying properties, like reaction in category 2, increases the number of statements about each class and, therefore, the usefulness of the grouping.

4. The class interval of a differentiating characteristic must provide classes homogeneous for the objective.

When differentiation is based upon degree of expression of an attribute, the limiting value of that property between classes of a continuous series may be placed arbitrarily at any point in the series. Not all points within such a series are equally pertinent for a given objective, however, and the establishment of the class interval for the most useful grouping is not arbitrary. Accessory characteristics may not be straight-line functions of the differentiating property, and the best limits of classes for a given objective may be largely determined by them. The graph of percentage base saturation against pH, for example, is a characteristic titration curve. In northeastern United States many mineral soils are roughly 30 percent base-saturated at pH 5.0; 80 percent, at pH 6.0; and 95 percent at pH 7.0. Thus a significant break in the curve occurs near pH 6.0; that pH is also associated with important changes in the solubility of iron, aluminum, and phosphorus. Soil classification must rely on the data of observation and experiment for establishment of the significant limiting values of classes. The points of greatest significance may vary not only among different objectives but also among different soils for the same objective.

As They Affect Relationships Among Categories

1. *The differentiating characteristic must classify all individuals in any single population.*

Nikiforoff[3] calls this the "principle of wholeness of taxonomic categories." Every category must include all existing individuals of the population; therefore, the differentiating characteristic of each category must apply to all individuals, or some will remain unclassified. Violation of this principle was a serious error in Marbut's Classification of soils in 1935 (4); his "family groups," which were azonal and intrazonal soils, were not classified by the criteria used in higher categories. This does not mean that a system of classification must immediately provide a pigeonhole for every individual in every category. It must provide for expansion in the number of classes based on a given differentiating property to accomodate new individuals as they are discovered. (In many cases one class may be defined as the zero degree of the differentiating characteristic.)

2. *Greatly different "kingdoms" require different differentiating characteristics at the same level of abstraction.*

This principle rests upon a concept of degrees of difference among groups of things at different levels of abstraction. All living things might be considered a unit separate and distinct from all things that do not possess life. Each is a segment of the universe and might conceivably be included in one master natural scheme of classification. It would be futile, however, to attempt to differentiate within both groups on the basis of the same property; they have too few important things in common. All living matter, in turn, may be classified into two kindgoms, plants and animals, each of which is a distinct unit at a lower level of abstraction. Again

---

[3] The author is indebted to C. C. Nikiforoff for many of the ideas expressed in this paper, particularly for the original expression of the principles of "wholeness of taxonomic categories" and "ceiling of independence of differentiating characteristics."

it would be futile to attempt to differentiate within both on the basis of a single property. Such contrasting populations are differences in "kind," as Mill used the term (5), and require classification in different systems[4] using different criteria for differentiation at the same level of abstraction. Within the natural phenomenon called "soils," there may be populations that have so few important common properties that a single differentiating characteristic at a given level of abstraction would not frame the important classes in each. The breech between organic and inorganic soils may be of that order of magnitude.

3. *All classes of the same category of a single population should be based on the same characteristics.*

This is a corollary of the "principles of wholeness of taxonomic categories," but it needs some explanation in the light of the preceding concept. The objective of classification is accomplished by arranging the individuals in an orderly manner commensurate with order as conceived in the mind. To differentiate on different properties at the same categorical level complicates the problem of visualizing relationships. It should be resorted to only when two kinds of things have so little in common that the important properties of one do not occur in the other. At some level of abstraction, differences no longer outweigh common properties; at that and all lower levels the "principle of wholeness of taxonomic categories" applies.

4. *A differentiating characteristic in one category must not separate like things in a lower category.*

Every characteristic has a *ceiling of independence* above which it cannot be used to differentiate without separating like things in categories below it. This is illustrated in table 1, where the objective is to show the most important similarities related to color value and reaction. Color value, a property with few accessory characteristics, is used at the highest categorical level. When each of the two classes based on color is subdivided on the basis of reaction in category 1, four classes are formed. Two of those classes are acid and two are alkaline. In no category in the system are all acid soils segregated in one group and all alkaline soils in another. Reaction is associated with many accessory characteristics that make similarities in that property more significant than similarities in color value, but individuals of like reaction are separated by differentiation on the basis of color at a higher level. Differentiation at a high categorical level on any basis separates on that same basis throughout all lower categories; consequently, the properties used to differentiate at high levels of generalization must be more important for the objective than those used at lower levels. The importance of a differentiating characteristic must be commensurate with the level of abstraction at which it is used. Failure to observe this principle is a major error in Shaw's (7) classification of soils, in which origin of parent material as a differentiating characteristic in a high category separates like profiles throughout all lower categories.

---

[4] The term "system of classification" is restricted in this article to those schemes in which a single differentiating characteristic is used throughout the population in any single category. Two or more such systems for distinctly different populations may be tied together by a common property in a more inclusive scheme.

CLASSIFICATION OF SOILS

The Soil as a Population

The dimensions of the ultimate individual of the soil population are fixed vertically by the thickness of the soil profile and horizontally by the practical limits of space required for its observation. Vertically, the soil unit must extend from the surface into the parent material; any lesser depth would divide the complete natural body. Horizontally, the limits are not sharply defined; the unit must extend in two directions far enough to allow sampling and accurate determination of the properties that can be observed in the field. It must be large enough to permit observation of relationships of horizons to the rooting of plants. An almost infinite number of these individuals make up the population—the soils of the world.

It is impractical, however, to attempt to deal with all these small units in any system of classification or in most practical problems involving use of the land. The range of the properties of each is too narrow to be significant; their numbers are too great to allow individual treatment; the area represented is too small to serve as a practical land unit in most operations. These individuals, however, are the sampling units upon which must depend definition of soil of larger areas feasible of treatment for most problems. These more inclusive units, as typified by the soil type or phase, may be considered classes of the lowest category of soil classification. They are more than a categorical grouping of individuals, however, because their variation is fixed partly by the geographic association of the ultimate individuals in areas large enough to be feasible of treatment. The definition of these classes is a problem in sampling to determine the characteristics of the modal profile and the deviations from it. Just as in the definition of a species of plants, no attempt is made to study all individuals and group them into a class of the lowest category. A sample is drawn, and from it are estimated the properties of the class.

Sources of Criteria

For the most part, the criteria used to classify are those that can be observed or determined rapidly by simple tests in the field. This is inevitable because the practical limitations imposed by requirements of an adequate sample (1) of such a variable population preclude laboratory determinations as criteria for application on an areal basis. Consequently, until techniques are developed that will allow rapid chemical determinations in the field, one should expect homogeneity of chemical properties of soil units only to the extent that they are accessory to the observable characteristics used to classify in the field.

One is not confined to direct observation, however, in choosing criteria or their class intervals. Controlled experiments establish relationships that enable selection of those criteria to which many properties that cannot be observed are accessory. They not only indicate important criteria but also indicate significant class intervals.

For every controlled experiment there are thousands of natural experiments from which criteria of properties that cannot be observed readily may be deduced. Data from these experiments are not in orderly arrangement; they must be collected in many places, classified, and applied to soils by the correlation methods of science. The correlation of natural vegetation types with soil conditions, for example, is a principle criterion for the placement of soil boundaries. The behavior of crops under known management may indicate soil properties that cannot be observed easily.

Enough is known about soil formation to establish broad factors of the process and some of their effects. We expect a difference between two soils if any one of the factors varies. A change in one of the factors is a warning to look at the soil again if no differences have been observed. Genetic factors, though not criteria of classification in themselves, are indexes to soil properties that are criteria.

Criteria of Classification

Soil classification is passing through a series of approximations in which the system is being built from the lowest category upward by a process of reducing homogenity in each successively higher category. If our knowledge were complete, we should be able to choose the differentiating characteristic of each category, but at present not only must we establish the importance of many known relationships but undoubtedly we are still unaware of many relationships that will be discovered. Our choice of differentiating characteristics in the higher categories is limited by our knowledge not only of soil properties but also of relationships among soil properties. As a direct result of requirements imposed by the "principle of a ceiling of independence of differentiating characteristics," the limitations imposed by lack of knowledge are greater, the higher the level of generalization in the system. Let us examine the possible criteria at our disposal.

No one has yet improved appreciably upon the following list of criteria proposed by Marbut (3), for differentiation among soils at the level of the soil type:

1. Number of horizons in the soil profile.
2. Color of the various horizons, with special emphasis on the surface one or two.
3. Texture of the horizons.
4. Structure of the horizons.
5. Relative arrangement of the horizons.
6. Chemical composition of the horizons.
7. Thickness of the horizons.
8. Thickness of the true soil.
9. Character of the soil material.
10. Geology of the soil material.

Each of the 10 factors listed varies narrowly in a soil type within the limitations of precision of their measurement. Long experience with the soil type has proved that it, as defined, is a unit adequately homogeneous for most of the practical problems of the land so far as the soil profile is concerned. No better unit has been suggested at the categorical level. Cases of inadequate homogeneity are the result either of lack of precise application of one or more of the criteria listed or of the importance of features other than characteristics of the profile, such as slope or degree of erosion. Lack of precision is not a fault of the system but of its application; techniques for feasible evaluation of chemical properties, for example, are not adequate. Such characteristics as slope are differentiated in the soil phase or its equivalent in practical problems. One must conclude, therefore, that Marbut's criteria provide a workable basis for classification of soil profiles in the lowest category; when properly applied, they provide units about which the number, precision, and importance of statements are adequate for practical problems in soils.

Now consider the implications of the "principle of accumulating differentia" in relation to the proposition that the properties listed by Marbut are adequate for differentiation at the level of the soil type. All of those properites except the one used to differentiate soil types within a soil series must be accumulated from the differentiating and accessory characteristics of higher categories. The list undoubtedly is not a complete accumulation of all those characteristics, but each property in the list must be either differentiating at a higher level or accessory to a property that is differentiating. It would be sheer accident if any property could be found to differentiate at higher categorical levels that is not either (a) a characteristic listed by Marbut, or (b) a characteristic to which one of the properties listed by Marbut is accessory.

The properties listed by Marbut were not intended as bases of differentiation in higher categories, and careful consideration will show that no single characteristic listed could be used at a level higher than one category above the soil series without exceeding its ceiling of independence. Its use would separate like things in lower categories and defeat the objective of a natural classification. One must conclude, therefore, that these properties are accessory characteristics of those attributes whose ceilings of independence are high enough to justify their use in the higher categories. This is one important reason why the "formula" type of system in which individual soil properties are accumulated in a symbol in some specified order is not a natural classification.

The first step in the selection of differentiating characteristics of higher categories, therefore, is to define the characteristics to which the properties listed by Marbut are accessory. Most of those listed are characteristics of individual horizons. All of them, collectively, plus inferences from them, however, define the whole soil, not only in terms of all of its horizons but also in terms of relationships among horizons. It is to this definition of the soil type that one must turn for criteria whose ceilings of independence permit their use at high categorical levels. A Podzol, for example, is not just any soil with a bleached horizon; it is a complete natural body definable in terms of all of its horizons *and the relationships among them.*

At a given level of abstraction, for example, the kind and sequence of horizons defines a specific "kind of profile." This is a characteristic of the whole soil and has a ceiling of independence far above that of soil texture. The degree of expression of those horizons is also a property of the whole soil; its ceiling of independence is obviously below that of "kind of profile" but still above that of soil texture. Kind of parent material is reflected throughout the whole soil; its ceiling of independence is below that of degree of expression of horizons but slightly above that of soil texture —in fact, it is roughly commensurate with the level of abstraction of the soil series as used at present. It is from properties such as these that the criteria for differentiation in the various categories above the soil type must come. Their definition is controlled by the state of knowledge about specific soil characteristics and especially about relationships among horizons. We may expect many approximations before knowledge will be adequate to frame, in final form, the generalizations necessary for definition of appropriate criteria at the various categorical levels.

REFERENCES

1. Cline, M. G. 1944 Principles of soil sampling Soil Sci. 58: 275–287.
2. Kellogg, C. E. 1937 Soil Survey manual. U.S. Dept. Agr. Misc. Pub. 274.
3. Marbut, C. F. 1922 Soil classification. Life and Work of C. F. Marbut, p. 85–94. Artcraft Press, Columbia, Missouri.
4. .... 1935 Atlas of American Agriculture, Part III. Soils of the United States. U.S. Government Printing Office, Washington, D. C.
5. Mill, J. S. 1874 A System of Logic, ed. 8, vols. I and II. New York.
6. Orvedal, A. C., and Edwards, M. J. 1942 General principles of technical grouping of soils. Soil Sci. Soc. Amer. Proc. (1941) 6: 386–391.
7. Shaw, C. F. 1947 The basis of classification and key to the soils of California. First Internatl. Cong. Soil Sci. Proc. and Papers. Comm. V:65–103.

GENERAL CONSIDERATIONS ON THE PROBLEM OF
SOIL CLASSIFICATION

G. Manil

(Laboratoire de Pedologie, Gembloux, Belgium)

I. INTRODUCTION

At the 6th International Congress of Soil Science, held in Paris in 1956, I submitted a synthesis of the general problem of soil classification. Taking that report as a starting-point I now wish to submit for discussion some general considerations suggested by various classification schemes presented at or before the Congress. It seems worth while trying to elucidate a few definite issues, while excluding, if possible once for all, several false or insoluble problems which sometimes still result from lack of mutual understanding. Experience has indeed shown that specialists are often very near agreement when they have succeeded in restricting the discussion to a limited number of issues. It seems no mere wishful thinking to say that even now international agreement is quite possible on the fundamental aspects of the problem of soil classification.

II. THE PROBLEM OF GENERAL CLASSIFICATION

A. Preliminaries

(a) Definition of the subject. As Stewart (1954) and Stephens (1954) have pointed out, there are three groups of problems to be solved, (i) definition, (ii) nomenclature, (iii) classification. But before attempting an examination of specific issues of definition, it is necessary in my opinion to reach agreement on a number of general principles of classification itself so as to put an end to the confusion and misunderstanding that sometimes still prevail among pedologists.

(b) Definition of the term 'classification'. As is usually understood, a *classification* constitutes a co-ordinated, synthetic and, if possible, natural system of grouping different objects which are generally classed at several levels of generalization. As a matter of fact, confusion still exists, especially in oral discussion, between *method of classification* and *methods of classing*. Classing is accidental and corresponds in principle to a well-defined practical purpose. It may be merely geographical, as in the case of *a. sociation*, in the commonly accepted meaning of the word. For practical reasons of land use or soil conservation, soils which are adjacent to one another in a geographical unit must sometimes be grouped together technically, although

Reproduced with permission from *Journal of Soil Science*, Vol. 10, 1959, p. 5-13.
Published by the British Society of Soil Science, England.

they may be placed far apart in a proper classification. The best-known association, the *catena*, corresponds to topographic juxtaposition. The necessity for such a method of grouping also appears when printing a pedological map, even on a large scale. It is not generally possible to reproduce in all particulars all the soil formations actually identified in the field.

Another method of classing that is often used for utilitarian and specific purposes is the division into *phases*. Phases are used in large-scale mapping, when it is worth while giving prominence to some well-defined ecological or technological factors which can often be expressed by 'single values' such as useful depth of soil, content of nutrient elements, pH, humus content, slope, &c. The phases may correspond to natural division into types, series, or other units of classification; but they may also be spread over several such units.

In spite of the necessity to make use of such phases for some practical purpose, it is not possible to include all imaginable phases in a complete system of classification. If this conclusion is accepted, a frequent cause of argument and misunderstanding will have been ruled out. In other words, it must be acknowledged that the best system of classification will never be able to give all the information necessary for all practical purposes. In addition to a general system of classification, with all its usefulness, it is necessary to allow in some cases for another method of classing soils. In botany, for instance, it is not possible to include in one and the same systematization the classification by anatomical and physiological characteristics and the utilitarian properties of plants.

B. General Notes on the Problem of Soil Classification

(a) To begin with, why do several kinds of soil classification exist, whereas there is, in general, international agreement on botanical, zoological, mineralogical, &c., classifications?

This side of the problem has already been the object of numerous comments which amount to saying that *soil is a multi-dimensional system in space and time;* as Bergson would have said, the actual description of a given soil appears to us with all the static quality of a picture of a moving object. Accordingly, soil cannot be defined with absolute rigour. At any level of generalization whatever, a definition of it is always partly imperfect and arbitrary, like the definition of all complex things, such as works of art. Moreover, the terms that we use to describe a specific pedological formation can never be identified with pure ideas, with abstractions. It must be admitted as a matter of fact that lecture-room discussions slip all too easily into abstractions instead of dealing with actual soils.

In practice, however, the pedologist still often comes up against the following difficulties:

1. The technical (often merely financial) impossibility of determining all the important properties of known soils with adequate accuracy. It is enough only to mention the hydrological properties of soils.
2. The scale and purpose of the work, about which more will be said later.
3. The difference of method and accuracy in the description of various characteristics of soil. Even if accurate means of determining definite properties of soil

are used, it is none the less true that different authors are apt to be at variance in setting limits between two closely related soils. Such discordance is likely to be still more marked if the descriptions are purely qualitative.

4. Differences in frame of mind according to race and form of civilization. Some types of culture favour reasoning from ideas to facts, others from facts to ideas. It should not be overlooked, as Leeper (1956) points out, that it is sometimes possible to detect behind arguments issues of national, political, or racial prestige.

(b) *'Natural' or 'universal' classifications.* When discussions are held there appears to be a misunderstanding which it is desirable to clear up. Care must be taken to distinguish between *natural classifications* and classifications founded on natural characteristics, often immediately perceptible. As several colleagues have pointed out, the former should command 'natural', unquestionable recognition by the very nature of the things it aims at classifying. Most workers are convinced that such a system is not even conceivable, and would set more realistic bounds to their ambitions, hoping, however, that in the not too distant future pedologists would agree on a *universal classification,* i.e. universally accepted after discussion and mutual concessions. It might simply be a system universally accepted as a system of reference without necessarily being universally applied.

(c) *Complete or incomplete classifications.* A classification is *complete* when it includes all categories, from the most general to the most detailed category which makes large-scale mapping possible. A classification is *incomplete* when the highest or the lowest categories are missing. For example, it is incomplete at the bottom when it deals only with the higher categories, in which case its chief interest lies in the scientific side, though it could be used for the schematic description of vast areas as natural regions. A classification is incomplete at the top when the pedologist turns his attention exclusively to those lower categories which are essential for more immediate practical purposes, as is often the case in soil surveying.

Most of us would grant that it is possible for one specialist to construct a complete classification. It should be noted, however, that in the setting up of higher or lower categories different considerations and a different frame of mind are at work and these cannot always be reconciled in actual fact. To make this point clear, it is enough to point to the frequent arguments between two groups of pedologists. Those on the practical side tend to regard classifications that are incomplete at the bottom as a product of purely academic labour, eminently respectable perhaps, but without practical meaning. On the other hand, those concerned only with the higher terms are sometimes tempted to look down on practical classifications, incomplete at the top, as a more or less incoherent juxtaposition of facts which it would be difficult to integrate into a co-ordinated system. It is a manifestation of the ever-recurring controversy between the theoretically and practically minded people.

I propose to limit the discussion to the various types of complete classifications.

(d) (i) *General characristics of various types of proposed complete classifications.* A classification can be represented as a more or less truncated pyramid. The top corresponds to the number of highest categories in the classification, e.g. 10 for that used in France or 12 for that used in Russia. The base may be very wide, depending on the number of lower categories—usually very large. Whatever the method of classification, it may be asked whether there do not exist levels of categories more or less common to all proposed systems, and, of course, there are.

Descending the scale of categories, there is towards the base a level at which one finds definite categories, more or less comparable with botanical or zoological species. At this level, for instance, a given soil may be described as 'le sol brun lessive sur loess'.

In several classifications, specific terms are found down to a level which, to use a commonly accepted word, we shall call 'series'. In poly-type series or complex series it is necessary to go down to types or sub-types, i.e. to terms suitable for practical large-scale cartography. Just below the top of our truncated pyramid there is a level at which the characteristics are specific enough to make a representation of the soil possible as, for instance, in a sketch. Such a sketch could be used to represent an iron podzol in general, but it obviously cannot be used to convey such qualities as zonality in a soil.

The following table is a tentative linking of the reference levels of several types of classification. We have included in it the German classification of Muckenhausen (1954), those of Avery (1956) for Britain and Stephens (1954) for Australia, and also that of Kubiena (1953), although they apply only to limited areas. Their chief interest lies in the tendencies. Since this is not meant to be a complete synthesis it was not thought necessary to mention all classifications that have ever been proposed.

Types of classification	Higher level	Lower level
I. Australian. Stephens (1954)	Great soil groups	From the series or down, types and phases
II. Kubiena (1953)	Types	Lokalformen
III. U.S.S.R. Ivanova (1956)	Types	Species and varieties
IV. French. Aubert and Duchaufour (1956)	Sub-groups, sometimes groups	From the series or down
V. German. Muckenhausen (tentative scheme, 1954)*	Types	Facies
VI. British. Avery (1956)	Sub-groups	Series and sub-series
VII. U.S.A. (tentative scheme, 1956)†	Upper categories VI and V	Series or types

* Quoted by kind permission of Prof. Dr. E. Muckenhausen.
† Quoted by kind permission of Dr. C. E. Kellogg and Dr. G. D. Smith.

It should not be very difficult for the authors of these various schemes to agree on the definition or on the naming of the reference levels. This would be a decisive step towards the elaboration of a universal system of reference.

(ii) *The method of elaboration.* There are two main methods of working. The first is analytic and descending: it starts from general facts and principles and goes down to more and more detailed categories as observation proceeds. The second method is synthetic or ascending: a great many data are first gathered and then classed into more and more general categories.

In the analytic method, which is usually genetic, there are again several ways of working according as one relies directly on some pedogenetic factors, pedogenetic processes, or properties that reflect genetic characteristics. The synthetic method may rely on morphological characteristics chosen with or without pedogenetic considerations or various chemical, physical, &c., characteristics chosen objectively because of their practical importance, but without genetic considerations.

It is appreciated that it is not possible to define the various types of classification rigorously in a single phrase, but it does not seem absurd to describe some of the tendencies of the proposed systems in the following terms:

1. Descending classification based on the genetic factors: U.S.S.R. system proposed by Ivanova (1956).
2. Descending classifications based on pedogenetic processes: French system (Aubert and Duchaufour, 1956), Kubiena's system (1953), German system (Muckenhausen, tentative scheme, 1954).
3. Descending classifications based on properties that reflect pedogenetic factors or processes: British system (Avery, 1956), Australian system (Stephens, 1954).
4. Ascending classification based chiefly on morphology, with pedogenetic considerations: U.S. system (tentative scheme, 1956).
5. Ascending classification based on various characteristics objectively chosen for their practical value without pedogenetic consideration: Leeper's scheme (1954).

Broadly speaking, it can be said that a descending system is the only possible one when no large amounts of accurate data are available, as in the form of small-scale soil maps. The classification may then be of the *a priori* type, in which case it must be improved as new findings are made. Descending systems are of necessity essentially genetic, since only the previous knowledge of the genetic factors or processes makes deductive reasoning possible. For instance, it may be assumed *a priori* that, in an area whose climate and geological structure are known, the soils will come under one of the great soil groups such as 'Sols bruns' or 'Chernozem'.

An advantage of the ascending type of classification is that it is founded on a large amount of detailed data resulting chiefly from soil surveying. It is accordingly rather of an *a posteriori* type. Serious difficulties may, however, be occasioned when it comes to elaborating higher categories from a large number of data spread over a lower level.

(iii) *Types of construction.* Another characteristic which could possibly be used to distinguish between types of classification is the *type of construction.* Ideally, the best solution would be a *simple construction,* characterized by more and more detailed subdivision of a single factor, according to a single phylum—*simple classification,* but owing to the complexity in the origin of soils and the number of characteristics necessary for their description, this method is purely theoretical and unsuitable in pedology. *Mixed classification* is already more complex. It assumes a different but single factor at each level of categorization. *Empirical classification* is founded on several factors at one and the same level of categorization, in order to take into account the full complexity of soils. The various systems mentioned above fit, on the whole, with this type of construction, which, logically, is the least perfect, but, practically, the most used by soil specialists.

C. Attempting to Simplify the Issue

In discussions on soil classifications the various issues are easily multiplied as experience often shows. The main thing is to determine those which are really worth considering, to limit their number and discuss them in turn. It is generally acknowledged that agreement has been reached on the following points:

(i) It is necessary to make a clear distinction between questions of definition, nomenclature, and classification.

(ii) The adoption of an international system of taxonomy is not yet possible. It is necessary first of all to reach agreement on numerous problems of definition and nomenclature.

(iii) It is already possible to exclude a number of issues with which the discussions often become involved to no avail. This could be achieved (a) by not confusing problems of *soil classification* or *taxonomy* and problems of soil *classing,* and (b) by limiting discussion to types of *complete classification* or, at least, to systems that have reached the same degree of elaboration, in order to avoid the misunderstanding that often arises between theorists proposing classifications incomplete in the lower parts and practical workers offering systems incomplete in the higher parts.

(iv) The first main theme for discussion could be a comparison of the advantages and disadvantages of the methods of elaboration in systems of classification, both of ascending and descending methods. However, it appears that in our present state of knowledge both methods are necessary for mutual control.

(v) A study of the *descending* methods leads, as we have shown, to a first rough division into three groups, which could probably readily be reduced to one system. It would be easiest, as a first step, to determine the similarities between the units included at the *higher level* that can be represented by sketching a profile, as has been mentioned above.

(vi) However, as it is certainly premature to try to elaborate a single system at present, it is more convenient to propose a *common system of reference,* for which we would suggest the French system of Aubert and Duchaufour. This has the advantage of being, at one and the same time, both complete and general, and standing between two extremes. Indeed a pedogenetic process stands between the podogenetic factors and the properties brought about by pedogenesis. If it be done in a constructive spirit it would be worth while attempting to find links with the provisional reference system which would doubtless lead to the elaboration of an *international reference system of soil classification.* The idea of such a system would appear, for the present at least, less Utopian and more practical interest than a *universal system* that would stand little chance of being used by everybody.

D. Notes on Some Problems of Immediate Interest

Recent pedological literature and reports by participants in the discussion during the Paris Congress raise a number of issues of immediate importance in soil classification. It is satisfactory to note that the opinions expressed were in general identical. We shall consider three issues which, if discussed, might lead quickly to complete agreement.

(a) *The utilitarian trend in soil classification.* As we have already shown, an unquestionably 'natural' classification is hardly conceivable. It is not even possible to find single terms to express all the complexity of any objective whatever at any level of generalization. A system of taxonomy is necessarily a compromise between purely scientific and speculative logic and some practical necessities. Economic and social needs which are now arising all over the world demand that pedological problems, often of a purely cartographical nature, should be solved. This makes it a duty to direct the work of soil classification and mapping towards utilitarian aims, as far as is compatible with serious scientific work. In order to be utilitarian, classification must, at least in the lower categories, provide surveyors in charge of pedological map-making with the simplest criteria possible. Preference must be given to morphological characteristics, on condition that these have a real agronomical meaning, i.e. that they correspond to factors of unquestionable importance for the growth of plants and the technology of soils.

(b) *The trend towards 'actual' description of soils.* As our knowledge increases, chiefly as a result of cartographic studies, it is ever more clearly noticeable that the characteristics used to define a pedological unit at any level of generalization have no clear-cut limits, either in time or in space. There is a 'law of continuity in time' and a 'law of continuity in space', as Duchaufour pointed out.

The first of these two laws is expressed by the fact that we notice more and more frequently the presence of paleopedological characteristics, especially in those parts of the world that have remained free from the recent alterations of the Quaternary ice ages. The most logical and convenient way of handling this time factor is to include those characteristics in the lower categories, for instance, at the level where variations of parent material appear.

Let us take the case of soils of recent, almost present-day, genesis like those of temperate zones, which were covered with forest after the latest glaciations. Alterations of this vegetable cover brought about by the latest post-glacial climatic fluctuations and the influence of man caused certain pedological properties, which are still generally considered as being actual, to become fossil. There are, for instance, typical *grey-brown podzolic soils* or *sol bruns lessives* or *Parabraunerde* which have in fact becomes *sols bruns acides* of the A/C type. We also know *podzols* of typical morphology that, to judge by the type of humification and the nature of vegetation *(chenaie a charme),* now function like *sols bruns.*

It is for this reason that we are often compelled, for practical and ecological reasons, to introduce two different concepts in the interpretation of profiles (Manil, 1956): (1) the pedological profile, and (2) the edaphic profile. A *pedological profile* is defined by its general morphological genetic characteristics to the exclusion of clearly paleopedological features.

An *edaphic profile* is defined by its biological tendencies and more particularly by its type of humification.

(c) *The trend towards giving the human factor all its actual importance.* It becomes more and more evident that man has played an essential part in the genesis of the present properties of our soils by modifying the vegetal cover; by being the indirect cause of numerous forms of alteration by erosion, or inversely, by accumulation of particles brought by wind, running water, or gravity; by modifying in one way or another the quantity of water percolating through the profile, or by modifying the position of the underground water table; and by adding organic or mineral amendments and fertilizers to the soil, and so on. Among pedological formations which have reached some degree of development there are seldom any to be found which can be regarded as being 'virgin' or 'natural'.

There is a real difficulty in choosing the level of categorization at which the human factor is to be introduced. Agreement is far from being general on this point. The problem becomes somewhat simpler when soil is studied with its actual particularities. It would become still simpler, however, if provision were made in the classification for pedogenetic processes which would specially take human influence, direct or indirect, into account. This question alone would deserve a full report which would certainly not fail to make further discussions more profitable and less academic.

One process which is typically of human origin could be recognized at once, and it might be termed *catenization*. Over an area whose soils are assumed to be homogeneous at the outset, clearing and especially deforestation lead to erosion which brings about the succession in space of more or less eroded profiles, and more or less colluvial or alluvial profiles following one another in 'catena' form according to Milne's conception of the word.

III. GENERAL CONCLUSIONS AND PROPOSALS

A. The systematic examination of the various types of proposed classifications shows clearly that there is no fundamental opposition between the workers on the problem. Moreover, agreement is getting more and more general on the three trends specially mentioned above, namely, the utilitarian trend, the priority of actual characteristics, the importance of the human factor.

B. Co-ordination of endeavours at the international level could easily be achieved in two stages:

(a) preliminary choice of one system as a provisional *frame of reference*, for which the French classification seems to be the most suitable;

(b) starting from this, one could elaborate an *international system* which should be checked by comparison with both the descending and the ascending systems of classification.

ACKNOWLEDGEMENTS

It is my duty to recall here the part taken by prominent scientists in the general discussion, opened on the occasion of the last Congress in Paris, on the general problem of classification of soils, and more especially by Messrs. Aubert, Avery, Duchaufour, Edelman, Ehrart, Ivanova, Glangeaud, Kellogg, Kovda, Kubiena, Muckenhausen, Muir, Smith, Stremme, von Kries, Yerkhina, Zavalashin, and others. I have much pleasure in expressing my deepest thanks to Dr. Muir, past Chairman of the 5th Commission of the Congress, 1956, for his kind assistance in reading over the manuscript of this paper.

REFERENCES

1. Aubert, G., and Duchaufour, P. 1956. Projet de classification des sols. 6th Int. Cong. Soil Sci. E, 597.
2. Avery, B. W. 1956. A classification of British soils. 6th Int. Cong. Soil Sci. E, 279.
3. Ivanova, E. N. 1956. Attempt at a general soil classification. 6th Int. Cong. Soil Sci. E, 387.
4. Kubiena, W. 1953. The Soils of Europe. Murby, London.
5. Leeper, G. W. 1956. The classification of soils. J. Soil Sci. 7, 59.
6. Manil, G. 1956. Aspects dynamiques du profil pedologique. 6th Int. Cong. Soil Sci. E, 439.
7. Muckenhausen, E. 1954. A plan of a classification system of the soils of Germany. 5th Int. Cong. Soil Sci. 4, 210.
8. Stephens, C. G. 1954. The classification of Australian soils. 5th Int. Cong. Soil Sci. 4, 155.
9. Stewart, G. A. 1954. Some aspects of soil taxonomy. 5th Int. Cong. Soil Sci. 4, 109.

(Received 4 June 1958)

THE RUSSIAN APPROACH TO SOIL CLASSIFICATION
AND ITS RECENT DEVELOPMENT

J. J. Basinski [1]

I. INTRODUCTION

Ever since Dokuchaev (1879) published his first classification of the soils of Nizhnyi Novgorod Province in 1879, the minds of Russian pedologists have been exercised by the problems of soil taxonomy, probably far more than those of their Western counterparts. Russian literature on this subject is so voluminous that to summarize it for the English reader would involve prolonged and intensive study but for a number of excellent reviews published recently, mainly in one of the journals of the Soviet Academy of Sciences, *Pochvovedenie (Pedology)*.

The number and extent of quotations from early works found in contemporary Soviet literature on soil taxonomy and used in support of current arguments are striking to the Western reader. It is, however, the best evidence of the evolutionary rather than revolutionary development of Russian thought on the subject. All recent developments are so closely linked with past achievements that it is impossible to consider them apart from the traditional Russian school of pedology and the conditions under which it developed.

II. TRADITIONAL RUSSIAN APPROACH TO SOIL SCIENCE AS A WHOLE

Russian pedologists have been fortunate in the geographical position of their country—in the middle of the Eurasian continent—and its vast extent. They have been able to study a wide variety of environments and vegetation types as well as soils, and to make extensive comparisons. This has also undoubledly led to the broad outlook which has persisted in their thinking. In addition, the presence of soil undisturbed by man in a wide range of environmental conditions makes it possible for them to be studied in their natural state and form.

The Russian school of pedology in general and soil classification in particular must also have been influenced appreciably by the fact that it developed under the stimulus of the necessity of classifying and mapping land for utilization purposes often without the opportunity of studying it intensively.

The mental climate of Russia in the late nineteenth and early twentieth centuries must also be taken into account. It was the time when modern scientific thinking,

[1]Division of Land Research and Regional Survey, C.S.I.R.O., Canberra, A.C.T.

Reproduced with permission from *Journal of Soil Science,* Vol. 10, 1959, p. 14-26.
Published by the British Society of Soil Science, England.

seeking not only to establish and record the facts and laws of nature, but also to explain them, received its main impetus. The teaching of Darwin and his disciples often provided the basis of explanation, and hence the evolutionary approach was fashionable.

While western European and American scientists were still considering soil as a geological material (Hilgard) or a complicated mixture of chemical compounds (Liebig), the early Russian pedologists were the first to regard soils as an independent body with a definite morphological organization reflected in the profile. They were the first to show the broad but definite inter-relationship between environment, soils, and vegetation, and the first to recognize soil as the product of a process governed by environmental factors rather than by soil parent material. This led to recognition of the fact that soil is a dynamic and not a static body, a living organism allied in the plane of development to biological bodies.

This Russian concept of soil and its place in nature has, in the words of Marbut (1936), 'established the study of soils firmly as an independent science with criteria, point of view, method of approach, process of development applicable to soil alone and inapplicable to any other series of natural bodies'. It also had a predominant influence on the development of Russian taxonomy.

III. TRADITIONAL RUSSIAN APPROACH TO SOIL CLASSIFICATION

One of the primary aims of soil-classification systems as proposed or employed by Russian pedologists since the time of Dokuchaev's first soil classification is to group the soils according to their productivity and utilization problems, and to determine, compare, and explain their fertility differences. Dokuchaev (1893), writing of his first classification, stressed 'the close connexion existing between soil types on the one hand and yields, kind of crops and husbandry methods on the other'. In many recent papers on the subject, Russian pedologists continue to stress the importance of soil productivity in taxonomic work. For example, Ivanova (1956) states, 'fertility is an essential property of the soil and consequently soil classification must reflect this property'. She writes further, 'soil world groups, constituted on the basis of radiation energy, define the main ways of utilizing natural resources in national economy. Classes and subclasses define the type of husbandry. Soil types, regional groups, families, subtypes and forms permit more concrete zoning of types of agriculture and husbandry systems, give indispensable amelioration measures, define the order of soil suitability for cultivation, use in agriculture etc.' This stress on utilization aspects in the Russian approach to soil taxonomic work is often forgotten by those outside observers who lose themselves in the theoretical and philosophical arguments of Russian pedologists.

The Russians have always recognized the 'genetic soil type' as the fundamental unit. Their classification schemes are essentially a series of attempts to link soil types into progressively larger groups and to subdivide them into progressively more defined variants. The definition of soil type is usually based on three criteria first established by Sibirtsev towards the end of the last century, namely:

1. Sameness of genetic properties of the soil.
2. Sameness of the pedogenetic processes determining these properties.
3. Sameness of pedogenetic factors defining and directing the pedogenetic processes.

The choice and extent of the 'genetic soil properties' taken into account when defining 'soil types' have differed from time to time, although the morphological structure of the profile has always been of primary importance. Moreover, since the days of Sibirtsev, Russian pedologists have considered that only the combination of the attributive and genetic approach can lead to an identification of soil types and their classification which will permit the proper appraisal of soil fertility. This point of view is still generally accepted amongst them (Rozov, 1957).

Because one of the fundamental concepts of pedology as developed mainly in Russia is that soil is a product of geographical environment which determines the process of its formation and which is in itself a resultant of separate environmental factors, the attention of Russian soil classifiers has, since early days, focused on environment, environmental factors, and pedogenetic processes rather than on the soil itself.

It is true that the father of Russian soil taxonomy, Dokuchaev, stressed in connection with his first classification that 'grouping of the soils should always be based on the sum of existing characters of a given body' (its profile, clay content, chemical characteristics, &c.). As pointed out recently by Rode (1957), however, 'many of Dokuchaev's followers, amongst whom were some eminent scientists, did not always adhere to this principle, and developed their own classification schemes, basing them mainly on conditions of pedogenesis'. Even when the properties of the soils themselves provided the basis of a classification system, the classifications as such were based on genesis rather than on soil attributes, on the assumption that all soil-material characteristics are merely the reflexion of their development processes as directed by environment.

Also, because soils and their pedogenesis are regarded as a single system, it is often very difficult for outside students of Russian pedology to distinguish whether the reference or argument concerns soil as such or the process of its formation, which to a Russian are one and the same thing. This is well illustrated by a recent review of soil-classification systems by Gerasimov (1954) who, dealing for example with Kossovitch, Tumin, Glinka, Gedroitz, Neustruev, and Prasolov's systems, describes them as 'based on intrinsic properties of the soil', while in fact they are based on intrinsic soil-forming processes.

The existence of a definite relationship between geographical environment, soil, and its vegetative cover on which Russian classifications are based, justifies also the inclusion of environmental (geographical) and ecological terms in the classification systems.

The evolutionary character of soil formation makes it possible to explain soil differences as expressions of different stages of their evolution as well as expressions of different conditions governing evolutionary processes. This concept of soil as a product of evolution has played an increasingly important part in the thought of Russian pedologists and in their approach to soil classification.

The experimentation in soil genesis and evolution has not yet been developed as a well-established method of attack on the problems involved. Consequently, reasons for the soil differences found in the field or laboratory must be reached by interpretation of correlations between soil types and factors influencing its development. In this deductive approach to soil taxonomy, Soviet scientists are prepared to go much farther than Western pedologists.

IV. DIFFERENCES IN THE RUSSIAN APPROACH
TO SOIL CLASSIFICATION

All Russian soil classifications are based on a genetic approach. However, within this general approach five different categories of classification systems may be recognized, according to whether the systems are based on conditions of pedogenesis, the factors governing pedogenesis, the character of pedogenetic processes or evolutionary stages in these processes, or a single process. This grouping of then existing classification systems has been adopted by Gerasimov (1954) in his recent review. His terminology, however, when translated is apt to confuse the Western reader, and has not been adopted here it its entirety.

(a) Geographic-Environmental Classifications

In these classification systems the soil types clearly related to bio-climatic conditions of regions where they are found are classed as 'normal' or 'zonal'. Those not so related are classed as 'transitional' and 'abnormal' or 'intrazonal' and 'azonal'.

Thus, Dokuchaev (1896) in his final classification grouped glacial, light grey podzolic, brown forest, chernozemic, dark chestnut, light greyish brown, red, dark brown swampy and whitish secondary solonetz soil types into the class of 'normal' or 'zonal' soils. He also recognized a class of 'transitional' or 'intrazonal' soils, and a class of 'abnormal' or *'cosmopolitan'* soils, including aeolian, alluvial, and swampy soil types.

Sibirtsev (1895, 1898, 1900) classified soils into classes and types. The class of 'zonal' soils included the following types: lateritic, aeolian loess, desert-steppe soils, chernozemic, grey forest, grassland, podzolic, and tundra soils. The 'intrazonal' class included solonetzic, swamp, and humic-carbonate soil types. The class of 'azonal' soils included skeletal, coarse, and riverain types.

In the classification proposed by Afanasev (1922, 1927) who in the 1920's developed further the ideas of Dokuchaev and Sibirtsev, each of five climatic belts (cold, cool, temperate, subtropical warm, and tropical hot) is divided into two complexes, maritime and continental. Each soil type has an equivalent in the corresponding complex. Further subdivision is based on soil changes as influenced by the type of vegetation (forest, grassland-forest, and grassland). Finally, differences due to different phases of evolution influenced by degradation and salinization processes are also considered.

In constructing classification systems in this category, the authors—as stated by Sibirtsev (1895)—attempted 'to explain the soil cover of the earth's surface in its genetic entity and geographical variability'.

(b) Factorial Classifications

These classifications are based on separate factors of pedogenesis or their combinations. Glinka (1902, 1915), who was the first to adopt this approach, divided soils into two main groups, 'ectodynamomorphic' and 'endodynamorphic'. The former is the result of external (mainly climatic) factors, while the character of the latter is determined by the parent material. Further classification is based on the moisture regime.

Vilenskii's (1925) classification is typical of this category although, like Dokuchaev, he divides soils into 'zonal' and 'intrazonal'. Zonal soils in his system are divided horizontally into five belts, based on Köppen's temperature zones (polar, cold, temperate, subtropic, and tropic) and five corresponding soil divisions (hydrogenic, phytohydrogenic, phytogenic, thermophytogenic, and thermogenic). Each of these belts is subdivided vertically into columns according to Weigner's humidity regions (arid, semi-arid, weakly arid, semi-humid, and humid). Intrazonal soils are divided horizontally into five divisions (halogenic, phytohalogenic, hydrohalogenic, thermohalogenic, and thermohydrogenic). The first two divisions correspond to the temperate zone and the last two to the subtropical and tropical zones. The first two are also divided vertically according to humidity regions. In addition, the soils of the mountain region are grouped in the orogenic division.

Zakharov's (1927) system is essentially similar, zonal soil complexes being divided into climatogenic, orogenic, hydrohalogenic, fluviogenic, and lithogenic divisions, and classified further according to climatic and ecological conditions.

Vysotskii (1906) also divides soils into zonal, intrazonal, and undeveloped, subdividing them further according to climate and parent material.

The most recent factorial classification is that of Volobuev (1955) who groups the soils into climatic communities, subdividing each community into two orders: automorphic and hydromorphic. Swamp soils and solonchaks are regarded as intrazonal soil types. Further classification is based according to vegetation communities associated with the soils.

(c) Process Classifications

These classification systems are based on differences and similarities in the process of soil formation. As has already been pointed out, owing to the lack of distinction between the processes and their result, some of the Russian soil taxonomists who adopted this approach claimed that their classifications were based on intrinsic soil properties, although in fact they were based on the pedogenetic processes.

Kossovitch (1910), for example, wrote, 'genetic soil classification should be based on intrinsic properties and characteristics of the soils themselves'. In his classification, however, he divided soils according to types of pedogenesis. In the group of 'genetically independent' (eluvial) soils he recognized the following types of pedogenesis related to bio-climatic conditions: desert type, semi-desert (solonetzic) type. steppe (chernozemic) type, humid-cool (podzolic) type, humid-hot (lateritic) type, and polar (tundra) type. The class of genetically dependent (illuvial) soils embraced the corresponding types of pedogenesis as affected by impeded drainage. In the case of each type of pedogenesis, transformation and translocation of mineral and organic substances were considered, special attention being given to changes in organic matter.

Tumin's (1907) classification is basically the same. His classes were divided into families according to quantitative expression of the pedogenetic process (degree of development), and some families were sub-divided into forms, e.g. podzols were divided into podzols proper, podzolic and weakly podzolic, while chernozems were divided into chernozems proper and southern chernozems. There was also division into groups according to parent material.

Glinka (1922, 1924), in his later work, recognized five basic types of pedogenesis (lateritic, podzolic, chernozemic, solonetzic, and swampy) and stressed that since pedogenetic processes lead to transformation of organic matter and decomposition of mineral matter and translocation of the products of these two processes, the soil properties are born in pedogenesis itself.

In Neustruev's (1926) classification there are two broad divisions of soil-forming processes, 'automorphic' active under normal moisture conditions, and 'hydromorphic' active under conditions of excessive moisture. The processes are further sub-divided according to their effect on the state of decomposition of the mineral constituents, transformation of organic matter, and translocation of the products of pedogenesis.

Prasolov (1934) classifies the processes into eluvial, salinizing, and desalinizing, and hydromorphic. According to his system, eluviation results in three principal soil groups: soils of the humid regions, soils of the semi-humid and semi-arid regions, and soils of the arid regions. These groups are further divided into genetic soil types defined on the basis of interrelation between biological elements (mainly vegetation) and parent material on the one hand and pedogenetic processes on the other.

(d) Evolutionary Classification

Although his classification in its final form was based on types of pedogenesis Kossovitch (1906), in his earlier work, regarded soils as phases in evolutionary development governed by two processes based on acid and alkaline weathering. His ideas undoubtedly influenced other Russian soil taxonomists.

In Polynov's uncompleted classification, the influence of Kossovitch's concept can easily be recognized. Polynov (1933) considered that soil evolution proceeds along two lines, one governed by eluviation and one by salinization or desalinization. In the eluvial evolution Polynov recognized two basic processes, acid and alkaline weathering, and considered that soil types merely reflect evolution's many stages due to progressive de-alkalinization. Thus alkaline weathering produces alkaline, pre-chernozemic, and chernozemic phases, while acid weathering results in prepodzolic, podzolic, and swampy phases. With increased humidity, alkaline weathering may give place to acid weathering and thus the two series may be regarded as continuous. Halogenic evolution consists of phases corresponding to transition from the solonchak group through the carbonic group to the swamp group.

Until recently, Viliams's (1939) concept of a single pedogenetic process—a part of his much wider theory of environment and life evolution—completely dominated Soviet pedology. This, according to Rozov (1957), is at least partly responsible for 'many unclear and undecided theoretical problems in [contemporary Soviet soil] science'. The wide concept of Viliams undoubtedly stimulated thought, but, being advanced dogmatically, it was also placing thought in 'chains'.

Viliams regarded soil evolution as phenomenon connected with geological history of life on earth, as a part of a single process of life development. Since living organisms affect soil development directly and indirectly through their effect on environment and pedogenetic processes, life was also considered as the main moving force in pedogenesis. Consequently, the processes of synthesis and decomposition of organic matter are regarded as particularly important in soil formation.

In addition, Viliams's theory postulates that soil evolution proceeds along a single path determined by the development of relief and shifts of climatic conditions and vegetation zones. For example, he thought that 'all the great territory in the U.S.S.R. in turn passed through all the phases of pedogenetic evolution, beginning with tundra'. Thus, according to his theory, all existing soils represent merely different phases in a single evolutionary development, being simply a function of time.

Recently this approach has been strongly criticized by Soviet pedologists. However, during the time when Viliams's views reigned supreme, a number of attempts were made to classify soils entirely in accordance with his principles. Tsyganov's (1955) classification may serve as an example. It is based on a single process of evolution connected with the geological growth and drying out of continents. The swampy, podzolic, grassland steppe and desert soils are regarded as evolutionary zonal phases with intrazonal phases based on the development of relief.

V. RECENT DEVELOPMENT IN THE RUSSIAN APPROACH

Recent trends in Russian pedology in general and soil taxonomy in particular cannot be described as revolutionary. They constitute merely a further development of the traditional school of thought of Dokuchaev and his early successors, and of Viliams and his followers. The genetic-evolutionary approach still universally accepted is, however, based on a much firmer foundation, made possible by the ever-increasing volume of pedological material. Especially since the 1939-45 war, Soviet soil-survey and mapping activites have been considerably increased, to embrace the lesser known polar and tropical regions of the Soviet Union. Close co-operation with eastern Eurpoean and Chinese scientists has extended the zone of activities of Soviet pedologists even further and has brought new, often valuable minds to the Russian school of pedology. Material for soil inventories has been greatly extended and, since the war, the compilation of such inventories has taken a place of great importance in Russian work. Field and laboratory studies of different soil types also have been intensified and made more detailed.

(a) Standardizing Nomenclature and Methods of Diagnosis of Soil Taxonomic Units

As may easily be understood from the preceding sections, which describe the development of Russian pedology and soil taxonomy, soil nomenclature and methods of recognizing and defining taxonomic units were, until comparatively recently, allowed to develop without any check or co-ordination. This inevitably led to a great profusion of ill-defined technical terms and diagnostic methods, resulting in constant misunderstandings and general confusion. Since the war, work has begun, mainly in the Soil Institute of the Academy of Sciences of the U.S.S.R., to bring order to this chaos in nomenclature and methodology. This culminated in the appointment by the Academy of Sciences in 1956 of a special permanent commission including forty leading Soviet pedologists. Opening the first session of the Commission in February 1957, the Chairman, Academician Tyurin, stated that 'the main task of the Commission appears to be unification of soil nomenclature, systematics and methods of diagnosis. These topics cannot, however, be discussed apart from classification problems. The Commission, although it is unable to undertake the task of developing classification schemes, which is beyond its powers, can nevertheless direct this work by considering them and making the necessary recommendations.'

The minutes of this first meeting (Rozov et al., 1957) stress the considerable discrepancy in the meanings of many pedological terms in the minds of different workers. The commission began its work by defining soil types and subordinate units:

Type

Major soil group, developing in a single type of bioclimatic and hydrological conditions, characterized by a clear manifestation of the basic processes of soil formation, possibly in combination with other pedogenetic processes. Characteristic points of soil type are defined by:
1. same type of accumulation of organic matter, its rate and character of distribution;
2. same type of processes in decomposition of mineral substances and synthesis of new mineral and organic-mineral products;
3. same type of translocation of soil materials;
4. same type of structure of soil profile;
5. same direction of measures for increasing and maintaining soil productivity.

Sub-type

Groups of soils within the range of soil type differing qualitatively in the manifestation of one of the superimposed soil-forming processes and in the intensity with which they reflect the main pedogenetic process. Measures for increasing and maintaining soil fertility are more alike for a sub-type than for a type.

In differentiating a sub-type, the subzonal as well as regional change in environmental conditions is taken into account. (Zonal conditions in the Russian approach are those determined by latitude or altitude—i.e. mainly temperature; regional conditions are determined by the type of climate, continental or maritime.)

Family (Rod)

Group of soils within a sub-type, with qualitative peculiarities dependent on local conditions, for example parent material (including chemistry of ground water), past history of soil development (relics of previous stages), &c.

Form (Vid)

Soils within family divisions differing in the degree of development of pedogenetic process (degree of podzolization, quantity of humus and strength of humic horizon, degree of salinization, &c.).

The Commission also recommended further study and discussion of methods of recognition of soil types and their description as the basis of future standardization.

Since its first meeting Rode (1957) has published a very interesting paper on this subject in which he stresses the necessity of basing genetic soil classification on a proper recognition ('diagnosis') of different soil types. This diagnosis, he advocates, should be based on a wide use of the methods of chemical and physical analysis, as well as on field observations, He also recommends, as far as possible, a quantitative approach to the definition of soil taxonomic units. According to him, these units should be based on similarity of a wide variety of soil attributes. These should be presented in the form of curves illustrating changes in different properties within the soil profile.

He considers that each soil type or lower taxonomic unit should have its own 'passport', a document containing the following parts:

1. Morphological column illustrating schematically the morphological structure of the soil profile by the use of agreed symbols.
2. A very short morphological description of separate horizons corresponding to their illustrations in the morphological column.
3. Graphs illustrating distribution in the profile of various soil characteristics, e.g. clay fraction, humus, carbonates, total salts, exchangeable bases, pH, &c.
4. Graph of mechanical composition.
5. Graph of moisture and other physical properties.
6. Graph showing root distribution.
7. Graph showing distribution of main groups of organic matter.
8. Graphs showing schematically the characteristic points of water and heat regime, &c.

Rode considers that these soil 'passports' should play a most important part in the preparation of soil-classification systems. Finally, he advocates the establishment of soil collections which should have a similar function to that of herbaria in plant taxonomy.

(b) Approach to Classification

The genetic approach is still accepted by Soviet pedologists as the only right approach to soil classification. As we have already seen, Viliams's theory of a single pedogenetic process has lately been subjected to considerable criticism. However, many Soviet pedologists still regard it as the best basis for genetic classification systems (Rozov et al., 1957). Moreover, in all current attempts to devise such systems, the evolution concept plays a very important part.

The predominant significance of biological and biochemical processes in soil formation is also universally accepted, though weathering of minerals and translocation of mineral compounds currently receives more attention than in the years when Viliams dominated Russian pedology. At the same time the importance of the direct influence of vegetation on pedogenesis is unquestioned.

Within the framework of the genetic evolutionary approach, the question of whether genetic soil properties and processes or conditions of pedogenesis and pedogenetic factors should be taken as the basis of classification is still alive. New ideas are emerging, however, which envisage the possibility of a combination of all the traditional methods to form a classification system.

The system developed by Rozov (1956) and Ivanova (1956), and shown in

GROUPS	Sub-classes / Orders / Classes	Biogenic Soils — Atmospheric wetting	Biogenic Soils — Periodic ground wetting	Biogenic Soils — Permanent ground wetting	Biohalogenic Soils — Atmospheric wetting	Biohalogenic Soils — Periodic ground wetting	Biohalogenic Soils — Permanent ground wetting	Biolithogenic Soils — Atmospheric wetting	Biolithogenic Soils — Periodic ground wetting	Biolithogenic Soils — Permanent ground wetting
SUB-BOREAL AND BOREAL	Class A Arctic tundra soils	1A Arctic / 2A Tundra / 3A Sub-arctic turf		4A Tundra swampy	—	—	5A Tundra solonchak-like	—	—	—
SUB-BOREAL AND BOREAL	Class B Seasonally frozen taiga soils	1B Taiga iron enriched / 2B Taiga pale yellow	3B Taiga gleyed pale yellow	4B Seasonally frozen swampy	5B Seasonally frozen solods	6B Seasonally frozen gleyed solods				
SUB-BOREAL AND BOREAL	Class C Taiga forest soils	1C Podzolic / 2C Grey forest	3C Podzolic swampy / 4C Grey forest gleyed	5C Swampy	—	—	—	6C Turf carbonaceous	7C Gleyed turf carbonaceous	8C Lowland swampy
SUB-BOREAL AND BOREAL	Class D Moist forest soils	1D Acid forest (non-podzolic) / 2D Brown forest / 3D Prairie chernozemic	4D Gleyed acid forest / 5D Gleyed brown forest / 6D Gleyed prairie chernozem-like	7D Swampy	—	—	—	8D Humic carbonaceous	9D Gleyed humic carbonaceous	
SUB-BOREAL AND BOREAL	Class E Steppe soils	1E Chernozems / 2E Chestnut	3E Meadow chernozems / 4E Meadow chestnut	5E Meadow swampy	6E Steppe solonetz	7E Solods / 8E Meadow solonetz	9E Solonchaks	—	—	—
SUB-BOREAL AND BOREAL	Class F Desert soils	1F Brown semi-desert / 2F Gleyed brown desert	3F Brown meadow desert		4F Desert solonetz	5F Desert meadow solonetz / 6F "Takyr"	7F Desert solonchaks	—	—	—
SUB-TROPICAL	Class G Sub-tropical moist forest soils	1G Yellow earths / 2G Red earths	3G Gleyed yellow earths / 4G Gleyed red earths	5G Sub-tropical swampy	—	—	—			
SUB-TROPICAL	Class H Sub-tropical dry forest and savannah soils	1H Buff / 2H Grey buff	3H Meadow buff / 4H Meadow grey buff	5H Sub-tropical meadow swampy	6H Sub-tropical solonetzic	7H Sub-tropical meadow solonetzic			8H "Smolnitzy" (Tar-like soils)	
SUB-TROPICAL	Class I Sub-tropical desert soils	1I Grey earths / 2I Sub-tropical desert	3I Meadow grey				4I Sub-tropical solonchaks	—	—	—
TROPICAL	Class J Tropical moist forest and savannah soils	1J Lateritic / 2J Red of tall grass savannah	3J Gleyed lateritic / 4J Gleyed red	5J Tropical swampy	—	—	—			
TROPICAL	Class K Tropical dry forest and savannah soils	1K Red buff of dry forests / 2K Red brown of dry savannahs	3K Meadow red buff	5K Tropical meadow swampy		6K Tropical meadow solonetzic		7K Tropical black	8K Tropical gleyed black	
TROPICAL	Class L Tropical desert soils	1L Red brown of denudated savannahs / 2L Tropical desert	4K Meadow red brown				3L Tropical solonchaks	—	—	—

Fig. 1—Tabular representation of Rozov's (1956) scheme for the genetic grouping of soil types showing their evolutionary-genetic relationships.

Figs. 1 and 2, provides a good example of this tendency. From the geographical-environmental point of view, soils are divided into zonal and intrazonal, and further subdivided into types according to zonal and regional characteristics of their pedogenesis resulting primarily from bioclimatic conditions. From a factorial point of view, the soil types are vertically linked according to the main complexes of pedogenetic factors. For process classification the seventy-seven soil types are differentiated on the basis of differences in their pedogenesis and grouped on the basis of differ-

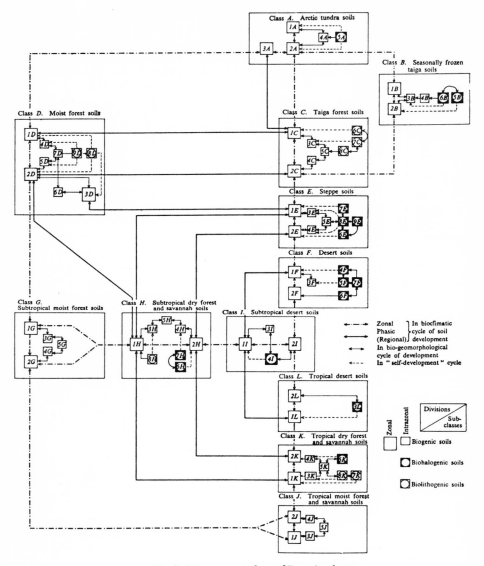

Fig. 2—Diagrammatic form of Rozov's scheme.

ences in salinization and the character and degree of influence of biological and weathering processes. From the evolutionary viewpoint, this scheme presents the main evolutionary-genetic connexions between soil types and permits them to be regarded as historical-genetic phases.

The same combined genetic approach is advocated by Rode (1957) in the paper mentioned above.

The subdivision of soil types which include a rather wide range of genetically and morphologically similar soils has also received increased attention in the work of Soviet pedologists. The recently standardized definition, quoted above, of sub-type, family, and form illustrates the direction which type subdivision is taking. Further subdivision of soils into variants according to the degree of change of natural profile by cultivation and erosion, and into varieties according to their mechanical composition has been proposed by Ivanova (1956). In this connexion, the growing interest in systematics of cultivated soils should also be mentioned.

SUMMARY

Due largely to the conditions in which they were working, Russian pedologists were the first to establish pedology as an independent science. From the beginning they regarded soil as an independent body with a definite morphological organization, expressed mainly in the structure of the profile, and resulting from pedogenetic processes determined and directed by environmental factors. This concept of soil led them to adopt a genetic approach to problems of soil classification. Russian soil classifications differed according to the basis accepted, whether bioclimatic, geographical conditions, factors of pedogenesis, pedogenetic processes, or soil evolutionary history. In recent years attempts have been made to construct classification systems based on all these aspects of pedogenesis. The current Soviet trends in soil taxonomy must be regarded mainly as a further development of the traditional approach. Measures are taken to standardize soil nomenclature and improve methods of recognizing (diagnosing) and describing soil types, which are regarded as basic taxonomic units. The evolutionary-genetic approach is considered the only proper approach to soil-classification problems. The importance of organic aspects of soil evolution and formation processes is emphasized. More attention is given to the genetic subdivision of soil types into smaller and better defined soil groups. Interest in the systematics of cultivated soils is also growing.

REFERENCES

1. Afanasev, Ya. N. 1922. Zonal soil systems. Zap. Gorets. sel. Khoz. Inst.
2. .... 1927. Classification problems in Russian pedology. Proc. 1st Int. Cong. Soil Sci.
3. Dokuchaev, V. V. 1879. Short historical description and critical analysis of the more important existing soil classifications. Trav. Soc. Nat., St. Petersb. 10, 64-67 (Collected Works, vol. ii, Acad. Sci. U.S.S.R., 1950).
4. .... 1882. Materials for appraisal of lands of Nizhegorod Province. Collected Works, vol. iv, Acad. Sci. U.S.S.R., 1951.
5. .... 1893. About the question of overvaluation of lands of European and Asiatic Russia. Collected Works, vol. vi, Acad. Sci., U.S.S.R., 1951.
6. .... 1896. The catalogue of soil collection of Prof. V. V. Dokuchaev and his students. Collected Works, vol. vii, Acad. Sci., U.S.S.R., 1953.
7. Gerasimov, I. P. 1954. Scientific bases of soil systematics and classification. Pedology, 8, 52-64.
8. Glinka, K. D. 1902. Post-tertiary formations and soils of Pskov, Novgorod and Smolensk Provinces (Classification of Soils). Annu. Geol. Miner. Russ. 4-5.
9. .... 1915. Pedology. St. Petersburg, 1st ed.
10. .... 1922. Soil, its Properties and the Natural Laws of Distribution. Edition of N. Dereven, Moscow.

11. Glinka, K. D. 1924. Differents types d'apres lesquels se forment les sols et la classification de ces derniers. Comite Int. Pedologie, IV. Commis. No. 20.

12. Ivonova, E. N. 1956. An experiment in general soil classification. Pedology, No. 6, 82-102.

13. Kossovitch, P. S. 1906. The problem of soil genesis and the bases of genetical soil classification. Russ. J. Exp. Agric. 7 (2).

14. .... 1910. Pedogenetic process as the basis of soil classification. Russ. J. Exp. Agric. 11 (5).

15. Marbut, C. F. 1936. In 'Introduction to Pedology' by J. S. Joffe. Rutgers Univ. Press.

16. Neustruev, S. S. 1926. An experiment in classification of soil development processes in connection with soil genesis. Izv. Geogr. Inst. 6.

17. Polynov, B. B. 1933. Bases of constructing soil classification—preliminary thesis. Trud. Sov. Sekts. M.A.P. Kom. V. 2 (1).

18. Prasolov, L. I. 1934. The problem of soil classification and nomenclature. Trav. Inst. Dokoutchaiev, 8.

19. Rode, A. A. 1957. Problems of organization of work on nomenclature, systematics and classification of soils. Pedology, No. 9, 89-95.

20. Rozov, N. N. 1956. Problems and principles of constructing genetic soil classification. Pedology, No. 6, 76-81.

21. .... 1957. Provisional results of the discussion on the problems of soil classification in the journal 'Pedology' in 1955-1956. Pedology, No. 4, 71-79.

22. ...., Karavayeva, N. A., and Rode, A. A. 1957. First plenary session of the Commission on nomenclature, systematics and classification of soils attached to the Academy of Sciences of U.S.S.R. Pedology, No. 8, 60-65.

23. Sibirtsev, N. M. 1895. The basis of genetical soil classification. Mem. Inst. Agron. Novo-Alex. 9 (7).

24. .... 1898. Short reviews of the main soil types of Russia. Mem. Inst. Agron. Novo-Alex. 11 (3).

25. .... 1900. Pedology. Collected Works, vol. i, 1951.

26. Tsyganov, M. S. 1955. Fundamental principles of genetic classification and nomenclature of soils. Pedology, No. 12, 52-63.

27. Tumin, G. M. 1907. Principle of classification schemes of Dokuchaev, Rospolozhenskii, Sibirtsev, Glinka, Selzkin and Kossovitch. Annu. Geol. Miner. Rus. 8 (10).

28. Vilenskii, D. G. 1925. The classification of soils on the bases of analogous series in soil formation. Proc. Int. Soc. Soil Sci. 1 (14), 224-41.

29. Viliams, V. R. 1939. Pedology. Selkhozgiz, Moscow.

30. Volobuev, V. R. 1955. Some problems of genetic soil types. Pedology, No. 11, 59-69.

31. Vysotskii, G. N. 1906. Oro-climatic bases of soil classification. Pedology, Nos. 1-4, 1-18.

32. Zakharov, S. A. 1927. Course of pedology.

(Received 19 August 1958)

SOIL CLASSIFICATION IN THE UNITED STATES

Classification of soils at any point in history
largely reflects current understanding of soil genesis.

Roy W. Simonson[1]

Much that is of importance to mankind takes place in the soil. It is the foothold, directly or indirectly, for much of the life on this planet. It serves as a foundation for buildings and for roads. It is the realm wherein living creatures mingle with the shell of weathered and weathering rock. As Coffey (1) wrote some 50 years ago, "It is the one great formation in which the organic and inorganic kingdoms meet and derives its distinctive character from this union." Earlier, Shaler (2) argued that "this slight and superficial and inconstant covering of the earth should receive a measure of care which is rarely devoted to it." If this measure of care is to be provided, the nature of soil and the kinds of soils and their distribution must first be known.

Present over nearly all land areas, the soil mantle is like a surface film. It is a minor part of the outer crust, and the crust in turn is a small part of the earth as a whole. The soil is the outermost part of the regolith, commonly between 1 and 6 feet thick in vertical cross section. The upper boundary of soil is clear, but the lower boundary is often obscure. As a rule, no distinct break sets soil apart from the remainder of the regolith, but the changes in the regolith that give rise to soil profiles occur largely in the uppermost few feet. Thus, the soil forms a veneer at the surface of the earth (Fig. 1), a thin mantle of major importance to food production and of substantial scientific interest.

Even though it is so widely distributed as to be commonplace, soil is highly complex. Every soil body consists of a variety of minerals, an assortment of particles of many sizes, a collection of dilute solutions, and a mixture of gases. Under natural conditions it harbors immense numbers of microorganisms and is host to numerous plant roots and small animals. The reactions among the components of the soil and between the soil and the life within it are many and varied, at least during the growing season and in many cases throughout the year. Every body of soil is thus a dynamic system, one which is open rather than closed. The multitude of reactions that occur in the formation of soil and in its continuing change are controlled by larger cycles in the wearing down and building up of land surfaces, the march of climate, and the succession of different forms of life.

The complexity of soil, both in composition and in the variety of reactions under way within it, dictates the approach to its effective study. Such study must draw up-

---

[1]The author is director of soil classification and correlation, Soil Survey, U.S. Department of Agriculture, Soil Conservation Service, Washington, D. C.

Reproduced with permission from *Science,* Vol 137, 1962, p. 1027-1034. Copyright © 1962, American Association for the Advancement of Science, Washington, D. C. 20005, USA.

on a number of other sciences—for example, geology, physics, chemistry, and biology. Substantial progress in all of these, and in others, is a prerequisite for the successful study of soils. This is but one requirement.

Recognition that the soil is a natural body worthy of attention in itself is also a prerequisite for its effective study. Only within the last century has it been recognized that a soil is a collection of natural bodies paralleling those of flora, fauna, and rock formations. Before this fact was recognized, construction of systems of soil classification applicable to wide areas was not possible. Furthermore, the construction of such systems required some knowledge of the charactistics and distribution of this collection of natural bodies. This is readily evident from a review of a few past efforts in soil classification.

PAST EFFORTS IN CLASSIFICATION

The earliest attempt to classify soils systematically seems to have occurred in China some 40 centuries ago (3). The soils of the kingdom were reportedly graded into nine classes, apparently on the basis of their known productivity, during the reign of the Yao dynasty (2357-2261 B.C). The best grade were the yellow, soft soils of Yung Chow (Shensi and Kansu), whereas the next best were the red, rich clayey soils of Su Chow (Shantung, Kiangsu, and Anhwei). Seven additional grades of soil were recognized and given names. Exactly what may have been done 40 centuries ago is not now determinable with any assurance. The available evidence does indicate, however, that soils of the kingdom were classified and that the size of individual land holdings and the tax to be paid the state were related to soil productivity. Comparable efforts to base tax assessment on soil productivity may have been made elsewhere in ancient times, but records of such efforts are lacking. All known attempts of this kind are part of recent history.

Marked impetus was given to the scientific study of soil by a much later effort to relate tax assessment to soil productivity. In fact, this later effort, which took place in Russia little more than a century ago (4), led directly to the establishment of pedology as a separate discipline. In 1882 the government of Nizhni-Novgorod employed V. V. Dokuchaiev, a geologist, to take charge of a program for classifying and mapping soils as a basis for tax assessment. This program was carried forward over a period of several years. At the outset, however, Dokuchaiev divided the assignment into two parts: (i) the establishment of a natural classification of soils, and (ii) the grading of those soils according to their agricultural potentiality. The program carried forward in Niahni-Novgorod included field studies of soil morphology, laboratory analyses of soil samples, construction of maps to show distribution of various kinds of soils, and measurements of crop yields on those soils. The kinds of soils were then graded on a scale ranging from 15 for the poorest to 100 for the best, to show their "natural value," and the ratings were used as a basis for tax levies.

As a result of his studies, Dokuchaiev broke sharply with the concept of soil held in his day by most scientists and by agriculturists. Soil was thought to be disintegrated rock mixed with some decayed organic matter, simply a product of rock weathering (5). This concept was widely held during the first few decades of the 20th century (6). Dokuchaiev argued (7) that soils should be considered as a sep-

Fig. 1—A soil profile about 4 feet deep showing, in downward succession, a dark A_1 horizon (12 inches thick), a light gray A_2 horizon (6 inches thick), a dark B horizon (12 inches thick), and a C horizon (bottom 6 inches of exposure). This profile represents Edina silt loam, a soil formed from loess under prairie vegetation on flat interfluves in south central Iowa and north central Missouri.

arate kingdom, similar to the kingdoms of rocks, plants, and animals: "Soil is an independent natural body which must not be mistaken for surface rocks. . . ."

Dokuchaiev and his students attempted to classify soils of Russia on the basis of this concept, using data available at the time. A brief description of the last scheme proposed by Dokuchaiev, in 1900, will illustrate his approach. The scheme consisted of two categories, the higher having three classes and the lower 13. The three classes in the higher category were designated "normal" soils (dryland vegetative or zonal soils), "transitional" soils, and "abnormal" soils (7, 8). There were seven subclasses under normal soils, three subclasses in each of the other two broad classes. The 13 subclasses were called "soil types" and were identified by names such as tundra (dark brown soils), light gray podzolized soils, chernozem, laterite or red soils, secondary alkali soils, and alluvial soils. Use of the name "normal" soils and the relating of each subclass of "normal" soils to climatic and vegetation zones seem to reflect a theory of soil formation in which first place is accorded climate and vegetation as factors in soil formation.

Dokuchaiev and his followers set out to describe and characterize soils as natural bodies rather than as mantles of weathered rock, giving attention first to exterior characteristics, or to soil morphology because it was the most obvious feature. Reporting on these efforts in 1927, Glinka (9) stated that pedologists in Russia had arrived at the conclusion that every soil "consists of several separate horizons, following one another in a vertical direction, and united by a common origin [genesis] . . ." The concept of the soil as an independent natural body possessing a degree of internal organization expressed in the profile, with its horizons, was a major contribution of the Dokuchaiev school of pedology. Recognition of the full soil profile and of the relationships between horizons was a gradual process which took place over a period of many years (10). Nevertheless, the ideas developed in Russia have had enormous impact on the study of soils throughout the world.

An immediate practical objective prompted the first efforts to classify and map soils of the United States, as had been the case earlier in China and Russia, though taxation of land was not involved. The first soil surveys in this country were made to increase production of a single crop, tobacco (11). Within a year or two the objectives had been expanded to include increasing the production of other crops and providing information on lands proposed for irrigation. Soils were considered a medium for plant growth, and attention was focused primarily on characteristics of soil important for plant growth and on local differences of consequence in crop production (12). The prevailing concept of soil as a mantle of disintegrated rock mixed with some organic matter is clearly reflected in a scheme proposed in 1911 (13) for the classification of soils.

The first clear argument in the United States for the recognition of soil as a distinct natural entity was offered by Coffey in 1912 (1). In a report on soils of this country he states that "the soil is an independent, natural body, a bio-geological formation, differing essentially from the rock which underlies it, although closely related to it. . . ." Coffey later lists requirements for an ideal classification of soils, emphasizing the importance of recognizing inherent differences in the soil itself as fundamental and arguing that each soil had a definite genesis and has a distinct nature of its own. Before listing these requirements, Coffey briefly summarizes and appraises prior approaches in the classification of soils, including that of the Dokuchaiev school in Russia.

One part of Coffey's study is a proposal for classifying soils of the United States. He states that five broad classes, or divisions as he calls them, are known well enough to be recognized. These five are defined on the basis of characteristics of the soils themselves, though some terms relating to climate and vegetation are used in the names. The five divisions are as follows: (i) arid or unleached soils low in humus; (ii) dark-colored prairie soils or semi-leached soils rich in humus; (iii) light-colored timbered or leached soils low in humus; (iv) dark-colored or swampy leached soils high in organic matter; and (v) organic soils or peat and muck. The several hundred soil series recognized in the soil surveys completed prior to 1912 were thought to be classifiable into the five divisions, though the classification was not made at the time.

The first effort in the United States to devise a comprehensive scheme of soil classification, one which might be useful outside as well as within this country, was presented by Marbut (14) to the First International Congress of Soil Science in 1927. The scheme consisted of six categories with two classes in the highest category, several thousand in the lowest category, and intermediate numbers of classes in the intermediate categories.

The two classes of soils in the highest category were named pedocals and pedalfers. Pedocals were soils in which calcium carbonate had accumulated while horizons were being differentiated in the profile. Such soils were thought to be restricted in their occurrence to regions of low rainfall. Pedalfers were soils in which aluminum and iron had accumulated in the profile. These were thought to occur only in regions of moderate-to-high rainfall. The information available about soils in 1927 indicated that these two classes were mutually exclusive, though it has since been learned that they are not.

In the construction of this scheme Marbut attempted to meet the requirements for an ideal classification outlined earlier by Coffey (1) and himself (15). Clearly, he thought of the soil as an independent natural body. His criteria for differentiating classes are mainly characteristics of the soils themselves. As additional information has become available since 1927, however, it has become evident that some of the criteria are inferences as to genesis rather than actual characteristics of soils. Moreover, features outside of the soils themselves seem to have been actual differentiae in some cases. Weaknesses of this kind are not peculiar to the scheme outlined by Marbut; they are evident in the schemes proposed by Dokuchaiev and in schemes that have been proposed since 1926 (16).

It is possible to develop many different classification schemes for natural objects as complex as soils. Many have therefore been constructed, and more can be expected in the future. Therefore, not all the schemes devised in the past are reviewed here. A few examples have been considered to indicate what has been done. These few examples also lend support to certain general conclusions about the process of constructing schemes.

GENERAL PROBLEMS

Two general conclusions stand out among those that can be drawn from critical study of schemes developed thus far. First of all, no scheme can be any better than the state of knowledge in the soil science of its day. As a matter of fact, the validity of any scheme is a direct reflection of the knowledge of soils and their characteristics on the part of its author or authors. Secondly, the construction of each scheme is circumscribed by the current understanding of soil genesis, the knowledge of soil formation. Whether consciously or otherwise, the selection of characteristics as definitive for classes or as criteria for differentiating classes is governed by the understanding of soil genesis. The relative weights given to individual characteristics of the soil when a number of them must be considered collectively in classification are also largely determined by theories of soil genesis.

Given the importance of theories of soil genesis to the classification of soils, it might be argued that direct use of interpretations of soil genesis as a basis for constructing a scheme would be desirable. Unfortunately, such direct use leads to serious weaknesses in schemes for soil classification. This is due to a combination of reasons.

The genesis of many—perhaps of most—soils seems to have been more complex than is generally realized even now. Certainly, evidence accumulated during the last decade or two clearly points toward more complex histories than were inferred earlier to explain the present characteristics of soils. It now seems that many soils have been subject to all, or part, of more than one cycle of horizon differentiation, even though it may not be possible to identify the features that reflect each of the entire or partial cycles. The simplest cases are explainable, but their existence is in itself an argument for the occurrence of complex cases.

The explanation that can be offered at any point in time for the genesis of a given soil is a matter of inference rather than one of direct observation or experiment. Current understanding of soil genesis is limited. Furthermore, it also seems that the genesis of a number of soils is obscure. Inferences can be made as to the probable path of genesis of a given soil, but the factual basis for such inference is always modest.

The basing of classification schemes solely on interpretations of soil genesis is consequently subject to large risks of error. Difficulties may arise in one or more of several ways. Direct reliance on inferences about the genesis of given soils as a basis for their classification may lead to the placing of indistinguishable soils into different classes. Similarly, soils that are not alike in morphology and composition may be placed together in the same class because of the interpretation that their genesis was the same. Finally, there is always the danger that classification will be based on the inferred causes of the present soil characteristics rather than on the characteristics themselves. The importance of using characteristics rather than possible explanations for those characteristics has been stressed by Coffey (1) and Marbut (15).

The danger that markedly unlike soils will be classed together and that like soils will be put in separate classes exists with an approach in classification, but it is greater in some approaches than in others. In the current status of soil science, the use of morphology and composition of soils as criteria for differentiating classes seems to present the smallest risk of error. The selecting and weighting of characteristics as criteria are best done in the light of current understanding of soil genesis. For the sake of brevity, a scheme so constructed may be called a morphogenetic system. Theories of soil genesis are an important part of the background for choosing criteria in such a system, but the criteria themselves are characteristics which can be observed and measured, not inferences, which cannot be rigorously tested.

CURRENT EFFORT IN THE UNITED STATES

Because it can be no better than the state of knowledge in the soil science of its day, any scheme must eventually be modified or replaced. This is the only way whereby new data or improved understanding of available data can be reflected in soil classification. The need for modifying or replacing old schemes was evident in the several reports on work in progress made to the Seventh International Congress of Soil Science in 1960 (17). Among the progress reports was one on the current effort in this country (18). The scheme being developed in this country is outlined in its present stage in a monograph (19), copies of which were distributed to participants in the congress. Attention is centered on this scheme in the discussion that follows.

The scheme presented by American pedologists to the 1960 congress has been carried through a succession of stages over a period of years. For purposes of identification, these stages have been numbered, and the stage presented to the 1960 congress is identified as the 7th Approximation of a comprehensive system of soil classification. This approximation is currently being tested, as were earlier stages, and some modifications are likely to follow. These are expected to be modifications in details of the scheme, however, rather than in general structure. Hence, it seems that the scheme embodied in the 7th Approximation will be adopted, with minor changes, in this country within the next few years.

The prime difficulty in all efforts to classify soils arises from the fact that soil forms a continuum on the land surface. With few exceptions, changes within the continuum are gradual in character, though horizontal differences in the soil may be substantial over distances measured in meters or tens of meters. Marked differences exist between soils of widely separated regions or even within the continuum as it occurs in a single square mile. Despite the existence of these differences within the continuum, discrete entities, comparable to single plants or animals, do not exist. Hence, there is the initial problem of defining the basic entity or entities that are to be grouped into classes in some way.

The approach toward solution of this problem followed in the 7th Approximation differs from earlier approaches in several ways. An attempt is being made to define a small volume of soil as the basic entity, one for which the term *pedon* (plural, *pedons*) has been suggested (20). *Pedon* is proposed as a generic term for small volumes of soil, each large enough for the study of horizons and their interrelationships within the profile and having a roughly circular lateral cross section of between 1 and 10 square meters (19, 21).

A group of contiguous pedons belonging to a single class of the lowest category (soil series) in the 7th Approximation is identified as a "soil individual" in the monograph (19). Since the monograph was prepared it has seemed that use of some other term to identify such groups of contiguous pedons would be desirable. Consequently, the term *polypedon* (plural, *polypedons*) has been proposed. A single polypedon is defined as a group of pedons contiguous within the soil continuum and having a range in characteristics within the limits of a single soil series.

Like other schemes developed earlier in this country, the 7th Approximation is a multiple-category system. Six categories are used in the scheme. These are identified, from top to bottom, as orders, suborders, great groups, subgroups, families, and series. Among these categories, that of the soil series has been used in the United States for a long time. The concept of the soil series has been changed over the years, but further change is not proposed in the 7th Approximation. In contrast to the category of the soil series, other categories in the scheme do not correspond exactly in level of generalization to any that have been used previously in this country or elsewhere, so far as is known. The "suborder" category in the 7th Approximation does approach in level of abstraction the category of the great soil group currently in use in this country, but the two are not fully equivalent.

Some measure of the span in properties permitted within classes is indicated by the numbers of classes in the categories. The 7th Approximation provides for the recognition of ten classes in the "order" category. The numbers of classes in the other categories (in rounded numbers) are as follows: suborders, 40; great groups, 120; subgroups, 400; families, 1500; and series, 7000. It should be mentioned that the totals for the three lowest categories cover only the soils of the United States. These totals would be appreciably larger if soils of other continents were included. On the other hand, the total number of each of the orders, suborders, and great groups is expected to remain the same, or virtually so, whether the scheme is applied to the United States or to the world as a whole. The intent has been to provide a place in the scheme for all known soils in the world, though this goal may not have been reached. In the construction of the scheme it is recognized that soils not known to the authors of the scheme may have been omitted. It is also recognized that modification of this scheme or its replacement will eventually become necessary as the knowledge and understanding of soils continue to grow.

The nomenclature proposed in the 7th Approximation represents a marked departure from past practice in soil classification. A new nomenclature is proposed for the classes in each of the four highest categories. The proposed names for classes in the order, suborder, great group, and subgroup categories consist of coined terms in which Greek and Latin roots are largely used. The names are distinctive for the classes in each category, so that a name itself will indicate the category to which a given class belongs. Moreover, the names are designed so that each subgroup may be identified, by its name, with the great group, suborder, and order in which it is classified.

The names of the ten orders consist of three or four syllables, and every name ends in the suffix *sol*. The names of the ten orders are "entisols," "vertisols," "inceptisols," "aridisols," "mollisols," "spodosols," "alfisols," "ultisols," "oxisols," and "histosols" (the letter *s* is added for the plural form).

The name of each suborder is a two-syllable rather than a three- or four-syllable term. Each name consists of a prefix syllable with a specific connotation plus a syllable for the name of the order in which the suborder is classified. Fourteen formative elements are used as prefixes in the construction of suborder names. Thus, for example, suborders in the order of entisols are identified as "aquents," "ustents," and "udents."

The name of each great group consists of either three or four syllables. For the most part, the names are three-syllable words, but a few have four syllables. Each name has been constructed by adding a second prefix to the name of the appropriate suborder. Twenty-seven formative elements, in addition to the 14 used in constructing suborder names, are used in constructing names for the great groups. Thus, for example, four great groups in the suborder of udents are the "cryudents," "agrudents," "hapludents," and "plaggudents."

Binomials have been used as names for subgroups. Each binomial is constructed by placing an adjective before the name of the great group to which the subgroup belongs. For each great group, a typifying subgroup is first selected. That subgroup is then named by a combination of the word *orthic* with the name of the great group —for example, "orthic hapludents." The names of other subgroups within a great group are constructed in the same way, except that the adjectives are formed from the names of other groups or of suborders. Thus, in the 7th Approximation, the hapludents, a great group in the suborder of udents and in the order of entisols, comprise several subgroups in addition to the central one. Examples of the names are "grumaquertic hapludents" and "udalfic hapludents".

Several objectives have been kept in mind in developing the proposed nomenclature. Efforts were made to devise names that were distinctive and could be easily remembered, would suggest a few characteristics of the soils in each class, would identify the categorical level to which a class belonged, would fit into the existing pattern of language readily, and would provide convenient adjective as well as substantive forms (18). An effort to reach all of these objectives simultaneously is ambitious, and the several are not compatible in all cases. Hence, it is not surprising that some defects have already been noted in the proposed nomenclature (18). In all probability, more will be discovered. It is hoped, however, that the nomenclature can be improved as a result of scrutiny of the names and definitions of classes by a larger group of scientists than could participate in the construction of the scheme.

The major problems in constructing the scheme embodied in the 7th Approximation were encountered in defining classes in the several categories. This is not surprising; the selection and weighting of characteristics as criteria for the definition and differentiation of classes at all levels is a central and continuing problem in the classification of soils (22). Efforts to construct schemes of soil classification in the past have not gone far toward defining individual classes fully. General descriptions of classes, often brief, have been offered, without attempts at detailed definition. Furthermore, definitions of many classes have been expressed in terms either of inferences as to genesis or of features external to the soils, or of both. Careful examination of a sample of the schemes proposed in the past will provide a test of this statement. It is not my intent to decry the value of schemes of soil classification devised in the past, but the deficiencies of existing schemes must be recognized before they can be corrected.

Definitions of the classes in the different categories of the 7th Approximation are in terms of morphology and composition of the soils—that is, in terms of soil characteristics themselves. Moreover, an attempt is made to have the definitions as nearly quantitative as currently available data will permit.

The definitions are generally given in two parts. A norm or central concept is given as the first part of the definition in most instances. This consists of a full description of the morphology of a soil profile plus certain analytical data, by horizons, of that profile. This information is meant to provide a ready first picture of the class. The second part of the definition is a statement of the limits of the class, with emphasis on characteristics that set the class apart from the other classes most like it. The limits for classes are given, insofar as possible, in terms of characteristics that can observed through field study of soils, but some of the characteristics used as definitive can be observed only through laboratory analysis. In all instances, however, an attempt has been made to define classes in terms of soil characteristics that can be observed and measured by competent pedologists.

The ten orders are set apart on the basis of one or more of the following factors: gross composition, degree of horizonation, the presence or absence of certain horizons, and what is in effect a combined index of weathering and weatherability of minerals. The characteristics selected to distinguish the orders are believed to reflect major differences in paths of horizon differentiation (23), in stages reached in horizon differentiation, or in both. To state this another way, the intent has been to choose as differentiating characteristics properties that reflect major differences in genesis of the soils. Whether the selections have been successful for this purpose, and if they have been, to what degree, will become evident only after the scheme has been tested for a time.

The bases for distinguishing the ten orders may be made clearer by some illustrations. Full definitions will not be given here for any of the orders, but the principal differentiae for the histosols, entisols, mollisols, and spodosols will be sketched briefly.

The histosols are organic soils, mainly those known as peats and mucks. These are distinguished from soils of the other nine orders by differences in gross composition: histosols are high in organic matter (20 percent or more). The balance among processes of horizon differentiation in soils so high in organic matter is very different from that in dominantly mineral soils.

The entisols are mineral soils with low degrees of horizonation, mainly those that have been identified as lithosols, regosols, and alluvial soils in the United States in recent years. The entisols have few and faint horizons in their profiles. These soils are in early stages of horizon differentiation. Some are forming in regoliths consisting of highly resistant minerals; others in areas where accretions of fresh materials keep pace with horizon differentiation; still others in areas where removal by erosion keeps pace with horizon differentiation.

The mollisols are mineral soils which have a characteristic known as a mollic epipedon (9) (Fig. 2). This is a darkened surface layer of considerable thickness, relatively high in organic matter, high in base saturation, and friable. For ident-

Fig. 2—Profile of a soil with a mollic epipedon, a friable dark surface horizon relatively high in organic matter and high in base status. The thickness of the mollic epipedon is slightly more than 12 inches in this profile, which represents a "brunizem" or "hapludoll," one of the well-drained mollisols derived from glacial drift in the Corn Belt. The scale shows depth in feet.

ification as a mollic epipedon, minimum requirements for thickness, color, base saturation, level of organic matter, and consistence are given. Unlike the histosols and entisols, mollisols tend to occur within certain geographic zones. Such soils are the major ones of the Corn Belt and Great Plains in the United States. Mollisols have been formed almost entirely under prairie vegetation in semiarid-to-subhumid climates. Included in the mollisols are the chernozems, studied almost a centruy ago by Dokuchaiev (7) in Russia.

The spodosols are mineral soils which have a characteristic known as a spodic horizon (19) (Fig. 3). This is a subsurface horizon of illuvial accumulation of humus, usually in conjunction with accumulation of iron or aluminum, or both. The spodic horizon corresponds closely to the B horizon of podzols, as those soils have been described in North America and western Europe. Like the mollisols, the spodosols tend to be associated with certain climatic and vegetation types. These soils are found in cool, humid regions, for the most part, and they are formed mainly under coniferous forest or under vegetation dominated by plants such as heather. The spodosols occur extensively in eastern Canada, in New England and

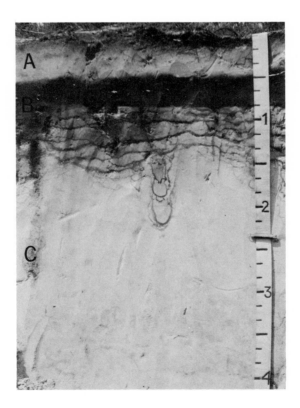

Fig. 3—Profile of a soil with spodic horizon—a subsurface horizon of illuvial accumulation of humus with or without concurrent accumulation of aluminum and iron. The dark layer below a depth of 6 inches is the spodic horizon. The soil is a podzol or spodosol formed from sand under heather near Eindhoven, Holland. The scale shows depth in feet.

the northern Lake States, and in the taiga region of the Soviet Union. Such soils often have strikingly different horizons in the same profile, and this may be why they were among the first to be studied with care.

The basic approach followed in defining orders in the 7th Approximation is carried down to the suborder and great-group categories, though the same characteristics are not used as criteria. Additional characteristics of the soil are introduced as criteria for distinguishing classes at each level.

The kinds of characteristics used in differentiating suborders within orders are moisture regimes, temperature, mineralogy, and specific kinds of horizons. One suborder is set apart in each of eight orders because of the evidence of wetness in the morphology of the soils. In two of the orders, one pair of suborders is distinguished mainly on the basis of temperature. The mineralogy of the soil—for example, very high levels of quartz, dominance of allophane, or high proportions of calcium carbonate—provides criteria for recognizing at least one suborder in each of four orders. Characteristics such as an argillic horizon, a cambic horizon, and the tonguing of an albic horizon into an argillic horizon are definitive for at least one suborder in each of five orders.

The setting apart of great groups within suborders is based on the same kinds of criteria as is the distinguishing of suborders within orders. Great groups are distinguished within suborders by the presence or absence of characteristic horizons or other features, the occurrence of horizons extraneous to the sequence required for the suborder, and temperature. The range of definitive characteristics within individual classes has been reduced step by step in coming down the ladder from the order to the suborder to the great group. Thus, the soils of a great group are more homogeneous in their characteristics than are soils of classes in higher categories. For each great group, the soils have the same kinds of horizons in the same sequence within pedons, except for surface horizons, which may be obliterated by plowing or by erosion.

The approach in defining subgroups differs from that followed in defining classes in higher categories. As explained earlier, a typifying subgroup is first defined for each great group and identified by the term *orthic* preceding the great-group name. This subgroup has the median expression of the definitive characteristics of the great group. In addition to the orthic subgroup, other subgroups are set apart as intergrade or extragrade subgroups. Intergrade subgroups have some characteristics definitive of another great group, either in the same order or in some other order. Extra-grade subgroups have some properties that are not definitive of any known great group. In both intergrade and extragrade subgroups, however, the soils are more like the orthic or central subgroup of the great group to which each belongs than to any other known kind of soil. Recognition of orthic, intergrade, and extragrade subgroups is one device for recognizing that the soil mantle forms a continuum in which changes are gradational rather than abrupt.

Mention has already been made of the family and series as the two lowest categories in the 7th Approximation. Work is still in progress on the selection of appropriate criteria for differentiating families within subgroups. There are a number of difficulties to be overcome before the known soil series of the United States can be grouped into families on a uniform basis. Possible approaches have been tested through trial groupings of soil series into families, and these tests are being continued (19).

The soil series has been used in the classification of soils in the United States since the early days of this century (22). The concept of the series has evolved greatly during this time. However, changes in the concept of the soil series have been discussed elsewhere (22) and have not been considered in this article. The concept of the soil series and the relationship of that category to the higher categories in the scheme are discussed in the monograph on the 7th Approximation (19).

CONCLUDING REMARKS

The scheme of soil classification now being developed in the United States differs from earlier schemes prepared in this country and elsewhere in several ways which are important. This scheme reflects evolution in the concept of soil itself. Basic to the scheme is the concept that soil comprises a continuum on the land surface, one which can be subdivided into classes in a variety of ways. Also basic to the scheme is an effort to achieve more quantitative definitions than have been devised heretofore. Definitions of classes at every categoric level are expressed in terms of properties that can be observed or measured. These are important departures from schemes developed earlier for classifying soils.

The basic objectives of the classification scheme are essentially the same as those of earlier schemes, despite the differences in approach. The scheme must first of all organize, define, and name classes in the lowest category, and it must group these classes into progressively broader classes in higher categories and provide names for these classes. Its general purpose is to make the characteristics of soils easier to remember, to bring out relationships among soils and between the soils and other elements of the environment, and to provide a basis for developing principles of soil genesis and soil behavior that have prediction value. It is hoped that these purposes may be served better by the new scheme than by earlier ones, though only time will tell whether this hope has been realized.

REFERENCES AND NOTES

1. G. N. Coffey, U. S. Dept. Agr. Bur. Soils Bull. No. 85 (1912), p. 7-40.
2. N. S. Shaler, U. S. Geol. Survey Ann. Rept. No. 12 (1891), pt. 1, p. 219.
3. M. Ping-Hua Lee, Columbia Univ. Studies in History, Economics, and Public Law 99, 33 (1921).
4. A. A. Yarilov, "Russian Pedological Investigation No. 11," Publ. Acad. Sci. U.S.S.R. (1927).
5. Fr. Fallou, Pedologie oder allgemeine und besondere Bodenkunde (Dresden, 1862), p. 180-182.
6. C. F. Marbut, H. H. Bennet, J. E. Lapham, M. H. Lapham, U. S. Dept. Agr. Bur. Soils Bull. No. 96 (1913); E. Blanck, in Handbuch der Bodenlehre (Springer, Berlin, 1921), vol. 1, p. 1-28.
7. J. N. Afanasiev, "Russian Pedological Investigations No. 5," Publ. Acad. Sci. U.S.S.R. (1927).
8. I. P. Gerasimov and E. I. Ivanova, Soils Fertilizers 22, 239 (1959).
9. K. D. Glinka, "Russian Pedological Investigations No. 1," Publ. Acad. Sci. U.S.S.R. (1927).
10. A. Muir, Advan. Agron. 13, 1 (1961).
11. M. Whitney, Yearbook Agr. (U.S. Dept. Agr.) 1901, 117 (1901).
12. "Instructions to field parties," Publ. Bur. Soils, U.S. Dept. Agr. (1914), p. 5-6.
13. E. O. Fippin, J. Am. Soc. Agron. 3, 76 (1911).
14. C. F. Marbut, Trans. Intern. Congr. Soil Sci., 1st (1927), vol4, p. 1-31.
15 ...., Am. Soil Survey Workers Rept. No. 3 (1922), p. 24-32.
16. J. J. Basinski, J. Soil Sci. 10, 14 (1959); M. Baldwin, C. E. Kellogg, J. Thorp, Yearbook Agr. (U. S. Dept. Agr.) 1938, 979 (1938).

17. See Trans. Intern. Congr. Soil Sci., 7th (1960), vol. 4.

18. G. D. Smith, ibid. (1960), vol. 4, p. 105-108.

19. Soil Survey Staff, Soil Classification, A Comprehensive System—7th Approximation (U.S. Department of Agriculture Soil Conservation Service, Washington, D.C., 1960).

20. The word *pedon* is pronounced with the accent on the first syllable.

21. R. W. Simonson and D. R. Gardner, Trans. Intern. Congr. Soil Sci., 7th (1960), vol. 4, p. 127-131.

22. R. W. Simonson, Soil Sci. 74, 249 (1952).

23. ....m Soil Sci. Soc. Am. Proc. 23, 152 (1959).

SUBJECT INDEX

(Note: After the item, page numbers are given, and in a few instances, definitions also. Refer to the *USDA Soil Survey Manual, Soils and Men,* the *7th Approximation,* the *SSSA Glossary of Soil Science Terms,* and general soil science textbooks for other definitions.)

NOTE: This index was prepared by F. D. Hole, Geological and Natural History Survey, The University of Wisconsin, Madison, Wisconsin, November 6, 1968.

22-302